# Finding America

## The American Experience in Multicultural Literature

### Patricia Osborn

AMSCO SCHOOL PUBLICATIONS, INC.
315 Hudson Street / New York, N.Y. 10013

In addition to required English courses, Patricia Osborn has taught electives in composition, drama, Russian literature, and journalism. She has experience in all grades from 9–12 and at all levels, basic to honors; has advised school newspapers; and has served as English department chairperson. Before becoming a teacher, Ms. Osborn was a general news reporter and advertising copywriter. Her stories and articles have appeared in magazines ranging from *Educational Digest* to *TV Guide*, and she has published a number of books relating to the study of English.

Cover photo: Comstock Inc.

When ordering this book, please specify:
*either* **R 623 S** *or* FINDING AMERICA

ISBN 1-56765-025-2
*NYC Item 56765-025-1*

Printed in the United States of America

5  6  7  8  9  10          02  01  00

# CONTENTS

# 6 Search for the Spirit  329

# 7 A Sense of Place  403

# 8 A Sense of Pride  503

# ACKNOWLEDGMENTS

Grateful acknowledgment is made to the following sources for permission to reprint copyrighted materials. Every effort has been made to obtain permission to use previously published material. Any errors or omissions are unintentional.

Page 3. "The Three Swimmers and the Educated Grocer," by William Saroyan. From MY NAME IS ARAM, copyright 1940 by William Saroyan, reprinted by permission of Harcourt Brace Jovanovich, Inc.

Page 12. "A Tornado Struck," from AN AMERICAN CHILDHOOD, by Annie Dillard. Copyright © 1987 by Annie Dillard. Reprinted by permission of Harper Collins Publishers, Inc.

Page 18. The excerpt "Foxes and Hounds" from THE EDUCATION OF LITTLE TREE by Forrest Carter, published by the University of New Mexico Press, is reprinted by arrangement with Eleanor Friede Books, Inc. Copyright © 1976 by Forrest Carter. All rights reserved.

Page 27. "The Sick Child," by Angel DeCora. From THE SINGING SPIRIT: EARLY SHORT STORIES BY NORTH AMERICAN INDIANS, by Bernd Peyer. Copyright © 1989, The University of Arizona Press.

Page 31. "The Day the World Almost Came to an End," by Pearl Crayton. Published in NEGRO DIGEST, August 1965. Copyright © 1965 by Negro Digest.

Page 38. "One Throw," by W. C. Heinz. Reprinted by permission of the William Morris Agency, Inc., on behalf of the author. Copyright © 1950, renewed 1978 by W. C. Heinz.

# UNIT 1

# Trying Your Wings

THE SEARCH TO FIND AMERICA starts where you are. Growing up, kids need to ask questions, to look in secret places, to cross the boundaries—real or imaginary—set by others. It sometimes includes doing what's called dangerous or even wrong, just to make sure.

It's called "trying your wings."

The first attempts to explore your world also lead to self-discovery. What are your limits? What can you do? How far can you go? The limits are often artificial. They are set by parents, by society, and even by your own fears.

Trying your wings may cause conflict. Adults often settle into a narrow groove. They need to protect their own judgment, to insist on the rightness of their habitual responses and opinions.

Kids don't accept "because I said so" as a good answer. They want to break loose, to test the rules. And they want to see for themselves and make their own choices.

In the following selections, you'll meet young Americans who are trying their wings. Read to share their discoveries about their own piece of turf and to see how they gain a clearer understanding of themselves and the people around them.

# The Three Swimmers and the Educated Grocer

## by William Saroyan

**Home state:** *California*
**Birth name:** *Sirak Goryan*
**Early jobs:** *Western Union telegraph messenger, branch manager*
**Famous as:** *Author, composer, and playwright*

THE DITCHES WERE DRY MOST of the year, but when they weren't dry, they were roaring. As the snows melted in the Sierra Nevadas the ditches began to roar and from somewhere, God knows where, arrived frogs and turtles, water snakes and fish. In the spring of the year the water hurried, and with it the heart, but as the fields changed from green to brown, the blossoms to fruit, the shy warmth to arrogant heat, the ditches slowed down and the heart grew lazy. The first water down the mountains and the hills was cold, swift, and frightening. It was too cold and busy to invite the naked body of a boy.

Alone, or in a group, a boy would stand on the bank of a ditch and watch the water for many minutes, and then, terribly challenged, fling off his clothes, make a running dive, come up gasping, and swim across to the other side. If the boy was the first of a group to dive, the others would soon follow, in order not to walk home in shame. It wasn't simply that the water was cold. It was more that it had no time for boys. The springtime water was as unfriendly as anything could be.

One day in April I set out for Thompson Ditch with my cousin Mourad and a pal of his named Joe Bettencourt, a Portuguese who loved nothing more than to be free and out-of-doors. A schoolroom made Joe stupid. It embarrassed him. But once out of school, once off the school-grounds, he was as intelligent, as good-natured, casual, sincere, and friendly as anyone could possibly be. As my cousin Mourad said, Joe ain't dumb—he just doesn't want an education.

It was a bright Saturday morning. We had two baloney sandwiches each, and ten cents between the three of us. We decided to walk to the ditch so that we would get there around noon, when the day would be warm. We walked along the railroad tracks to Calwa. Along the state highway to Malaga. And then east through the vineyard country to the ditch. When we said Thompson Ditch, we meant a specific place. It was an intersection of country roads, with a wooden bridge and a headgate. The swimming was south of the bridge. West of the ditch was a big fenced-in pasture, with cows and horses grazing in it. East of the ditch was the country road. The road and the ditch traveled together many miles. The flow was south, and the next bridge was two miles away. In the summertime a day of swimming was incomplete until a boy had gone downstream to the other bridge, rested a moment in the pasture land, and then came back up, against the stream, which was a good workout.

By the time we got out to Thompson Ditch the brightness of morning had changed to a gloom that was unmistakably wintry; in fact, the beginning of a storm. The water was roaring, the sky was gray, growing black, the air was cold and unfriendly, and the landscape seemed lonely and desolate.

Joe Bettencourt said, I came all this way to swim and rain or no rain I'm going to swim.

So am I.

*You* wait, my cousin Mourad said. Me and Joe, we'll see how it is. If it's all right, you can come in. Can you really swim?

Aw shut up, I said.

This is what I always said when it seemed to me that somebody had unwittingly insulted me.

Well, Joe Bettencourt said, *can* you?

Sure I can swim.

If you ask *him*, my cousin Mourad said, he can do anything. Better than anybody in the world.

Neither of them knew how uncertain I was as to whether or not I could swim well enough to negotiate a dive and a swim across that body of cold roaring water. If the truth were known, when I saw the dark water roaring I was scared, challenged, and insulted.

Aw shut up, I said to the water.

I brought out my lunch and bit into one of the sandwiches. My cousin Mourad whacked my hand and almost knocked the sandwich into the water.

We eat after we swim, he said. Do you want to have cramps?

I had plumb forgotten. It was because I was so challenged and scared.

One sandwich won't give me cramps.

It'll taste better after we swim, Joe said.

He was a very kind boy. He knew I was scared and he knew I was bluffing. I knew *he* was scared, but I knew he was figuring everything out a little more wisely than I was.

Let's see, he said. We'll swim across, rest, swim back, get dressed, eat, and unless the storm passes, start for home. Otherwise we'll swim some more.

This storm isn't going to pass, my cousin Mourad said. If we're going to swim, we're going to have to do it in a hurry.

By this time Joe was taking off his clothes. My cousin Mourad was taking off his, and I was taking off mine. We stood together naked on the bank of the ditch looking at the unfriendly water. It certainly didn't invite a dive, but there was no other honorable way to enter a body of water. If you tried to walk in, you were just naturally not a swimmer. If you jumped in feet first it wasn't exactly a disgrace, it was just bad style. On the other hand, the water was utterly without charm, altogether unfriendly, uninviting, and sinister. The swiftness of the water made the distance to the opposite bank seem greater than it was.

Without a word Joe dived in. Without a word my cousin Mourad dived in. The second or two between splashes seemed like long days dreamed in a winter dream because I was not only scared but very cold. With a bookful of unspoken words on my troubled mind, I dived in.

The next thing I knew—and it wasn't more than three seconds later—I was listening to Joe yelling, my cousin Mourad yelling, and myself yelling. What had happened was that we had all dived into mud up to our elbows, had gotten free only with great effort, and had each come up worried about what had happened to the other two. We were all standing in the cold roaring water, up to our knees in soft mud.

The dives had been standing dives. If they had been running dives we would have stuck in the mud up to our ankles, head first, and remained there until summer, or later.

This scared us a little on the one hand and on the other hand made us feel very lucky to be alive.

The storm broke while we stood in the mud of the ditch.

Well, Joe said, we're going to get caught in the rain anyhow, so we might as well stay in for a while.

We were all shivering, but it seemed sensible that we should try our best to make a swim of it. The water wasn't three feet deep; nevertheless, Joe managed to leap out of the mud and swim across, and then back.

We swam for what seemed like a long time, but was probably no more than ten minutes. Then we got out of the water and mud and dressed and, standing under a tree, ate our sandwiches.

Instead of stopping, the rain increased, so we decided to set out for home right away.

We may get a ride, Joe said.

All the way to Malaga the country road was deserted. In Malaga we went into the general store and warmed ourselves at the stove and chipped in and bought a can of beans and a loaf of French bread. The proprietor was a man named Darcous who wasn't a foreigner. He opened the can for us, divided the beans into three parts on three paper plates, gave us each a wooden fork, and sliced the bread for us. He was an old man who seemed funny and young.

Where you been, boys? he said.

Swimming, Joe said.

Swimming?

Sure, Joe said. We showed that river.

Well, I'll be harrowed, the grocer said. How was it?

Not three feet deep.

Cold?

Ice-cold.

Well, I'll be cultivated. Did you have fun?

Did we? Joe asked my cousin Mourad.

Joe didn't know whether it had been fun or something else.

I don't know, Mourad said. When we dived in we got stuck in the mud up to our elbows.

It wasn't easy to get loose from the mud, Joe said.

Well, I'll be pruned, the grocer said.

He opened a second can of beans, pitched an enormous forkful into his mouth, and then divided the rest onto the three paper plates.

We haven't got any more money, I said.

Now, tell me, boys, what made you do it.

Nothing, Joe said with the finality of a boy who has too many reasons to enumerate at a moment's notice, and his mouth full of beans and French bread.

Well, I'll be gathered into a pile and burned, the grocer said. Now, boys, tell me—of what race are you? Californians, or foreigners?

We're all Californians, Joe said. I was born on G Street in Fresno. Mourad here was born on Walnut Avenue or someplace on the other side of the Southern Pacific tracks, I guess, and his cousin somewhere in that neighborhood, too.

Well, I'll be irrigated. Now, tell me, boys, what sort of educations have you got.

We ain't educated, Joe said.

Well, I'll be picked off a tree and thrown into a box. Now, tell me, boys, what foreign languages do you speak?

I speak Portuguese, Joe said.

*You* ain't educated? I have a degree from Yale, my boy, and I can't speak Portuguese. And you, son, how about you?

I speak Armenian, my cousin Mourad said.

Well, I'll be cut off a vine and eaten grape by grape by a girl in her teens. I can't speak a word of Armenian and I'm a college graduate, class of 1892. Now, tell me, son, what's *your* name?

Aram Garoghlanian.

I think I can get it. Gar-oghlan-ian. Is that it?

That's it.

Aram.

Yes, sir.

And what strange foreign language do *you* speak?

I speak Armenian, too. That's my cousin, *Mourad* Garoghlanian.

Well, I'll be harrowed, cultivated, pruned, gathered into a pile, burned, picked off a tree, and let me see what else? Thrown into a box, cut off a vine and eaten grape by grape by a girl in her teens. Yes, sir. All them things, if this doesn't beat everything. Did you encounter any reptiles?

What's reptiles? Joe said.

Snakes.

We didn't see any. The water was black.

Black water. Any fish?

Didn't see any, Joe said.

A Ford stopped in front of the store and an old man got out and came across the wood floor of the porch into the store.

Open me a bottle, Abbott, the man said.

Judge Harmon, the grocer said, I want you to meet three of the most heroic Californians of this great state.

The grocer pointed at Joe, and Joe said, Joseph Bettencourt—I speak Portuguese.

Stephen L. Harmon, the Judge said. I speak a little French.

The grocer pointed at my cousin Mourad and Mourad said, Mourad Garoghlanian.

What do you speak? the Judge said.

Armenian, my cousin Mourad said.

The grocer gave the Judge the opened bottle, the Judge lifted it to his lips, swallowed three swigs, beat his chest, and said, I'm mighty proud to meet a Californian who speaks Armenian.

The grocer pointed at me.

Aram Garoghlanian, I said.

Brothers? the Judge asked.

Cousins.

Same thing. Now, Abbott, if you please what's the occasion for this banquet and your poetic excitement, if not delirium?

These boys have just come from showing that old river, the grocer said.

The Judge took three more swigs, beat his chest three times slowly and said, Come from *what*?

They've just come from swimming.

Have any of you fevers? the Judge said.

Fever? Joe said. We ain't sick.

The grocer busted out with a roar of laughter.

Sick? he said. Sick? Judge, these boys dived naked into the black water of winter and came up glowing with the warmth of summer.

We finished the beans and the bread. We were thirsty but didn't know if we should intrude with a request for a drink of water. At least *I* didn't know, but Joe apparently didn't stop to consider.

Mr. Abbott, he said, could we have a drink of water?

Water? the grocer said. Water's for swimming in, not for drinking.

He fetched three paper cups, went to a small barrel with a tap, turned the tap, and filled each cup with a light golden fluid.

Here, boys. Drink. Drink the lovely juice of the golden apple, unfermented.

The Judge poured the grocer a drink out of his bottle, lifted the bottle to his lips, and said, To your health, gentlemen.

Yes, sir, Joe said.

The Judge screwed the top onto the bottle, put the bottle into his back pocket, looked at each of us carefully, as if to remember us for the rest of his life, and said, Good-by, gentlemen. Court opens in a half hour. I must pass sentence on a man who says he *borrowed* the horse, *didn't* steal it. He speaks Mexican. The man who says he *stole* the horse speaks Italian. Good-by.

Good-by, we said.

By this time our clothes were almost dry, but the rain hadn't stopped.

Well, Joe said, thanks very much, Mr. Abbott. We've got to get home.

Not at all, the grocer said. *I* thank you.

The grocer seemed to be in a strange silence for a man who only a moment before had been so noisy with talk.

We left the store quietly and began to walk down the highway. The rain was now so light it didn't seem like rain at all. I didn't know what to make of it. Joe was the first to speak.

That Mr. Abbott, he said, he's some man.

The name on the sign is Darcous, I said. Abbott's his first name.

First or last, Joe said, he sure is some man.

That Judge was somebody too, my cousin Mourad said.

Educated, Joe said. I'd learn French myself, but who would I talk to?

We walked along the highway in silence. After a few minutes the black clouds parted, the sun came through, and away over in the east we saw the rainbow over the Sierra Nevadas.

We sure showed that old river, Joe said. Was he crazy?

I don't know, my cousin Mourad said.

It took us another hour to get home. We had all thought about the two men and whether or not the grocer was crazy. Myself, I believed he wasn't, but at the same time it seemed to me had acted kind of crazy.

So long, Joe said.

He went down the street. Fifty yards away he turned around and said something almost to himself.

What? my cousin Mourad shouted.

He was, Joe said.

Was what? I shouted.

Crazy.

How do you know?

How can you be cut off a vine and eaten grape by grape by a girl in her teens?

Suppose he *was* crazy? my cousin Mourad said. What of it?

Joe put his hand to his chin and began to consider. The sun was shining for all it was worth now and the world was full of light.

I don't think he was crazy, Joe shouted.

He went on down the street.

He was pretty crazy, my cousin Mourad said.

Well, I said, maybe he's not always.

We decided to let the matter rest at this point until we went swimming again, at which time we would visit the store again and see what happened.

A month later when, after swimming in the ditch, the three of us went into the store, the man who was in charge was a much younger man than Mr. Abbott Darcous. He wasn't a foreigner either.

What'll it be? he said.

A nickel's worth of baloney, Joe said, and a loaf of French bread.

Where's Mr. Darcous? my cousin Mourad said.

He's gone home.

Where's that? I said.

Some place in Connecticut, I think.

We made sandwiches of the baloney and French bread and began to eat.

At last Joe asked the question.

Was he crazy?

Well, the young man said, that's hard to say. I thought he was crazy at first. Then I decided he wasn't. The way he ran this store made you think he was crazy. He gave away more than he sold. Otherwise he was all right.

Thanks, Joe said.

The store was all in order now, and a very dull place. We walked out, and began walking home.

*He's* crazy, Joe said.

Who? I said.

That guy in the store now, Joe said.

That young fellow?

Yeah. That new fellow in there that ain't got no education.

I think you're right, my cousin Mourad said.

All the way home we remembered the educated grocer.

Well, I'll be cultivated, Joe said when he left us and walked on down the street.

Well, I'll be picked off a tree and thrown in a box, my cousin Mourad said.

Well, I'll be cut off a vine and eaten grape by grape by a girl in her teens, I said.

He sure was some man. Twenty years later, I decided he had been a poet and had run that grocery store in that little run-down village just for the casual poetry in it instead of the paltry cash.

## For Better Reading: Asking Questions

Why are good readers different from tape recorders? Because they don't simply record things in order to "play them back" later. Good readers take an active part in what they're reading.

Good readers are always asking questions, as if they're engaging in conversation with the author. And, because you aren't talking face to face, you can be sure that good writers try to anticipate your questions.

And, you shouldn't hesitate to ask them.

Writers, also, sometimes like to keep you in suspense. Be alert to the difference between the questions to be answered right away and those meant to keep you guessing ... and reading to the end.

If the story's a mystery, the answer to "Who's guilty?" likely comes last. But, wide-awake readers ask questions and spot clues all along the way.

Good readers aren't like tape recorders. They're more like detectives and lawyers—whether they're reading short stories, novels, or poems, nonfiction books, essays, or articles. They're always posing questions, weighing evidence, making decisions—to get to the heart of what they read.

## Important Details

1. The boys go swimming (a) in defiance of their parents' orders (b) on a cold, stormy spring day (c) to escape the summer heat of the city (d) for a last fling before the start of school.
2. Their diving and swimming were dangerous because of the (a) polluted and unsafe water (b) extreme depth and strong current (c) muddy bottom and shallow depth (d) boys' inexperience.
3. The grocer Abbott Darcous says that he (a) knows a little French (b) is a Yale graduate (c) majored in psychology (d) has published a book of poetry.

## Questioning the Story

1. In "The Three Swimmers and the Educated Grocer," the question is "Was Mr. Abbott Darcous crazy or wasn't he?" What are three things he did that might make him seem crazy?
2. When the grocer calls the boys "heroic" and says they've just come "from showing that old river," how does this reveal his understanding of the boys' point of view?
3. How does the Judge express a more typically adult attitude?
4. How do the descriptions of the water at the beginning of the story reveal the boys' attitude toward diving into the ditch?
5. "Aw shut up" is Aram's response when something unwittingly insults him. How do both Joe and the river insult Aram?
6. What evidence in the story suggests that Aram is younger than both Joe and his cousin Mourad?
7. Although Joe doesn't take to schooling, what does he do and say to show his intelligence? Find at least two examples.
8. How does Mr. Darcous compare his education to the boys'? How is his attitude toward the boys' backgrounds different from that which others might have?
9. One reason for thinking Mr. Darcous crazy is the "crazy" words he uses. When he says, "Well, I'll be cultivated" or "I'll be picked off a tree and put in a box," what kind of feelings does he wish to express? How do many other people express the same idea?
10. What is the new grocer's only reason for thinking Mr. Darcous crazy? What good qualities of Mr. Darcous does the young grocer lack?

## Looking Deeper
### I. What Is an American?

That's a question raised in the story when Joe says, "We're all Californians," not foreigners. What point is author William Saroyan, who has an Armenian background, making about many people's attitudes towards boys like Aram, Mourad, and Joe? How does the Judge describe the two men involved in the trial of horse theft? Should they rightfully be called Californians or foreigners? Why do you think the Judge looked at the three boys so carefully before he left?

### II. Why Is the Grocer "Sure Some Man"?

Although he's called a poet at the end, why doesn't Mr. Darcous fit the usual image of a poet? Not counting his imaginative use of words, how does he look at the world in an original way, as a poet might? How does the new grocer show himself more interested in "paltry cash" than "casual poetry"?

### III. What Made You Do It?

"Nothing, Joe said—for he had too many reasons to name them all at a moment's notice." What do you think are some of the reasons? Without a river for diving and swimming, what similar kinds of things do kids do in other places for much the same reasons?

# A tornado struck . . . from *An American Childhood*

## by Annie Dillard

**Home state:** *Pennsylvania*
**Famous as:** *Columnist for Wilderness Society, poet, and author*

---

**A** TORNADO HIT OUR NEIGHBORHOOD one morning. Our neighborhood was not only leafy Richland Lane and its hushed side streets, but also Penn Avenue, from which Richland Lane loftily arose. Old Penn Avenue was a messy, major thoroughfare still cobblestoned in the middle lanes, and full of stoplights and jammed traffic. There were drugstores there, old apartment buildings, and some old mansions. Penn Avenue was the city—tangled and muscular, a broad and snarled fist. The tornado broke all the windows in the envelope factory on Penn Avenue and ripped down mature oaks and maples on Richland Lane and its side streets—trees about which everyone would make, in my view, an unconscionable fuss, not least perhaps because they would lie across the streets for a week.

After the tornado passed I roamed around and found a broken power line. It banged violently by the Penn Avenue curb; it was shooting sparks into the street. I couldn't bring myself to leave the spot.

The power line was loosing a fireball of sparks that melted the asphalt. It was a thick twisted steel cable usually strung overhead along Penn Avenue; it carried power—4,500 kilovolts of it—from Wilkinsburg ("City of Churches") to major sections of Pittsburgh, to Homewood and Brushton, Shadyside, and Squirrel Hill.

It was melting a pit for itself in the street. The live wire's hundred twisted ends spat a thick sheaf of useless yellow sparks that hissed. The sparks were cooking the asphalt gummy; they were burning a hole. I watched the cable relax and sink into its own pit; I watched the yellow sparks pool and crackle around the cable's torn end and splash out of the pit and over the asphalt in a stream toward the curb and my shoes. My bare shins could feel the heat. I smelled tarry melted asphalt and steel so hot it smoked.

"If you touch that," my father said, needlessly, "you're a goner."

I had gone back to the house to get him so he could see this violent sight, this cable all but thrashing like a cobra and shouting a torrent of sparks.

While the tornado itself was on—while the buckeye trees in our yard were coming apart—Mother had gathered Amy and Molly and held them with her sensibly away from the windows; she urged my father and me to join them. Father had recently returned from his river trip and was ensconced tamed in the household again. And here was a pleasant, once-in-a-lifetime tornado, the funnel of which touched down, in an almost delicate point, like a bolt of lightning, on our very street. He and I raced from window to window and watched; we saw the backyard sycamore smash the back-porch roof; we saw the air roaring and blowing full of sideways-flying objects, and saw the leafy buckeye branches out front blow white and upward like skirts.

"With your taste for natural disaster," Mother said to me later, "you should try to arrange a marriage with the head of the International Red Cross."

Now the torn cable lay near the curb, away from traffic. Its loose power dissipated in the air, a random destructiveness. If you touched it, you would turn into Reddy Kilowatt. Your skin would wiggle up in waves like an electrified cat's in a cartoon; your hair would rise stiff from your head; anyone who touched you by mistake would stick to you wavy-skinned and paralyzed. You would be dead but still standing, the power surging through your body in electrical imitation of life. Passersby would have to knock you away from the current with planks.

Father placed a ring of empty Coke bottles around the hissing power line and went back home to call Duquesne Light. I stayed transfixed. Other neighborhood children showed up, looked at the cable shooting sparks, and wandered away to see the great killed trees. I stood and watched the thick billion bolts swarm in the street. The cable was as full as a waterfall, never depleted; it dug itself a pit in which the yellow sparks spilled like water. I stayed at the busy Penn Avenue curb all day staring, until, late in the afternoon, someone somewhere turned off the juice.

Streetcars ran on Penn Avenue. Streetcars were orange, clangy, beloved things—loud, jerky, and old. They were powerless beasts compelled to travel stupidly with their wheels stuck in the tracks below them. Each streetcar had one central headlight, which looked fixedly down its tracks and nowhere else. The single light advertised to drivers at night that something was coming that couldn't move over. When a streetcar's tracks and wires rounded a corner, the witless streetcar had to follow. Its heavy orange body bulged out and blocked two lanes. Any car trapped beside it had to cringe stopped against the curb until it passed.

Sometimes a car parked at the curb blocked a streetcar's route. Then the great beast sounded its mournful bell: it emitted a long-suffering, monotonous bong ... bong ... bong ... and men and women on the sidewalk shook their heads sympathetically at the motorman inside, the motorman more inferred than seen through the windshield's bright reflections.

Penn Avenue smelled of gasoline, exhaust fumes, trees' sweetness in the spring, and, year round, burnt grit. On the blocks from Lang to Richland Lane were buildings in wild assortment: two drugstores, Henry Clay Frick's mansion with his old daughter somewhere inside, a dark working-class bar called the Evergreen Cafe, a corner grocery store, the envelope factory, a Westinghouse plant, some old apartment buildings, and a parklike Presbyterian seminary.

. . . The streetcars' overhead network of wires made of Penn Avenue a loose-roofed tunnel. The wires cut the sky into rectangles inside which you could compose various views as you walked. Here were a yellow brick apartment top and some flattened fair-weather clouds; here were green sycamore leaves in the foreground, and a faded orange rooftop advertising sign, and a yellow streetlight, and a slab of neutral sky.

Streetcars traveled with their lone trolley sticks pushed up by springs into these overhead wires. A trolley stick carried a trolley wheel; the trolley wheel rolled along the track of hot electric wire overhead as the four wheels rolled along the cold grooved track below. At night, and whenever it rained, the street-cars' trolleys sparked. They shot a radiant fistful of sparks at every crossing of wires. Sometimes a streetcar accidentally "threw the trolley." Bumping over a switch or rounding a bend, the trolley lost the wire and the spring-loaded stick flew up and banged its bare side crazily against the hot wire. Big yellow sparks came crackling into the sky and fell glowing toward the roofs of cars. The motorman had to brake the streetcar, go around to its rear, and haul the way-ward, sparking trolley stick down with a rope. This happened so often that there was a coil of rope for that purpose at the streetcar's stern, neat and cleated like a halyard on a mast.

So the big orange streetcars clanged and spat along; they stopped and started, tethered to their wires overhead and trapped in their grooves below. Every day at a hundred intersections they locked horns with cars that blocked their paths—cars driven by insensible, semiconscious people, people who had just moved to town, teenagers learning to drive, the dread Ohio drivers, people sunk in rapturous conversation.

"Bong bong," bleated the stricken streetcar, "bong," and its passengers tried to lean around to see what was holding it up, and its berserk motorman gestured helplessly, furiously, at the dumb dreaming car—a shrug, a wave, a fist:

I'm a streetcar!
What can I do?
What can I do
but wait for you jerks
to figure out that I'm a streetcar!

I tried to kill a streetcar by overturning it.

Pin Ford and I were hiding under a purple beech tree on the lawn of the Presbyterian seminary on Penn Avenue.

Through the beech's low dense branches she and I could make out Penn Avenue's streetcar lanes. It was midafternoon. Now a streetcar was coming toward us. We had been waiting. We had just stuck a stone in the streetcar track. This one seemed like a stone big enough to throw it over. Would the streetcar go over? Did we hope it would go over? We spotted its jiggling trolley stick first, high above the roofs of cars. Then we saw its round orange shoulder, humped like a cobblestone, and its lone simple eye. I pressed a thumb and finger between ribs on both side of my breastbone, to try to calm myself.

It had started with pennies. A streetcar's wheel could slick a penny and enlarge it into a stripe. What would it do to a stone? It would crunch and crumble a stone. How big a stone? We ran between moving cars and placed ever bigger stones in the streetcar track; we ran back under the beech tree to watch.

This last stone was a coarse gray conglomerate, five inches by two by two. Was it reinforced concrete? Through the low-slung beech boughs we saw the streetcar draw nigh; we covered our lower faces with our hands.

The streetcar hit the stone audibly and rose like a beached whale. Its big orange body faltered in the air, heaved toward the lane of cars beside it, trembled, and finally fell down on its track and broke the stone. And went on, bumping again only slightly when the rear wheel went over it. Pin Ford and I lay low.

In that instant while the streetcar stopped upraised over its track like an animal bewildered, while it swayed over the cars' lane and hung on its side and its trolley stick dangled askew, I saw it continue its roll; I saw precisely which cars it would fall on, and which dim people silhouetted inside the cars and the streetcar would be the most surprised. I saw, too, in that clear instant, that if the streetcar did derail, I would have to come forward and give myself up to the police, and do time, and all that, for the alternative was living all the rest of life on the lam.

## For Better Reading: What's Important

"A tornado struck . . ." With those three words, a dozen questions should pop into your head. Where did it hit? What damage did it do? Was anyone hurt? How strong was it? Where were you?

Those are the questions you should read to answer in the first part of Annie Dillard's account of her childhood in Pittsburgh.

In some ways, reading is like watching the movies or TV. You have to keep your eyes on the action. Although there is much in the background to make the scene seem real, you pay attention to the characters—what they do and say.

Dillard brings many details to her story—to fill in the background and create the reality of her hometown. What happens in the foreground is most important: finding out what happened when Dillard encountered a tornado and how she tried to kill a streetcar. Always try to have what's important in mind so you can concentrate more easily when you read.

## Making Inferences

1. Annie reacts to the tornado as a (a) pleasant, once-in-a-lifetime experience (b) disaster revealing the best and worst in people (c) chance to

prove her courage and daring (d) terrifying example of nature's devastating power.

2. Annie remains watching the downed cable until (a) someone turns off the central power (b) she is chased away by Electric Company technicians (c) her father comes to make her go home (d) friends tell her about the wrecked streetcar.

3. Annie tries to "kill a streetcar" by (a) cutting one of its power lines (b) breaking a connecting trolley stick (c) laying pennies on the rails (d) putting large stones on the track.

## Questioning the Selection

1. What are three examples of damage that the tornado did to Dillard's neighborhood and yard?
2. In what ways does Dillard seem more like her father than her mother?
3. Why would the other children be more interested in the "great killed trees" than the downed cable? What questions of their own were they trying to answer?
4. Give three examples of the force, power, and destructiveness of the broken line.
5. Dillard writes that the power line "banged violently." Find three other phrases that make it seem almost alive.
6. Why do you think Dillard "couldn't leave the spot" where the cable fell? What was its fascination for her?
7. How does Dillard personify the streetcars, making them seem more like living creatures or people than mechanical objects? Find at least five examples, with no more than one per paragraph.
8. Although Dillard says she "tried to kill a streetcar," what kinds of questions was she really trying to answer?
9. How was the streetcar's reaction to the last stone both different from and the same as before?
10. In the final paragraph, Dillard writes that she "saw precisely which cars it would fall on" and "which dim people ... would be the most surprised." Since the car didn't derail, where must she have "seen" this?
11. How and why does the final paragraph prove that Dillard wasn't really "trying to kill a streetcar"?
12. Would you call the affair of the streetcar a crime, prank, or experiment? Support your answer from the selection.

## Looking Deeper
### I. But, Is It true?

Judging from its details and from your own knowledge, do you consider Dillard to be a good and accurate reporter? Use details and points from this selection to uphold your viewpoint.

## II. How Actions Reveal Character

Curiosity, a sense of responsibility, concern for others, a spirit of daring, imagination—these and many other qualities are better proved by what someone does than what he or she says.

For example, Dillard showed great intellectual curiosity by staying to watch the downed cable and discovering its power to dig an ever deeper pit and shoot billions of sparks that never depleted.

In what other instances does Dillard display this and other inner qualities by her actions? Give at least three additional examples.

## III. Breaking the Stereotype

How do Annie Dillard and her friend Pin Ford fit your image—or stereotype—of the typical girl of the 50's or today? In what ways are they typical or untypical? Be prepared for differences of opinion and ready to support your point of view.

# Foxes and Hounds

*by Forrest Carter*

**Born in:** *Tennessee*
**Orphaned:** *Age 10*
**Lived in:** *Wyoming, Texas*
**Careers:** *Woodchopper, ranch hand, author of Western fiction*

(From *The Education of Little Tree*, the tale of a small boy who goes to live with his half Cherokee grandfather and full Cherokee grandmother after the death of his parents.)

IT WAS LATE OF A winter afternoon when Granpa took ol' Maud and Ringer into the cabin because he said he didn't want them embarrassed before the other hounds. I figured something was to happen. Granma already knew. Her eyes were twinkling like black lights and she put a deer shirt on me, just like Granpa's, and placed her hand on my shoulder like she done him, and I felt might near growed-up.

I didn't ask, but I hung around. Granma gave me a sack with biscuits and meat and said, "I'll sit on the porch tonight and listen; and I will hear you."

We went into the yard and Granpa whistled up the dogs and off we set, up the hollow by the spring branch. The hounds ran back and forth, hurrying us up.

Granpa kept his hounds for only two reasons. One was his corn patch where every spring and summer, he assigned ol' Maud and Ringer to stay and guard against deer, 'coon, hogs and crow getting all his corn.

Like Granpa said, ol' Maud had no smell sense at all and was practical worthless on a fox trail; but she had keen hearing and eyesight, and this gave her something she could do and take pride in knowing she was of worth. Granpa said if a hound or anybody else has got no feeling of worth then it's a bad thing.

Ringer had been a good trail dog. He was getting old now. His tail was broke, which made him look disheartened, and he couldn't see nor hear very well. Granpa said he put Ringer with ol' Maud so he could help and feel that he was of worth in his old age; that it sort of dignified him, which it did for Ringer walked around right stiff-legged and dignified, especially during the periods when he was working at the corn patch.

Granpa fed ol' Maud and Ringer at the barn up in the hollow during corn raising time, for this wasn't far from the corn patch. They stayed there faithful. Ol' Maud was Ringer's eyes and ears. She would see something in the corn patch and take off after it, raising howls like she owned that corn patch, and Ringer would follow, doing the same.

They'd go crashing through the corn; and maybe ol' Maud would run right past a 'coon if she didn't see it, for she sure couldn't smell it, but Ringer, following behind her, could. He'd put his nose to the ground and go braying after that 'coon. He'd run that 'coon out of the patch and hold onto his trail by smell until he run into a tree. Then he'd come back kind of sad; but him and ol' Maud never give up. They done their job.

The other reason Granpa kept hounds was for pure fun, trailing fox. He never used dogs to hunt game. He didn't need them. Granpa knew the watering and feeding places, the habit and trails, even the thinking and character of all the game, far better than any hound could learn.

The red fox runs in a circle when he is chased by hounds. With his den in the center, he will start on a circle swing that measures maybe a mile, sometimes more, across the middle. All the time he's running, he'll use tricks: backtracking, running in water and laying false trails; but he'll stick to the circle. As he grows tired, he will make the circle smaller and smaller, until he retreats to his den. He "dens up," they call it.

The more he runs, the hotter he gets, and his mouth sweats out stronger smells that the dogs pick up on the trail, and so get louder with their baying. It is called a "hot trail."

When the gray fox runs, he runs in a figure 8, and his den is just about where he crosses his trail each time to make the 8.

Granpa knew the thinking of the 'coon too and laughed at his mischievous ways, and swore a solemn oath that on occasion, the 'coon had laughed at him. He knew where the turkey ran, and could track a bee from water to hive with a look of his eye. He could make the deer come to him, because he knew his curious nature; and he could ease through a covey of quail without stirring a wing. But he never bothered them, except for what he needed and I *know* they understood.

Granpa lived *with* the game, not *at* it. The white mountain men were a hardy lot and Granpa bore with them well. But they would take their dogs and clatter all over the mountains chasing game this way and that, until everything would run for cover. If they saw a dozen turkey, why they killed a dozen turkey, if they could.

But they respected Granpa as a master woodsman. I could see it in their eyes and the touching of their hat brims when they met him at the crossroads store. They stayed out of Granpa's hollows and mountains with their guns and dogs, whilst they complained a lot about the game getting scarcer and scarcer where they was. Granpa often shook his head at their comments and never said anything. But he told me. They would never understand The Way of the Cherokee.

With the dogs loping behind, I trotted close behind Granpa because it was that mysterious, exciting time in the hollows when the sun had sunk and the light faded from red to shady blood, and kept changing and darkening, as if the daylight was alive but dying. Even the dusk breeze was sly with a whisper as if it had things to tell that it couldn't say out open.

The game was going to its beds and the night creatures was coming out for the hunt. As we passed the meadow by the barn, Granpa stopped and I stood practical under him.

An owl was flying toward us down the hollow, moving in the air not higher than Granpa's head; and passed right by, making no sound, not a whisper nor whir of wing and settled silent as a ghost in the barn.

"Screech owl," Granpa said, "the one ye hear sometimes at night that sounds like a woman paining. Going to catch some rats." I sure didn't want to disturb that ol' owl and rat catching, and kept Granpa between me and the barn as we passed.

Dark fell in close, and the mountains moved in on either side as we walked. Before long, we came to a Y in the trail, and Granpa taken the left. Now there was no more room for the trail except right on the edge of the spring branch. Granpa called this the "Narrows." Seemed like you could stretch out your arms on either side and touch the mountains. Straight up they went, dark and feathered with treetops, and left a thin slice of stars above us.

Way off, a mourning dove called, long and throaty, and the mountains picked it up and echoed the sound over and over, carrying it farther and farther away until you wondered how many mountains and hollows that call would travel—and it died away, so far, it was more like a memory than a sound.

It was lonesome, and I trotted right up on Granpa's heels. None of the hounds stayed behind me, which I wished they would. They stayed ahead of Granpa, running back to him now and then, whining and wanting him to send them off trailing.

The Narrows sloped upward, and before long I could hear big water running. It was a creek that crossed what Granpa called "Hangin' Gap."

We moved off the trail, up into the mountain above the creek. Granpa sent the dogs off. All he had to do was point and say, "Go!" and off they went, giving little yelps, like young'uns going berry picking Granpa said.

We sat down in a pine thicket above the creek. It was warm. Pine thickets give off heat, but if it's summertime, you want to sit amongst oak or hickory or some such, because pine gets plumb hot.

The stars were watering and moving around in the creek, riding on ripples and splashes. Granpa said we could commence to listen for the hounds in a little while, when they picked up ol' Slick's trail. That's what he called the fox.

Granpa said we was in ol' Slick's territory. He said he had knowed him about five years. Most people think that all fox hunters kill foxes, but it's not true. Granpa never killed a fox in his life. The reason for fox hunting is the hounds—to listen to their trailing. Granpa always called off the hounds when the fox denned up.

Granpa said that when things had got monotonous for ol' Slick he had gone so far as to come and set in the edge of the cabin clearing, trying to get Granpa and the hounds to trail him. It sometimes caused Granpa all manner of trouble with the hounds, as they yelped and bayed, with ol' Slick leading them up the hollow.

Granpa said he like to slip up on ol' Slick when he was cantankerous and not in the mood for trailing. When a fox wanted to den up, he will use ingenious tricks to throw off the hounds. When he is playful, he will play all over the countryside. He said the best part was that ol' Slick would *know* he was being paid back for sashaying round the cabin and troubling Granpa.

Sure enough, the moon broke over the mountain, a quarter used up. It sprinkled patterns through the pines and splashed lights off the creek, and made thin silver boats of the fog tearings sailing slow through the Narrows.

Granpa leaned back against a pine and spraddled out his legs. I done the same thing, and put the vittle sack right by me as it was my responsibility. Not far off a big bay sounded, long and hollow.

"That's ol' Rippitt," Granpa said, and laughed low, "and it's a damn lie. Rippitt knows what's wanted ... but he can't wait, so he makes out like he's hit a trail-scent. Listen to how falsified his bay sounds. He knows he's a'lying." Sure enough, it *did* sound that-a-way.

"He's damn shore lying," I said. Me and Granpa could cuss when we wasn't around Granma.

In a minute the other hounds let him know, as they howled around him, not baying. In the mountains they call such a "bluffer dog." There was silence again.

In a little while a deep bay broke the stillness. It was long and far off, and I knew right then it was the real thing, because it carried excitement in it. The other hounds took it up.

"That was Blue Boy," Granpa said, "up and comin' to have the best nose in the mountains; and that's Little Red right behind him ... and there's Bess." Another bay chimed in, this one kind of frantic. Granpa said, "And there's ol' Rippitt, gittin' in on the last."

They was in full voice now, moving farther away; their chorus echoing backward and forward until it sounded like hounds all around. Then the sound disappeared.

They're on the backside of Clinch Mountain," Granpa said. I listened hard, but I couldn't hear anything.

A nighthawk went "SEEeeeeee!" from the side of the mountain behind us, cutting the air with a sharp whistle. Across the creek, a hoot owl answered him, "WHO ... WHO ... WHOAREYouuuuu!"

Granpa laughed low. "Owl stays in the hollow, hawk stays on the ridges. Sometimes ol' hawk figures there's easy pickins around the water and ol' owl don't like it."

A fish flopped a splash in the creek. I was beginning to get worried. "Reckin," I whispered to Granpa, "that them hounds is *lost?*"

"Nope," Granpa said, "we'll hear 'em in a minute, and they'll come out on t'other side of Clinch Mountain and run across that ridge in front of us."

Sure enough they did. First they sounded far-off, then louder and louder; and then they came, baying and yelping, longways along the ridge facing us and crossed the creek somewhere down below. Then they came along the side of the mountain behind us and set off again for Clinch Mountain. This time they ran on the near side of Clinch Mountain and we heard them all the way across it.

"Ol' Slick is tightening up the circle," Granpa said, "this time, after they cross the creek, ol' Slick may lead 'em right in front of us." Granpa was right. We heard them splashing and baying across the creek not far below us . . . and while they was splashing and baying Granpa set up straight and grabbed my arm.

"There he is," Granpa whispered. And there he was. Coming along through willow poles on the creek bank, it was ol' Slick. He was trotting, with his tongue hanging out and a bushy tail dangling kind of careless behind him. He had pointed ears, and he jogged along real pickety, taking his time to go around a pile of brush. Once he stopped, lifted a front paw and licked it; then he turned his head back toward the baying of the hounds and came on.

Down in front of me and Granpa, there were some rocks that stuck up in the water, five or six of them that went out nearly to the middle of the creek. When ol' Slick reached where the rocks were, he stopped and looked back, like he was judging how far away the hounds was. Then he sat down, calm as you please with his back to us, and just sat there, looking at the creek. The moon glinted red off his coat, and the hounds was coming closer.

Granpa squeezed my arm. "Watch him now!" Ol' Slick jumped from the creek bank out onto the first rock. He stopped there a minute and danced on the rock. Then he jumped to the next one and danced again, then the next and the next until he reached the last one, nearly in the middle of the creek.

Then he came back, jumping from rock to rock, until he reached the one closest to the creek bank. He stopped and listened again, then stepped into the water and splashed up the creek, until he was out of sight. He sure cut the time close, because he had no more than disappeared when here come the hounds.

Blue Boy was leading with his nose right on the ground. Ol' Rippitt was crowding him, and Bess and Little Red was bunched right behind. Now and then, one of them would raise their nose and give out a "OOOWOOOOoooooooooh!" that tingled your blood.

They came to where the rocks went out into the creek and Blue Boy never hesitated; out he went, jumping from rock to rock, and the rest of them right behind.

When they reached the last rock in the middle of the creek, Blue Boy stopped but ol' Rippitt didn't. He jumped right in, like there wasn't no doubt about it, and started swimming for the other bank. Bess jumped in behind him and started swimming too.

Blue Boy raised his nose and commenced to sniff the air, and Little Red stayed there on the rock with him. In a minute here come Blue Boy and Little Red jumping back on the rocks toward us. They reached the bank, and Blue Boy led the way. Then he hit ol' Slick's trail and bayed long and loud, and Little Red chimed in.

Bess reversed herself while she was still swimming and come back, while ol'

Rippitt was running up and down the other back at a total loss. He was howling and yelping and running back and forth with his nose on the ground. When he heard Blue Boy, he hit the creek water in a dive and swam so hard he splashed water over his head until he made it to the bank and took up the trail behind the rest of them.

Me and Granpa laughed so hard we nearly fell off the mountain. I did lose my foot-bracing hold on a pine sapling and rolled into cocklebur bushes. Granpa pulled me out and we was still laughing while we picked the burrs out of my hair.

Granpa said he *knowed* ol' Slick would pull that trick, and that's why he chose the place for us to set. He said that, without a doubt, ol' Slick had set close by and watched the dogs his own self.

Granpa said the reason ol' Slick had waited so long for the hounds to get close is that he wanted his scent to be fresh on the rocks, figuring that the hounds' *feelings* would take over from the *sense*, when they got excited. It worked too, with ol' Rippitt and Bess; but not with Blue Boy and Little Red.

Granpa said he had many's the time seen that same kind of thing, feelings taking over sense, make as big a fools out of people as it had ol' Rippitt. Which I reckin is so.

It had broke day and I hadn't even noticed. Me and Granpa moved down to the creek bank clearing and et our sour biscuits and meat. The dogs was baying back around and coming along the ridge in front of us.

The sun topped the mountain, sparkling the trees across the creek and brought out brush wrens and a red cardinal.

Granpa slid his knife under the bark of a cedar tree and made a dipper by twisting one end of the bark. We dipped water from the creek, cold, where you could see the pebbles on the bottom. The water had a cedary taste that made me hungrier, but we had et all the biscuits.

Grandpa said ol' Slick *might* come up the farther creek bank this time, and we would get to see him again; but we would have to sit quiet. I didn't move, not even when the ants crawled up on my foot, though I wanted to. Granpa saw them, and said it was all right to brush them off—ol' Slick wouldn't see me do that. Which I did.

In a little while the hounds were below us again, down the creek, and then we saw him, lazying up the creek bank on the other side with his tongue hanging out. Granpa give a low whistle and ol' Slick stopped and stared across the creek at us. He stood there a minute, with his eyes crinkled up like he was grinning at us; then he snorted and trotted on out of sight.

Granpa said ol' Slick snorted because he was disgusted, being caused all this inconvenience. I remembered ol' Slick had it coming to him.

Granpa said some fellers told that they had heard about foxes "swapping out," but he had actually seen it. He said years ago, he had been fox trailing and was sittin' on a hillock above a meadow clearing. He said the fox, a red one, come along with the hounds behind him and stopped at a hollow tree and give a little bark. He said another fox come out of that hollow tree, and the first one got in. Then the second fox trotted off, leading the dogs on the trail. He said he moved close to that tree and could hear that ol' fox actually *snoring* while the hounds was passing a few feet from him. He said that ol' fox had so much confidence in hisself that he didn't give a lick-damn *how* close them dogs come around him.

Here comes Blue Boy and the pack up the creek bank. They bayed every step or two . . . it was a strong trail. They passed out of sight and in a minute, one bay split off from the rest and broke up into yelps and howls.

Granpa cussed. He said, "Damn! Ol' Rippitt is trying to cut acrost again and cheat on ol' Slick. He's gone and got hisself lost." In the mountains, such is known as a "cheater hound."

Granpa said we would have to set up a hollering and baying ourselves to guide ol' Rippitt back to us, and that would call off the trailing, because the other dogs would come too. So we did.

I couldn't give the long holler like Granpa—it was almost like a yodel—but I did tolerable well, Granpa said.

In a little while here they come, and ol' Rippitt was ashamed of what he had done. He hung back behind the others; hoping, I reckin, that he would pass unnoticed. Granpa said it served him right and maybe *this* time it would learn him that you can't cheat without making unnecessary trouble for yourself. Which proves out as reasonable.

The sun had slanted into the afternoon when we left Hangin' Gap, back down the Narrows toward home. The dogs dragged their feet in the trail and I knew they were tired. I was too and would have had a hard time making it if Granpa hadn't been so tuckered that he walked along slow.

It was dusk evening when we sighted the cabin clearing and Granma. She was out on the trail to meet us. She picked me up, though I could have made it, and put an arm around Granpa's waist. I guess I was tuckered, for I fell asleep on her shoulder and didn't know when we got to the cabin.

## For Better Reading: Through a Child's Eyes

Forrest Carter does not write about life with his Cherokee grandparents as an adult looking back on his boyhood. Instead, he writes as if the story were being told by himself as a little boy, then called Little Tree.

Little Tree expresses childish wonder and uses less than perfect English. And, he doesn't understand all that he sees.

Adult writers often take a child's point of view because children look at things with fresh, curious eyes—they are full of questions and open to new ideas.

Yet, all is not as innocent as it seems. For, the writer shapes the story with adult skill and expects the reader to see more than the child can knowingly express or understand.

So it is with the story of Little Tree. As you consider the questions, discover how Forrest Carter has revealed much that Little Tree, his childhood self, did not realize.

## Determining Outcomes

1. Granpa tells Little Tree that ol' Slick (a) had killed some of his chickens (b) had a bounty put on his head by the mountain men (c) cannot legally be shot on the reservation (d) enjoys playing tricks on the hounds.
2. The mountain men (a) ignore the "No Hunting" signs on the reservation (b) feel Granpa is ignorant and foolish (c) respected Granpa as a master woodsman (d) resented Granpa's trying to advise them.
3. The result of the fox hunt was (a) the loss and injury of a hound (b) Granpa's calling off the trailing (c) Little Tree's being fooled by ol' Rippitt (d) Grandpa's bagging the limit of two foxes.

## Questioning the Selection

1. "Granpa says if a hound or anybody else has got no feeling of worth then it's a bad thing."
   a. How does Granpa show concern and understanding towards ol' Maud and Ringer to give them a feeling of worth?
   b. Though Little Tree does not realize it, what ways does Granpa make him feel worthy and important?
2. Granpa says the white mountain men "would never understand The Way of the Cherokee."
   a. How does the white men's attitude towards hunting differ from Granpa's, which is the Cherokee way?
   b. When the white men complain that game is getting scarcer and scarcer, what don't they realize?
3. Why does it seem that both ol' Slick and Granpa like to play tricks and outwit one another? Give examples for each.
4. According to Granpa, how do foxes sometimes fool hunting dogs by "swapping out"?
5. Granpa says, "feelings taking over sense [can] make as big a fools out of people as it had ol' Rippitt."
   a. What does Rippitt do to make Granpa say this?
   b. By saying this, what effect do you think Granpa hoped to have on Little Tree?
6. Granpa says, "You can't cheat without making unnecessary trouble for yourself."
   a. How does Rippitt try to cheat ol' Slick?
   b. What trouble does he get into and how does he feel when he comes back?
7. Little Tree says he "would have had a hard time making it if Granpa hadn't be so tuckered that he walked along slow."
   a. What is probably the real reason Granpa walked slowly?
   b. How does Granma show her awareness of Little Tree's feelings, both at the beginning and end of the selection?

## Looking Deeper

### I. Which Way of Looking at Nature Is Better?

The white hunters looked at animals as objects in a sport while Granpa as a Cherokee "lived *with* the game, not *at* it." How did their different outlooks affect their thinking and behavior? Which viewpoint of nature do you think is better? Why?

### II. What Will Little Tree Take with Him?

Forrest Carter's book is called *The Education of Little Tree*. What qualities does Granpa have that make him a good teacher? What lessons does Little Tree learn that serve someone well as an adult? Do you think the story would have been more or less effective if Carter wrote it through an adult's eyes? Why?

# The Sick Child

*by Angela DeCora*

**Born:**        *Winnebago Reservation, Nebraska*
**Indian name:** *Henook-Makhewe-Kelenaka*
                 *(Woman Coming on the Cloud in*
                 *Glory)*
**Career:**      *Artist, book illustrator, lecturer,*
                 *writer*

It WAS ABOUT SUNSET WHEN I, a little child, was sent with a handful of powdered tobacco leaves and red feathers to make an offering to the spirit who had caused the sickness of my little sister. It had been a long, hard winter, and the snow lay deep on the prairies as far as the eye could reach. The medicine-woman's directions had been that the offering must be laid upon the naked earth, and that to find it I must face toward the setting sun.

I was taught the prayer: "Spirit grandfather, I offer this to thee. I pray thee restore my little sister to health." Full of reverence and a strong faith that I could appease the anger of the spirit, I started out to plead for the life of our little one.

But now where was a spot of earth to be found in all that white monotony? They had talked of death at the house. I hoped that my little sister would live, but I was afraid of nature.

I reached a little spring. I looked down to its pebbly bottom, wondering whether I should leave my offering there, or keep on in search of a spot of earth. If I put my offering in the water, would it reach the bottom and touch the earth, or would it float away, as it had always done when I made my offering to the water spirit?

Once more I started on in my search of the bare ground.

The surface was crusted in some places, and walking was easy; in other places I would wade through a foot or more of snow. Often I paused, thinking to clear the snow away in some place and there lay my offering. But no, my faith must be in nature, and I must trust to it to lay bare the earth.

It was a hard struggle for so small a child.

I went on and on; the reeds were waving their tasselled ends in the wind. I stopped and looked at them. A reed, whirling in the wind, had formed a space round its stem, making a loose socket. I stood looking into the opening. The reed must be rooted in the ground, and the hole must follow the stem to the earth. If I poured my offerings into the hole, surely they must reach the ground; so I said the prayer I had been taught, and dropped my tobacco and feathers into the opening that nature itself had created.

No sooner was the sacrifice accomplished than a feeling of doubt and fear thrilled me. What if my offering should never reach the earth? Would my little sister die?

Not till I turned homeward did I realize how cold I was. When at last I reached the house they took me in and warmed me, but did not question me, and I said nothing. Everyone was sad, for the little one had grown worse.

The next day the medicine-woman said my little sister was beyond hope; she could not live. The bitter remorse was mine, for I thought I had been unfaithful, and therefore my little sister was to be called to the spirit-land. I was a silent child, and did not utter my feelings; my remorse was intense.

My parents would not listen to what the medicine-woman had said, but clung to hope. As soon as she had gone, they sent for a medicine-man who lived many miles away.

He arrived about dark. He was a large man, with a sad, gentle face. His presence had always filled me with awe, and that night it was especially so, for he was coming as a holy man. He entered the room where the baby lay, and took a seat, hardly noticing anyone. There was silence saving only for the tinkling of the little tin ornaments on his medicine-bag. He began to speak: "A soul has departed from this house, gone to the spirit-land. As I came I saw luminous vapor about the house. It ascended, it grew less, it was gone on its way to the spirit-land. It was the spirit of the little child who is sick; she still breathes, but her spirit is beyond our reach. If medicine will ease her pain, I will do what I can."

He stood up and blessed the four corners of the earth with song. Then, according to the usual custom of medicine-doctors, he began reciting the vision that had given him the right to be a medicine-man. The ruling force of the vision had been in the form of a bear. To it he addressed his prayer, saying: "Inasmuch as thou hast given me power to cure the sick, and in one case allowing me to unite spirit and body again, if thou seest fit, allow me to recall the spirit of this child to its body once more." He asked that the coverings be taken off the baby, and that it be brought into the middle of the room. Then, as he sang, he danced slowly around the little form. When the song was finished, he blessed the child, and then prepared the medicine, stirring into water some ground herbs. Then he took it into his mouth and sprinkled it over the little body. Another mixture he gave her to drink.

Almost instantly there was a change; the little one began to breathe more easily, and as the night wore on she seemed to suffer less. Finally she opened her eyes, looked into mother's face, and smiled. The medicine-man, seeing it, said that the end was near, and though he gave her more medicine, the spirit, he said, would never return.

After saying words of comfort, he took his departure, refusing to take a pony and some blankets that were offered him, saying that he had been unable to hold the spirit back, and had no right to accept gifts.

The next morning I found the room all cleared away, and my mother sat sewing on a little white gown. The bright red trimming caught my eye. I came to her and asked, "Please mother, tell me for whom is that, and why do you make it so pretty?" She made no answer, but bent over her work. I leaned forward that I might look into her face and repeat my question. I bent down, and, oh! the tears were falling fast down her cheeks. Then we were told that our little sister was gone to the spirit-land, and we must not talk about her. They made us look upon her. We felt of her and kissed her, but she made no response. Then I realized what death meant. Remorse again seized me, but I was silent.

## For Better Reading: Big Questions

It doesn't matter if it's classed as fiction or non-fiction. Some writing strikes you as phony, and other writing impresses you as true. It depends mostly on whether you can freely say, "Yes, this writer seems to know what he or she is talking about." And, if you think, "This is how I would feel, put in a similar situation."

You, of course, must decide this for yourself. Yet, when most readers agree that they can share the feelings in a story, a poem, or a piece labeled non-fiction, it's said to have *universality*. This means there's a quality that speaks across miles and years, saying, "This is something that all people face and learn, feel and ask. Although backgrounds and lifestyles differ, some things remain the same."

Angela DeCora was born in 1871, shortly after the Civil War, and died in 1920, just after World War I. Her story, "The Sick Child," was published in *Harper's Monthly* magazine in 1899. So long ago—yet what questions does it concern that still are ours today?

## Cause and Effect

1. Told to find naked earth, the child is not sure she has followed directions because she (a) brushed off the snow with her hand (b) dropped the offering into a spring (c) forgot part of the ceremonial chant (d) poured the offering into a hole surrounding a reed stem.
2. The child expresses being afraid of (a) her parents (b) nature (c) death (d) magic.
3. Because the medicine-woman says the case is hopeless, the parents (a) have her perform a spirit rite of passage (b) become angry at the older girl (c) assure the girl she'd done her best (d) send for a medicine-man.

## Questioning the Selection

1. The story simply calls the narrator, "a little child," without giving a further description. Judging by small children you know, how old to you think the child is? What in the story influences your conclusion?
2. There is a question whether "The Sick Child" is autobiographical. Although the author is a woman, might a boy feel and act as the narrator does? Use evidence from the story to back your opinion.
3. Why are "white monotony" fitting words to describe the prairies at that time of year? Consider the meanings of both *monotone* and *monotony*.
4. What three things does the medicine-woman order the child to do?
5. Based on evidence in the story, give two reasons that the child might say, "I was afraid of nature."
6. Why might the child fear that the medicine-woman's orders to "trust nature" were not being totally fulfilled?
7. On returning home, why does the child feel "bitter remorse"—guilt and shame?
8. What shows that the parents do care, and what explains why they didn't try to ease the child's feeling of guilt?
9. Give three examples of the medicine-man's behavior that show him to be an honest, caring, and honorable man.
10. How were the children led to realize "what death meant"? How did the mother's words and actions contribute to the child's understanding of the expected way to respond?


# Looking Deeper

## I. But, Is It True?

What conflicts and fears does the little child feel when starting out to make the sacrifice? Do most children—and even adults—have certain fears of nature's power? If you agree, give specific examples. How do the sick child's parents react to her illness and death? How is this similar to or different from the way people react today?


## II. What Changes, What Doesn't?

In what ways does the medicine-man provide good care for his small patient and offer help to her family? How is he either like or different from your previous image of an Indian medicine-man? How is the Winnebago religion like or different from others you know about? Although you find both likeness and differences, do you feel Angela DeCora's story has universality? Why or why not?

# The Day the World Almost Came to an End

## by Pearl Crayton

**Born on:** *A plantation in Louisiana*
**Careers:** *Weekly newspaper editor, story writer*

IF YOU HAVEN'T HAD THE world coming to an end on you when you're twelve years old and a sinner, you don't know how lucky you are! When it happened to me it scared the living daylights and some of the joy of sinning out of me and, in a lot of other ways, messed up my life altogether. But if I am to believe Ralph Waldo Emerson's "Compensation," I guess I got some good out of it too.

The calamity befell me back in 1936. We were living on a plantation in Louisiana at the time, close to the earth and God, and all wrapped up in religion. The church was the axis around which plantation life revolved, the Mother to whom the folks took their problems, the Teacher who taught them how the Lord wanted them to live, the Chastiser who threatened the sinful with Hell.

In spite of the fact that my parents were churchgoing Christians, I was still holding on to being a sinner. Not that I had anything against religion, it was just a matter of integrity. There was an old plantation custom that in order to be baptized into the church a sinner had to "get religion," a mystical experience in which the soul of the sinner was converted into Christian. A Christian had to live upright, and I knew I just couldn't come up to that on account of there were too many delicious sins around to get into. But a world coming to an end can be pretty hard on a sinner.

The trouble began when my cousin Rena came upon me playing in the watermelon patch, running like the devil was behind her. I was making a whole quarter of mud cabins by packing dirt over my foot in the shape of a cabin, putting a chimney on top, then pulling my foot out. The space left by my foot formed the room of the cabin. I'd broken some twigs off chinaberry and sycamore trees which I planted in the ground around the cabins to make "trees." Some blooming wild flowers that I had picked made up a flower yard in front of each cabin. It was as pretty a sight as you ever want to see before she came stepping all over everything. I let her know I didn't like it real loud, but she didn't pay what I said any attention, she just blurted out, "The end of the world is coming Saturday; you'd better go get you some religion in a hurry!"

That was on a Friday afternoon, getting late.

A picture of Hell flashed across my mind but I pushed it back into the subconscious. "The world's NOT coming to an end!" The confidence I tried to put in my voice failed; it quaked a little. "Who told you the world is coming to an end?"

"I heard Mama and Miss Daya talking about it just now. There's going to be an eclipse Sunday. You know what an eclipse is, don't you?"

I didn't know but I nodded anyhow.

"That's when the sun has a fight with the moon. If the sun whips, the world goes on; if the moon whips, then the world comes to an end. Well, they say that Sunday the moon is going to whip the sun!"

I wasn't going to be scared into giving up my sinning that easily. "How do they know the moon is going to whip?"

"They read it in the almanac. And it's in the Bible too, in Revelation. It says in Revelation that the world is supposed to end this year. Miss Daya is a missionary sister and she knows all about things like that."

"Nobody knows anything about Revelation, my daddy says so," I rebutted. "Ain't never been nobody born smart enough to figure out Revelation since that Mister John wrote it. He's just going to have to come back and explain it himself."

She acted like she didn't hear that. "And Reverend Davis said in church last Sunday that time is winding up," she said.

"He's been saying that for years now, and time hasn't wound up yet."

"That's what I know, he's been saying it for years, and all the while he's been saying it time's been winding right along, and now it's just about all wound up!"

That made sense to me and I began to consider that maybe she could be right. Then that Miss Daya happened by.

"Lord bless you down there on your knees, baby! Pray to the Lord 'cause it's praying time!"

I hadn't gotten up from where I'd been making mud cabins, but I jumped up quick to let her know I wasn't praying.

"Both of you girls got religion?" she asked, and without waiting for an answer, "That's good. You're both big girls, big enough to go to Hell. You all be glad you all got religion 'cause the Lord is coming soon! He said he was coming and he's coming SOON!" And she went on towards our cabin before I could ask her about the world ending Sunday.

Rena just stood there and looked at me awhile, shaking her head in an "I told you so," and advised me again to get some religion in a hurry. Then she ran off to warn someone else.

Although I was a sinner, I was a regular churchgoing sinner and at our church we had a hellfire-preaching pastor. He could paint pictures of Hell and the Devil in his sermons horrible enough to give a sinner a whole week of nightmares. Nobody with a dime's worth of sense wanted to go to a hot, burning Hell where a red, horned Devil tormented folks with a pitchfork, but I'd been taking a chance on enjoying life another thirty years or so before getting some religion—getting just enough to keep me out of Hell. I hadn't figured on time running out on me so soon, and I still wasn't taking anybody's word before asking my daddy about it first. But it was plowing time and Daddy was way back in the cornfield where I'd already run across a rattlesnake, so I figured even the world coming to an end could wait until suppertime.

I went around the rest of that day with my mind loaded down. Now I didn't exactly believe that the world was coming to an end, but I didn't exactly believe it wasn't either. About two years before, I'd went and read the worst part of Revelation and it had taken my daddy two weeks to convince me that I didn't understand what I had read, which still didn't keep me from having bad dreams about the moon dripping away in blood and a lot of other distressing visions aroused from misunderstood words.

Those dreams were only a vague and frightening memory the Friday I'm talking about, and Revelation an accepted mystery. Yet things like that have a way of sneaking back on you when you need it the least. I got to "supposing" the world did come to an end with earthquakes and hail and fire raining down from the sky and stars falling, exactly like it read in Revelation, and "supposing" the Devil got after me and took me to Hell like folks on the plantation said he would, and "supposing" Hell really and truly was as horrible as the preacher said it was. The way the preacher told it, in Hell a person got burned and burned up and never died, he just kept on burning, burning, burning. With "supposing" like that going through it, my mind was really loaded down! I figured there was no use talking to Mama about what was bothering me because that Miss Daya had stayed at our cabin for over an hour, and I was sure she had convinced Mama that the moon was going to whip the sun.

It seemed to me like it took Daddy longer than ever to come home. It was the Friday of Council Meeting at the church, and Daddy, a deacon, had to be there. I knew he wouldn't have much time to talk to me before he'd have to leave for the church, so I started walking up the turnrow through the fields to meet him. When I finally saw him riding towards home on his slide I ran to meet him.

Daddy always hitched a plank under his plow to keep the plow blades from cutting up the turnrow when he came home from plowing the fields. The plank, which we called a slide, was long enough behind the plow for him to stand on and ride home, pulled by his plow horse. Whenever I ran to meet him he'd let me ride home with him on the slide.

"Daddy," I said as soon as he'd put me on the slide in front of him and "gee'd" the horse to go on, "is the world going to come to an end Sunday?"

"I don't know, honey," he replied. "Why do you want to know?"

I told him about Rena's prophecy. That really tickled him! He laughed and laughed like that was the funniest thing he'd ever heard! I laughed a little too, though I didn't get the joke in it.

"There's always somebody coming around prophesying that the world's coming to an end," he said after he laughed himself out. "Folks been doing that ever since I was a boy, they were doing it when my daddy was a boy, aw, they've been doing that for hundreds of years and the world is still here. Don't you ever pay any attention to anybody that comes around telling you the world is going to end, baby."

"But ain't the world *ever* going to end?" I wanted to know.

"Yeah, but don't anybody know when. Only the Lord knows that. Why, the world might not end for another thousand years, then again it might end tonight, we just don't know ..."

"TONIGHT! You mean the world might end TONIGHT?"

"Sure. I'm not saying it will but it could. A person never can tell about a thing like that. But if you let that bother you, why you'll be scared to death every day of your life looking for the world to end. You're not going to be that silly, are you?"

"Aw, shucks no," I lied. I was that silly. Right then and there I got to looking for the world to end, right there on the *spot*!

Like anybody expecting a calamity, I decided to sit up all night that night but Mama made me go to bed. My room was full of the plantation, the darkest of the darkness. Before Daddy returned from church Mama put out the coal oil lamp and went to bed.

The lazy old moon was on its vacation again; there was no light anywhere, not a speck. Although my eyes couldn't see anything in that awful dark, my mind had always been very good at seeing things in the dark that weren't there. I got to "seeing" how it was going to be when the world ended, the whole drama of it paraded right before my mind. Then my imagination marched past me up before the judgment seat to give account for my past sins and I tried to figure out how much burning I'd get for each offense. Counting up all the ripe plums and peaches I'd saved from going to waste on the neighbors' trees, neglecting to get the owners' permission, the fights I'd had with that sassy little Catherine who lived across the river, the domino games I'd played for penny stakes with my sinner-cousin, Sam, the times I'd handled the truth careless enough to save myself from a whipping, and other not so holy acts, I figured I'd be in for some real hot burning.

While I lay there in that pitch-black darkness worrying myself sick about burning in Hell, a distant rumbling disturbed the stillness of the night, so faint that at first I wasn't sure I'd heard it. I sat up in the bed, straining my ears listening. Sure enough there was a rumbling, far away. The rumbling wasn't thunder, I was sure of that because thunder rumbled, then died away, but this rumbling grew louder and louder and LOUDER. A slow-moving, terrible, loud rumbling that was to my scared mind the earth quaking, the sky caving in, the world ending!

I got out of there, I got out of there *fast*! I didn't even think about being dressed only in my nightgown or the awful dark outside being full of ghosts and bogeymen and other horrors, I just ran!

"The world is ending! The world is ending! Run! Run for your life" I shouted a warning to Mama, and I just kept on hollering as I ran down the road past the other plantation cabins. "The world is ending! The world is ending! Run! Run for your life!"

Doors opened and folks came out on the cabin porches, some holding coal oil lamps in their hands. They'd look at me in my witch nightgown running down the road as fast as a scared rabbit, then look up at the sky, rumbling like it was caving in, and a few of them hollered something at me as I passed by, but I couldn't make out what any of them said.

I might have run myself plumb to the ocean or death if Daddy and some other deacons hadn't been coming up the road on their way from church. Daddy caught me. He had a hard time holding me though. The fear of the Devil and Hell was stronger in me than reason. I was dead set on escaping them.

Daddy had heard my hollering about the world ending as I ran down the road towards them, so he kept telling me, "That's just an old airplane, honey, the world's not ending. That's just an old airplane making all that racket!"

When his words got through the fear that fogged my mind I calmed down a bit. "Airplane?" I'd only heard about airplanes, never had I seen or heard one passing by.

Daddy laughed. "You were just about outrunning that old airplane and keeping up almost as much racket!" He pointed toward the sky. "Look up there, you see, it's gone now. See that light moving towards town? That's it. Those old airplanes sure have scared a lot of folks with all that racket they make."

I looked up. Sure enough there was a light that looked like a star moving across the sky. The rumbling was way off in the distance, going away slowly like it had come. And the sky was whole, not a piece of it had caved in! I broke down and cried because I was so relieved that the world wasn't coming to an end, because I'd been so scared for so long, because I'd made such a fool of myself, and just because.

Daddy pulled off his suit coat and wrapped it around me to hide the shame of my nightgown from the deacons. After I'd had a real good cry we walked home.

As we walked up the ribbon of road bordering the plantation on our way home I felt a new kind of happiness inside of me. The yellow squares of light shining from the black shapes of the plantation cabins outlined against the night made a picture that looked beautiful to me for the first time. Even the chirping of the crickets sounded beautiful, like a new song I'd never heard before. Even the darkness was beautiful, everything was beautiful. And I was alive, I felt the life within me warming me from the inside, a happy feeling I'd never had before. And the world was there all around me, I was aware of it, aware of all of it, full of beauty, full of happy things to do. Right then and there I was overwhelmed with a desire to *live*, really *live* in the world and enjoy as much of it as I could before it came to an end. And I've been doing so ever since.

## For Better Reading: Taking Part in Dialogue

To be sure what's going on, you have to pay close attention to what the other person says. That's true with reading, just as for everyday conversations and discussions.

When someone speaks, there's often more to his or her words than strikes your ears. For example, read the following sentence and see how many "educated guesses" you can make about the speaker and situation.

*"Please, Dad, you gotta' believe me!"*

From just this one line of dialogue, what do you learn about the relationship of those involved? What doubt or fear does the speaker seem to have? What can you infer or conclude about a previous action of the speaker?

How would the following changes affect your conclusions?

"Please, Father, I would like you to believe me."

In making judgments about dialogue, wild guesses don't count. Be sure you have valid clues in the dialogue or elsewhere in the selection to back up your conclusions. By reading closely, you'll discover that what someone says frequently reveals much more than you might, at first, think.

## Main Idea

The main idea is best expressed by which of the following statements?
a. No one can accurately foresee the future.
b. One should live every day as if the world will end tomorrow.
c. The worst kind of punishment is self-punishment.
d. Expecting the worst makes the imagination run wild.

## Making Inferences

1. By describing the sins she had in mind as "delicious," the main character shows she (a) wants to have fun, not do evil (b) doesn't care what others think of her (c) is not honest with herself or others (d) doesn't believe in religion.
2. The main character puts her greatest trust in the opinion and ideas of (a) her father (b) her minister (c) her cousin Rena (d) herself.

## Questioning the Story

1. When her cousin Rena first warns her that the world's about to end, what is the main character doing that shows her to have a good imagination?
2. How does the narrator react when Rena asks, "You know what an eclipse is, don't you?" Why does she react this way?
3. How is Rena herself mistaken in her definition of an eclipse? How does this affect her entire argument?

4. Although Rena uses Miss Daya as an authority, how does the mission- ary sister show her lack of understanding that caused her to say, "Lord bless you . . ." to the girls?

5. When Miss Daya tells the girls, "He said he was coming and he's coming SOON," how does she express a different version from Rena's of the coming event?

6. What pictures does the main character have in her imagination, increas- ing her fear of the end of the world and going to hell? (Find at least three examples, each from a different paragraph.)

7. Why does the main character decide not to confide in her mother? Why does she decide to go meet her father on his way home from the fields?

8. Describe three things that the main character has done that make her consider herself a sinner. What are the proper names for each of these "sins"?

9. By trying to answer his daughter's questions honestly, how did the father actually add to her fears?

10. What did the main character do that caused her to feel she had made a fool of herself? Why shouldn't she blame herself for being utterly foolish?

## Looking Deeper

### I. Laughing with or at Someone

Writer Pearl Crayton didn't mean you to take this story too seriously. After all, the world wasn't really coming to an end. But she probably thought you'd be able to see yourself in it. Perhaps you found the ending an *anticlimax*, or something of a letdown. After all, an airplane wouldn't scare anyone today, unless . . .

In order to be so frightening, how must the plane have been flying? Can you think of anything—manmade or natural—that might similarly terrify a child today?

### II. What Imagination Can Do

Why does the main character seem like a smart and thoughtful child? How does her background contribute to her reaction? What things today fill some children with fear or cause their imaginations to run wild because they're so hard to understand?

What was the attitude of the main character's father towards questions, such as when the world would end, that are too big to understand?

At the beginning, the narrator mentions *compensation*, or getting back something of equal value for what is given up. What did the main character feel was her *compensation* for the hours of terror she'd gone through?

# One Throw

## by W. C. Heinz

**Born in:**     Mt. Vernon, New York
**Worked as:**   Copy boy, reporter, war
                   correspondent, sports columnist

---

**I** CHECKED INTO A HOTEL CALLED the Olympia, which is right on the main street and the only hotel in the town. After lunch I was hanging around the lobby, and I got to talking to the guy at the desk. I asked him if this wasn't the town where that kid named Maneri played ball.

"That's right," the guy said. "He's a pretty good ballplayer."

"He should be," I said. "I read that he was the new Phil Rizzuto."

"That's what they said," the guy said.

"What's the matter with him?" I said. "I mean if he's such a good ballplayer what's he doing in this league?"

"I don't know," the guy said. "I guess the Yankees know what they're doing."

"What kind of a kid is he?"

"He's a nice kid," the guy said. "He plays good ball, but I feel sorry for him. He thought he'd be playing for the Yankees soon, and here he is in this town. You can see it's got him down."

"He lives in this hotel?"

"That's right," the guy said. "Most of the older ballplayers stay in rooming houses, but Pete and a couple other kids live here."

He was leaning on the desk, talking to me and looking across the hotel lobby. He nodded his head. "This is a funny thing," he said. "Here he comes now."

The kid had come through the door from the street. He had on a light gray sport shirt and a pair of gray flannel slacks.

I could see why, when he showed up with the Yankees in spring training, he made them all think of Rizzuto. He wasn't any bigger than Rizzuto, and he looks just like him.

"Hello, Nick," he said to the guy at the desk.

"Hello, Pete," the guy at the desk said. "How goes it today?"

"All right," the kid said but you could see he was exaggerating.

"I'm sorry, Pete," the guy at the desk said, "but no mail today."

"That's all right, Nick," the kid said. "I'm used to it."

"Excuse me," I said, "but you're Pete Maneri?"

"That's right," the kid said, turning and looking at me.

"Excuse me," the guy at the desk said, introducing us. "Pete, this is Mr. Franklin."

"I'm glad to know you," the kid said, shaking my hand.

"I recognize you from your pictures," I said.

"Pete's a good ballplayer," the guy at the desk said.

"Not very," the kid said.

"Don't take his word for it, Mr. Franklin," the guy said.

"I'm a great ball fan," I said to the kid. "Do you people play tonight?"

"We play two games," the kid said.

"The first game's at six o'clock," the guy at the desk said.

"I'll be there," I said. "I used to play a little ball myself."

"You did?" the kid said.

"With Columbus," I said. "That's twenty years ago."

"Is that right?" the kid said . . .

That's the way I got talking with the kid. They had one of those pine-paneled taprooms in the basement of the hotel, and we went down there. I had a couple and the kid had a Coke, and I told him a few stories and he turned out to be a real good listener.

"But what do you do now, Mr. Franklin?" he said after a while.

"I sell hardware," I said. "I can think of some things I'd like better, but I was going to ask you how you like playing in this league."

"Well," the kid said, "I suppose it's all right. I guess I've got no kick coming."

"Oh, I don't know," I said. "I understand you're too good for this league. What are they trying to do to you?"

"I don't know," the kid said. "I can't understand it."

"What's the trouble?"

"Well," the kid said. "I don't get along very well here. I mean there's nothing wrong with my playing. I'm hitting .365 right now. I lead the league in stolen bases. There's nobody can field with me, but who cares?"

"Who manages this ball club?"

"Al Dall," the kid said. "You remember, he played in the outfield for the Yankees for about four years."

"I remember."

"Maybe he is all right," the kid said, "but I don't get along with him. He's on my neck all the time."

"Well," I said, "that's the way they are in the minors sometimes. You have to remember the guy is looking out for himself and his ball club first. He's not worried about you."

"I know that," the kid said. "If I get the big hit or make the play he never says anything. The other night I tried to take second on a loose ball and I got caught in the run-down. He bawls me out in front of everybody. There's nothing I can do."

"Oh, I don't know," I said. "This is probably a guy who knows he's got a good thing in you, and he's looking to keep you around. You people lead the league, and that makes him look good. He doesn't want to lose you to Kansas City or the Yankees."

"That's what I mean," the kid said. "When the Yankees sent me down here they said, 'Don't worry. We'll keep an eye on you.' So Dall never sends a good report on me. Nobody ever comes down to look me over. What chance is there for a guy like Eddie Brown or somebody like that coming down to see me in this town?"

"You have to remember that Eddie Brown's the big shot," I said, "the great Yankee scout."

"Sure," the kid said. "I never even saw him, and I'll never see him in this place. I have an idea that if they ever ask Dall about me he keeps knocking me down."

"Why don't you go after Dall?" I said. "I had trouble like that once myself, but I figured out a way to get attention."

"You did?" the kid said.

"I threw a couple of balls over the first baseman's head," I said. "I threw a couple of games away, and that really got the manager sore. I was lousing up his ball club and his record. So what does he do? He blows the whistle on me, and what happens? That gets the brass curious, and they send down to see what's wrong."

"Is that so?" the kid said. "What happened?"

"Two weeks later," I said, "I was up with Columbus."

"Is that right?" the kid said.

"Sure," I said, egging him on. "What have you got to lose?"

"Nothing," the kid said. "I haven't got anything to lose."

"I'd try it," I said.

"I might try it," the kid said. "I might try it tonight if the spot comes up."

I could see from the way he said it that he was madder than he'd said. Maybe you think this is mean to steam a kid up like this, but I do some strange things.

"Take over," I said. "Don't let this guy ruin your career."

"I'll try it," the kid said. "Are you coming out to the park tonight?"

"I wouldn't miss it," I said. "This will be better than making out route sheets and sales orders."

It's not much of a ball park in this town—old wooden bleachers and an old wooden fence and about four hundred people in the stands. The first game wasn't much either, with the home club winning something like 8 to 1.

The kid didn't have any hard chances, but I could see he was a ballplayer, with a double and a couple of walks and a lot of speed.

The second game was different, though. The other club got a couple of runs and then the home club picked up three runs in one inning, and they were in the top of the ninth with a 3-2 lead and two outs when the pitching began to fall apart and they loaded the bases.

I was trying to wish the ball down to the kid, just to see what he'd do with it, when the batter drives one on one big bounce to the kid's right.

The kid was off for it when the ball started. He made a backhand stab and grabbed it. He was deep now, and he turned in the air and fired. If it goes over the first baseman's head, it's two runs in and a panic—but it's the prettiest throw you'd want to see. It's right on a line, and the runner is out by a step, and it's the ball game.

I walked back to the hotel, thinking about the kid. I sat around the lobby until I saw him come in, and then I walked toward the elevator like I was going to my room, but so I'd meet him. And I could see he didn't want to talk.

"How about a Coke?" I said.

"No," he said. "Thanks, but I'm going to bed."

"Look," I said. "Forget it. You did the right thing. Have a Coke."

We were sitting in the taproom again. The kid wasn't saying anything.

"Why didn't you throw that ball away?" I said.

"I don't know," the kid said. "I had it in my mind before he hit it, but I couldn't."

"Why?"

"I don't know why."

"I know why," I said.

The kid didn't say anything. He just sat there, looking down.

"Do you know why you couldn't throw that ball away?"

"No," the kid said.

"You couldn't throw that ball away," I said, "because you're going to be a major-league ballplayer someday."

The kid just looked at me. He had that same sore expression.

"Do you know why you're going to be a major-league ballplayer?"

The kid was just looking down again, shaking his head. I never got more of a kick out of anything in my life.

"You're going to be a major-league ballplayer," I said, "because you couldn't throw that ball away, and because I'm not a hardware salesman and my name's not Harry Franklin."

"What do you mean?" the kid said.

"I mean," I explained to him, "that I tried to needle you into throwing that ball away because I'm Eddie Brown."

## For Better Reading: Preparing for a Surprise

Written mostly in dialogue, "One Throw" builds to what you might call a surprise ending. Yet, just as a good ballplayer has a keen sense for clues found in an opposing player's stance and almost unconscious movements, so a good reader picks up clues along the way, sometimes without realizing it.

In "One Throw," there's a lot to learn from dialogue, not only from what the "kid" says but also what he doesn't say. Sometimes, by asking yourself what else a character could say, you'll discover how much the chosen piece of dialogue reveals. By careful reading, you'll find there's often more to a casual-seeming conversation than first meets the eye.

## Making Inferences

1. Concerning Pete's being in the minors, the desk clerk comments, "I guess the Yankees know what they're doing." This implies that the desk clerk (a) has faith in the Yankees' judgment (b) has doubts about management's actions (c) plans to tell the head office what's going on (d) thinks the stranger is acting suspiciously.
2. The Yankees' home office told Pete, "We'll keep an eye on you." This can be taken as a clue that:
    a. Al Dall has been sending false reports.
    b. Pete suspects the truth about the stranger.
    c. The stranger is not who he says he is.
    d. The desk clerk is a spy for the league headquarters.
3. By suggesting that Pete throw the game away, the stranger is trying to (a) get the attention of the main office (b) cause problems for both Pete and Al Dall (c) test whether Pete deserves being called up (d) help Pete repeat the same trick he did.

## Questioning the Story

1. How does Nick, the desk clerk, create a positive attitude towards Pete, even before he's introduced in the story?
2. What does the narrator mean by commenting "you could see he was exaggerating" about Pete's saying "All right"?
3. When Nick said, "Pete's a good ballplayer," Pete might have said, "You're the only one around here who's noticed." How would this change your attitude toward him? Can you think of any other replies he might have made? Why do you think Pete says, "Not very"?
4. When first asked how he likes playing in the farm club league, Pete says he guesses he had no kick coming. Does his answer give you a favorable or unfavorable impression? What kind of person does it show him to be?
5. Who introduces the idea of Pete's being treated unfairly, and how is it brought up?
6. What explains the league manager's motives for giving Pete a hard time and sending the Yankees bad reports? Who provides this explanation?
7. What does the narrator offer as a plan to make the Yankee home office aware of Pete's situation? What clues alert you that the narrator's motives aren't open and straightforward?
8. What did the narrator really hope that Pete would do? Find at least two pieces of proof for your answer.
9. What are early clues that the narrator isn't who he says he is? Be sure to explain how each provides a tip to the narrator's identity.
10. How does Pete feel when he returns from the ballpark? Why? What

reasons would cause the narrator to think it necessary to assume a false identity?

## Looking Deeper

### I. Proving One's Worth

Pete says he doesn't know why he couldn't throw the ball away, and the narrator's explanation goes around in circles. What difference would it have made in the game if Pete had thrown the ball away? What would it have shown about Pete's attitude towards himself, his team, and the sport of baseball if he had followed Brown's advice? Based on this, what kept him from making the throw? From what you know of the narrator, do you believe his story of "lousing up" and being sent to Columbus? Why or why not?

### II. Making Everything Fit

What double meaning can you find in the title, "One Throw"? How would the effect be different if the title were "The Test" or "The Chance"? When you reread the first paragraph, what shows that it was always Brown's intention to check up on Pete? Although some details put this story in the past, do you find it has universality for you? Why or why not?

# The Gift

## by Li-Young Lee

| | |
|---|---|
| **Born in:** | *Jakarta, Indonesia, of Chinese parents* |
| **Father:** | *Political prisoner before fleeing to Hong Kong* |
| **In America:** | *Studied at universities in Pennsylvania, Arizona, and New York* |
| **Career:** | *Poet, artist for fashion accessories company in Chicago, Illinois* |

To pull the metal splinter from my palm
my father recited a story in a low voice.
I watched his lovely face and not the blade.
Before the story ended, he'd removed
the iron sliver I thought I'd die from.                    5

I can't remember the tale,
but hear his voice still, a well
of dark water, a prayer.
And I recall his hands,
two measures of tenderness                                10
he laid against my face,
the flames of discipline
he raised above my head.
Had you entered that afternoon
you would have thought you saw a man                     15
planting something in a boy's palm,
a silver tear, a tiny flame.
Had you followed that boy
you would have arrived here,
where I bend over my wife's right hand.                  20

Look how I shave her thumbnail down
so carefully she feels no pain.

Watch as I lift the splinter out.
I was seven when my father took my hand like this,
and I did not hold that shard                                    25
between my fingers and think,
*Metal that will bury me,*
christen it Little Assassin,
One Going Deep for My Heart.
And I did not lift up my wound and cry,                          30
*Death visited here!*
I did what a child does
when he's given something to keep.
I kissed my father.

# For Better Reading: The Poem and You

Among different kinds of writers, poets expect their readers to take the
most active part. It's not that poets purposely try to be difficult or write
in riddles you can't understand. In fact, poets don't like to waste words.
They choose each one as carefully and exactly as they can.

Poets put their trust in words, and they put their trust in readers, too.
They believe people share the same feelings. They believe that if you bring
yourself to a poem, you will make it more real for you. By putting yourself
in a poem, by weighing and measuring its words, as the poet has before
you, you'll find yourself becoming a part of a poem and it a part of you.

## Questioning the Poem

1. What past situation is described at the beginning of the poem? What
   are the boy's feelings when he first brings his hurt to his father?
2. What is the father's purpose in reciting the story?
3. In lines 10–12 the poet writes of both "measures of tenderness" and
   "flames of discipline." What kind of discipline does the father give the
   boy: self-discipline or obedience to rules? Explain the reason for your
   choice.
4. How does the situation in lines 18–22 parallel that in the first stanza of
   the poem?
5. What qualities seen in his father does the speaker now exhibit?
6. From lines 23–29, what other attitude does the speaker say he might
   have taken toward the metal splinter or shard that pierced into his palm?
   What would be his feelings?
7. If he would "lift up [his] wound and cry," what feelings would this show
   about himself and what would he be asking of others?
8. Considering that the poet's father was imprisoned in Indonesia for his

political beliefs, how might the metal sliver stand for much more than an object that could hurt a child's hand?

## Looking Deeper
### A Father's Gift

Explain what the poem means by the "gift" the father has given the child to keep.

# Incident

*by Countee Cullen*

| | |
|---|---|
| ***Birthplace:*** | *Unknown, possibly Kentucky or New York* |
| ***Adopted at:*** | *Age 15* |
| ***Careers:*** | *Poet, French teacher, children's book author* |

Once riding in old Baltimore,
    Heart-filled, head-filled with glee,
I saw a Baltimorean
    Keep looking straight at me.

Now I was eight and very small,          5
    And he was no whit bigger,
And so I smiled, but he poked out
    His tongue, and called me, "Nigger."

I saw the whole of Baltimore
    From May until December;         10
Of all the things that happened there
    That's all that I remember.

## Questioning the Poem

1. What must the speaker have first thought was the reason for the other boy's looking straight at him? Is this kind of staring typical of small children you know? If so, how and why?
2. In lines 7 and 8 what words does the poet use in an attempt to surprise and shock the reader? What is the purpose of creating this effect?
3. Why must this experience have made such an indelible mark on the boy's memory?

# Looking Deeper
## Lasting Aftereffects

The word *incident* can mean a happening that seems of minor importance yet that can have major consequences. How does this definition help explain the theme or idea behind the poem?

# The Courage That My Mother Had

## by Edna St. Vincent Millay

**Born:**      Rockland, Maine, 1892
**Early life:** Raised by mother as a single parent
                with little income
**Careers:**   Freelance writer, actress, playwright,
                short story writer

The courage that my mother had
Went with her, and is with her still:
Rock from New England quarried;
Now granite in a granite hill.

The golden brooch my mother wore          5
She left behind for me to wear;
I have no thing I treasure more:
Yet, it is something I could spare.

Oh, if instead she'd left to me
The thing she took into the grave!—        10
That courage like a rock, which she
Has no more need of, and I have.

## Questioning the Poem

1. By comparing courage to a rock, what elements of courage does the poem bring to mind? In what kinds of situation might someone need a granite-like courage?
2. What proves that the mother never lost her courage, no matter what?
3. How much does the speaker value her mother's golden brooch? What does this show about her feelings for her mother?
4. In spite of her feeling, what would make her wish to give up her mother's piece of jewelry?
5. What emotions does the speaker express in lines 9 and 10?
6. What does the speaker feel about herself in comparison to her mother?

7. The last words, "and I have," say a great deal about the speaker's present life. What do they show?

## Looking Deeper
### A Mother's Gift

Considering the poem, does it seem that the speaker has or has not gained some of the qualities she admires in her mother? Explain the reasons for your answer.

# Blasphemy

## by Leroy V. Quintana

| | |
|---|---|
| **Born:** | *Albuquerque, New Mexico, 1944* |
| **Early jobs:** | *Roofer, family and alcoholism counselor* |
| **In Vietnam:** | *Served in U.S. Army, Airborne division* |
| **Later careers:** | *Newspaper sports and feature writer, poet, novelist* |

**W**ANT TO BET? NO MATTER the challenge, everyone in the gang likes to prove he can win. After reading this poem, decide what was the purpose of Santos's game.

Santos wasn't too bright in school, but
he always thought he was better
and because he didn't cuss very much
he devised a game as we walked home
from school one day: If anybody cussed                5
the rest of us got to punch him once
on the shoulder, as hard as possible.
But the only thing wrong was every time
somebody cussed and got punched
he would cuss even more, screaming              10
¡Cabron! from the pain or ¡Jodido! in anger
and the more he cussed the more he got hit
until he had to switch shoulders and shut up
and we finally had to drop the game entirely;
it got to where we would walk entire blocks       15
in silence.

*Leroy V. Quintana*

## Questioning the Poem

1. How does line 3 explain why Santos "thought he was better"?
2. How does line 3 also prove why Santos invented this particular game and set of rules?
3. Considering Santos's belief that he was superior to the others, why did the rest of the boys go along with the game?
4. For what reason, not expressly given in the poem, might a boy use a cuss word even though trying to play the game?
5. What two reasons does the poem give for a boy to "cuss even more" after getting punched?
6. How are all the boys finally able to find a way to avoid cussing?
7. Judging by the first three lines, do you think Santos was ever punched for cussing?

## Looking Deeper

### Where's the Joke?

*Blasphemy* may be serious word, but this is a poem you shouldn't take too seriously. *Blasphemy* is one form of "cussing," and it also is "the crime of assuming to oneself the rights or qualities of God." In what way did Santos try to act as if he were above the other boys? Which do you think Santos wanted more: to make the boys stop swearing or to watch them punch one another and feel himself superior? In your opinion, did Santos come out as a "winner"? Why or why not? What makes this a humorous poem?

# Walking Down Park

*by Nikki Giovanni*

| | |
|---|---|
| **Born in:** | *Tennessee* |
| **Makes home in:** | *Cincinnati, Ohio* |
| **Career:** | *Poet, writer, lecturer, professor; has written books of poetry for both children and adults* |
| **Honors:** | *Named Outstanding Woman of Tennessee in 1985; member of Ohio Women's Hall of Fame* |

walking down park
amsterdam
or columbus do you ever stop
to think what it looked like
before it was an avenue                                5
did you ever stop to think
what you walked
before you rode
subways to the stock
exchange (we can't be on                               10
the stock exchange
we are the stock
exchanged)

did you ever maybe wonder
what grass was like before                             15
they rolled it into a ball and called
it central park
where syphilitic dogs
and their two-legged tubercular
masters fertilize                                      20
the corners and sidewalks
ever want to know what would happen
if your life could be fertilized
by a love thought
from a loved one                                       25
who loves you

ever look south
on a clear day and not see
time's squares but see
tall birch trees with sycamores                                              30
touching hands
and see gazelles running playfully
after the lions
ever hear the antelope bark
from the third floor apartment                                               35

ever, did you ever, sit down
and wonder about what freedom's freedom
would bring
it's so easy to be free
you start by loving yourself                                                 40
then those who look like you
all else will come
naturally

ever wonder why
so much asphalt was laid                                                     45
in so little space
probably so we would forget
the Iroquois, Algonquin
and Mohicans who could caress
the earth                                                                    50

ever think what Harlem would be
like if our herbs and roots and elephant ears
grew sending
a cacophony of sound to us
the parrot parroting black is beautiful black
        is beautiful                                                         55
owls sending out whooooo's making love ...
and me and you just sitting in the sun trying
to find a way to get a banana from one of the monkeys
koala bears in the trees laughing at our listlessness

ever think it's possible                                                     60
for us to be
happy

## Questioning the Poem

There is more than one way of testing your wings. Sometimes it's just as important to stretch your imagination as to try your courage or prove yourself to others.

Nikki Giovanni has invited you to go along as she lets her imagination run free while she's "Walking Down Park" Avenue in New York City.

1. In addition to being New York avenue names, what connection do Amsterdam and Columbus have with New York and American's past?
2. How do you picture New York before there were subways?
3. On what two meanings of *stock* does Giovanni base a pun in lines 10–13. Why would she state that black Americans have been looked on as "stock exchanged"?
4. In lines 14–21 what imagined picture of the past does Giovanni ask you to compare to the present? What does the poet feel would most enrich or fertilize life in the present?
5. In lines 27–35 Giovanni lets her imagination run free. What does she name that could belong to America of the past? What's not native to America? What relates to the present?
6. Although Times Square exists in the heart of New York, the poet has written "time's squares" in line 29. How many ways can you think of that make modern life and time seem cut into squares?
7. What does the poem state as the beginning of true freedom? Considering the steps given in lines 40 and 41, what is the "all else" that "will come naturally?"
8. In lines 44–50 Giovanni touches another part of America's story. Why might she feel modern Americans want to forget the Iroquois, Algonquin, and Mohicans?
9. What is the message from the parrots and owls? What is the surprise in line 59 that proves Giovanni's imagination is breaking many boundaries?
10. What is your answer to the question in lines 60–62? What does the poet imply might make this possible?

## Looking Deeper

### Did You Ever?

Did you notice how many times Giovanni uses phrases such as "did you ever stop to think ..." in this poem? What was her purpose? What different kinds of things did she ask you to think about? What other, similar kinds of things do you and others sometimes think about when you let your mind roam free?

---

## REFLECTIONS

In many ways, reading stories and poems is like looking into a mirror in which you catch reflections of yourself or, perhaps, get a whole new angle from which to look at life.

As you look back on the selections in "Trying Your Wings," you can see common threads—or themes—running through them. One was the difficulties of trying to live up to others' expectations—with adults you can look up to and others you can't. There's the need to find out about yourself and your place in the world. And, there are the feelings involved in stretching and growing—the love, the doubt, the curiosity, the courage, and maybe, most of all, the questioning. Are there other themes important to you?

If you found yourself saying, "I know how he felt," or recognized a situation that you might have met in a somewhat different shape, you're already on your way to finding America.

## To Write About or Discuss

1. Choose the selection with the most universality to you. Explain why you found it easiest to "put yourself" in the selection.
2. Think of an adult influence—either positive or negative.
3. Crazy or not? Tell about a person you know—or maybe yourself—who might seem crazy to someone who didn't really understand.
4. Trying your wings: the place may be anywhere—big city, country, or small town—but how was it necessary to prove yourself, to yourself and others?
5. Let your mind roam free. Discuss an important idea or let your imagination loose on a subject inspired by what you've read.

# UNIT 2

# A Change of Focus:
# Them and Us

CHOOSING SIDES COMES NATURALLY TO PEOPLE. Whether it's your friends, a favorite team, your family heritage, or your country, everyone likes to feel part of a group. By identifying yourself with others, you gain a sense of belonging and a way of defining who you are and what you believe in.

As part of a group, you know the need to be loyal and see your group as Number One—the best there is. And, of course, it is Number One, because it's *yours*. Yet, the need to be loyal can also blind you. It can make you close your eyes to similarities and see other people from one side only—as if team colors, symbols, and slogans said it all.

With what groups do you identify? The older you grow, the wider your choices. It's a natural part of growing up to face conflicts between your friends' ideas and family's wishes. Or between your own beliefs and the demands of others. When you find yourself pulled between loyalties, taking sides becomes more difficult ... and at times seems overwhelming. Yet, the need for making such choices comes with a maturing change of focus. And, it can also lead to important questions, discoveries, and decisions if you ask yourself the reason behind the differences and realize that no one is ever "just" a member of a group, but also an individual.

Are all people alike? Or are all people different? As you continue the search to find America, you might be surprised to find the answer to both questions is "Yes."

Much depends upon which side you're looking from and what you're looking for.

# My First Eccentric

## *by John Steinbeck*

**Home state:** *California*
**Early jobs:** *Fruit packer, hod carrier, painter, reporter*
**Famous as:** *Pulitzer Prize winning novelist, author of* The Grapes of Wrath, Of Mice and Men

**I** WAS TWELVE OR THIRTEEN years old when I became deeply involved with my first real eccentric. There are verities beyond question when one is thirteen—a haunted house is a haunted house, and there is no sense or purpose in questioning it. There is good luck and bad luck, and the penalty for inspection of these is bad luck. Then there are misers, and misers hoard gold. We had a miser; I shall call him Mr. Kirk. Kirk and his wife and daughter lived in a little, old, dark house in a five-acre orchard not far from the center of Salinas. Of course it had once been in the country, until the town crept out and surrounded it. The Kirk place was much too valuable as town lots to be left as a grove of apples and pears and plums, and even those trees so old that they were long past good bearing. The Kirks had been a decent, well-to-do farm family for generations, and it occurred to me only much later why Mr. Kirk was known as a miser. He couldn't be tempted, or bribed, or threatened into selling his valuable acres, to root out his trees, take his profit, and build a white house with a wrought-iron fence and a grave-plot-sized lawn. He hoarded his five acres; and he was peculiar.

Kirk dressed in a blue shirt and overalls like all farm people, but he left his orchard only once a week. On Saturday he came to a little feed store my father owned and bought ten cents' worth of middlings—about five pounds, I suppose. Middlings were simply ground wheat with the chaff left in; it would be called whole wheat now, but then it was sold for chicken and pig feed. His weekly purchase was remarkable because the Kirks had neither chickens nor pigs. Mrs. Kirk and the daughter were rarely seen. They never left the orchard, but we could peer through the black cypress hedge which surrounded the orchard and see two gaunt, gray women, so much alike that you couldn't tell which was mother and which was daughter. As far as anyone ever knew, the ten cents' worth of middlings was all Mr. Kirk ever bought. First the daughter faded and sickened and died, and soon after, Mrs. Kirk went the same way. The coroner said they had starved to death; we would call it malnutrition now—but there was no evidence of violence. People did mind their own business then. But I do know that after they died, Mr. Kirk bought five cents' worth of middlings a week.

Having a genuine miser of our own had a great impact on me and on the three other little boys I ran with. The dark and gloomy orchard and the little unpainted house, mossy with dampness, drew us. I remember being out at night a good deal and I can't for the life of me remember how I got out or back into my own house again. The four of us chicken-necked kids hid in the black shadow of the cypress hedge and looked at the lighted window glowing among the trees, and eventually, by boasting and daring one another, we overcame our cowardice and moved quietly into the orchard and crept with held breaths toward the uncurtained window. Mr. Kirk's face and his right hand and forearm seemed to hang in the air, yellow-lighted by the butterfly flame of a kerosene barn lantern. He was writing feverishly in a big old ledger with red leather corners, his face twisted and contorted with concentration. Now and then his upper teeth clamped on his lower lip. Suddenly he looked up, I presume in thought, but in our timid state we thought he looked right into our peering faces. All of us jumped back, but one boy's foot slipped and fetched a heavy kick on the wall of the house.

Mr. Kirk leaped to his feet, and we froze in the darkness. He did not look at the window; he addressed a presence to his left so that his profile stood against the lantern. Through the closed window we could hear his voice; he cried out on Satan, on the Devil, on Beelzebub. He argued, pleaded, threatened, and after a few moments collapsed into his chair by the table and put his head down on his arms while we trembled in fear and ecstasy. Nothing there is in nature as thoughtlessly cruel as a small boy, unless it be a small girl. As we hid in the deep shadows, our terror abated and we felt that our entertainer had let us down. Then one of us, and I don't know which of us it was, crept back to the house and struck the wall three great, portentous raps. Instantly Mr. Kirk was on his feet again, fighting his brave and hopeless combat against Satan, while we glowed with excitement and a sense of power. Again he collapsed, and again we roused him, until finally he fell to the floor and did not get up. Now I am horrified at our wantonness, but I cannot remember that we felt any pity whatever.

In the ensuing weeks we ranged the darkness of the orchard every night, so that our parents wondered at our sluggishness in the daytime and put it down to what was called "growing pains." Since Mr. Kirk was a known miser, we began to dig about the roots of the fruit trees, searching for his golden hoard, while, to keep him busy, one of us would crouch under his window and with measured knockings employ him at his job against Satan.

We found no gold, but we were making a horrid mask of paper mounted on a stick to stimulate our victim to new heights of despair, when Mr. Kirk disappeared. No light glowed in his window, and a strange, sweet sickliness hung over the night orchard. Two weeks later we heard that Mr. Kirk had not gone away. He had died in his house, probably helped on by us, and he was in very bad shape when the sheriff and the coroner took him out and splashed the house with creosote.

We could hardly wait for the darkness to fall; we invaded through a window, our pockets full of candles. Every cranny we inspected for his gold; we dug up the earthen floor of his cellar, knocked on walls, searching for hidden hiding places, and we found nothing but his big ledgers. I took one away and read it: gibberish; words and word sounds repeated, "read, reed, wrote, rotten, Robert," or, "sea, sky, sin, sister, soon." I know now that these were symptoms of his sickness.

In the end we were fortunate, but it was long before we knew it to be good fortune. We found no gold, but when Kirk's distant cousins took over their inheritance and prepared to sell off the orchard for building lots, they found a canvas bag wedged in a U-pipe of the sink trap, and in the bag were gold pieces—over five thousand dollars' worth. If we had found them, we would have tried to spend them and—well, it's better we were unlucky.

This was our eccentric; every town must have one or more—strange, hidden, frightened, half-mad people are always with us. Only when they hurt someone or die do we discover them.

## For Better Reading: Making Connections with Words

Why did John Steinbeck choose the word *eccentric* to describe the boys' feelings about Mr. Kirk?

The dictionary lists "strange, different, odd" as its synonyms. But Mr. Kirk requires a stronger word than one of these. To be precise, he was *eccentric*.

What makes one word a better choice than another?

Often a list of synonyms doesn't tell enough. Missing are the word's special sense and flavor that make it the one word that expresses a writer's intention exactly.

*Eccentric* is related to *center*, as in center stage, center of a circle, a social circle, a circle of friends. To fit into a social circle, you have to conform, to dress and act in a way that others will accept. Someone who's *eccentric* is "off center" in some way. Eccentric people won't or can't fit in. By not following the accepted pattern of behavior, they often become the object of rumors, ridicule, and sometimes fear.

Eccentric Mr. Kirk is a prime example.

Form the habit of looking for natural connections between unfamiliar words and those you already know well. By taking an active part in making new words your own, you can find an extra dimension in what you read.

## Drawing Conclusions

1. The boys considered Kirk eccentric because he (a) never cut his hair and wore out-of-date clothing (b) played mean tricks on them (c) was known as a peculiar old miser who avoided associating with the townspeople (d) had threatened to "shoot to kill" trespassers.
2. Steinbeck leads the reader to conclude that Kirk made a weekly purchase of middlings (a) to feed himself and his family (b) as provisions for his cattle (c) to mix with poison for ridding his barn of rats (d) because he could afford nothing more.
3. Steinbeck reveals his belief that he and his friends (a) were less prejudiced than adults (b) behaved with thoughtless cruelty (c) deserved to find the buried treasure (d) had seen an evil spirit haunting the farmhouse.

## Questioning the Selection

1. How had the situation and condition of Kirk's property changed through the years?
2. From the townspeople's viewpoint, what would be the advantages of selling the property, both for themselves and Kirk? What is a logical reason for Kirk's not wanting to sell it?
3. Kirk's wife and daughter died of malnutrition, but Kirk was not accused of murder. Explain whether or not you feel that Kirk intentionally starved them and deserved to be put on trial as a murderer. Use evidence from the selection to support your conclusion.
4. How did the boys "overcome their cowardice" the first time they went close to Kirk's house? Why is this a frequently used technique among circles of friends?
5. What was the boys' first real indication that Kirk was crazy or half-crazy?
6. Steinbeck writes, "We felt that our entertainer had let us down." What does the word *entertainer* reveal about the boys' attitude towards Kirk? Later, Steinbeck calls Kirk "frightened" and "half-mad." How do these words show a change of focus?
7. Steinbeck writes that Kirk fought a "brave and hopeless combat against Satan." In what way was his combat hopeless? How does he prove himself brave?
8. Kirk "died in his house, probably helped on by us." What indicates that the boys could have hastened his death?
9. Compare the deaths of Kirk's wife and daughter with that of Kirk himself. Why might Kirk be considered responsible in the first case and the boys in the second? Is either or both cases actually the crime of murder? Why or why not?
10. How did the town's gossip about Kirk's being an eccentric miser affect

the boys' actions? Although they did not find gold, what did the boys find that Steinbeck terms "symptoms" of his condition?

## Looking Deeper

### I. Weighing the Consequences

How would it have changed the boys' actions and attitudes if they had found the gold hidden on Kirk's property? Why would Steinbeck conclude, "Well, it's better we were unlucky" for not finding it?

### II. Taking a Mature Focus

John Steinbeck is writing as an adult, looking at himself at age 12 or 13. How has his focus changed towards eccentrics like Kirk? What does he realize now that he didn't then? Do you feel his attitude at 12 or 13 was typical of kids at this age? Why or why not?

### III. What Is a True Eccentric?

According to Steinbeck, not everyone who behaves strangely is truly an eccentric. Before deciding, you need to know the cause.

He writes, "A number of years ago when I was working on a New York newspaper the police picked up a pretty young girl walking naked on Park Avenue, leading a fawn with a collar and leash. She was brought into the precinct station, booked, and then brought before a magistrate, who said that he found it eccentric but he wondered if she might not be opening in some show someplace; and it turned out that she was."

As with Kirk, true eccentrics don't make an effort to be different although they are thought abnormal by people around them.

Consider someone you know, have seen in the news, or have read about who might be labeled "strange" or "different." Describe what makes this person seem "off center," the cause for his or her odd appearance or behavior, and whether or not you believe this person is truly eccentric.

# It's All in How You Say It

*by Mickey Roberts*

| | |
|---|---|
| ***Member:*** | *Nooksack tribe* |
| ***Home state:*** | *Washington* |
| ***Jobs:*** | *Executive secretary, researcher, free-lance writer* |
| ***Cause:*** | *Gain federal recognition for Nooksack Indian tribe* |

EVER SINCE I WAS A small girl in school, I've been aware of what the school textbooks say about Indians. I am an Indian and, naturally, am interested in what the school teaches about natives of this land.

One day in the grammar school I attended, I read that a delicacy of American Indian people was dried fish, which, according to the textbook, tasted "like an old shoe, or was like chewing on dried leather." To this day I can remember my utter dismay at reading these words. We called this wind-dried fish "sleet-schus," and to us, it was our favorite delicacy and, indeed, did not taste like shoe leather. It took many hours of long and hard work to cure the fish in just this particular fashion. Early fur traders and other non-Indians must have agreed, for they often used this food for subsistence as they traveled around isolated areas.

I brought the textbook home to show it to my father, leader of my tribe at that time. My father was the youngest son of one of the last chiefs of the Nooksack Indian Tribe of Whatcom County in the state of Washington. On this particular day, he told me in his wise and humble manner that the outside world did not always understand Indian people, and that I should not let it hinder me from learning the good parts of education.

Since those early years I have learned we were much better off with our own delicacies, which did not rot our teeth and bring about the various dietary problems that plague Indian people in modern times. I was about eight years old when this incident happened and it did much to sharpen my desire to pinpoint terminology in books used to describe American Indian people, books which are, most often, not very complimentary.

At a later time in my life, I had brought a group of Indian people to the county fairgrounds to put up a booth to sell Indian-made arts and crafts. My group was excited about the prospect of making some money selling genuine Indian artifacts. We thanked the man who showed us our booth and told him it was nice of him to remember the people of the Indian community. The man expanded a little and remarked that he liked Indian people. "In fact," he went on to state, "we are bringing some professional Indians to do the show!"

As we stood there in shock, listening to this uninformed outsider, I looked at my dear Indian companion, an eighty-year-old woman who could well remember the great chiefs of the tribe who once owned all the land of this county before the white man came bringing "civilization," which included diseases and pollution. My friend said not a word, but took the hurt as Indian people have done for many years, realizing outsiders are very often tactless and unthinking.

Of course, we all knew that the "professional Indians" were not Indians at all, but dressed in leather and dancing their own dances. And, anyway, how does one become a "professional Indian"?

I remembered my father's words of so long ago and said to my friend as my father had said to me, "They just don't understand Indian people."

## For Better Reading: The Personal Essay

In its first dictionary entry, *essay* is defined as a short piece of writing about a particular theme or subject.

So a personal essay is a short piece of writing about a subject of personal interest to the writer.

But there's more to the word *essay* than that, as you probably guessed. To *essay* means to try, to attempt, to put to the test. So you can think of a personal essay as being a writer's attempt to test ideas on paper and share them with a reader.

Personal essays are concerned with the writer's thoughts and impressions as much as with details and facts. For a good reader, they're a way of looking at life from someone else's focus and testing how closely your conclusions and reactions match the writer's own.

## Fact or Opinion

Tell which of the following should be accepted as fact and which as opinion.
1. The dried fish eaten by Indians tasted like old shoe leather.
2. The diet of Indian people in modern times frequently causes various dietary problems.
3. The professional Indians were better performers than the people of the Indian community.

## Questioning the Selection

1. When and how does Roberts learn that textbooks are not always correct?
2. After seeing his daughter's book, what advice does the father give her?
3. How did this childhood incident "sharpen" the author's focus on books about American Indians?
4. What proves that the man at the fairgrounds was actually well-meaning, in spite of being tactless?
5. The two women were shocked by the man's saying, "We are bringing some professional Indians to do the show." How does the 80-year-old woman's reaction echo the attitude of Roberts' father?
6. *Professional* means to be involved in an activity to earn a livelihood or for gain. Why therefore is it impossible to be a "professional" Indian?

## Looking Deeper

### I. How Attitude Shows Character

Roberts says that her father, a tribal leader, was "wise and humble." How does his advice about the textbook illustrate both qualities? You might expect a chief's son also to be proud. Is it possible to be proud and humble at the same time? You may wish to define the words *proud* and *humble* for yourself or as a class before giving your answer.

### II. "They Just Don't Understand . . ."

The group of Indian people had been excited by the chance to sell genuine Indian artifacts. Considering the words of Mickey Roberts' father, what was important about their being genuine? What was wrong with "professional" Indians being included in the event?

### III. Speaking Without Thinking

Trying to be friendly, the man at the fairgrounds said he liked Indian people. Consider similar statements made to someone with a different background, such as "I like people from big cities," or "I like people with red hair," or "I like handicapped people." What is wrong with this kind of comment, causing it to be offensive?

# Don't Misread My Signals

*by Judith Ortiz Cofer*

| | |
|---|---|
| ***Family background:*** | *Puerto Rican* |
| ***Growing up:*** | *New Jersey* |
| ***Lived in:*** | *Florida, Georgia* |
| ***Career:*** | *Bilingual teacher, English instructor, poet, novelist* |

GROWING UP IN NEW JERSEY and wanting most of all to belong, I lived in two completely different worlds. My parents designed our life as a microcosm of their *casas* on the island—we spoke in Spanish, ate Puerto Rican food bought at the *bodega* and practiced strict Catholicism complete with Sunday mass in Spanish.

I was kept under tight surveillance by my parents, since my virtue and modesty were, by their cultural equation, the same as their honor. As teenagers, my friends and I were lectured constantly on how to behave as proper *señoritas*. But it was a conflicting message we received, since our Puerto Rican mothers also encouraged us to look and act like women by dressing us in clothes our Anglo schoolmates and their mothers found too "mature" and flashy. I often felt humiliated when I appeared at an American friend's birthday party wearing a dress more suitable for a semiformal. At Puerto Rican festivities, neither the music nor the colors we wore could be too loud.

I remember Career Day in high school, when our teachers told us to come dressed as if for a job interview. That morning, I agonized in front of my closet, trying to figure out what a "career girl" would wear, because the only model I had was Marlo Thomas on TV. To me and my Puerto Rican girlfriends, dressing up meant wearing our mothers' ornate jewelry and clothing.

At school that day, the teachers assailed us for wearing "everything at once"—meaning too much jewelry and too many accessories. And it was painfully obvious that the other students in their tailored skirts and silk blouses thought we were hopeless and vulgar. The way they looked at us was a taste of the cultural clash that awaited us in the real world, where prospective employers and men on the street would often misinterpret our tight skirts and bright colors as a come-on.

It is custom, not chromosomes, that leads us to choose scarlet over pale pink. Our mothers had grown up on a tropical island where the natural environment was a riot of primary colors, where showing your skin was one way to keep cool as well as to look sexy. On the island, women felt freer to dress and move provocatively since they were protected by the traditions and laws of a Spanish/Catholic system of morality and machismo, the main rule of which was: *You may look at my sister, but if you touch her I will kill you.* The extended family and church structure provided them with a circle of safety on the island; if a man "wronged" a girl, everyone would close in to save her family honor.

Off-island, signals often get mixed. When a Puerto Rican girl who is dressed in her idea of what is attractive meets a man from the mainstream culture who has been trained to react to certain types of clothing as a sexual signal, a clash is likely to take place. She is seen as a Hot Tamale, a sexual firebrand. I learned this lesson at my first formal dance when my date leaned over and painfully planted a sloppy, overeager kiss on my mouth. When I didn't respond with sufficient passion, he said in a resentful tone: "I thought you Latin girls were supposed to mature early." It was only the first time I would feel like a fruit or vegetable—I was supposed to *ripen*, not just grow into womanhood like other girls.

These stereotypes, though rarer, still surface in my life. I recently stayed at a classy metropolitan hotel. After having dinner with a friend, I was returning to my room when a middle-aged man in a tuxedo stepped directly into my path. With his champagne glass extended toward me, he exclaimed, "Evita!"

Blocking my way, he bellowed the song "Don't Cry For Me, Argentina." Playing to the gathering crowd, he began to sing loudly a ditty to the tune of "La Bamba"—except the lyrics were about a girl named Maria whose exploits all rhymed with her name and gonorrhea.

I knew that this same man—probably a corporate executive, even worldly by most standards—would never have regaled a white woman with a dirty song in public. But to him, I was just a character in his universe of "others," all cartoons.

Still, I am one of the lucky ones. There are thousands of Latinas without the privilege of the education that my parents gave me. For them every day is a struggle against the misconceptions perpetuated by the myth of the Latina as whore, domestic worker or criminal.

Rather than fight these pervasive stereotypes, I try to replace them with a more interesting set of realities. I travel around the U.S. reading from my books of poetry and my novel. With the stories I tell, the dreams and fears I examine in my work, I try to get my audience past the particulars of my skin color, my accent or my clothes.

I once wrote a poem in which I called Latinas "God's brown daughters." It is really a prayer, of sorts, for communication and respect. In it, Latin women pray "in Spanish to an Anglo God/with a Jewish heritage," and they are "fervently hoping/that if not omnipotent,/at least He be bilingual."

# For Better Reading: Beyond Stereotyping

Stereo:   hard, solid, three dimensional

Type:    a number of things or persons sharing a particular characteristic or trait; also, a piece of metal used in printing and typing to reproduce letters and symbols

Words don't just "happen." People make them, often by putting several meaningful parts together to create a new word. By knowing what each part means, you gain a better understanding of the whole.

The meaning of *stereotype* shows in its parts. First, it's a word for a three-dimensional mold or plate used by printers to reproduce the same impression or image over and over.

How does it carry over to stereotyping people? It means to assume that a group of people—whether English, Latino, or Indian—share certain traits, just as if they were nearly identical copies of one another, printed from a stereotype.

Through stereotyping, people often assign good traits to their own side and negative ones to others. In your reading, try to become aware of elements of stereotyping that color reactions and attitudes, sometimes without your realizing it.

## Important Details

1. Growing up, the author felt herself stereotyped as (a) modest and virtuous (b) stupid and backward (c) bold and provocative (d) shy and unfriendly.
2. The author's parents (a) welcomed their daughter's Anglo friends into their home (b) tried to maintain the life style of Puerto Rico (c) taught their daughter to stereotype anyone who was not Latin (d) believed that a woman's place was in the home, not in college.
3. As an adult, the author tries to deal with the stereotypes by (a) deciding all people have a right to their own opinion (b) trying to replace stereotypes with reality (c) changing her appearance to blend with the majority (d) refusing to associate with people who prejudge others.

## Questioning the Selection

1. While growing up in New Jersey, the author wanted "most of all to belong." Explain the factors that made belonging difficult for her.
2. As teenagers, what conflicting messages did the author and her friends receive from their Puerto Rican mothers?

3. What shows that the teachers, as well as other students in class, stereotyped the Puerto Rican girls instead of trying to understand and help them?
4. Why did traditions of both family and church allow girls to dress and behave more freely on the island than on the mainland?
5. How does the author attempt to understand, not stereotype, the middle aged man who sang a vulgar song to her?
6. Explain what the author means by stating, "I was just a character in his universe of 'others,' all cartoons."
7. Why does having an education make it easier for the author to avoid being stereotyped? For someone who is poor and uneducated, why do stereotypes often seem to feed upon themselves?

## Looking Deeper

### I. The Easy Way Out

Terms like "hot tamale" are often used to stereotype certain groups of people. Besides showing their prejudice, why do some people like to use such terms? Women, men, Irish, teenagers, teachers ... is there any group of people who cannot be stereotyped? Explain why or why not, giving examples to support your viewpoint.

### II. "At Least . . . Bilingual"

At the end of her essay, Judith Ortiz Cofer quotes several lines from one of her poems. By writing "in Spanish to an Anglo God/with a Jewish heritage," she means the Catholic church, the Christian religion. What is her intention in using the words *Spanish*, *Anglo*, and *Jewish*? In the final line Cofer states the Latin women's hope that God, if not omnipotent or all powerful, will at least be bilingual. Since the prefix "bi-" means two, what is humorous about hoping God is bilingual? Considering the entire selection, why might "God's brown daughters" have this fear when they pray?

# One Christmas Eve

*by Langston Hughes*

| | |
|---|---|
| ***Born:*** | *Joplin, Missouri* |
| ***Early schooling:*** | *Kansas, Ohio* |
| ***Youthful experience:*** | *Did odd jobs, shipped on freighters to Africa, Europe, lived a year in Mexico* |
| ***Famous as:*** | *Poet, novelist, lecturer, and playwright* |

**S**TANDING OVER THE HOT STOVE cooking supper, the colored maid, Arcie, was very tired. Between meals today, she had cleaned the whole house for the white family she worked for, getting ready for Christmas tomorrow. Now her back ached and her head felt faint from sheer fatigue. Well, she would be off in a little while, if only the Missus and her children would come on home to dinner. They were out shopping for more things for the tree which stood all ready, tinsel-hung and lovely in the living-room, waiting for its candles to be lighted.

Arcie wished she could afford a tree for Joe. He'd never had one yet, and it's nice to have such things when you're little. Joe was five, going on six. Arcie, looking at the roast in the white folks' oven, wondered how much she could afford to spend tonight on toys. She only got seven dollars a week, and four of that went for her room and the landlady's daily looking after Joe while Arcie was at work.

"Lord, it's more'n a notion raisin' a child," she thought.

She looked at the clock on the kitchen table. After seven. What made white folks so darned inconsiderate? Why didn't they come on home here to supper? They knew she wanted to get off before all the stores closed. She wouldn't have time to buy Joe nothin' if they didn't hurry. And her landlady probably wanting to go out and shop, too, and not be bothered with little Joe.

"Dog gone it!" Arcie said to herself. "If I just had my money, I might leave the supper on the stove for 'em. I just got to get to the stores fo' they close." But she hadn't been paid for the week yet. The Missus had promised to pay her Christmas Eve, a day or so ahead of time.

Arcie heard a door slam and talking and laughter in the front of the house. She went in and saw the Missus and her kids shaking snow off their coats.

"Umm-mm! It's swell for Christmas Eve," one of the kids said to Arcie. "It's snowin' like the deuce, and mother came near driving through a stop light. Can't hardly see for the snow. It's swell!"

"Supper's ready," Arcie said. She was thinking how her shoes weren't very good for walking in snow.

It seemed like the white folks took as long as they could to eat that evening. While Arcie was washing dishes, the Missus came out with her money.

"Arcie," the Missus said, "I'm so sorry, but would you mind if I just gave you five dollars tonight? The children have made me run short of change, buying presents and all."

"I'd like to have seven," Arcie said. "I needs it."

"Well, I just haven't got seven," the Missus said. "I didn't know you'd want all your money before the end of the week, anyhow. I just haven't got it to spare."

Arcie took five. Coming out of the hot kitchen, she wrapped up as well as she could and hurried by the house where she roomed to get little Joe. At least he could look at the Christmas trees in the windows downtown.

The landlady, a big light yellow woman, was in a bad humor. She said to Arcie, "I thought you was comin' home early and get this child. I guess you know I want to go out, too, once in awhile."

Arcie didn't say anything for, if she had, she knew the landlady would probably throw it up to her that she wasn't getting paid to look after a child both night and day.

"Come on, Joe," Arcie said to her son, "Let's us go in the street."

"I hears they got a Santa Claus down town," Joe said, wriggling into his worn little coat. "I wants to see him."

"Don't know 'bout that," his mother said, "but hurry up and get your rubbers on. Stores'll all be closed directly."

It was six or eight blocks downtown. They trudged along through the falling snow, both of them a little cold. But the snow was pretty!

The main street was hung with bright red and blue lights. In front of the City Hall there was a Christmas tree–but it didn't have no presents on it, only lights. In the store windows there were lots of toys–for sale.

Joe kept on saying, "Mama, I want . . ."

But mama kept walking ahead. It was nearly ten, when the stores were due to close, and Arcie wanted to get Joe some cheap gloves and something to keep him warm, as well as a toy or two. She thought she might come across a rummage sale where they had children's clothes. And in the ten-cent store, she could get some toys.

"O-oo! Lookee . . . ," little Joe kept saying, and pointing at things in the windows. How warm and pretty the lights were, and the shops, and the electric signs through the snow.

It took Arcie more than a dollar to get Joe's mittens and things he needed. In the A.&P. Arcie bought a big box of hard candies for 49c. And then she guided

Joe through the crowd on the street until they came to the dime store. Near the ten-cent store they passed a moving picture theatre. Joe said he wanted to go in and see the movies.

Arcie said, "Ump-un! No, child! This ain't Baltimore where they have shows for colored, too. In these here small towns, they don't let colored folks in. We can't go in there."

"Oh," said little Joe.

In the ten-cent store, there was an awful crowd. Arcie told Joe to stand outside and wait for her. Keeping hold of him in the crowded store would be a job. Besides she didn't want him to see what toys she was buying. They were to be a surprise from Santa Claus tomorrow.

Little Joe stood outside the ten-cent store in the light, and the snow, and people passing. Gee, Christmas was pretty. All tinsel and stars and cotton. And Santa Claus a-coming from somewhere, dropping things in stockings. And all the people in the streets were carrying things, and the kids looked happy.

But Joe soon got tired of just standing and thinking and waiting in front of the ten-cent store. There were so many things to look at in the other windows. He moved along up the block a little, and then a little more, walking and looking. In fact, he moved until he came to the white folks' picture show.

In the lobby of the moving picture show, behind the plate glass doors, it was all warm and glowing and awful pretty. Joe stood looking in, and as he looked his eyes began to make out, in there blazing beneath holly and colored streamers and the electric stars of the lobby, a marvellous Christmas tree. A group of children and grown-ups, white, of course, were standing around a big jovial man in red beside the tree. Or was it a man? Little Joe's eyes opened wide. No, it was not a man at all. It was Santa Claus!

Little Joe pushed open one of the glass doors and ran into the lobby of the white moving picture show. Little Joe went right through the crowd and up to where he could get a good look at Santa Claus. And Santa Claus was giving away gifts, little presents for children, little boxes of animal crackers and stick-candy canes. And behind him on the tree was a big sign (which little Joe didn't know how to read). It said, to those who understood, MERRY XMAS FROM SANTA CLAUS TO OUR YOUNG PATRONS.

Around the lobby, other signs said, WHEN YOU COME OUT OF THE SHOW STOP WITH YOUR CHILDREN AND SEE OUR SANTA CLAUS. And another announced, GEM THEATRE MAKES ITS CUSTOMERS HAPPY-SEE OUR SANTA.

And there was Santa Claus in a red suit and a white beard all sprinkled with tinsel snow. Around him were rattles and drums and rocking horses which he was not giving away. But the signs on them said (could little Joe have read) that they would be presented from the stage on Christmas Day to the holders of the lucky numbers. Tonight, Santa Claus was only giving away candy, and stick-candy canes, and animal crackers to the kids.

Joe would have liked terribly to have a stick-candy cane. He came a little closer to Santa Claus, until he was right in the front of the crowd. And then Santa Claus saw Joe.

Why is it that lots of white people always grin when they see a Negro child? Santa Claus grinned. Everybody else grinned, too, looking at little black Joe—who had no business in the lobby of a white theatre. Then Santa Claus stooped down and slyly picked up one of his lucky number rattles, a great big loud tin-pan rattle such as they use in cabarets. And he shook it fiercely right at Joe. That was funny. The white people laughed, kids and all. But little Joe didn't laugh. He was scared. To the shaking of the big rattle, he turned and fled out of the warm lobby of the theatre, out into the street where the snow was and the people. Frightened by laughter, he had begun to cry. He went looking for his mama. In his heart he never thought Santa Claus shook great rattles at children like that—and then laughed.

In the crowd on the street he went the wrong way. He couldn't find the ten-cent store or his mother. There were too many people, all white people, moving like white shadows in the snow, a world of white people.

It seemed to Joe an awfully long time till he suddenly saw Arcie, dark and worried-looking, cut across the side-walk through the passing crowd and grab him. Although her arms were full of packages, she still managed with one free hand to shake him until his teeth rattled.

"Why didn't you stand where I left you?" Arcie demanded loudly. "Tired as I am, I got to run all over the streets in the night lookin' for you. I'm a great mind to wear you out."

When little Joe got his breath back, on the way home, he told his mama he had been in the moving picture show.

"But Santa Claus didn't give me nothin'," Joe said tearfully. "He made a big noise at me and I runned out."

"Serves you right," said Arcie, trudging through the snow. "You had no business in there. I told you to stay where I left you."

"But I seed Santa Claus in there," little Joe said, "so I went in."

"Huh! That wasn't no Santa Claus," Arcie explained. "If it was, he wouldn't a-treated you like that. That's a theatre for white folks—I told you once—and he's just a old white man."

"Oh . . . ," said little Joe.

## For Better Reading: The Help of Omniscience

Omni:      all
Science:   knowledge, or a particular branch of systematized knowledge

Having *omniscience*, being *omniscient* means knowing everything there is to know about a subject . . . being in possession of all knowledge.

For writers and readers, *omniscience* has a special sense. It means the writer has assumed the privilege of looking into characters' minds and can tell what they're thinking. It's an ability that doesn't happen outside of literature and fiction, and, when an author chooses to use it, omniscience can help a reader understand the reasons for a character's behavior.

But, a word of caution. The writer chooses the thoughts that a character expresses. Many times the author wants the reader to be aware that those thoughts reveal even more than the character actually realizes. That's true in this story by Langston Hughes.

For example, near the beginning of the story Arcie wonders, "What made white folks so darned inconsiderate?" Arcie herself can't answer the question, and her thoughts show that she's trapped in a situation she can't control. By revealing Arcie's puzzlement, the author invites readers to seek the answer themselves, through the incidents, characters' thoughts, and other evidence included throughout the story.

On the surface "One Christmas Eve" is a simple story about simple people. Yet, by using omniscience, Hughes permits you to see that their lives are not so simple as they'd seem if you weren't privileged to share their thoughts.

## Making Inferences

1. Working as a maid for a white family in the 1930's, Arcie (a) thought seven dollars a week were generous wages (b) felt too poor to put up a Christmas tree (c) got a bonus for working overtime on Christmas Eve (d) spent most of her salary on food and clothing.
2. Arcie shows her consideration for others by thinking (a) her landlady probably wanted to shop, too (b) she might leave the supper on the stove if she had her money (c) her shoes weren't very good for walking in the snow (d) it was best not to argue about her pay.
3. Arcie allowed Joe to wander off by himself because (a) she was too tired to chase after him (b) they were separated in the crowded store (c) she was trying on a pair of overshoes (d) she wanted to surprise Joe on Christmas.

## Questioning the Story

1. Using omniscience, Hughes writes, "Arcie wished she could afford a tree for Joe." What other advantages does the white family have that Arcie lacks? Does or doesn't Arcie feel jealous of her white employers? Use proof from the story to support your position.
2. Arcie asks herself, "What made white folks so darned inconsiderate?" Give three examples to illustrate their lack of consideration. What attitudes do your examples reveal? Why did Arcie think, but not voice, her complaint?
3. How was Arcie's landlady also affected by the Missus' lack of consideration? Why didn't Arcie attempt to explain?
4. When Joe first asked to go to the movies, Arcie told him, "In these here small towns, they don't let colored folks in. We can't go in there." What else might Arcie have told him, but didn't add?

5. Looking into the theater lobby, Joe thinks, "No, it was not a man at all. It was Santa Claus!" What does this reveal about Joe's belief about Santa and Christmas?
6. If he could have read the signs in the lobby, would Joe have realized he was not welcome? Have reasons to support your reply. What must the theater owners have assumed?
7. The white people, kids and all, were cruel to Joe by laughing at him after the Santa Claus scared him and laughed, too. Why might they think they were not really "hurting" Joe? What did they fail to understand?
8. Why did Arcie say, "Serves you right," when Joe explained what happened? What combination of feelings were included in her anger? What caused her to feel this way?

## Looking Deeper

### I. "Oh . . . ," said little Joe.

Sometimes an expression like "oh" can carry a great deal of meaning. This was Joe's answer after Arcie told him, "That wasn't no Santa Claus . . . just a old white man." Since Joe was only five, he didn't realize and didn't have the words to express what he'd learned "One Christmas Eve." Explain at least three lessons Joe had learned at the theater and from his mother that day, concerning himself and his place in the world.

### II. Past to Present

In reading a story written in the past, it's natural to compare how conditions, appearances, and even language have changed. And, also important to discover how people "back then" were really like ourselves today.

The fact that Arcie could live on $7 a week shows the great difference between the dollar's value in the 1930's and its buying power today. What other comparisons does the story provide, as far as money is concerned? What does the author want you to feel about Arcie's economic situation, and which details prove this?

Find three or more uses of language that differ from those more common today. Explain what you believe accounts for the differences.

Although the setting of this story is in the past, how are Arcie's problems as a single parent similar to those faced by many families now? What other feelings and attitudes of characters in "One Christmas Eve" are evident in life today?

# His Big Chance

## by John Hildebidle

**Born:** Hartford, Connecticut
**Career:** Junior high social studies teacher,
literature teacher at Massachusetts
Institute of Technology, poet, author

OH, JIMMY WAS A PIP; everyone knew it. It helped to be a Fontaine in a town where the hotel that family had bought and named for itself loomed a story higher than anything else on Main Street. And it helped that he was clever, and tall, and had just *that* smile. But what topped it all off was baseball. When he went off to college, he was still, as his mother liked to say, a little ahead of himself; but after a year of schoolwork and ballplaying (whenever the ground was dry enough) and three jobs on top of that (there wasn't enough of Grandpa's money left to pay the way), he'd really grown into something, tall as ever but now broad across the shoulders too, and the arms that used to dangle as if they were looking for a place to hide had turned hard as two-by-fours.

Jimmy was supposed to spend that summer learning the hotel business, but before long he was playing ball all the time. He certainly could show those farm boys a thing or two, mostly with the bat; but he was no slouch behind the plate either. What could be better? Good exercise and fresh air and good money when you added it all up, and there was no harm in having a hero in the family, either.

So with one thing and another, Uncle Ralph's daffy idea made a kind of sense, at first. No one believed him when he bragged about connections; Ralph was always saying that, but all his connections had never gotten him further than two steps from the poorhouse. Still, you could read in the papers that some people actually made a good living playing baseball, and nobody could ignore how these days money got tighter and tighter, and maybe it was just some kind of luxury to have Jimmy off in college for most of the year. Grandpa was beside himself when he first heard. When he wanted to be the first college man in the family, he couldn't argue with what the ledger said. But he told himself that maybe college would be just a tryout, with Jimmy squeezing in some schoolwork during the winter.

The first surprise was that Uncle Ralph did seem to know somebody, maybe not Connie Mack or Christy Mathewson, but enough of a somebody to answer his letter. It was miles and miles to any big-league team and the letter Ralph got didn't offer any train fare, but it did mention that there were scouts who came that way every so often.

Whatever Ralph lacked in common sense, he at least had an eye for drama, and he knew that just letting Jimmy show up some townteam from Nashua or Concord might not be enough to capture the hard eye of a scout. The House of David team usually came through late in the summer but that was too long to wait; so off went another letter, to another somebody who handled a barnstorming negro team; and before Grandpa could even begin to point out how silly the whole thing was, it was all set: The posters run up (on speculation) by a job-printer Ralph had taken fishing a few times, and the mayor, once he was promised he could umpire, convinced him he could dig up the money to add some fireworks afterward.

Of course it didn't take all that just to draw a crowd for a ballgame, especially once Ralph, now convinced he was Mr. Ban Johnson himself, managed to put together a roster of the best players from all the teams for miles around, and hired a fellow from Manchester who'd had a few so-so years pitching for the New York Highlanders and who could still throw a baseball, and even had some control of it—when he was sober. Before long everybody—not just Ralph and Jimmy and of course Grandpa—looked upon it as a great occasion, and the selectmen, without being asked, hired some of the high-school boys to take the worst bumps out of the playing field and give the wooden stands a new coat of whitewash.

Jimmy made a point of telling himself this was all just a lark, but he couldn't keep his hopes from rising. The morning of the game he was awake well before sunrise, and he nearly cried when dawn revealed heavy clouds and a wind that promised rain. Uncle Ralph was certain he had all the necessary charms working, however, and the two of them sat down in the dining room to a huge breakfast. By late morning it looked as if he were right; the rain held off and then the clouds broke and it was as fine and hot a summer day as you could wish for.

Most of the town went down to the station to see the visiting team come in, but Ralph got all his players together early at the ball field and put them through their paces. The big pitcher, whom Ralph had kept under a teetotal eye for three days, looked grumpy but ready. He let Jimmy warm him up a little, and the fast ball had a sweet little hop to it. Jimmy tried to talk about signals but the pitcher said he'd throw the first couple quick, up and in, and "Then those duds will just wave at anything else I throw anyhow. They're like that."

By noon the crowd was building, every seat full and people standing well out along each foul line, and the fellow from the general store doing quite a business in scorecards and lemonade. The visitors had marched down Main Street like a drill team and then sat together in center field, eating box lunches. They didn't look like much; their uniforms didn't quite match and hung on them as if they were borrowed, and the only one who looked big at all had a roll of fat around his middle. When they started to loosen up, though, the uniforms somehow began to fit better; and there was something in their gestures that suggested that they were on good terms with the scuffed baseballs they threw around. The fat guy caught; it was surprising how quickly he could raise all that weight out of a crouch. But the pitcher looked like a bad joke: thin, squeaky-voiced, coffee-colored, with flapping sleeves and shoes about three sizes too big. He was lobbing them up like wedding invitations and every time he tried to throw a curve ball it bounced at least twice before it got anywhere near home plate. Jimmy almost felt sorry for him.

Ralph and Grandpa had fine seats right behind home plate, and beside them were two strangers, with straw boaters and flashy ties and little slips of paper they kept looking at and writing on, whom Jimmy supposed were the scouts. The point of all of Ralph's plots and plans could hardly have been kept secret, and when the mayor shouted "Play ball," Jimmy had the warm feeling of being the object of every eye. Ralph had conceded last ups to the visitors, and Jimmy, who was of course batting fourth, was convinced he'd get an early chance to show what he could do. But the skinny pitcher wasn't lobbing any more, and it took him ten pitches to set down three batters, only one of whom managed so much as a foul tip. Still, that just made it seem more of a challenge, and Jimmy crouched down behind the plate with his confidence intact. It was his day and he knew it.

The first batter hit from a deep crouch and the hired pitcher did just what he said he would; his best fast ball came just behind the batter's head. The batter didn't move an inch; and when the next pitch came in—a pretty fair curve, down and away—he stepped into it and sent it on a line back over the pitcher's mound and nearly took the pitcher's ample belly along with it. But the pitcher was, in his way, a man of principles, and it took four more hitters, two runs, and an out that came only because the center fielder was even luckier than he was fast, before he began to realize the high-and-tight fast ball wasn't the key to success. Jimmy went out to talk to him but he just turned his back.

The crowd was still pretty noisy but somehow you could hear a skeptical edge begin to take hold. On the next pitch Jimmy knew he was in trouble; he could see the ball jerk and twitch, the spit flying off of it, and all he could do was go to his knees to try to block it, which he did but with the part of his body that hurt the worst. He lay face down next to the plate telling himself first to breathe, then to stand up, but his body wasn't listening. By the time he could see or hear another run had scored. He went out to the mound again, very slowly, and said he'd need to know when the spitball was coming, but the hired pitcher just said, "Maybe I should roll it in?"

By the end of the inning Jimmy was still a little woozy; he wasn't sure whether five or six runs had scored, and he was beginning to suspect it might not matter. The skinny pitcher didn't take any warm ups. "No use wearing it out," he said to the crowd, which by now knew where the entertainment was. But they let out a healthy roar for Jimmy, their own boy. Jimmy couldn't find a bat that didn't feel like a wagon-tongue. When he finally got himself settled at the plate, he saw the pitcher smile at him: "Hey College Boy, I hear you're really something." Then the ball came right at him, and although his eyes told him it was a curve—it must be, it had to break, his body broke first and he felt himself back away and wave as—sure enough—it broke over the plate. "Don't you be nervous, College Boy," the pitcher said.

Jimmy watched, or rather heard, one fast ball. Then he fouled off another one, and he knew he'd just about measured it. All his preservation instincts made him give up on another curve that started out straight for his head; but the mayor had some local pride left and called it a ball. "Merry Christmas, College Boy," the pitcher said. He tried another fast ball, outside, but Jimmy was ready and got most of it, his swing just the slightest bit late but the ball still went singing down the right-field line, barely foul. "My, my, I *am* impressed," the pitcher said; and went into the longest wind-up Jimmy had ever seen, topped off with a head-jerk that looked like a bee had just stung his neck. Jimmy kept his eye on the ball the whole time and he was ready this time to turn the fast ball into two bases. The ball floated and floated, visibly slowing down and Jimmy just couldn't hold back; as he finished his swing he could see the ball still coming. "That was Mr. Restful," the pitcher said; and the crowd, all on his side now, cheered.

From the bench, Jimmy got to watch one more strike out and a sad excuse for a pop-up; and then, from behind the plate, he had plenty of time to admire what the visitors could do with a bat. The fat catcher could hit the ball so far he hardly had to run; and the skinny pitcher would announce just where hits would land. "You got to study this game, College Boy," he said to Jimmy, whom he'd made his interlocutor. By the third inning no one even bothered to announce the score. The skinny pitcher started alternating which hand he'd throw with, and the fielders did about every trick you could think of, catching balls behind their backs and what not. The mayor did his best to get the home team some base runners by calling balls when the pitches were obvious strikes, but it didn't do much good. Meanwhile the hired pitcher had disappeared and Jimmy found himself catching a bright-eyed farmhand who had volunteered from the stands.

It was still a lovely day but there were shadier places to enjoy it, and the crowd dwindled rapidly. Ralph and Grandpa and the two scouts stuck it out, of course; and so did the mayor's wife, who was more or less obligated to, and a crowd of younger brothers who enjoyed laughing and the old fellows who usually napped on the hotel porch. By the time Jimmy got to bat again even the skinny pitcher's good humor had started to wear out, and he threw one hard one at Jimmy's belt buckle, just to put things on a serious footing, and then the curve ball one more time. But Jimmy had by now fallen back on sheer desperation, which was stronger even than the reflex which told him to back away.

He knew exactly where the ball was headed and got his whole body into it and could tell without looking just what a beautiful arc the ball described as it rose out toward the creek that was beyond the left fielder. As he rounded first he saw the outfielders still chasing it, and he decided there was nothing on God's green and ample earth that could keep him from going all the way around.

Past second he could feel the ache in his groin start to deepen but he kept his legs moving. The third baseman tried to decoy him, crouching down as if a throw was on its way, but Jimmy went right by him and on toward home, where the fat catcher stood in the way.

Jimmy was no midget himself and went head first into the catcher just as the throw finally arrived. The two of them rolled toward the dust-covered plate. Jimmy reached out with one hand but the catcher's knee pressed down on his belly and held him fast; and Jimmy could see the ball, absurdly small in the catcher's hand, as it came toward his chin, where it hit with a resolute thud. "No sir," the catcher said, quietly but clearly, "No sir, you're on my property." Jimmy's hand was still a foot from the plate; just far enough to break utterly his last weak grip on common sense.

Before he was even aware he'd moved, Jimmy was up and swinging wildly at the catcher, who bobbed away from the punches, smiling. Still Jimmy swung, again and again, so enraged by it all that no one dared to try and stop him, although he could vaguely hear the mayor making conciliatory noises. Suddenly a wiry arm grabbed him and turned him around; it was the pitcher shouting. "Out is out, College Boy." Jimmy stopped in mid-swing and looked around at what was left of the crowd, all staring hard at him, some even cheering him on; all except the two scouts, who seemed mostly interested in the one or two clouds overhead. "Game called," the mayor announced; and Jimmy, all his energy now spent, limped over to the bench to collect his gear.

Grandpa was gone, but Ralph, who after all knew a good deal about failure, kept an only slightly worn smile on his face as he brought the two scouts over to shake Jimmy's hand. They were polite, of course, and explained that just now the big club was neckdeep in catchers but they'd keep him in mind. Ralph walked the two scouts down to the train station, gabbing the whole time, as if it were all still a matter of charm and careful pre-arrangement. Jimmy walked home, his groin aching badly, his chin swollen, his knuckles raw and his belly bruised.

Grandpa, a poor loser but a gentle winner, had a hot bath waiting for Jimmy, who let the water soak through his aches while the fireworks rumbled in the distance. His appetite wasn't bruised, and Grandpa made sure the kitchen did its best for him. Afterward the two of them took a walk, Jimmy limping along at the old man's usual sedate pace, up Main Street, out past the Methodist Church and all the wide-porched houses, where people resting in the cool evening nodded and sometimes even said kind things about how far that last hit had gone; and then down the other side of the street, the hotel gliding closer to them in the twilight, the town at ease. As they climbed the two steps on to the hotel porch, where his usual rocker waited, Grandpa finally said, "So. College I guess."

"Yeah. College," Jimmy said.

## For Better Reading: Colorful Language

"My, my, I *am* impressed," said the opposing pitcher after Jimmy swung late and hit a foul, on his way to striking out.

The comment, of course, was meant as irony. Often more effective than direct criticism, irony is a verbal jab of humor which really means the opposite of what's openly stated.

Even though you're likely to use and hear irony every day with friends, it's easy to miss when you're reading. Because you have to "get" the point of irony, it sometimes carries a delayed response and, just like a fast ball, can whiz right past.

Like slang, puns, and other colorful uses of language, irony can add life, fun, and humor to a story if you and the author are on the same wave length. But stories—like jokes—merely seem stupid when an author's attempt at humor is taken the wrong way.

When reading, it pays to take a second look at a colorful or unexpected turn of phrase. You might discover a stroke of humor that's well worth noticing—and where there's one, you're almost certain to find more.

### Inference

1. Considering the entire first paragraph, "pip" is seen as a slangy word characterizing Jimmy as (a) a special hometown favorite (b) a conceited young puppy (c) a typical self-centered teenager (d) an easy mark for a practical joke.
2. In writing "Ralph did seem to know somebody," the author uses "somebody" to mean (a) the mayor of Jimmy's town (b) the manager of the barnstorming team (c) a person connected with a big-league team (d) the one person who took his bragging seriously.
3. In order to impress the scouts, Ralph (a) tried to bribe the opposing pitcher (b) provided new uniforms for the hometown boys (c) brought in out-of-town players (d) got a former major-leaguer to write Jimmy a recommendation.

### Questioning the Story

1. "Uncle Ralph's daffy idea made a kind of sense, at first." What examples of foreshadowing in this sentence and the two following paragraphs give clues to the story's outcome?
2. Why did the visiting team's appearance make them seem like no real threat to Ralph's plans? What was the first clue to their ability?
3. The author writes that Jimmy was "of course batting fourth." Why was

he in this spot? What did Jimmy expect of his side's first time at bat? What did happen?

4. "Maybe I should roll it in?" the hired pitcher told Jimmy. Describe the situation that led to his sarcastic comment.

5. The crowd "by now knew where the entertainment was." Why was there no longer entertainment in the game itself? Explain what people now found entertaining, giving at least three examples.

6. Why did each inning of the game last exceptionally long?

7. How did each of the following react as the game wore on: the hired pitcher? the majority of the crowd? the visiting scouts? Ralph?

8. What position had Ralph offered the mayor to win his support? In this position, how did the mayor try to help Jimmy's team? How did he stop the scuffle between Jimmy and the catcher?

# Looking Deeper

## I. "His Big Chance"

The title is in some ways ironical. How was its ending the opposite of what was hoped and expected? Nevertheless, consider the following before deciding whether or not the ending was unhappy in fact. How did Jimmy prove he was not a quitter? What did Jimmy learn on the walk he took down Main Street, after the game? How did the game affect Jimmy's plans for the future?

## II. Beyond the Stereotypes

The setting of this story is in the past, at a time when black baseball players were not accepted by major league teams. How does the barnstorming team at first seem a likely victim for stereotyping? Explain how the story breaks these stereotypes, giving at least three examples.

## III. Responding to Humor

How someone reacts to humor is a very personal thing. What about this story—either its use of language, incident, or character trait—did you find most humorous and why? If you didn't find it humorous, explain your reasons for feeling as you do.

# An Independent Thinker

## by Mary Wilkins Freeman

| | |
|---|---|
| **Born:** | *Mary Ella Wilkins in Randolph, Massachusetts* |
| **Early life:** | *Suffered from poverty, ill health, death of mother* |
| **Adult life:** | *Published first story at age 29, married at age 50, spent final years in New Jersey* |

ESTHER GAY'S HOUSE WAS LITTLE and square, and mounted on posts like stilts. A stair led up to the door on the left side. Morning-glories climbed up the stair-railing, the front of the house and the other side were covered with them, all the windows but one were curtained with the matted green vines. Esther sat at the uncurtained window, and knitted. She perked her thin, pale nose up in the air, her pointed chin tilted upward too; she held her knitting high, and the needles clicked loud, and shone in the sun. The bell was ringing for church, and a good many people were passing. They could look in on her, and see very plainly what she was doing. Every time a group went by she pursed her thin old lips tighter, and pointed up her nose higher, and knitted more fiercely. Her skinny shoulders jerked. She cast a sharp glance at every one who passed, but no one caught her looking. She knew them all. This was a little village. By and by the bell had stopped tolling, and even the late church-goers had creaked briskly out of sight. The street, which was narrow here, was still and vacant.

Presently a woman appeared in a little flower-garden in front of the opposite house. She was picking a nosegay. She was little and spare, and she bent over the flowers with a stiffness as of stiff wires. It seemed as if it would take mechanical force to spring her up again.

Esther watched her. "It's dretful hard work for her to git around," she muttered to herself.

Finally, she laid down her knitting and called across to her. "Laviny!" said she.

The woman came out to the gate with some marigolds and candytuft in her hand. Her dim blue eyes blinked in the light. She looked over and smiled with a sort of helpless inquiry.

"Come over here a minute."

"I—guess I—can't."

Esther was very deaf. She could not hear a word, but she saw the deprecating shake of the head, and she knew well enough.

"I'd like to know why you can't, a minute. You kin hear your mother the minute she speaks."

The woman glanced back at the house, then she looked over at Esther. Her streaked light hair hung in half-curls over her wide crocheted collar, she had a little, narrow, wrinkled face, but her cheeks were as red as roses.

"I guess I'd better not. It's Sunday, you know," said she. Her soft, timid voice could by no possibility reach those deaf ears across the way.

"What?"

"I—guess I'd better not—as long as it's *Sunday*."

Esther's strained attention caught the last word, and guessed at the rest from a knowledge of the speaker.

"Stuff," said she, with a sniff through her delicate, uptilted nostrils. "I'd like to know how much worse 't is for you to step over here a minute, an' tell me how *she* is when I can't hear across the road, than to stop an' talk comin' out o' meetin'; you'd do that quick enough. You're strainin', Laviny Dodge."

Lavinia, as if overwhelmed by the argument, cast one anxious glance back at the house, and came through the gate.

Just then a feeble, tremulous voice, with a wonderful quality of fine sharpness in it, broke forth behind her,

"Laviny, Laviny, where be you goin'? Come back here."

Lavinia, wheeling with such precipitate vigor that it suggested a creak, went up the path.

"I wa'n't goin' anywhere, mother," she called out. "What's the matter?"

"You can't pull the wool over my eyes. I *seed* you a-goin' out the gate."

Lavinia's mother was over ninety and bedridden. That infinitesimal face which had passed through the stages of beauty, commonplaceness, and hideousness, and now arrived at that of the fine grotesqueness which has, as well as beauty, a certain charm of its own, peered out from its great feather pillows. The skin on the pinched face was of a dark-yellow color, the eyes were like black points, the tiny, sunken mouth had a sardonic pucker.

"Esther just wanted me to come over there a minute. She wanted to ask after you," said Lavinia, standing beside the bed, holding her flowers.

"Hey?"

"She *jest* wanted me to come over an' tell her how you was."

"How I was?"

"Yes."

"Did you tell her I was miser'ble?"

"I didn't go, mother."

"I *seed* you a-goin' out the gate."

"I came back. She couldn't hear 'thout I went way over."

"Hey?"

"It's all right, mother," screamed Lavinia. Then she went about putting the flowers in water.

The old woman's little eyes followed her, with a sharp light like steel.

"I ain't goin' to hev you goin' over to Esther Gay's, Sabbath day," she went on, her thin voice rasping out from her pillows like a file. "She ain't no kind of a girl. Wa'n't she knittin'?"

"Yes."

"Hey?"

"Yes, she was knittin', mother."

"Wa'n't knittin'?"

"Y-e-s, she was."

"I knowed it. Stayin' home from meetin' an' knittin'. I ain't goin' to hev you over thar, Laviny."

Esther Gay, over in her window, held her knitting up higher, and knitted with fury. "H'm, the old lady called her back," said she. "If they want to show out they kin, I'm goin' to do what I think's right."

The morning-glories on the house were beautiful this morning, the purple and white and rosy ones stood out with a soft crispness. Esther Gay's house was not so pretty in winter—there was no paint on it, and some crooked outlines showed. It was a poor little structure, but Esther owned it free of encumbrances. She had also a pension of ninety-six dollars which served her for support. She considered herself well to do. There was not enough for anything besides necessaries, but Esther was one who had always looked upon necessaries as luxuries. Her sharp eyes saw the farthest worth of things. When she bought a half-cord of pine wood with an allotment of her pension-money, she saw in a vision all the warmth and utility which could ever come from it. When it was heaped up in the space under the house which she used for a woodshed, she used to go and look at it.

"Esther Gay does think so much of her own things," people said.

That little house, which, with its precipitous stair and festoons of morning-glories, had something of a foreign picturesqueness, looked to her like a real palace. She paid a higher tax upon it than she should have done. A lesser one had been levied, and regarded by her as an insult. "My house is worth more'n that," she had told the assessor with an indignant bridle. She paid the increased tax with cheerful pride, and frequently spoke of it. Today she often glanced from her knitting around the room. There was a certain beauty in it, although it was hardly the one which she recognized. It was full of a lovely, wavering, gold-green light, and there was a fine order and cleanness which gave a sense of peace. But Esther saw mainly her striped rag-carpet, her formally set chairs, her lounge covered with Brussels, and her shining cooking-stove.

Still she looked at nothing with the delight with which she surveyed her granddaughter Hatty, when she returned from church.

"Well, you've got home, ain't you?" she said, when the young, slim girl, with her pale, sharp face, which was like her grandmother's, stood before her. Hatty in her meeting-gown of light-brown delaine, and her white meeting-hat trimmed with light-brown ribbons and blue flowers was not pretty, but the old woman admired her.

"Yes," said Hatty. Then she went into her little bedroom to take off her things. There was a slow shyness about her. She never talked much, even to her grandmother.

"You kin git you somethin' to eat, if you want it," said the old woman. "I don't want to stop myself till I git this heel done. Was Henry to meetin'?"

"Yes."

"His father an' mother?"

"Yes."

Henry was the young man who had been paying attention to Hatty. Her grandmother was proud and pleased; she liked him.

Hatty generally went to church Sunday evenings, and the young man escorted her home, and came in and made a call. Tonight the girl did not go to church as usual. Esther was astonished.

"Why, ain't you goin' to meetin'?" said she.

"No; I guess not."

"Why? why not?"

"I thought I wouldn't."

The old woman looked at her sharply. The tea-things were cleared away, and she was at her knitting again, a little lamp at her elbow.

Presently Hatty went out, and sat at the head of the stairs, in the twilight. She sat there by herself until meeting was over, and the people had been straggling by for some time. Then she went down-stairs, and joined a young man who passed at the foot of them. She was gone half an hour.

"Where hev you been?" asked her grandmother, when she returned.

"I went out a little way."

"Who with?"

"Henry."

"Why didn't he come in?"

"He thought he wouldn't."

"I don't see why."

Hatty said nothing. She lit her candle to go to bed. Her little thin face was imperturbable.

She worked in a shop, and earned a little money. Her grandmother would not touch a dollar of it; what she did not need to spend for herself, she made her save. Lately the old woman had been considering the advisability of her taking a sum from the saving's bank to buy a silk dress. She thought she might need it soon.

Monday, she opened upon the subject. "Hatty," said she, "I've been thinkin'—don't you believe it would be a good plan for you to take a little of your money out of the bank an' buy you a nice dress?"

Hatty never answered quickly. She looked at her grandmother, then she kept on with her sewing. It was after supper, her shop-work was done, and she was sitting at the table with her needle. She seemed to be considering her grandmother's remark.

The old woman waited a moment, then she proceeded: "I've been thinkin'—you ain't never had any real nice dress, you know—that it would be a real good plan for you to take some money, now you've got it, an' buy you a silk one. You ain't never had one, an' you're old enough to."

Still Hatty sewed, and said nothing.

"You might want to go somewhar," continued Esther, "an'—well, of course, if anythin' should happen, if Henry—It's jest as well not to hev' to do everythin' all to once, an' it's consider'ble work to make a silk dress—Why don't you say somethin'?"

"I don't want any silk dress."

I'd like to know why not?"

Hatty made no reply.

"Look here, Hatty, you an' Henry Little ain't had no trouble, hev' you?"

"I don't know as we have."

"What?"

"I don't know as we have."

"Hatty Gay, I know there's somethin' the matter. Now you jest tell me what 'tis. Ain't he comin' here no more?"

Suddenly the girl curved her arm around on the table, and laid her face down on it. She would not speak another word. She did not seem to be crying, but she sat there, hiding her little plain, uncommunicative face.

"Hatty Gay, ain't he comin'? *Why* ain't he comin'?"

Hatty would give the old woman no information. All she got was that obtained from ensuing events. Henry Little did not come; she ascertained that. The weeks went on, and he had never once climbed those vine-wreathed stairs to see Hatty.

Esther fretted and questioned. One day, in the midst of her nervous conjectures, she struck the chord in Hatty which vibrated with information.

"I hope you want too forrard with Henry, Hatty," said the old woman. "You didn't act too anxious arter him, did you? That's apt to turn fellows."

Then Hatty spoke. Some pink spots flared out on her quiet, pale cheeks.

"Grandma," said she, "I'll tell you, if you want to know, what the trouble is. I wasn't goin' to, because I didn't want to make you feel bad; but, if you're goin' to throw out such things as that to me, I don't care. Henry's mother don't like you, there!"

"What?"

"Henry's mother don't like you."

"Don't like me?"

"No."

"Why, what hev I done? I don't see what you mean, Hatty Gay."

"Grace Porter told me. Mrs. Little told her mother. Then I asked him, an' he owned up it was so."

"I'd like to know what she said."

Hatty went on, pitilessly, "She told Grace's mother she didn't want her son to marry into the Gay tribe anyhow. She didn't think much of 'em. She said any girl whose folks didn't keep Sunday, an' stayed away from meetin' an' worked, wouldn't amount to much."

"I don't believe she said it."

"She did. Henry said his mother took on so he was afraid she'd die, if he didn't give it up."

Esther sat up straight. She seemed to bristle out suddenly with points, from her knitting-needles to her sharp elbows and thin chin and nose. "Well, he kin give it up then, if he wants to, for all me. I ain't goin' to give up my principles fir him, nor any of his folks, an' they'll find it out. You kin git somebody else jest as good as he is."

"I don't want anybody else."

"H'm, you needn't have 'em then, ef you ain't got no more sperit. I shouldn't think you'd want your grandmother to give up doin' what's right yourself, Hatty Gay."

"I ain't sure it is right."

"Ain't sure it's right. Then I s'pose you think it would be better for an old woman that's stone deaf, an' can't hear a word of the preachin', to go to meetin' an' set there, doin' nothin' two hours, instead of stayin' to home an' knittin', to airn a leetle money to give to the Lord. All I've got to say is, you kin think so, then. I'm a-goin' to do what's right, no matter what happens."

Hatty said nothing more. She took up her sewing again; her grandmother kept glancing at her. Finally she said, in a mollifying voice, "Why don't you go an' git you a leetle piece of that cake in the cupboard; you didn't eat no supper hardly."

"I don't want any."

"Well, if you want to make yourself sick, an' go without eatin, you kin."

Hatty did go without eating much through the following weeks. She laid awake nights, too, staring pitifully into the darkness, but she did not make herself ill. There was an unflinching strength in that little, meagre body, which lay even back of her own will. It would take long for her lack of spirit to break her down entirely; but her grandmother did not know that. She watched her and worried. Still she had not the least idea of giving in. She knitted more zealously than ever Sundays; indeed, there was, to her possibly distorted perceptions, a religious zeal in it.

She knitted on week-days too. She reeled off a good many pairs of those reliable blue-yarn stockings, and sold them to a dealer in the city. She gave away every cent which she earned, and carefully concealed the direction of her giving. Even Hatty did not know of it.

Six weeks after Hatty's lover left, the old woman across the way died. After the funeral, when measures were taken for the settlement of the estate, it was discovered that all the little property was gone, eaten up by a mortgage and the interest. The two old women had lived upon the small house and the few acres of land for the last ten years, ever since Lavinia's father had died. He had grubbed away in a boot-shop, and earned enough for their frugal support as long as he lived. Lavinia had never been able to work for her own living; she was not now. "Laviny Dodge will have to go to the poorhouse," everybody said.

One noon Hatty spoke of it to her grandmother. She rarely spoke of anything now, but this was uncommon news.

"They say Laviny Dodge has got to go to the poorhouse," said she.

"What?"

"They say Laviny Dodge has got to go to the poorhouse."

"I don't believe a word on't."

"They say it's so."

That afternoon Esther went over to ascertain the truth of the report for herself. She found Lavinia sitting alone in the kitchen crying. Esther went right in, and stood looking at her.

"It's so, ain't it?" said she.

Lavinia started. There was a momentary glimpse of a red, distorted face; then she hid it again, and went on rocking herself to and fro and sobbing. She had seated herself in the rocking-chair to weep. "Yes," she wailed, "it's so! I've got to go. Mr. Barnes come in, an' said I had this mornin'; there ain't no other way. I've—got—to go. Oh, what would mother have said!"

Esther stood still, looking. "A place gits run out afore you know it," she remarked.

"Oh, I didn't s'pose it was quite so near gone. I thought mebbe I could stay—as long as I lived."

"You'd oughter hev kept account."

"I s'pose I hed, but I never knew much 'bout money-matters, an' poor mother, she was too old. Father was real sharp, ef he'd lived. Oh, I've got to go! I never thought it would come to this!"

"I don't think you're fit to do any work."

"No; they say I ain't. My rheumatism has been worse lately. It's been hard work for me to crawl round an' wait on mother. I've got to go. Oh, Esther, it's awful to think I can't die in my own home. Now I've got—to die in the poorhouse! I've—got—to die in the poorhouse!"

"I've got to go now," said Esther.

"Don't go. You ain't but jest come. I ain't got a soul to speak to."

"I'll come in agin arter supper," said Esther, and went out resolutely, with Lavinia wailing after her to come back. At home, she sat down and deliberated. She had a long talk with Hatty when she returned. "I don't care," was all she could get out of the girl, who was more silent than usual. She ate very little supper.

It was eight o'clock when Esther went over to the Dodge house. The windows were all dark. "Land, I believe she's gone to bed," said the old woman, fumbling along through the yard. The door was fast, so she knocked. "Laviny, Laviny, be you gone to bed? Laviny, Dodge!"

"Who is it?" said a quavering voice on the other side, presently.

"It's me. You gone to bed?"

"It's you, Mis' Gay, ain't it?"

"Yes. Let me in. I want to see you a minute."

Then Lavinia opened the door and stood there, her old knees knocking together with cold and nervousness. She had got out of bed and put a plaid shawl over her shoulders when she heard Esther.

"I want to come in jest a minute," said Esther. "I hadn't any idee you'd be gone to bed."

The fire had gone out, and it was chilly in the kitchen, where the two women sat down.

"You'll ketch your death of cold in your night-gown," said Esther. "You'd better git somethin' more to put over you."

"I don't keer if I do ketch cold," said Lavinia, with an air of feeble recklessness, which sat oddly upon her.

"Laviny Dodge, don't talk so."

"I don't keer. I'd ruther ketch my death of cold than not; then I shouldn't have to die in the poorhouse." The old head, in its little cotton night-cap, cocked itself sideways, with pitiful bravado.

Esther rose, went into the bedroom, got a quilt and put it over Lavinia's knees. "There," said she, "you hev that over you. There ain't no sense in your talkin' that way. You're jest a-flyin' in the face of Providence, an' Providence don't mind the little flappin' you kin make, any more than a barn does a swaller."

"I can't help it."

"What?"

"I—can't help it."

"Yes, you kin help it, too. Now, I'll tell you what I've come over here for. I've been thinkin' on't all the arternoon, an' I've made up my mind. I want you to come over and live with me."

Lavinia sat feebly staring at her. "Live with you!"

"Yes. I've got my house an' my pension, an' I pick up some with my knittin'. Two won't cost much more'n one. I reckon we kin git along well enough."

Lavinia said nothing, she still sat staring. She looked scared.

Esther began to feel hurt. "Mebbe you don't want to come," she said, stiffly, at last.

Lavinia shivered. "There's jest—one thing—" she commenced.

"What?"

"There's jest one thing—"

"What's that?"

"I dunno what—Mother—You're real good; but—Oh, I don't see how I kin come, Esther!"

"Why not? If there's any reason why you don't want to live with me, I want to know what 'tis."

Lavinia was crying. "I can't tell you," she sobbed; "but, mother—If—you didn't work Sundays. Oh!"

"Then you mean to say you'd ruther go to the poorhouse than come to live with me, Lavinia Dodge?"

"I—can't help it."

"Then, all I've got to say is, you kin go."

Esther went home, and said no more. In a few days she, peering around her curtain, saw poor Lavinia Dodge, a little, trembling, shivering figure, hoisted into the poorhouse covered wagon, and driven off. After the wagon was out of sight, she sat down and cried.

It was early in the afternoon. Hatty had just gone to her work, having scarcely tasted her dinner. Her grandmother had worked hard to get an extra one today, too, but she had no heart to eat. Her mournful silence, which seemed almost obstinate, made the old woman at once angry and wretched. Now she wept over Lavinia Dodge and Hatty, and the two causes combined made bitter tears.

"I wish to the land" she cried out loud once—"I wish to the land I could find some excuse; but I ain't goin' to give up what I think's right."

Esther Gay had never been so miserable in her life as she was for the three months after Lavinia Dodge left her home. She thought of her, she watched Hatty, and she knitted. Hatty was at last beginning to show the effects of her long worry. She looked badly, and the neighbors began speaking about it to her grandmother. The old woman seemed to resent it when they did. At times she scolded the girl, at times she tried to pet her, and she knitted constantly, week-days and Sundays.

Lavinia had been in the almshouse three months, when one of the neighbors came in one day and told Esther that she was confined to her bed. Her rheumatism was worse, and she was helpless. Esther dropped her knitting, and stared radiantly at the neighbor. "You said she was an awful sight of trouble, didn't you?" said she.

"Yes; Mis' Marvin said it was worse than takin' care of a baby."

"I should think it would take about all of anybody's time."

"I should. Why, Esther Gay, you look real tickled 'cause she's sick!" cried the woman, bluntly.

Esther colored. "You talk pretty," said she.

"Well, I don't care; you looked so. I don't s'pose you was," said the other, apologetically.

That afternoon Esther Gay made two visits: one at the selectmen's room, in the town-hall, the other at Henry Little's. One of her errands at the selectmen's room was concerning the reduction of her taxes.

"I'm a-payin' too much on that leetle house," said she, standing up, alert and defiant. "It ain't wuth it." There was some dickering, but she gained her point. Poor Esther Gay would never make again her foolish little boast about her large tax. More than all her patient, toilsome knitting was the sacrifice of this bit of harmless vanity.

When she arrived at the Littles', Henry was out in the yard. He was very young; his innocent, awkward face flushed when he saw Esther coming up the path.

"Good afternoon," said she. Henry jerked his head.

"Your mother to home?"

"Ye—s."

Esther advanced and knocked, while Henry stood staring.

Presently Mrs. Little answered the knock. She was a large woman. The astonished young man saw his mother turn red, in the face, and rear herself in order of battle, as it were, when she saw who her caller was; then he heard Esther speak.

"I'm a-comin' right to the p'int afore I come in," said she. "I've heard you said you didn't want your son to marry my granddaughter because you didn't like some things about me. Now, I want to know if you said it."

"Yes; I did," replied Mrs. Little, tremulous with agitation, red, and perspiring, but not weakening.

"Then you didn't have nothin' again' Hatty, you nor Henry? Twa'n't an excuse?"

"I ain't never had anything against the girl."

"Then I want to come in a minute. I've got somethin' I want to say to you, Mrs. Little."

"Well, you can come in—if you want to."

After Esther had entered, Henry stood looking wistfully at the windows. It seemed to him that he could not wait to know the reason of Esther's visit. He took things more soberly than Hatty; he had not lost his meals nor his sleep; still he had suffered. He was very fond of the girl, and he had a heart which was not easily diverted. It was hardly possible that he would ever die of grief, but it was quite possible that he might live long with a memory, young as he was.

When his mother escorted Esther to the door, as she took leave, there was a marked difference in her manner. "Come again soon, Mis' Gay," he heard her say; "run up any time you feel like it, an' stay to tea. I'd really like to have you."

"Thank ye," said Esther, as she went down the steps. She had an aspect of sweetness about her which did not seem to mix well with herself.

When she reached home she found Hatty lying on the lounge. "How do you feel to-night?" said she, unpinning her shawl.

"Pretty well."

"You'd better go an' brush your hair an' change your dress. I've been over to Henry's an' seen his mother, an' I shouldn't wonder if he was over here to-night."

Hatty sat bolt upright and looked at her grandmother. "What do you mean?"

"What I say. I've been over to Mrs. Little's, an' we've had a talk. I guess she thought she'd been kind of silly to make such a fuss. I reasoned with her, an' I guess she saw I'd been more right about some things than she'd thought for. An' as far as goin' to meetin' an' knittin' Sundays is concerned—Well, I don't s'pose I kin knit any more if I want to. I've been to see about it, an' Laviny Dodge is comin' here Saturday, an' she's so bad with her rheumatiz that she can't move, an' I guess it'll be all I kin do to wait on her, without doin' much knittin'. Mebbe I kin git a few minutes evenin's, but I reckon 't won't amount to much. Of course I couldn't go to meetin' if I wanted to. I couldn't leave Laviny."

"Did she say he—was coming?"

"Yes; she said she shouldn't wonder if he was up."

The young man did come that evening, and Esther retired to her little bedroom early, and lay listening happily to the soft murmur of voices outside. Lavinia Dodge arrived Saturday. The next morning, when Hatty had gone to church, she called Esther. "I want to speak to you a minute," said she. "I want to know if—Mr. Winter brought me over, and he married the Ball girl that's been in the post-office, you know, and somethin' he said—Esther Gay, I want to know if you're the one that's been sendin' that money to me and mother all along?"

Esther colored, and turned to go. "I don't see why you think it's me."

"Esther, don't you go. I know 'twas; you can't say 'twa'n't."

"It wa'n't much, anyhow."

"'T was to us. It kept us goin' a good while longer. We never said anythin' about it. Mother was awful proud, you know, but I dunno what we should have done. Esther, how could you do it?"

"Oh, it wa'n't anythin'. It was extra money. I airn'd it."

"Knittin'?"

Esther jerked her head defiantly. The sick woman began to cry. "If I'd ha' known, I would ha' come. I wouldn't have said a word."

"Yes, you would, too. You was bound to stan' up for what you thought was right, jest as much as I was. Now, we've both stood up, an' it's right. Don't you fret no more about it."

"To think—"

"Land sakes, don't cry. The tea's all steeped, and I'm goin' to bring you in a cup now."

Henry came that evening. About nine o'clock Esther got a pitcher and went down to the well to draw some water for the invalid. Her old joints were so tired and stiff that she could scarcely move. She had had a hard day. After she had filled her pitcher she stood resting for a moment, staring up at the bright sitting-room windows. Henry and Hatty were in there: just a simple, awkward young pair, with nothing beautiful about them, save the spark of eternal nature, which had its own light. But they sat up stiffly and timidly in their two chairs, looking at each other with full content. They had glanced solemnly and bashfully at Esther when she passed through the room; she appeared not to see them.

Standing at the well, looking up at the windows, she chuckled softly to herself. "It's all settled right," said she, "an' there don't none of 'em suspect that I'm a-carryin' out my p'int arter all."

## For Better Reading: Getting Acquainted

"She perked her thin, pale nose up in the air, her pointed chin tilted upward too; she held her knitting high, and the needles clicked loud, and shone in the sun."

You can discover a lot about a character from just one sentence, as this example from the first paragraph of "An Independent Thinker" proves.

What does it indicate if someone's nose is in the air and chin points upward? It's often a sign of being stuck-up. Or it could describe a person trying to make people think that she doesn't care who's watching.

Why does she hold her knitting high and click her needles sharply? Does she want to be seen? Or is it just because she's a very deaf, eccentric old lady?

The first paragraphs of stories or novels offer the opportunity for adding words together, trying to see where the author is heading, making and testing judgments.

To support your ideas, it's important to watch for repetitions, trusting the author to offer evidence that you're on the right track.

"Every time a group went by she ... pointed up her nose higher, and knitted more fiercely." It's the introduction to "An Independent Thinker."

## Words in Context

It's not always necessary to use a dictionary to know what a word means. Using sentences from the story as clues, choose the probable definition of each word in italics.

1. "The woman came out to the gate with some marigolds and *candytuft* in her hand." *Candytuft* is (a) a type of homemade taffy (b) a kind of flower (c) fuzzy, lightweight yarn (d) a crocheted bedspread.
2. I—guess I—can't." After Laviny's refusal, the author writes: "Esther ... could not hear a word, but she saw the *deprecating* shake of the head, and she knew well enough." *Deprecating* means (a) belittling, thinking badly of (b) angry and bitter (c) encouraging, hopeful (d) proud and haughty.
3. "But Esther saw mainly her striped rag-carpet, her formally set chairs, her lounge covered with *Brussels.* ..." In this context, *Brussels* must be (a) a kind of vegetable (b) a city in Europe (c) a breed of dog (d) a type of fabric.

## Questioning the Story

1. Why did Esther's neighbor and other townspeople object to her knitting? Why did Esther believe she was doing what was right?
2. How did Esther also prove herself an independent thinker with regard to the tax on her house?
3. What change in the life of her granddaughter, Hatty, concerned Esther? What did Hatty finally admit was the reason for this change?
4. Esther said, "I'm a-goin' to do what's right, no matter what happens." How might Hatty question her grandmother's stand? Why do you agree or disagree with Esther's viewpoint?
5. After the death of her mother, what choice did Laviny Dodge make and why?
6. "I wish ... I could find some excuse; but I ain't goin' to give up what I think's right." How does this statement by Esther explain why she looked pleased to discover Laviny was now helpless and confined to bed?
7. Why was Esther able to get a reduction of her taxes, and why did she want this? How did Esther convince Harry Little's mother to accept her?
8. What was Esther's secret purpose for the money she made from knitting? According to Esther, Laviny also stood up for what she thought was right. How is Esther's belief true?

# Looking Deeper

## I. Just a Stubborn, Eccentric Old Woman?

"It's all settled right," said Esther at the end, "an' there don't none of 'em suspect that I'm a-carryin' out my p'int after all." Why did Esther feel she had won her point instead of giving in? The author describes Esther as having a "religious zeal" or passion toward her Sunday knitting, that was "possibly distorted." Do you think she carried her determination "to do what she believed was right" too far? Why or why not?

## II. From the Other Viewpoint

Why did the townspeople feel threatened by Esther and try to avoid her? In what ways was Esther truly an independent thinker, instead of just eccentric? Are there still kinds of "unacceptable" behavior today that might cause people to be talked about or shunned? Have reasons and examples to support your opinion.

# El Patrón

## by Nash Candelaria

| | |
|---|---|
| **Home state:** | *California* |
| **Background:** | *Descendent of founding family of Albuquerque, New Mexico* |
| **Military service:** | *U.S. Air Force, became second lieutenant* |
| **Career:** | *Chemist, technical editor, novelist, short story writer* |

**M**Y FATHER-IN LAW'S IIIERARCHY IS, in descending order: Dios, El Papá, y el patrón. It is to these that mere mortals bow, as in turn el patrón bows to El Papá, and El Papá bows to Dios.

God and the Pope are understandable enough. It's this el patrón, the boss, who causes most of our trouble. Whether it's the one who gives you work and for it pay, the lifeblood of hardworking little people—or others: our parents (fathers affectionately known as jefe, mothers known merely as mama, military commanders el capitán), or any of the big shots in the government (el alcalde, el gobernador, el presidente and never forget la policía).

It was about some such el patrón trouble that Señor Martínez boarded the bus in San Diego and headed north toward L.A.—and us.

Since I was lecturing to a mid-afternoon summer school class at Southwestern U., my wife, Lola, picked up her father at the station. When I arrived home, they were sitting politely in the living room talking banalities: "Yes, it does look like rain. But if it doesn't rain, it might be sunny. If only the clouds would blow away."

Lola had that dangerous look on her face that usually made me start talking too fast and too long in hope of shifting her focus. It never worked. She'd sit there with a face like a brown-skinned kewpie doll whose expression was slowly turning into that of an angry maniac. When she could no longer stand it, she'd give her father a blast: "You never talk to me about anything important, you macho, chauvinist jumping bean!" Then it would escalate to nastiness from there.

But tonight it didn't get that far. As I entered Señor Martínez rose, dressed neatly in his one suit as for a wedding or a funeral, and politely shook my hand.

Without so much as a glance at Lola, he said, "Why don't you go to the kitchen with the other women."

"There are no other women," Lola said coldly. She stood and belligerently received my kiss on the cheek before leaving.

Señor Martínez was oblivious to her reaction, sensing only the absence of "woman," at which he visibly relaxed and sat down.

"Rosca," he said, referring to me as he always did by my last name. "Tito is in trouble with the law."

His face struggled between anger and sadness, tinged with a crosscurrent of confusion. Tito was his pride and joy. His only son after four daughters. A twilight gift born to his wife at a time when he despaired of ever having a son, when their youngest daughter, Lola, was already ten years old and their oldest daughter twenty.

"He just finished his examinations at the state university. He was working this summer to save money for his second year when this terrible thing happened."

I could not in my wildest fantasies imagine young Vicente getting into any kind of trouble. He had always impressed me as a bright, polite young man who would inspire pride in any father. Even when he and old Vicente had quarreled about Tito going to college instead of working full-time, the old man had grudgingly come around to seeing the wisdom of it. But now. The law! I was stunned.

"Where is he?" I asked, imagining the nineteen-year-old in some filthy cell in the San Diego jail.

"I don't know." Then he looked over his shoulder toward the kitchen, as if to be certain no one was eavesdropping. "I think he went underground."

Underground! I had visions of drug-crazed revolutionary zealots. Bombs exploding in federal buildings. God knows what kind of madness.

"They're probably after him," he went on. Then he paused and stared at me as if trying to understand. "Tito always looked up to you and Lola. Of all the family it would be you he would try to contact. I want you to help me." Not help *Tito*, I thought, but help *me*.

I went to the cabinet for the bottle that I keep there for emergencies. I took a swallow to give me enough courage to ask the question. "What . . . did . . . he do?"

Señor Martínez stared limply at the glass in his hand. "You know," he said, "my father fought with Pancho Villa."

Jesus! I thought. If everyone who told me his father had fought with Pancho Villa was telling the truth, that army would have been big enough to conquer the world. Besides—what did this have to do with Tito?

"When my turn came," he continued, "I enlisted in the Marines at Camp Pendleton. Fought los Japonés in the Pacific." Finally he took a swallow of his drink and sat up stiffly as if at attention. "The men in our family have never shirked their duty!" He barked like the Marine corporal he had once been.

It slowly dawned on me what this was all about. It had been *the* topic all during summer school at Southwestern U. Registration for the draft. "No blood for Mideast oil!" the picket signs around the campus post office had shouted. "Boycott the Exxon army!"

"I should never have let him go to college," Señor Martínez said. "That's where he gets such crazy radical ideas. From those rich college boys whose parents can buy them out of all kinds of trouble."

"So he didn't register," I said.

"The FBI is probably after him right now. It's a federal crime, you know. And the Canadians don't want draft dodgers either."

He took a deep swallow and polished off the rest of his drink in one gulp, putting the empty glass on the coffee table. There, his gesture seemed to say, now you know the worst.

Calmer now, he went on to tell me more. About the American Civil War; a greater percentage of Spanish-speaking men of New Mexico had joined the Union Army than the men from any other group in any other state in the Union. About the Rough Riders, including young Mexican-Americans, born on horseback; riding roughest of all over the Spanish in Cuba. About the War-to-End-All-Wars, where tough, skinny, brown-faced doughboys from farms in Texas, New Mexico, Arizona, Colorado, and California gave their all "Over There." About World War II, from the New Mexico National Guard captured at Bataan to the tough little Marines whom he was proud to fight alongside; man for man, there were more decorations for bravery among Mexican-Americans than among any other group in this war. Then Korea, where his younger brother toughed it out in the infantry. Finally Vietnam, where kids like his nephew, Pablo, got it in some silent, dark jungle trying to save a small country from the Communists.

By now he had lost his calm. There were tears in his eyes, partly from the pride he felt in this tradition of valor in war. But partly for something else, I thought. I could almost hear his son's reply to his impassioned call to duty: "Yes, Papá. So we could come back, if we survived, to our jobs as busboys and ditch diggers; *that's* why I have to go to college. I don't want to go to the Middle East and fight and die for some oil company when you can't even afford to own a car. If the Russians invaded our country, I would defend it. If a robber broke into our house, I would fight him. If someone attacked you, I would save you. But this? No, Papá."

But now Tito was gone. God knows where. None of his three sisters in San Diego had seen him. Nor any of his friends in the neighborhood or school or work.

I could hear preparations for dinner from the kitchen. Señor Martínez and I had another tragito while Lolita and Junior ate their dinner early, the sounds of their childish voices piercing through the banging of pots and pans.

When Lola called me Emiliano instead of by my nickname, Pata, I knew we were in for a lousy meal. Everything her father disliked must have been served. It had taken some kind of perverse gourmet expending a tremendous amount of energy to fix such rotten food. There was that nothing white bread that presses together into a doughy flat mass instead of the tortillas Papá thrived on. There was a funny little salad with chopped garbage in it covered by a blob of imitation goo. There was no meat. No meat! Just all those sliced vegetables in a big bowl. Not ordinary vegetables like beans and potatoes and carrots, but funny, wiggly long things like wild grass . . . or worms. And quivering cubes of what must have been whale blubber.

Halfway through the meal, as Señor Martínez shuffled the food around on his plate like one of our kids resisting what was good for them, the doorbell rang.

"You'd better get that, Emiliano," Lola said, daring me to refuse by her tone of voice and dagger-throwing glance.

Who needs a fight? In a sense I was the lucky one because I could leave the table and that pot of mess-age. When I opened the door, a scraggly young man beamed a weak smile at me. "I hitchhiked from San Diego," Tito said.

Before I could move onto the steps and close the door behind me, he stumbled past me into the house. Tired as he was, he reacted instantly to seeing his father at the table. "You!" he shouted, then turned and bolted out the door.

Even tired he could run faster than I, so I hopped into the car and drove after him while Lola and Sennor Martínez stood on the steps shouting words at me that I couldn't hear.

Two blocks later Tito finally climbed into the car after I bribed him with a promise of dinner at McDonald's. While his mouth was full, I tried to talk some sense into him, but to no avail. He was just as stubborn as his father and sister. Finally, I drove him to the International House on campus where the housing manager, who owed me a favor, found him an empty bed.

"You should have *made* him come back with you," Lola nagged at me that night.

"He doesn't want to be under the same roof with his father." From her thoughtful silence I knew that she understood and probably felt the same way herself. When I explained to her what it was all about—her father had said nothing to her—it looked for a moment as if she would get out of bed, stomp to the guest room, and heave Señor Martínez out into the street.

The next day seemed like an endless two-way shuttle between our house and the I House. First me. Then Lola. If Señor Martínez had had a car and could drive, he would have followed each of us.

Our shuttle diplomacy finally wore them down. I could at last discern cracks in father's and son's immovable positions.

"Yes. Yes. I love my son."

"I love my father."

"I know. I know. Adults should be able to sit down and air their differences, no matter how wrong he is."

"Maybe tomorrow. Give me a break. But definitely not at mealtime. I can't eat while my stomach is churning."

The difficulty for me, as always, was in keeping my opinions to myself. Lola didn't have that problem. After all, they were her brother and father, so she felt free to say whatever she pleased.

"The plan is to get them to talk," I said to her. "If they can talk they can reach some kind of understanding."

"Papá has to be set straight," she said. "As usual, he's wrong, but he always insists it's someone else who messed things up."

"He doesn't want Tito to go to jail."

"That's Tito's choice!" Of course she was right; they were both right.

The summit meeting was set for the next afternoon. Since I had only one late morning lecture, I would pick up Tito, feed him a Big Mac or two, then bring him to the house. Lola would fix Señor Martínez some nice tortillas and chili, making up for that abominable dinner of the night before last. Well fed, with two chaperones mediating, we thought they could work something out.

When Tito and I walked into the house, my hope started to tremble and develop goose bumps. It was deathly silent and formal. Lola had that dangerous look on her face again. The macho, chauvinist jumping bean sat stiffly in his suit that looked like it had just been pressed—all shiny and sharply creased, unapproachable and potentially cutting, an inanimate warning of what lay behind Señor Martínez's stone face.

Tito and I sat across from the sofa and faced them. Or rather I faced them. Both Tito and Señor Martínez were looking off at an angle from each other, not daring to touch glances. I smiled, but no one acknowledged it so I gave it up. Then Lola broke the silence.

"What this needs is a woman's point-of-view," she began.

That's all Señor Martínez needed. The blast his eyes shot at her left her open-mouthed and silent as he interrupted. "I don't want you to go to jail!" He was looking at Lola, but he meant Tito.

Tito's response was barely audible, and I detected a trembling in his voice. "You'd rather I got killed on some Arabian desert," he said.

The stone face cracked. For a moment it looked as if Señor Martínez would burst into tears. He turned his puzzled face from Lola toward his son. "No," he said. "Is that what you think?" Then, when Tito did not answer, he said, "You're my only son, and damn it! Sons are supposed to obey their fathers!"

"El patrón, El Papá, and Dios," Tito said with a trace of bitterness.

But Lola could be denied no longer. "Papá, how old were you when you left Mexico for the U.S.?" She didn't expect an answer, so didn't give him time to reply. "Sixteen, wasn't it? And what did your father say?"

Thank God that smart-ass smile of hers was turned away from her father. She knew she had him, and he knew it too, but he didn't need her smirk to remind him of it.

He sighed. The look on his face showed that sometimes memories were best forgotten. When he shook his head but did not speak, Lola went on. She too had seen her father's reaction, and her voice lost its hard edge and became more sympathetic.

"He disowned you, didn't he? Grandpa disowned you. Called you a traitor to your own country. A deserter when things got tough."

"I did not intend to stay in Mexico and starve," he said. He looked around at us one by one as if he had to justify himself. "He eventually came to Los Estados Unidos himself. He and Mamá died in that house in San Diego."

"What did you think when Grandpa did that to you?"

No answer was necessary. "Can't you see, Papá?" Lola pleaded, meaning him and Tito. He could see.

Meanwhile Tito had been watching his father as if he had never seen him before. I guess only the older children had heard Papá's story of how he left Mexico.

"I don't intend to go to jail, Papá," Tito said, "I just have to take a stand along with thousands of others. In the past old men started wars in which young men died in order to preserve old men's comforts. It just has to stop. There's never been a war without a draft. Never a draft without registration. And this one is nothing but craziness by el patrón in Washington, D.C. If enough of us protest, maybe he'll get the message."

"They almost declared it unconstitutional," I said. "They may yet."

"Because they aren't signing women," Papá said in disgust. But from the look on Lola's face, I'd pick her over him in any war.

"If they come after me, I'll register," Tito said. "But in the meantime I have to take this stand."

There. It was out. They had had their talk in spite of their disagreements.

"He's nineteen," Lola said. "Old enough to run his own life."

Señor Martínez was all talked out. He slumped against the back of the sofa. Even the creases in his trousers seemed to have sagged. Tito looked at his sister, and his face brightened.

"Papá," Tito said. "I . . . I'd like to go home, if you want me to."

On Papá's puzzled face I imagined I could read the words: "My father fought with Pancho Villa." But it was no longer an accusation, only a simple statement of fact. Who knows what takes more courage—to fight or not to fight?

"There's a bus at four o'clock," Señor Martínez said.

Later I drove them in silence to the station. Though it felt awkward, it wasn't a bad silence. There are more important ways to speak than with words, and I could feel that sitting shoulder to shoulder beside me, father and son had reached some accord.

Papá still believed in el patrón, El Papá, and Dios. What I hoped they now saw was that Tito did too. Only in his case, conscience overrode el patrón, maybe even El Papá. In times past, popes too declared holy wars that violated conscience. For Tito, conscience was the same as Dios. And I saw in their uneasy truce that love overrode their differences.

I shook their hands as they boarded the bus, and watched the two similar faces, one old, one young, smile sadly at me through the window as the Greyhound pulled away.

When I got back home, Junior and Lolita were squabbling over what channel to watch on TV. I rolled my eyes in exasperation, ready to holler at them, but Lola spoke up first.

"I'm glad Papá got straightened out. The hardest thing for parents with their children is to let go."

Yeah, I started to say, but she stuck her head into the other room and told Junior and Lolita to stop quarreling or they were going to to get it.

# For Better Reading: Making Words Add Up

| | |
|---|---|
| *Hierarchy:* | It's a word to make many readers wonder. |
| *Dios, El Papá, y el patrón:* | In the beginning of this short story, writer Nash Candelaria also includes words in Spanish to illustrate another way of taking sides: generation versus generation, old ways versus new. |

Yet sometimes, as in this story, several unfamiliar words are easier to understand than just one.

*Dios, El Papá, y el patrón.* Questions to ask yourself are: How are they all alike? How are they different? What relation do they have to one another? In what order are they written? Why?

You can trust a good writer to want you to know the answers. But as a reader, you too must do your part. For example, in the list of "big shots in the government," the author names *el alcalde, el gobernador,* and *el presidente.* The final two words are similar to English. Considering their order, would an *alcalde* most likely hold a federal, state or city office? How do you know?

Whether it's English or a foreign expression, intelligent reading requires paying thoughtful attention to the relationship between words.

## More Words in Context

1. "They were sitting politely in the living room talking *banalities*." Judging by the examples in the story, *banality* means their conversation was (a) pointless (b) witty (c) insulting (d) serious.
2. "You macho, chauvinistic jumping bean!" In saying these words to her father, Lola means to be (a) funny (b) insulting (c) forgiving (d) understanding.
3. "It had taken some kind of *perverse* gourmet expending a tremendous amount of energy to fix such rotten food." Taken in context, *perverse* shows that Lola's meal was (a) intentionally bad (b) carefully balanced (c) carelessly prepared (d) not given the praise she'd hoped to win.

## Questioning the Story

1. Identify the first-person narrator of "El Patrón," by giving his full name, the names of his wife and children, his profession, and the city where he and his family live. What is Rosca's nickname, and what is revealed by his wife's failure to use it?
2. How does Sr. Martínez express his attitude toward women shortly after

Rosca's arrival? Why does he consider Tito a "twilight gift," as well as his "pride and joy"?

3. What is the "terrible trouble" that Tito is in? Why isn't it so serious as his father imagines?

4. Why is Sr. Martínez justifiably proud of the Mexican-American tradition of valor? When he thinks "I could almost hear his son's reply to his impassioned call for duty," what does Rosca feel that Tito has considered about their country's regard for Mexican-Americans' contributions, but his father has not?

5. Tito says, "I just have to take a stand . . ." How did he once before take a stand concerning his future? What was the outcome?

6. Whom does Tito mean by "el patrón in Washington?" What message does Tito hope to participate in sending to him?

7. When he was sixteen, how and why had Sr. Martínez also rebelled against his own father? What was the eventual outcome?

8. Lola says, "The hardest thing for parents with their children is to let go." Although Lola can see the mistakes made by her father, how do both she and her husband react in a similar way at the story's end, concerning Junior and Lolita?

## Looking Deeper

### I. A Matter of Distance

As the narrator, why could Emiliano Rosca see the situation more clearly and less emotionally than Tito, Lola, and their father? Rosca notes that Sr. Martínez said, "I want you to help me," instead of help *Tito*. What does this show about Sr. Martínez's attitude?

Describe two ways that Lola shows her feelings towards her father. Does he deserve her resentment? Why or why not?

### II. "They Were Both Right"

Lola feels that Tito has the right to choose what he wants to do. In what ways does the narrator feel that both Lola and her father are right? In what way did all three family members show their stubbornness? How does Lola show her willingness to make up?

### III. "El Patrón, El Papá, and Dios"

In this story, the three most important influences on Tito's decision were the U.S. government, his father, and his conscience. Discuss how each affected him, and which you believe should be most important in making such decisions. How does the story support the narrator's conclusion that "love overrode their differences"?

# My Tribe

## by John Ciardi

**Born:** Boston, Mass.

**Military service:** B29 gunner in World War II, made technical sergeant

**Career:** Poet, editor, children's book author, college professor

Everyone in my tribe hates
everyone in your tribe.

Every girl in my tribe wants to
be there when we bring in anyone
from your tribe. Our girls save fagots*
in their hope chests for you.

Every boy in my tribe has a peg
from which to hang the scalp of
anyone in your tribe. Our boys
hone knives in their dreams of you.

Everyone in my tribe is proud of
our boys and their dreams, of our
girls and their trousseaus. Our lives
have dear goals across which we

shall all finally kick all of your
heads. We are united.

* *fagot* a bundle of sticks, twigs, or branches bound together and used as fuel.

# For Better Reading: A Vein of Irony

"You can't mean that!" When that's your reaction to something you read, you're probably right. The author didn't mean it and wants the reader to disagree with what the first-person speaker says.

Experienced readers, especially of poetry, learn to trust their instincts. Often the strongest way to make a point is through the use of irony, as in "My Tribe" by John Ciardi.

It may a single word used ironically, with the reader recognizing its opposite as true. When someone says, "Lovely day, isn't it?" and the sky is pouring rain ... that's irony. And the one word "lovely" signals its use.

Irony can also involve showing a common attitude or error in thinking to be obviously wrong, by carrying such viewpoints to ridiculous extremes. That's John Ciardi's goal in exaggerating the "attitude problem" of his poem's first-person speaker.

When you're on the alert for irony, you'll discover how an ironic light sharpens your awareness of "out of focus" ideas and attitudes that people frequently take for granted.

## Questioning the Poem

1. Assuming he is not the poet, what do you know about the speaker? What words indicate that "tribe" is not meant in the customary sense, such as a tribe of Indians or other traditionally tribal peoples?
2. In the first two lines, only three words are not repeated. What are they? What is the only difference between the two tribes? What isn't explained about the hatred they share?
3. Although the poet uses the word *tribe*, what other types of groups might the poem refer to?
4. According to the poem, the girls are keeping bundles of sticks, or "fagots" for bonfires, in their hope chests. How would these be used "for" the other tribe? What is ironic about the word *hope*?
5. What is ironic about Ciardi's use of the word *dreams*, considering that the boys dream of sharpening knives? What is ironic about using the word *dear* to describe their goals?"

## Looking Deeper
### I. "We Are United"

Although these are the final words of the poem, what are the only ways in which the tribe is united? What is missing that might make their goal seem more valid? Why are or why aren't there good reasons for feeling as the poem's speaker does? In what sense are both "My Tribe" and the "Other Tribe" themselves united with each other?

## II. Words Without Thought

Explain the underlying ideas about people and their attitudes that are contained in this poem.

Compare the attitude expressed by the speaker with that of some sports fans or with the words of a school fight song, such as the following:

Forward, Tigers!
Forward, Tigers!
Fight for GHS.
Show our spirit!
Make them fear it!
Fight for GHS.

Give other examples of the tendency to use words without sufficient thought of their meaning and intent.

# Nutshell

*by Julio Marzan*

**Born:** *Puerto Rico*
**Career:** *Spanish language and literature teacher,*
*New York universities, poet, and author*

Mr. Rodriguez
is superintendent
at 85th and Park

Some days
he chases a taxi
for Mrs. Mathews

He does this
because he thinks
she is a lady

Mrs. Mathews
appreciates that
because

she thinks
that he
is right

## Questioning the Poem

As with "My Tribe," this poem requires you to make educated guesses based on the evidence given. Be sure to give support from the poem for your answers.

1. Does the poem take place in a small town or major city?
2. Does Mrs. Mathews live in a private home or an apartment building?
3. Does Mr. Rodriguez's position involve supervising the building itself or supervising a company's operation?
4. What does Mr. Rodriguez do for Mrs. Mathews? Why?
5. Why does Mrs. Mathews think he does this?

# Looking Deeper

## I. Attitudes

The final stanza of the poem simply states, "She thinks that he is right." Explain what this reveals about Mrs. Mathews' attitude toward herself and Mr. Rodriguez. How do the names of the characters provide one reason for her attitude? What other reasons might she have? Why is the final statement ironical?

## II. "Nutshell"

A common expression speaks of summing something up "in a nutshell" or stating it briefly. In a sentence of 10-15 words, state what the poem is trying to express about the attitudes of people like Mrs. Mathews. You might wish to begin, "Some people believe ..."

# Southern Cop

## by Sterling A. Brown

**Born:**      Washington, DC
**Honors:**      Phi Beta Kappa Professor at: Howard,
              Alaska and New York universities,
              Vassar College
**Noted as:**      Poet, editor, critic

Let us forgive Ty Kendricks
The place was Darktown. He was young.
His nerves were jittery. The day was hot.
The Negro ran out of the alley.
And so Ty shot.                                                     5

Let us understand Ty Kendricks
The Negro must have been dangerous,
Because he ran;
And here was a rookie with a chance
To prove himself man.                                              10

Let us condone Ty Kendricks
If we cannot decorate.
When he found what the Negro was running for,
It was all too late;
And all we can say for the Negro is                                15
It was unfortunate.

Let us pity Ty Kendricks
He has been through enough,
Standing there, his big gun smoking,
Rabbit-scared, alone,                                              20
Having to hear the wenches wail
And the dying Negro moan.

## Questioning the Poem

1. In the first stanza what is the only reason given for Ty Kendricks' shooting the victim? Why does the speaker claim Kendricks deserves forgiveness? Give three reasons.
2. Line 7 states, "The Negro must have been dangerous." Why does the speaker draw this conclusion? What gap in logic does this contain? How does the word *rookie* provide other possible explanations for the shooting?
3. The first line of each stanza names Ty Kendricks, yet the victim's name is never given. What does this reveal about the speaker's attitude?
4. In line 12, why would the speaker think of "decorating" Kendricks in response to his deed? What do the words "It was all too late" in line 14 reveal about why the victim had been running?
5. What is ironic about the word *unfortunate* in line 16? Coming after stanza 3, why is "Let us pity Ty Kendricks" in line 17 especially ironical?
6. How is blame misplaced in the last two lines of the poem?

## Looking Deeper

### I. Taking Sides

Sterling A. Brown is a celebrated black poet. Do you think he has written a fair description of the young rookie policeman? Why or why not? Which is the real target of Brown's irony, Ty Kendricks or the speaker in the poem? Explain the reasons supporting your choice. What effect results from Brown's title, "Southern Cop"?

### II. Another Viewpoint

Read the following letter sent to newspaper columnist Ann Landers.

# Teens shouldn't push police officers too far

*Ann Landers*

DEAR ANN LANDERS: I don't want to go into too much detail, and I'm not signing my name, but if you use your imagination you can figure out what happened.

With so many guns loose these days, this letter could have come from Chicago, Memphis, Florida, or New York. Actually, I live in Los Angeles. Please, Ann, print this message:

DEAR TEENAGER: I didn't mean to break your mother's heart or bring your family grief.

If you were my son, I would have told you, "Son, if a policeman says, 'Stop!'—stop. Don't move. Drop whatever you're carrying and put your hands where he can see them. Treat him with respect. If you don't, you could make a lot more trouble for yourself and you already have plenty."

I also would tell my own kid, if you're driving a car and you see flashing red lights or hear a siren, stop. Pull over to the side of the road and put your hands where the officer can see them. Someone may have just been murdered, a child may have been raped, or a bank robbed.

I don't know if you're carrying a Bible or a sawed-off shotgun, but I'm not taking any chances. You may think I'm scared and you're right. I am scared to death. I'm scared that I might never see my family again. I'm scared that my little kids are going to grow up without a father. I've been to too many of my buddies' funerals to think it couldn't happen to me. You may think life is just a game, so you play the game for fun. I'm sorry, son, but I'm a policeman and I have to play for keeps. Those are the rules and nobody can change them.—LAW OFFICER IN CALIFORNIA

**DEAR OFFICER: That couldn't have been an easy letter to write. Thank you for sending it my way.**

## Questioning the Selection

Compare the feelings expressed by the law officer writing the letter with that of the poem, "Southern Cop." How are they alike and how different? What part do understanding and lack of understanding play in both poem and letter?

---
### REFLECTIONS
---

Age, background, sex, upbringing—there often seem more possibilities for dividing people into groups than for bringing them together.

As you look back on this unit, try to decide what basic issues or problems caused the conflict between "them and us" in each selection. In some cases, you may find more than one reason for the inability of people to share the same focus.

What causes people to be like those of whom Mickey Roberts' father said, "They just don't understand"? Feel free to take sides in your discussion, but try to agree upon three major reasons.


## To Write About or to Discuss

1. I wanted "most of all to belong," admits Judith Ortiz Cofer in her essay "Don't Misread My Signals." What are the importance, problems, and possible dangers of trying to belong, as it concerns today's teens?
2. "They just don't understand ..." Explain a way in which this is true about you, yours, or something that matters to you.
3. Alike but different. Compare two characters you've read about in this unit or compare a character with yourself or someone you know. How are the feelings and situations alike, in spite of outward "differences"?
4. A change of focus ... common bonds. What quality or qualities are shared by the selections in this unit? How?
5. Air a special viewpoint of your own, putting it in focus.

# UNIT 3

# The Stuff of Legends

WHERE DO YOU LOOK TO find a legend?

Legends often concern larger than life figures like fearless knights in bright armor and great Greek heroes such as clever Odysseus and mighty Hercules.

Legendary heroes embody the qualities and characteristics that a people or nation most admire. Almost too good to be true, yes, for they are ideals from a dim yet glorious past, still living in memory as inspiration for times present and future.

In some ways, America is a nation of shared legends. Although the land is old, the country called America was formed by those with other roots, each bringing tales of olden heroes from other lands and other peoples.

What legends can America call its own? According to the dictionary, a legend is a "nonhistorical or unverifiable story handed down ... from early times and popularly accepted as historical."

But America is the land of the eyewitness. Almost all of its heroes are truly historical like Washington and Lincoln, or figures of fantasy like Superman and of popular fashion like Elvis. Americans sometimes enjoy finding chinks in the armor of their heroes—either to make them seem more human or to search out their weaknesses, with the hope for future improvement.

An important step in finding America is looking to its legends, as its writers and poets from past and present pass the stuff of American legend to Americans of the future.

# The Simple Story of G. Washington

## by Robert J. Burdett

| | |
|---|---|
| ***Born:*** | *Pennsylvania* |
| ***Career:*** | *Railway clerk, linguist, newspaperman, lecturer, clergyman,* |
| ***Military service:*** | *Member 4th Illinois Regiment, Civil War* |

**O**NLY YESTERDAY, A LADY FRIEND on a shopping excursion left her little toddler of five bright summers in our experienced charge, while she pursued the duties which called her downtown. Such a bright boy; so delightful it was to talk to him! We can never forget the blissful half hour we spent looking that prodigy up in his centennial history.

"Now listen, Clary," we said—his name is Clarence Fitzherbert Alençon de Marchemont Caruthers—"and learn about George Washington."

"Who's he?" inquired Clarence, etc.

"Listen," we said; "he was the father of his country."

"Whose country?"

"Ours; yours and mine—the confederated union of the American people, cemented with the life blood of the men of '76, poured out upon the altars of our country as the dearest libation to liberty that her votaries can offer!"

"Who did?" asked Clarence.

There is a peculiar tact in talking to children that very few people possess. Now most people would have grown impatient and lost their temper when little Clarence asked so many irrelevant questions, but we did not. We knew, however careless he might appear at first, that we could soon interest him in the story, and he would be all eyes and ears. So we smiled sweetly—that same sweet smile which you may have noticed on our photographs, just the faintest ripple of a smile breaking across the face like a ray of sunlight, and checked by lines of tender sadness, just before the two ends of it pass each other at the back of the neck.

And so, smiling, we went on.

"Well, one day George's father—"

"George who?" asked Clarence.

"George Washington. He was a little boy then, just like you. One day his father—"

"Whose father?" demanded Clarence with an encouraging expression of interest.

"George Washington's; this great man we were telling you of. One day George Washington's father gave him a little hatchet for a—"

"Gave who a little hatchet?" the dear child interrupted, with a gleam of bewitching intelligence. Most men would have got mad, or betrayed signs of impatience, but we didn't. We know how to talk to children. So we went on:

"George Washington. His—"

"Who gave him the little hatchet?"

"His father. And his father—"

"Whose father?"

"George Washington's."

"Oh!"

"Yes, George Washington. And his father told him—"

"Told who?"

"Told George."

"Oh, yes, George."

And we went on just as patient and as pleasant as you could imagine. We took up the story right where the boy interrupted, for we could see that he was just crazy to hear the end of it. We said:

"And he told him that—"

"George told him?" queried Clarence.

"No, his father told George—"

"Oh!"

"Yes; told him that he must be careful with the hatchet—"

"Who must be careful?"

"George must."

"Oh!"

"Yes; must be careful with the hatchet—"

"What hatchet?"

"Why, George's."

"Oh!"

"Yes; with the hatchet, and not cut himself with it, or drop it in the cistern, or leave it out on the grass all night. So George went round cutting everything he could reach with his hatchet. And at last he came to a splendid apple tree, his father's favorite, and cut it down, and—"

"Who cut it down?"

"George did."

"Oh!"

"But his father came home and saw it the first thing, and—"

"Saw the hatchet?"

"No! saw the apple tree. And he said: 'Who has cut down my favorite apple tree?' "

"Whose apple tree?"

"George's father's. And everybody said they didn't know anything about it, and—"

"Anything about what?"

"The apple tree."

"Oh!"

"And George came up and heard them talking about it—"

"Heard who talking about it?"

"Heard his father and the men."

"What was they talking about?"

"About this apple tree."

"What apple tree?"

"The favorite apple tree that George cut down."

"George who?"

"George Washington."

"Oh!"

"So George came up, and he said, 'Father, I cannot tell a lie. It was—' "

"His father couldn't?"

"Why, no, George couldn't."

"Oh! George? Oh, yes!"

" 'It was I cut down your apple tree; I did—' "

"His father did?"

"No, no, no; said he cut down his apple tree."

"George's apple tree?"

"No, no; his father's."

"Oh!"

"He said—"

"His father said?"

"No, no, no; George said, 'Father, I cannot tell a lic. I did it with my little hatchet.' And his father said: 'Noble boy, I would rather lose a thousand trees than have you to tell a lie.' "

"George did?"

"No; his father said that."

"Said he'd rather have a thousand trees?"

"No, no, no; said he'd rather lose a thousand apple trees than—"

"Said he'd rather George would?"

"No; said he'd rather he would than have him tell a lie."

"Oh! George would rather have his father lie?"

We are patient, and we love children, but if Mrs. Caruthers, of Arch Street, hadn't come and got her prodigy at that critical juncture, we don't believe all Burlington could have pulled us out of the snarl. And as Clarence Fitzherbert Alençon de Marchemont Caruthers pattered down the stairs, we heard him telling his ma about a boy who had a father named George, and he told him to cut an apple tree, and he said he'd rather tell a thousand lies than cut down one apple tree. We do love children, but we don't believe that either nature or education has fitted us to be a governess.

## For Better Reading: A Sense of Humor

Perhaps it's called a *sense* of humor because writers rarely announce when they're using humor or trying to be funny. You have to *sense* it.

A good comedian never laughs at his own jokes, they say. And, the written word doesn't come with a laugh track.

Since it's no fun to take humor the wrong way, it pays to look for clues that a writer doesn't intend to be taken seriously. Here are a few:

1. *Incongruity*: something that just doesn't fit (like the very idea of a blissful half hour with a bratty, five-year-old).
2. *Pointed Repetition*: calling attention to something silly by repeating it ("George who?").
3. *Overstatement*: using words so strong and flowery they actually seem meaningless ("life blood poured ... as the dearest libation ... her votaries can offer").
4. *Use of the Ridiculous*: both in names and situations (Would you like the name of Clarence Fitzherbert Alençon de Marchemont Caruthers?).
5. *Surprise*: the humor in the unexpected (like someone slipping on a banana peel) instead of the straightforwardness of a serious approach.
6. Of course, *Irony*... and, you may discover more. Actually, if a selection is serious, it's nearly impossible to list specific clues. It just *is*. When a writer uses humor, you're sure to find evidence to prove it.

### Inference

1. The word *centennial* means 100th anniversary. Since this story was first published around 1870, the phrase "centennial history" refers to the history of (a) the Civil War (b) America's founding (c) territorial expansion (d) the industrial revolution.
2. Stating "most people would have grown impatient and lost their temper" is a humorous way of showing the narrator has (a) exceptional tact (b) an urge to blow his top (c) an appreciation of the boy's inquiring mind (d) an attitude both sweet and sad.
3. The narrator's photographs actually (a) have nothing to do with the "simple" story (b) are proof of his good nature (c) let Clarence see how annoyed the speaker is (d) confuse the child more than before.

### Questioning the Story

1. Briefly retell the story of young George Washington and the cherry tree as you know it. What is the moral or purpose behind this legendary tale?

2. In telling the story to Clarence, what details has the narrator added or changed?
3. In writing "the dear child interrupted," the author is using verbal irony. Clarence *dear*? Find at least three additional examples of verbal irony in this selection.
4. How does the author use exaggeration, either in his characterization of Clarence, of the narrator, or of both?
5. As he is leaving, how does Clarence change the moral or purpose of the legend as he retells it to his mother?
6. What other techniques of humor does the author use? There is room for differing opinions, so have good reasons to back your choices.
7. In some ways, the narrator also changes his own story. Compare the beginning of the story with last sentence, "... we don't believe that either nature or education has fitted us to be a governess" or teacher. What claims had he made earlier that contradict this conclusion?

## Looking Deeper

### On Target

Humor often makes fun of something or someone, pointing out common human faults and misguided beliefs in an indirect way. Humor can poke fun at traits such as pigheadedness or smugness, as well as larger problems like prejudice.

Decide who represents the target of the author's humor, Clarence, the narrator, or both. Name the trait or traits made fun of and describe how each is exhibited in the story.

# Tecumseh

## by Mary Oliver

**Born:** Cleveland, Ohio
**Education:** Two years of college
**Career:** Secretary to sister of poet Edna St. Vincent Millay, poet, visiting professor

I went down not long ago
to the Mad River, under the willows
I knelt and drank from that crumpled flow, call it
what madness you will, there's a sickness
worse than the risk of death and that's               5
forgetting what we should never forget.
Tecumseh lived here.
The wounds of the past
are ignored, but hang on
like the litter that snags among the yellow branches,   10
newspapers and plastic bags, after the rains.

Where are the Shawnee now?
Do you know? Or would you have to
write to Washington, and even then,
whatever they said,                                     15
would you believe it? Sometimes

I would like to paint my body red and go out into
the glittering snow
to die.

His name meant Shooting Star.                           20
From Mad River country north to the border
he gathered the tribes
and armed them one more time. He vowed
to keep Ohio and it took him
over twenty years to fail.                              25

After the bloody and final fighting, at Thames,
it was over, except
his body could not be found.
It was never found,
and you can do whatever you want with that, say          30

his people came in the black leaves of the night
and hauled him to a secret grave, or that
he turned into a little boy again, and leaped
into a birch canoe and went
rowing home down the rivers. Anyway,                      35
this much I'm sure of: if we ever meet him, we'll know it,
he will still be
so angry.

# For Better Reading: Prior Knowledge

Tecumseh, Johnny Appleseed, Daniel Boone, Betsy Ross, Pancho Villa. Not presidents or discoverers, their names still sound from America's past.

Although you may have heard of them before, the exact details of their deeds are harder to remember.

What then? If you meet such a name in a poem or story, should you check it out in a reference first? Not necessarily. You can often gain a truer sense of the strength and force of legends from poems and stories than from cold facts in reference books.

Poet Mary Oliver has strong feelings about the Indian chief Tecumseh and midwestern pioneer John Chapman, also known as Johnny Appleseed. By reading her poems carefully, you'll discover why their legends are still retold.

## Questioning the Poem

1. Is the first person speaker from modern times or the past? What words and lines prove you right?
2. What is the "sickness worse than the risk of death" that the speaker warns of?
3. Although the details are scattered, identify the following facts about Tecumseh and give the line where you found them:
    a. his tribe
    b. the English meaning of his name
    c. the territory belonging to his tribe

4. Explain Tecumseh's vow. What shows his determination to keep it? What caused his failure?
5. What is the mystery about Tecumseh's body? According to legend, what are its two possible fates?
6. By writing "if we ever meet him," what possibility does the speaker raise? Why will he "still be so angry"?

## Looking Deeper

### I. The Wounds of the Past

In stanza two, lines 12–16, the speaker raises a series of questions. Even though their original territories were east of the Mississippi, where are the reservations of many American Indian tribes now? Does the speaker expect you to know the location of today's Shawnee lands? Find support for your answer. According to the poem, what clearly happened to many Shawnee? What does the word "Washington" represent? What, concerning the Indians, might cause the speaker to express doubt about Washington?

"Sometimes . . ." As the poet introduces stanza three, she has the speaker express a strong and perhaps surprising desire to "paint my body red . . ." What does this reveal about the speaker's probable ancestors and attitude toward their possible deeds? The speaker also expresses a willingness to "go out . . . to die." How does this more fully explain the speaker's feelings about the "sickness worse than the risk of death" mentioned in lines 4 and 5?

### II. Remembering

What are some similar incidents of the past that many would like to forget or ignore? Even though the past cannot be changed, do you agree with the speaker that it's important to remember? Why or why not?

# JOHN CHAPMAN

*by Mary Oliver*

He wore a tin pot for a hat, in which
he cooked his supper
toward evening
in the Ohio forests. He wore
a sackcloth shirt and walked                                    5
barefoot on feet crooked as roots. And everywhere
    he went
the apple trees sprang up behind him lovely
as young girls.

No Indian or settler or wild beast
ever harmed him, and he for his part honored            10
everything, all God's creatures! thought little,
on a rainy night,
of sharing the shelter of a hollow log touching
flesh with any creatures there: snakes,
raccoon possibly, or some great slab of bear.            15

Mrs. Price, late of Richland County,
at whose parents' house he sometimes lingered,
recalled: he spoke
only once of women and his gray eyes
brittled into ice. "Some                                            20
are deceivers," he whispered, and she felt
the pain of it, remembered it
into her old age.

Well, the trees he planted or gave away
prospered, and he became                                        25
the good legend, you do
what you can if you can; whatever

the secret, and the pain,

there's a decision: to die,
or to live, to go on                                                30
caring about something. In spring, in Ohio,
in the forests that are left you can still find
sign of him: patches
of cold white fire.

## Questioning the Poem

1. Although the poem does not mention his legendary nickname, how does the first stanza explain the reason Chapman is popularly known as Johnny Appleseed?
2. In what ways does stanza one portray Chapman as an eccentric character?
3. What is the special relationship between Chapman and "all God's creatures"? Why does this relationship seem more like the "stuff of legend" than reality?
4. How do lines 6–8 make the existence of the apple trees seem almost miraculous? How do lines 24–25 explain this more realistically?
5. Stanza three helps explain why Chapman behaved so eccentrically. Considering that he "spoke only once of women" and then merely whispered, "Some are deceivers," give your version of the secret and painful story that must lie behind the facts, by adding three or more logical details.
6. How does Mrs. Price's reaction reveal the depth of feeling Chapman's three words expressed?
7. According to the poem, what choice lies before someone who suffers the pain that Chapman had? In view of this choice, what must have been the motive for Chapman's decision to plant "apple trees . . . lovely as young girls" throughout the Ohio countryside?
8. Does the poem lead you to believe Chapman kept his secret out of shame, pride, the genuineness of his love—or a combination of these emotions? Use proof from the poem to support your conclusion.

# Looking Deeper

## I. "The Good Legend"

The poem states that in the springtime, blooming apple trees in the remaining Ohio forests are signs of Chapman. What is contradictory about describing this as "cold white fire"? What would the word "white" refer to? How is "fire" a fitting expression of Chapman's motives, considering the choice he made? Why is this fire "cold"?

According to the introduction, legendary heroes embody the qualities and characteristics that a people or nation most admire. What admirable qualities does John Chapman, the man behind the legendary figure Johnny Appleseed, represent?

## II. A Point of Reference

After reading and thinking about these two poems by Mary Oliver, you might wish to learn more about the lives of one or both of these historical American figures. You're likely to find their names in dictionaries, in encyclopedias, in history textbooks, and in library books of American history. Check two or more references, and compare the ways they present their information.

You may decide that the poems make Tecumseh and Chapman seem more alive, or you may prefer the informative style of references. Explain your reaction, including a comparison of the poem with your findings in reference entries.

# Sourdough Sam, "Stummick Robber"

## *from Paul Bunyan*

## *by Stanley D. Newton*

**T**HOUSANDS OF AMERICANS COME TO the Upper Peninsula of Michigan in peace times each summer to enjoy the cool climate, and to see the woods where Paul Bunyan flourished.

Teachers, boys and girls are interested in the land where Hiawatha lived. Many others are eager to hear more about the famous Sourdough Sam. Most people like to eat, and Sam certainly was a wonderful cook.

Sam's pea soup was a mark of his genius and almost as celebrated as his soft-nosed non-skid sinkers. Pea Soup Lake in Delta County is named in honor of Sourdough Sam. One day the tote team was coming into camp from Gladstone with four tons of split peas. Team and sleigh broke through the ice while crossing the lake, and the peas went to the bottom, but the horses and driver escaped.

Sam knew that Johnny Inkslinger would charge up the peas to the cook camp, and he hatched a bright idea for saving them. At his suggestion Paul Bunyan ordered a lumberjack crew to build a dam across the creek outlet at the foot of the lake. When the job was done Sam ordered the 300 cookees to build dozens of bonfires, close together, all the way around the lake, which was half a mile long and a quarter of a mile wide.

The water in the lake soon began to boil, and the peas were cooked in a few hours. After that, when Sam wanted some pea soup for dinner, all the cookees had to do was to open a few faucets in the dam and draw off as much soup as needed, then heat it and put it on the tables. There was always a good supply of soup on hand, for the cookees dumped more peas into the lake from time to time and cooked them in the circle of bonfires.

Paul was proud of Sam because he handled the commissary department in such a big and efficient way. When Paul walked down Ludington Street in Escanaba or State Street in St. Ignace, folks turned their heads as he went by and said to each other: "There goes Paul Bunyan, the big logger and lumberman. His crew is so big that his cook makes a whole lake full of pea soup at one time."

Such remarks were sweet in Paul's ears, and when he overheard them he threw his chest out and looked bigger than ever. You just can't help liking folks who tell you that you're a big shot, even if you're no more than a big bootlegger. Paul liked everybody who told him that he was the world's greatest logger, and he always admitted it.

There was one thing about Pea Soup Lake that made trouble for Sam. The soup couldn't be stirred while it was cooking, and sometimes it burned around the edges of the lake. Sam put his brain to work on the problem, and he solved it by building and launching a stern-wheel steamboat on the lake. He anchored the boat in the center of the lake, and as the wheel turned over gently it stirred the soup and prevented burning. Just to make it perfect, Sam fastened rows of salt and pepper shakers on the wheel, and every lumberjack agreed that they gave the soup exactly the right flavor.

When Paul finished logging that part of the Upper Peninsula he sold the lake to Cap Fisher, who operated a hotel in Gladstone and drew his soup from Pea Soup Lake. The delicacy made his dining room famous, and Frenchmen and others were in the habit of traveling miles in order to enjoy a bowl of Cap's pea soup.

Pea Soup Lake was a great success in summer, but not even Sourdough Sam, with all his genius, was able to keep it operating as a pea soup supply base in winter. The cookees carried pea soup daily to the woods crew in cold weather, but the men complained that it reached them frozen so solidly in the kettles that they had to blast it out. Here was a knotty problem, but Sam went into conference with Joe Kadunk, the second cook, and solved it efficiently. The cookees knew that Sam was equal to any occasion within the bounds of possibilities, and they never doubted that he was the smartest cook that ever stuck his thumb into a bowl of soup.

Sam ordered the cookees to prepare two thousand pieces of tar rope, one and a half feet long. He dipped the ropes in the soup kettles, hung them outside the kitchen until the soup froze, and dipped them again. With a few dips and freezings there was plenty of soup on each piece of rope.

Then, when the pea soup ropes had been properly prepared, the cookees bunched them and carried them to the woods crew. Each man swallowed a piece of rope and held it until the soup melted. When the boys had enjoyed their lunch, the ropes were returned to the cook camp, soaked in a carbolic acid solution to destroy the germs if any, and made ready for next day's service. Before long every man had a piece of tar rope of his own, with his name on it, and eventually each member of the woods crew was provided with a new piece of rope daily, in compliance with the rules and regulations of the State Board of Health.

There was an occasional drawback to this arrangement, but it wasn't serious. Sometimes a hungry lumberjack loosened his hold on the rope and lost it down his gullet, or he held his piece of rope longer than necessary and found a tarry flavor in his soup. But in the main Sourdough Sam's modern soup delivery service appealed to the woods crew, and as for the cookees, they admired immensely his clever scheme for handling the winter pea soup problem.

"This is the proper time to settle once for all the arguments about the origin of the term 'hot dog'," says Tim. "The lumberjacks were forever arguing the question in the sleeping camp and in the woods. Joe Kadunk and I had a rather spirited discussion of this topic once. In the middle of the argument he bit a piece out of my left ear, but he did it in a gentlemanly way, and I didn't make any fuss about it.

"When the men in the woods were working not more than three miles from the cook camp, Sourdough Sam prepared a hot lunch and sent it out to them. The woods crew had breakfast each morning about half past three, and when nine o'clock came they were hungry. So at 8 o'clock daily Sam loaded a sled with kettles of frankfurts, pea soup ropes and other good food. Sometimes the cookees hauled the sled out to the men, and sometimes Elmer, the moose terrier, hauled it. When Elmer scooted down the woods road with the morning lunch, the men gave him a weenie or two from the kettle, if he didn't stop enroute to chase a moose.

"When the weather was very cold the steam rising from Elmer and the weenies made a fog like smoke in the woods. The men watched for Elmer's coming, and the minute he was in sight they hollered: 'Here's the hot dog sled coming at last.' The name was soon given to the weenies, and since that time boiled or roasted frankfurts were first known as hot dogs in Paul Bunyan's woods camps.

"Paul was very fond of Sam's special meat and vegetable stew, which we called mulligan. When Paul came in late from the woods on a cold night, Sam was always ready for him, and Paul was tickled when he sat down at the table with a big pan of mulligan before him.

"I remember how Paul came into camp at 10 o'clock one night—he had been running section lines in Dickinson county—and almost surprised us. Sam started to warm up the mulligan and we cookees bustled around the kitchen and helped to get Paul's supper ready. There was a shelf over the cook camp stove where Sam had put things that he wanted to have handy. When Sam's back was turned I reached up to the shelf for something, I don't remember what, and I accidentally knocked a bottle of brass polish, two cans of lye, a dozen bars of yellow washing soap and ten pounds of harness grease into the big mulligan pan that was simmering on the stove.

"I was so scared I couldn't talk, so I didn't mention the accident to Sam. I knew he would thump me if I did. He placed the piping hot mulligan before Paul, and I was sure there would be an explosion. I shook with fear when Paul grasped his mighty spoon. He was as hungry as a bear, and he swallowed plate after plate of mulligan and swore that he had never tasted mulligan that was half as good. He gave Sam a big raise in salary on the spot, but although Sam tried his best, he never again succeeded in making a mulligan stew with so delicious a flavor.

"The 27th of May was Paul's birthday and we always celebrated it with a party. I recollect that in '83 the party was held about the time we finished the spring drive down the Big Auger and through the Little Gimlet Creek to the Pink Onion River, near Pollywog Lake.

"There was a big attendance of friends from Grand Marais, Newberry, White-fish Point, Swedetown and Paradise Creek. The dinner table was so long that Paul arranged a miniature railroad along the center, and it carried the salt and pepper shakers and vinegar cruets from guest to guest. All hands agreed that nothing more classy could be found anywhere, and that Paul was a great man.

"Sourdough Sam, probably thinking of his great success at Pea Soup Lake, had dammed a branch of the Pink Onion River which flowed past the camp door. He rolled half a dozen hot stones into the pool, added flour and meat stock and seasoning, and soon he had a nice supply of grand gravy. Then he ordered the cookees to pump the gravy into a water tank which we used to sprinkle the ice roads in winter.

"The tank was on an incline and off balance, and the load of gravy tipped it over. The hot gravy spilled into the timber beside the road, and the woods fire that followed burned the ground clean almost to Seney. Miles of timber went up in smoke and flame, but Paul saved the forest north of Seney by taking off his boots and carrying water in them from Pollywog Lake to the scene of the fire.

"Paul docked Sam one month's pay and gave him a trimming because the gravy was spilled through his orders. 'You've never heard of my starting a woods fire,' said Paul. 'I'm careful with fire wherever I go in timber. Do you realize, Sam, that a minute's carelessness on your part has cost someone thousands of dollars? Do you think that timber grows overnight? Do you know that you passed sentence of death on thousands of fish and game when you started that fire? This time you have been no credit to the Paul Bunyan organization, and considering your years of experience in the woods, you should have known better.'

"Paul didn't fire Sam. He said Sam was too valuable a man to lose, and the lumberjacks agreed with him.

"The blaze in the Seney marshes calls to mind the fire which swept a part of the Tahquamenon swamp the same year," continued Tim. "Paul was operating a pulp wood camp in the swamp when a big fish hawk carried away a pile of 90-foot tamarack logs, which the loading crew had stacked on the river bank to be used for Lake Superior bean poles in the following spring.

"The hawk built her nest with the poles in a bog pivot pine that was the tallest tree for miles around. The nest was so close to the sun that it caught fire, and in a twinkling a wall of smoke and flame was racing across the swamp.

"We lumberjacks thought the swamp timber was doomed, but Paul saved the day with that great brain of his. He rushed Babe out of the barn and down to the river, and the big ox drank his fill. Then Paul kicked Babe in the ribs, and Babe belched just once and put out the fire.

"There's nothing like keeping your head and thinking things out when you get into a jam, and then acting without delay. It was that factor above all others that made Paul Bunyan a great man," said Tim.

# For Better Reading: The Tall Tale

There are many kind of heroes—legendary heroes, sports heroes, tragic heroes, and comic ones. And, then there is the folk hero, someone who comes from the people and whose story they created.

Paul Bunyan is America's biggest folk hero, in more ways than one.

Originally passed by word of mouth, the folk stories of Paul Bunyan spring from a day when many people couldn't read and television was almost beyond imagining. And, with every retelling, the deeds of Paul Bunyan grew more and more incredible. So the stories of Paul Bunyan rank as tall tales.

You see, Paul Bunyan and Babe, his blue ox, were so big, so strong, so wonderful that the stories about him kept getting bigger and more wonderful, too. Just as Paul could win every contest with other loggers, so creating tales about Paul became a sort of contest, too. The taller the tale, the better it was ... but wait till you hear the next one.

To enjoy tales like Paul Bunyan, you have to enter into the spirit. In spite of the exaggeration, you'll find Paul Bunyan and his crew have a combination of traits Americans admire.

## Inference

1. In dealing with the sunken peas, Sourdough Sam (a) relied on Paul Bunyan's suggestion (b) came up with a clever plan of his own (c) settled the matter democratically (d) showed more reliance on daring than strength.
2. When called "the world's greatest logger," Paul Bunyan (a) modestly denied it (b) gave most of the credit to his men (c) always admitted it was true (d) judged the compliment by its source.
3. Since Sam had 300 "cookees" working under him, the reader should infer that (a) much time was wasted in argument (b) the food was nourishing but not very tasty (c) Sourdough Sam was one of the world's great cooks (d) the logging crew numbered in the thousands.

## Questioning the Selection

1. According to the selection, what accident begins the tall tale about Pea Soup Lake in Delta County, Michigan? What details about this incident seem reasonably believable? What shows the truth is already beginning to be stretched?
2. A good tall tale gets a little taller with each new step. Explain what part each played in Sam's plan: (a) the dam (b) the bonfires (c) the faucets (d) the steamboat (e) the salt and pepper shakers.

3. What was the "winter pea soup problem"? How did Sourdough Sam operate his "modern soup delivery service"? What was one drawback for the men?
4. As the tale grows taller, what are the two final improvements to the soup delivery system? Why is stating this was "in compliance with the rules and regulations of the State Board of Health" also part of the humor?
5. According to Tim, what part does Elmer the moose terrier play in the origin of the term *hot dog*? And why, pray, is Elmer called a moose terrier?
6. What accident happened when Paul came back at 10 p.m. for a meal of Mulligan stew? Why didn't Tim confess to Sourdough Sam?
7. Considering the list of added ingredients, what effect would the stew have on the average person? Why? How did the stew affect Paul? Why must Paul's reaction to the stew have frustrated Sourdough Sam?
8. What went wrong with Sourdough Sam's plan for serving gravy at Paul's birthday party? How did Paul save the forest? How did he react to Sam's mistake?

## Looking Deeper

### I. Traits of a Folk Hero

Although the tales are tall and Paul Bunyan himself is larger than life, he exhibits qualities that everyone is able to recognize and admire. Explain how Paul displayed each of the following: honest self-appraisal; generosity; concern for nature; superhuman size; fairness; quick thinking. Use a different example for each trait.

### II. The Appeal of a Bunyan

What makes a folk hero like Paul Bunyan popular with people? Are there any special people today—real or fictional—who have the same sort of attraction? If not, why not? If so, give one or more examples describing stories about them that seem similar to tall tales, in spite or because of modern methods of communication.

# Who Made Paul Bunyan?

## by Carl Sandburg

| | |
|---|---|
| **Born:** | *Illinois in 1878, son of Swedish immigrants* |
| **Background:** | *Had little formal schooling, roamed US as hobo* |
| **Jobs:** | *Milk wagon driver, brickyard helper, stagehand, hotel dishwasher, railroad construction worker, harvest hand, and newspaperman* |
| **Gained fame as:** | *Poetry writer and reader, guitarist, and folksinger* |

**W**HO MADE PAUL BUNYAN, WHO gave him birth as a myth, who joked him into life as the Master Lumberjack, who fashioned him forth as an apparition easing the hours of men amid axes and trees, saws and lumber? The people, the bookless people, they made Paul and had him alive long before he got into the books for those who read. He grew up in shanties, around the hot stoves of winter, among socks and mittens drying, in the smell of tobacco smoke and the roar of laughter mocking the outside weather. And some of Paul came overseas in wooden bunks below decks in sailing vessels. And some of Paul is old as the hills, young as the alphabet.

The Pacific Ocean froze over in the winter of the Blue Snow and Paul Bunyan had long teams of oxen hauling regular white snow over from China. This was the winter Paul gave a party to the Seven Axmen. Paul fixed a granite floor sunk two hundred feet deep for them to dance on. Still, it tipped and tilted as the dance went on. And because the Seven Axmen refused to take off their hob-nailed boots, the sparks from the nails of their dancing feet lit up the place so that Paul didn't light the kerosene lamps. No woman being on the Big Onion river at that time the Seven Axmen had to dance with each other, the one left over in each set taking Paul as a partner. The commotion of the dancing that night brought on an earthquake and the Big Onion river moved over three counties to the east.

One year when it rained from St. Patrick's Day till the Fourth of July, Paul

Bunyan got disgusted because his celebration on the Fourth was spoiled. He dived into Lake Superior and swam to where a solid pillar of water was coming down. He dived under this pillar, swam up into it and climbed with powerful swimming strokes, was gone about an hour, came splashing down, and as the rain stopped, he explained, "I turned the dam thing off." This is told in the Big North Woods and on the Great Lakes, with many particulars.

Two mosquitoes lighted on one of Paul Bunyan's oxen, killed it, ate it, cleaned the bones, and sat on a grub shanty picking their teeth as Paul came along. Paul sent to Australia for two special bumble bees to kill these mosquitoes. But the bees and the mosquitoes intermarried; their children had stingers on both ends. And things kept getting worse till Paul brought a big boatload of sorghum up from Louisiana and while all the bee-mosquitoes were eating at the sweet sorghum he floated them down to the Gulf of Mexico. They got so fat that it was easy to drown them all between New Orleans and Galveston.

Paul logged on the Little Gimlet in Oregon one winter. The cook stove at the camp covered an acre of ground. They fastened the side of a hog on each snowshoe and four men used to skate on the griddle while the cook flipped the pancakes. The eating table was three miles long; elevators carried the cakes to the ends of the table where boys on bicycles rode back and forth on a path down the center of the table dropping the cakes where called for.

Benny, the Little Blue Ox of Paul Bunyan, grew two feet every time Paul looked at him, when a youngster. The barn was gone one morning and they found it on Benny's back; he grew out of it in a night. One night he kept pawing and bellowing for more pancakes, till there were two hundred men at the cook shanty stove trying to keep him fed. About breakfast time Benny broke loose, tore down the cook shanty, ate all the pancakes piled up for the loggers' breakfast. And after that Benny made his mistake; he ate the red hot stove; and that finished him. This is only one of the hot stove stories told in the North Woods.

## For Better Reading: Stories That Grew

It looks like prose. It appears written in paragraph form, instead of line for line like other poems. But as you read it to yourself or orally, you'll hear the rhythmic sound of poetry. In many ways, it's the rhythm of voices telling stories of Paul Bunyan: voices that were deep and almost hypnotic and caught listeners in their spell.

Read the poem through to enjoy its sound. Then look again to see how much poet Carl Sandburg packs into each line ... like the "hot stove" stories that grew and grew. Whopper seems piled upon whopper, as if each storyteller seems bursting to top the tale before. This makes careful rereading necessary as you question the poem, "Who Made Paul Bunyan?"

# Questioning the Poem

1. After asking "Who gave birth to Paul Bunyan?", what does Sandburg mean in answering the "bookless people"? In what sense did Paul "grow" in the shanties where his stories were told? Because his are folk tales, how can Paul Bunyan be both old and young at the same time?
2. Here come some more "whoppers." How did Paul solve the problem of having blue snow? Even though it was sunk two football fields deep, what happened to the granite floor at the party for the Seven Axmen? What does this imply about the Axmen's size? What provided light at the party? What was the cause and result of the earthquake?
3. How did Paul Bunyan stop the rain? By saying "I turned the dam thing off," what attitude does Paul express towards this deed? Explain the meaning of this tale's having "many particulars." Why would this be so?
4. There are often a number of steps to a tall tale: first, an incredibly big problem; next, the problem gets bigger; finally, a solution. How is this true of the tale about two mosquitoes?
5. Choose one of the tales concerning Sourdough Sam, and explain how it follows a similar pattern.
6. How does the tale about Benny follow the tall tale pattern described in question 4? How is its solution different?

# Looking Deeper

## I. The Many Sides to Paul Bunyan

Besides the difference between poetry and prose, how does the manner of telling the tales about Sourdough Sam differ from the way used by Sandburg? For example, which makes the greater attempt to bring the characters to life? Which is more fully packed with exaggeration? Which contains more dialogue and description? Have examples from each selection to support your choices.

What do you think was Stanley D. Newton's purpose in choosing his approach? What did Carl Sandburg wish to emphasize?

According to the "Sourdough Sam" story, Bunyan's logging camp was in northern Michigan while Sandburg mentions Oregon. Considering the source and origin of the tales, how do you account for this difference? What other similarities and differences do you find in the place names given in the two selections?

## II. "Who Made Paul Bunyan?"

How would you answer Sandburg's title question? Give three reasons why the manner of Bunyan's creation represents a typical American outlook. Why is "hot stove stories" a good term to describe the making of many Bunyan tales?

# Abraham Lincoln

*by Ralph Waldo Emerson*

| | |
|---|---|
| ***Born:*** | *Boston, Massachusetts, 1803* |
| ***Early life:*** | *Suffered from illness and poor vision* |
| ***Adult life:*** | *Settled in Concord, Mass., traveled Italy, France, Egypt, and England* |
| ***Famous as:*** | *Philosopher, poet, lecturer, and essayist* |

**W**E MEET UNDER THE GLOOM of a calamity which darkens down over the minds of good men in all civil society, as the fearful tidings travel over sea, over land, from country to country, like the shadow of an uncalculated eclipse over the planet. Old as history is, and manifold as are its tragedies, I doubt if any death has caused so much pain to mankind as this has caused, or will cause, on its announcement; and this, not so much because nations are by modern arts brought so closely together, as because of the mysterious hopes and fears which, in the present day, are connected with the name and institutions of America.

In this country, on Saturday, every one was struck dumb, and saw at first only deep below deep, as he meditated on the ghastly blow. And perhaps, at this hour, when the coffin which contains the dust of the President sets forward on its long march through mourning states, on its way to his home in Illinois, we might well be silent, and suffer the awful voices of the time to thunder to us. Yes, but that first despair was brief: the man was not so to be mourned. He was the most active and hopeful of men; and his work had not perished: but acclamations of praise for the task he had accomplished burst out into a song of triumph, which even tears for his death cannot keep down.

The President stood before us as a man of the people. He was thoroughly American, had never crossed the sea, had never been spoiled by English insularity or French dissipation; a quite native, aboriginal man, as an acorn from the oak; no aping of foreigners, no frivolous accomplishments, Kentuckian born, working on a farm, a flatboatman, a captain in the Black Hawk War, a country lawyer, a representative in the rural legislature of Illinois—on such modest foundations the broad structure of his fame was laid. How slowly, and yet by happily prepared steps, he came to his place. All of us remember—it is only a history of five or six years—the surprise and the disappointment of the country at his first nomination by the convention at Chicago. Mr. Seward, then in the culmination of his good fame, was the favorite of the Eastern States. And when the new and comparatively unknown name of Lincoln was announced (notwithstanding the report of the acclamations of that convention), we heard the result coldly and sadly. It seemed too rash, on a purely local reputation, to build so grave a trust in such anxious times; and men naturally talked of the chances in politics as incalculable. But it turned out not to be chance. The profound good opinion which the people of Illinois and of the West had conceived of him, and which they had imparted to their colleagues, that they also might justify themselves to their constituents at home, was not rash, though they did not begin to know the riches of his worth.

A plain man of the people, an extraordinary fortune attended him. He offered no shining qualities at the first encounter; he did not offend by superiority. He had a face and manner which disarmed suspicion, which inspired confidence, which confirmed good will. He was a man without vices. He had a strong sense of duty, which it was very easy for him to obey. Then, he had what farmers call a long head; was excellent in working out the sum for himself; in arguing his case and convincing you fairly and firmly. Then, it turned out that he was a great worker; had prodigious faculty of performance; worked easily. A good worker is so rare; everybody has some disabling quality. In a host of young men that start together and promise so many brilliant leaders for the next age, each fails on trial; one by bad health, one by conceit, or by love of pleasure, or lethargy, or an ugly temper—each has some disqualifying fault that throws him out of the career. But this man was sound to the core, cheerful, persistent, all right for labor, and liked nothing so well. . . .

Then his broad good humor, running easily into jocular talk, in which he delighted and in which he excelled, was a rich gift to this wise man. It enabled him to keep his secret; to meet every kind of man and every rank in society; to take off the edge of the severest decisions; to mask his own purpose and sound his companion; and to catch with true instinct the temper of every company he addressed. And, more than all, it is to a man of severe labor, in anxious and exhausting crises, the natural restorative, good as sleep, and is the protection of the overdriven brain against rancor and insanity.

He is the author of a multitude of good sayings, so disguised as pleasantries that it is certain they had no reputation at first but as jests; and only later, by the very acceptance and adoption they find in the mouths of millions, turn out to be the wisdom of the hour. I am sure if this man had ruled in a period of less facility of printing, he would have become mythological in a very few years, like Aesop or Pilpay, or one of the Seven Wise Masters, by his fables and proverbs. But the weight and penetration of many passages in his letters, messages and speeches, hidden now by the very closeness of their application to the moment, are destined hereafter to wide fame. What pregnant definitions; what unerring common sense; what foresight; and, on great occasion, what lofty, and more than national, what humane tone! His brief speech at Gettysburg will not easily be surpassed by words on any recorded occasion. This, and one other American speech, that of John Brown to the court that tried him, and a part of

Kossuth's speech at Birmingham, can only be compared with each other, and with no fourth.

His occupying the chair of state was a triumph of the good sense of mankind, and of the public conscience. This middle-class country had got a middle-class president, at last. Yes, in manners and sympathies, but not in powers, for his powers were superior. This man grew according to the need. His mind mastered the problem of the day; and as the problem grew, so did his comprehension of it. Rarely was man so fitted to the event. In the midst of fears and jealousies, in the Babel of counsels and parties, this man wrought incessantly with all his might and all his honesty, laboring to find what the people wanted, and how to obtain that. It cannot be said there is any exaggeration of his worth. If ever a man was fairly tested, he was. There was no lack of resistance, nor of slander, nor of ridicule. The times have allowed no state secrets; the nation has been in such ferment, such multitudes had to be trusted, that no secret could be kept. Every door was ajar, and we know all that befell.

Then, what an occasion was the whirlwind of the war. Here was place for no holiday magistrate, no fair-weather sailor; the new pilot was hurried to the helm in a tornado. In four years—four years of battle-days—his endurance, his fertility of resources, his magnanimity, were sorely tried and never found wanting. There, by his courage, his justice, his even temper, his fertile counsel, his humanity, he stood a heroic figure in the center of a heroic epoch. He is the true history of the American people in his time. Step by step he walked before them; slow with their slowness, quickening his march by theirs, the true representative of this continent; an entirely public man; father of his country, the pulse of twenty millions throbbing in his heart, the thought of their minds articulated by his tongue.

Adam Smith remarks that the axe, which in Houbraken's portraits of British kings and worthies is engraved under those who have suffered at the block, adds a certain lofty charm to the picture. And who does not see, even in this tragedy so recent, how fast the terror and ruin of the massacre are already burning into glory around the victim? Far happier this fate than to have lived to be wished away; to have watched the decay of his own faculties; to have seen—perhaps even he—the proverbial ingratitude of statesmen; to have seen mean men preferred. Had he not lived long enough to keep the greatest promise that ever man made to his fellow men—the practical abolition of slavery? He had seen Tennessee, Missouri and Maryland emancipate their slaves. He had seen Savannah, Charleston and Richmond surrendered; had seen the main army of the rebellion lay down its arms. He had conquered the public opinion of Canada, England and France. Only Washington can compare with him in fortune....

# For Better Reading: First-hand Knowledge

*Abraham Lincoln*: Like George Washington, Abraham Lincoln is a President whose life is wrapped in legend. There's the hardship of his early life in a log cabin, his nickname "Honest Abe," and the awe that he often inspires for holding America together and putting an end to slavery.

Yet Lincoln, too, is sometimes the target of Americans' tendency to hunt for chinks in the armor of their heroes. Where do you look to find the truth?

*Ralph Waldo Emerson*: A man known as America's greatest and perhaps only true philosopher, Emerson met Abraham Lincoln at the White House in 1862, and Lincoln recalled having attended an Emerson lecture. In 1865, on the day funeral services were held for the assassinated President, Emerson spoke at the meeting house in Concord, Massachusetts.

As you read Emerson's words, judge whether you find seeds of the legend and the ring of the truth.

## Inference

1. "The mysterious hopes and fears" that Emerson states "are connected with the name and institutions of America" refer to (a) hope for growth of international trade but fear of war (b) the belief that supernatural forces control human destiny (c) doubts whether the American dream of freedom could succeed and survive (d) the secrets that might still be hidden about Lincoln's presidency and assassination.
2. This selection by Emerson contains words spoken while (a) the government braced for further assassination attempts (b) the body of Lincoln was on its way to Illinois (c) the burial service in Washington was in progress (d) public unrest was threatening civil chaos.
3. According to Emerson, when Lincoln was first nominated for the presidency, the nation (a) was seeking a change (b) believed too little thought was given his selection (c) immediately recognized his superior abilities (d) realized the choice was between two relatively unknown candidates.

## Questioning the Selection

1. Emerson calls Lincoln "a man of the people." In what two ways was he "thoroughly American"? What are two early occupations that could be considered "modest foundations" for the presidency? What are two "happily prepared steps" that seem to lead more naturally to his final position?
2. Why might people be suspicious of someone who exhibited "shining

qualities at the first encounter"? Since Lincoln lacked these qualities, how did people tend to respond to him?

3. What does Emerson mean by stating Lincoln had a "long head"? What other positive quality did Lincoln have that, according to Emerson, many people lack?

4. Lincoln is sometimes criticized as being too fond of humor and joking, but Emerson considered this a "rich gift." Explain two ways that this "broad good humor" could help Lincoln deal with the innumerable visitors who came to seek his aid or influence his decisions. How was this sense of humor also personally important in a time of anxiety and crisis?

5. In what way did Lincoln's use of humor cause him to be misunderstood? By referring to the adoption of Lincoln's sayings in the "mouths of millions," what credit does Emerson give to the people of America?

6. Emerson states, "This middle-class country had got a middle-class president, at last." Compared with other lands, why might America be considered a "middle-class" country? In Emerson's eyes, why might earlier Presidents not be considered middle-class?

7. Why was Lincoln more severely and "fairly" tested than most American Presidents? Why would the times "have allowed no state secrets"?

8. Emerson calls Lincoln "the true history of the American people in his time." Although Lincoln is sometimes criticized for not acting more decisively to bring an end slavery, how does Emerson's characterization of Lincoln help explain his position?

## Looking Deeper

### I. Burning into Glory

In the last paragraph quoted, Emerson compares the assassination of Lincoln to the beheading of English kings and other "worthies." If not for this tragedy, what are three possible ways that fate might have dealt unfavorably with Lincoln? In what way had he kept "the greatest promise that ever man made to his fellow men?"

### II. The Life Behind the Legend

How does Emerson's portrayal of Lincoln compare with what you have read or heard about him? Do you respond to Emerson's description of Lincoln as seeming true to life, or as seeming too good to be true? Why or why not?

# Lincoln's Birthday
## *(For Pookie)*

### by Paulette White

**Born:** *Detroit, Michigan*
**Family:** *Married to artist Bennie White, parent*
*of five sons*
**Career:** *Writes poetry and short stories,*
*participates in writers' workshops and*
*inner-city arts program for girls*

How do you answer a son
who wants to know what slavery was
because his kindergarten teacher
told him it was Lincoln's birthday
and Lincoln freed the slaves                                   5
and he is already Black enough
to know it has something
to do with him and he is wise enough
to know that Teacher couldn't answer right
so he brought his question home to you           10
like an ugly rock in his pocket:
"Momma, what was slavery?"
and the *was* rolled around in your head
like the rock in his pocket.
Do you swallow the wild crush of words             15
that rises in you to devastate his innocence?
Do you smile and make the answer flow
honestly and easily and simply
because he is only five and you want him
to be more child than Black for awhile yet?        20
But his smile fades anyway
as he turns palms up to ask:
"Even a little boy like me?
But what could I do—

pick corn or something?"                                    25
And if he laughs deciding slavery is
the craaaziest thing he ever heard of,
have you answered him well?


## Questioning the Poem

1. In your own words, explain the problem facing the speaker at the beginning of the poem. What has caused the problem?
2. The poem states that the five-year-old kindergarten child is "already Black enough." What does this phrase suggest that he already realizes?
3. Line 9 states that "Teacher couldn't answer right." Why would this be so?
4. What does the repetition of the word "was" reveal about the difference between the mother's idea about the time of slavery's existence and the boy's?
5. Why does the speaker compare the word "was" in the boy's question to "an ugly rock"?
6. If the speaker had obeyed her impulse, what ideas might her "wild crush of words" express about slavery and its aftereffects? Why didn't she speak?
7. In line 20, the mother expresses a desire for her son to be "more child than Black for awhile yet." What awareness does she wish to protect him from?
8. While his mother is considering her answer, her son asks two questions more. What do they prove about his understanding of slavery?
9. In the final lines of the poem, the mother asks herself, "If he laughs ... have you answered him well?" Is thinking "slavery was the craaaziest thing he ever heard of" a good or bad decision for the little boy to reach? Consider both sides of the argument in making your answer.


## Looking Deeper

### I. Celebrating Lincoln's Birthday

What is the promise implied by the words "Lincoln freed the slaves"? How does this promise contrast with the situation still faced by many who are black? By inviting you to make this contrast, what irony does the poem bring out about America's celebration of Lincoln's birthday? Does or does not this take away from the legend of Lincoln and his place in American history? Give reasons for your answer.

What do the little boy's questions and his own responses to them show about his upbringing?

## II. Facing the Future

If you were the boy's parent, how would you try to explain slavery, Lincoln, and the place of African-Americans in our country today to your five-year-old son?

# For My People

## by Margaret Walker

**Born:** Birmingham, Alabama
**On faculty:** Jackson State College in Mississippi
**Famous as:** Poet, novelist, short story writer

For my people everywhere singing their slave songs repeatedly: their dirges and      1
their ditties and their blues and jubilees, praying their prayers nightly to an
unknown god, bending their knees humbly to an unseen power;

For my people lending their strength to the years, to the gone years and the      2
now years and the maybe years, washing ironing cooking scrubbing sewing
mending hoeing plowing digging planting pruning patching dragging along
never gaining never reaping never knowing and never understanding;

For my playmates in the clay and dust and sand of Alabama backyards playing      3
baptizing and preaching and doctor and jail and soldier and school and
mama and cooking and playhouse and concert and store and hair and Miss
Choomby and company;

For the cramped bewildered years we went to school to learn to know the      4
reasons why and the answers to and the people who and the places where
and the days when, in memory of the bitter hours when we discovered we
were black and poor and small and different and nobody cared and nobody
wondered and nobody understood;

For the boys and girls who grew in spite of these things to be man and woman,      5
to laugh and dance and sing and play and drink their wine and religion
and success, to marry their playmates and bear children and then die of
consumption and anemia and lynching;

For my people thronging 47th Street in Chicago and Lenox Avenue in New      6
York and Rampart Street in New Orleans, lost disinherited dispossessed
and happy people filling the cabarets and taverns and other people's pockets
needing bread and shoes and milk and land and money and something—something all our own;

For my people walking blindly spreading joy, losing time being lazy, sleeping      7
when hungry, shouting when burdened, drinking when hopeless, tied and
shackled and tangled among ourselves by the unseen creatures who tower
over us omnisciently and laugh;

For my people blundering and groping and floundering in the dark of churches    8
and schools and clubs and societies, associations and councils and commit-
tees and conventions, distressed and disturbed and deceived and devoured
by money-hungry glory-craving leeches, preyed on by facile force of state
and fad and novelty, by false prophet and holy believer;

For my people standing staring trying to fashion a better way from confusion,   9
from hypocrisy and misunderstanding, trying to fashion a world that will
hold all the people, all the faces, all the adams and eves and their countless
generations;

Let a new earth rise. Let another world be born. Let a bloody peace be written  10
in the sky. Let a second generation full of courage issue forth; let a people
loving freedom come to growth. Let a beauty full of healing and a strength
of final clenching be the pulsing in our spirits and our blood. Let the martial
songs be written, let the dirges disappear. Let a race of men now rise and
take control.

## For Better Reading: Companion Pieces

There is more than one approach to a piece of writing. Of course, every
worthwhile selection can and should be considered on its own, as an
expression of an individual's ideas, thoughts, and feelings. But it's also true
that reading helps you acquire a background of ideas that apply to future
reading.

Emerson's words about Lincoln cast a special light on Paulette White's
poem. Margaret Walker dedicated her poem to "My People," so you can
also think of it as a companion piece to "Lincoln's Birthday," illustrating
why the troubled mother found it so difficult to answer her son's question,
"What *was* slavery?"

### Questioning the Poem

1. In its form, how is this poem similar to "Who Made Paul Bunyan?"
   by Carl Sandburg? In some ways, Walker's poem also has a similarly
   hypnotic, continuously flowing rhythm. How do her choice of words
   and use of punctuation contribute to this effect?
2. What period in American history does the first segment refer to? By
   using the words "unknown" and "unseen" what does Walker imply
   about the feelings of her people toward their situation? Why might
   they feel this way?
3. In the second segment, how does the poem's focus change with respect
   to time? By repeating the word *never* four times, what unchanged
   situation does the poem emphasize?
4. What proves that segments 3 and 4 describe a time after the end of

slavery? How would you finish the following thoughts? "We went to learn the reasons why . . . ; the people who . . . ; the places where . . . ; the days when . . ." What bitter truth had the children discovered about themselves?

5. What contrast does the poet make in segment 5, concerning her people's lives? What would you conclude was responsible for their suffering greatly from consumption and anemia? For dying from having been lynched?

6. In segments 6 and 7, what change of setting occurs? What in her descriptions supports the people's being lost, disinherited, and dispossesed? What accounts for their being happy?

7. What in segments 6 and 7 sums up their greatest need? Who must be "the unseen creatures who tower over us omnisciently and laugh"?

8. According to segments 8 and 9, to what agencies have the people appealed in their "floundering" attempts to "fashion a better way"? What are three reasons the "better way" was not found?

9. How does the repetition of the word *all* at the end of stanza 9 show the desire for fairness in the hoped-for world?

10. The poem concludes by asking that a "race of men" now rise. Assuming this includes both men and women, what peoples will make up this race? What clues does the poem give as to how the change might be achieved? How will the world, as the speaker sees it, then be different in a "second generation"?

# Looking Deeper
## Companion Pieces

The poem "For My People" helps clarify the mother's reaction to her small son's questions in "Lincoln's Birthday." For instance, in stanza 4 Walker writes of discovering "we were black and poor and small and different" although no one seemed to care or understand. Although her son may not be poor, this expresses part of his mother's awareness. Find two or three additional examples, and explain them in your own words.

According to Margaret Walker, what besides the law was responsible for the situation faced by her people? Has America experienced the "bloody peace" and "martial songs" that Walker calls for? Considering both poems, have positive changes occurred since the writing of Walker's poem? Be sure to have thoughtful reasons and examples for all of your answers.

# Early Marriage

## by Conrad Richter

| | |
|---|---|
| **Born:** | *Pennsylvania, 1890* |
| **Early jobs:** | *Farm worker, store and bank clerk, reporter* |
| **Made home in:** | *New Mexico, where he wrote famous novels of western settlers and native Americans* |

## PART I

FOR TWO DAYS THE LEATHERY face of Asa Putman had been a document in cipher to anyone who could read the code. Since Saturday but one traveler had passed his solitary post, a speck of adobe and picket corrals lost on the vast, sandy stretch of the Santa Ana plain. Far as the eye could see from his doorway, the rutted El Paso trail, unfenced, gutterless, innocent of grading, gravel, culverts, or telephone poles, imprinted only by iron tires, the hoofs of horses and oxen, sheep and cattle, and the paw of the loping lobo wolf, lay with dust unraised.

Ordinarily, there were freighters with cracking whips and trailers rumbling on behind. Army trains to and from the forts set up their tents for the night beyond the springs. The private coaches of Santa Fe and Colorado merchants, of cattle kings and Government officials, stopped long enough for the Putman children to admire the ladies, the magnificent woodwork, and the luxurious cushions inside. Trail herds of gaunt red steers bawled for the water in the earthen tank, and pairs and companies of horsemen rode up and down.

But since Saturday not even a solitary buckboard[1] from the far settlements in the Cedar country had called for supplies or letters. Only a girl from the Blue Mesa had ridden in for her and her neighbors' mail. She had eaten dinner with the Putmans, refused to stay overnight and started her long ride home.

A stranger from the East would have spoken about the stillness, the deadly waiting, and asked uneasily why Uncle Gideon hadn't come as promised. But in the Putman household it was not mentioned.

Asa deliberately busied himself about the post, filling the bin beneath the

---

[1] buckboard: a horse-drawn vehicle with seats cushioned by a long, springy frame between the axles.

counter with navy beans and green coffee, leafing through the packet of letters in the drawer, and making a long rite out of feeding the occupants of the picket corrals—four horses of which were fresh for the next stage.

Rife, just turned fifteen, carried water and gathered cow chips in an old hide dragged by a rope to his saddle horn. Ignacita,[2] the Mexican housekeeper, spat sharply on her heavy irons in the torrid kitchen and kept glancing over her shoulder and out of the open door and windows.

And Nancy Belle, going on seventeen, packed and repacked the high, iron-bound trunk that her father had bought for her at Santa Fe and sang softly to herself in the way that women sang fifty and sixty years ago.

Saturday she was being married at Gunstock, two hundred miles away—five days' journey in a wagon, four in a saddle or buckboard.

For six months she had thought of little else. The almanac fell apart at June as naturally as her mother's Bible did at the Twenty-third Psalm. So often had she run her finger down the page that anyone might tell from the worn line of type the very day she and Stephen Dewee would be man and wife. The Dewees lived four hundred miles west across the territory in the Beaverhead country. She and Stephen were taking a mountain ranch near his people, and for the wedding they had compromised on Gunstock, nearly equidistant from both families and convenient to friends scattered up and down the Rio Grande.

She had lighted a candle in the dusk, when a figure appeared reluctantly in her doorway. Asa Putman had never been at ease in his daughter's bedroom. A tall, rawhide man in an unbuttoned sagging vest, he was visibly embarrassed by any furnishings that suggested refinement. Invariably he kept his hat on in the house. He had it on now, a flat top and a flat brim, not so much like the Western hats you see now. Nancy Belle knew that her mother's people had never forgiven him for bringing his young wife and their two small children to this lonely post, at the mercy of outlaws and the worse Apaches.

Tonight she could see that something bothered him. He gave her a sidewise glance, so sharp and characteristic.

"I don't expect, Nancy Belle, you could put off your weddin'?"

The girl stood quietly gazing at him with a face like the tintype of her mother. But under her sedate gray dress, with tight waist and full skirts to the instep, she had frozen. She looked much older than her years. Her air of gentlefolk and her wide-apart gray eyes came from her mother. But the chin, tipped up with resolute fearlessness, was her father's.

"No, papa!" Her two clear words held all the steady insistence of the desert.

"I figured how you'd feel," he nodded, avoiding her eyes. "I just wanted to put it up to you. I'd 'a' covered the *jornada*[3] on foot to be on time at my own weddin', but I didn't have to count on Gideon to hold me up."

"Are you telling me, papa, that you can't go to Gunstock tomorrow?" Her voice remained quiet, but a coldness had seized her. Of all the people she had

---

[2] Ignacita (ēg·nä·sē′tȧ).
[3] jornada (hôr·nä′dȧ): a journey, often used in the Southwest for a long stretch of desert country.

visualized at her wedding, the one next to Stephen she could least spare was the tall, grave figure of her father.

"I reckon I kind of can't, Nancy Belle," he said soberly. "Rife could tend to the stage all right and do the feedin'. But they's men come to this post no boy can handle." He shifted his position. "I figured once on closin' up the post till I got back. But the stage is comin' and the mail. And the freighters count on me for feed and grub. Then I got to protect my own property and the mail and freight for the Cedar country that's in the storage room."

"I know," Nancy Belle said steadily. "I can get to Gunstock all right."

Far back in her father's assaying eyes, she fancied she saw a glint of pride.

"You're pretty nigh a woman now, Nancy Belle. And Rife's a good slice of a man. It's a straight trail to the Rio Grande, once you turn at the old post. Both you and Rife's been over it before. Of course, I'd like to be at the weddin', but the boy can tell me about it." He went to the window. "Rife!" he called.

Nancy Belle's brother came in presently. A slight boy, with his father's blue eyes, he seldom made a fuss over anything, even when he shot a stray duck on the tank or when they braked down the last cedar hill into Santa Fe with all the open doors of the plaza shops in sight. And when his father told him now, he showed neither enthusiasm nor regret—merely straightened.

"Sure. I can take you, Nancy Belle," he said.

Something pulled under his sister's tight basque. She remembered the long miles they would have in the wagon, the camps at lonely places, the ugly shadow ever hovering over the outposts of this frontier country, and the blight that, since Saturday, seemed to have fallen on the trail. Her eyes swam. Now, at the last minute, she yielded.

"If you'll let me ride, papa, I'll wait another day for Uncle Gideon," she promised.

Her father's eyes moved to the ruffled red calico curtains at the shadeless windows.

"I don't hardly count on Gideon comin' any more, Nancy Belle. Besides, it's too long in the saddle to Gunstock—especially for a girl to get married. You'd be plumb wore out, and you wouldn't have your trunk. You couldn't get dressed for your weddin'."

He turned thoughtfully and went out, Rife close behind. Nancy Belle could hear her father's tones, slow and grave, coming from near one of the picket corrals.

It was too far to catch the words; but when they came in, she saw that her brother's features looked a little pale under the tan.

"You better get some sleep, Nancy Belle," her father said. "You and Rife are startin' before daylight. If Gideon comes, I'll ride after."

They had scarcely gone from the room when Ignacita came in from the kitchen, her black eyes glittering over a pile of freshly starched white in her arms.

"Nancy Belle, *chinita!*"[4] she whispered, plucking at the girl's sleeve. "You

[4] chinita (shē·nē′tä): a term of endearment.

150

don't say to your *papacito*[5] I talk to you! I have promise I don't scare you. But I can't see you go so far in the wilderness alone, *pobrecita!*[6] Sometimes people go safe from one place to the other, oh, *sí!*[7] But sometimes, *chinita*, they don't come back! You have not the oldness like Ignacita. Ay, I tell you these old eyes have seen men and women quartered from a tree like sheep or maybe tied over a stove like I don't have the words to say to you."

Nancy Belle did not answer except to lay, one by one, the ironed pieces in her trunk—a bride's muslin underwear trimmed with red and blue feather stitching; long petticoats stiffly flounced with ruffles, and nightgowns long in the sleeve and high in the neck, with ruffles at wrist and throat. The Mexican woman went on hoarsely. The girl folded away her winter's cashmere dress, buttoned up the front and with a white fichu.[8] She unwrapped and wrapped again in crumpled white tissue the red slippers the old gentleman on the stage had sent her as a wedding present from Philadelphia.

When Ignacita had left, she opened her keepsake box covered with colored shells. The mirror on the inside lid turned back a face as calm as the little golden clouds that hung of an evening over the east to catch the desert sunset. But after she had undressed and put on her nightdress, for a long time she was aware of the soft pound of her heart faintly swaying the bed on its rawhide springs.

At the first sound of Ignacita's hand on the kitchen stove, Nancy Belle sprang out of bed. She dressed on the brown pool of burro skin, the only carpet on her adobe floor. Through the west window she could see the morning star burning like a brilliant candle. It hung, she told herself, over Gunstock and the Beaverhead, where Stephen, at this moment, in their new log ranch house, lay thinking about her.

They ate in the kitchen by lamplight. She had never been so conscious of every detail—the great white cups and saucers, the familiar steel knives, the homey smell of the scorched paper lamp-shade, the unreadable eyes of her father, Rife, and Ignacita.

Asa Putman himself carried out the trunk. There was already hay in the wagon, a gunny sack of oats, food in a canned-tomato box and utensils in another, a water keg, bedroll tied in a wagon sheet, an ax, a bridle, and her own sidesaddle, made to order over a man's tree.[9] Her eyes caught the gleam of a rifle leaning up against the seat in the lantern light. Tethered to the rear of the wagon stood her saddle mare, Fancy, with pricked-up ears. She was going along to their new ranch home. Nancy Belle felt that she was still among intimate things, but outside the little circle of light lay darkness and the unknown.

When she said good-by to her father, he kissed her—something he had not done for years.

---

[5] papacito (pä′pä·sē′tō): "little" papa, a familiar, affectionate form.
[6] pobrecita (pō′brà·sē′tà): poor little one.
[7] sí (sē): Spanish for *yes*.
[8] fichu (fĭsh′ōō): a kind of kerchief of muslin or lace, worn about the neck.
[9] tree: saddletree, the wooden frame of a saddle.

"You haven't changed your mind, Nancy Belle?" he asked.

She climbed quickly up over the wheel to the spring seat of the wagon before he might see that she was crying. Rife swung up like a monkey on the other side and pushed the rifle into the crevice behind the seat cushion. The lines tautened and the wagon lurched.

"*Dios* go with you safe to your husband, Nancy Belle!" she heard Ignacita cry after her.

The morning star had set. They moved into a world of silent blackness. Nancy Belle could not see how the horses remained on the trail. When she looked back, the only light in all these square miles of black, unfriendly earth was the yellow window of her father's post.

It was almost a vision, golden and far away, like all beautiful things. She didn't trust herself to look again.

Two hours later the wagon was a lonely speck of boat rocking in an illimitable sage-green sea beneath the sun. The canvas wagon sheet fastened over the bows was a kind of sail, and eastward the sandy water did not stop rolling till it washed up at the foot of the faintly blue ramparts of the distant Espiritu Range.

Just before they turned west on the cross trail to the Rio Grande, a heavy wagon with a yoke of oxen in front and a cow behind toiled round the crumbling adobe walls of the old, abandoned post house. A bearded man and a thin woman with a white face sat on the seat. She held a baby in her arms, and three black-eyed children peered from under the wagon sheet.

The bearded man saluted and stopped his willing team. Rife did likewise. The woman spoke first. Her tongue was swift and slightly acid.

"You better turn around and follow us if you want to save your hair!" she called. "Yesterday a sheepherder told us he saw—"

A sharp word from the bearded man caused her to relapse into sullen silence. He asked Rife where he might be going, then climbed down to the trail and said he wanted to talk to him a little. The boy followed reluctantly behind his wagon. Nancy Belle could hear the bearded man's tones coming slow and grave like her father's, while the woman made silent and horribly expressive lip language.

Rife came back, walking stiffly. The bearded man climbed up beside the woman.

"They got to go on," he told her in a low tone, then saluted with his whip. "Good luck, boy! And you, miss!"

Rife raised his whip in stiff acknowledgment. The wagons creaked apart. Nancy Belle saw in front of her the trail to the Rio Grande, little more than a pair of wheel tracks, that lost itself on the lonely plain. Rife seemed relieved that she did not ask what the bearded man had said. But it was enough for her not to be able to forget the woman's fearful signs and mouthings and the horror in the curious eyes of the staring children.

Sister and brother talked very little. Nancy Belle saw her brother's eyes keep sweeping the country, scanning the horizons. Bunches of bear grass that might have been feathers pinioned his blue gaze, and clumps of cane cactus that seemed to hold pointing gun barrels. At arroyos[10] thick with *chamiso*[11] and Apache plume she could see his feet tighten on the footboard. Once he pulled out the rifle, but it was only a herd of antelopes moving across the desert page.

They camped for the night when the sun was still high. Nancy Belle asked no questions as the boy drove far off the trail into a grassy *cañada*.[12] She sang softly to herself as she fried the salt side bacon and put the black coffeepot to boil.

Rife hobbled Anton Chico and the Bar X horse and staked out Fancy close to the wagon.

She pretended not to notice when, before dark, he poured earth on the fire till not a spark or wisp of smoke remained. Out of one eye she watched him climb the side of the *cañada* and stand long minutes sweeping the country from the ridge, a slight, tense figure against the sullen glow of the sunset.

"It's all right," he said when he came down. "You can go to bed."

"What's all right?" she asked him.

"The horses," he said, turning away, and Nancy Belle felt a stab of pain that so soon this boy must bear a man's responsibilities and tell a man's lies.

She prayed silently on her blankets spread on the hay in the wagon box, and lay down with her head on the side-saddle, her unread Testament in her hand. She heard Rife unroll his camp bed on the ground beneath the wagon. It was all very strange and hushed without her father. Just to feel the Testament in her hand helped to calm her and to remember the day at the post when she had first met Stephen.

Her father had never let her come in contact with the men of the trail. Always, at the first sign of dust cloud on the horizon, he would tell both children to heap up the chip box, fill the water buckets and carry saddles and bridles into the house. But this day Asa Putman and Rife had gone to Fort Sumner. And to Nancy Belle, Uncle Gideon could seldom say no.

It had been a very hot day. She had been sitting in the shade of the earthen bank of the tank, moving her bare feet in the cool water, watching the ripples in the hot south wind. The leaves of the cottonwoods clashed overhead, and she heard nothing until she looked up, and there was a young man on a blue-gray horse with dust clinging to his hat brim and mustache. His eyes were direct as an eagle's. Firm lines modeled his lean face. But what she noticed most at the time was the little bow tie on his dark shirt.

Instantly she had tucked her bare, wet legs under her red dress. Her face burned with shame, but the young stranger talked to her about her father coolly, as if she, a girl of fifteen, had not been caught barefooted. Then he did what in her mind was a noble thing. When Uncle Gideon came out, he magnificently turned his back for her to run into the house and pull on shoes and stockings.

---

[10] arroyos (ă·roi′ōz): small, often dry, gullies or channels.
[11] chamiso (chá·me′·sō): a semidesert shrub.
[12] cañada (kä·nyá′dä): an open glade between mountains or ridges.

# PART II

She thought of Stephen constantly next day and the next. She had grown a little used to the journey without her father now—the still, uncertain nights under the wagon sheet, sitting, lying, listening, waiting; the less uncertain days with the sun on the endless spaces; her never-quiet perch on the high spring seat under the slanted bow; the bumps, creaks, and lumberings of the wagon; the sand sifting softly over the red, turning wheels; all afternoon the sun in their faces; ahead the far haze and heat waves in which were still lost Gunstock and the Rio Grande. Almost she had forgotten the bearded man with the oxen and the curious, detached horror in the eyes of his children.

Since morning of the third day their progress had been slower. The trail seemed level, except for the heavy breathing of the horses. But when Nancy Belle glanced back she could see the steady grade they had been climbing. Abruptly, in midafternoon, she found that the long, blue Espiritu Range had disappeared, vanished behind a high pine-clad hill which was its southernmost beginning. It was like the lizard that swallowed itself, a very real lizard. At this moment they were climbing over the lizard's tail.

"Cedars!" Rife said briefly, pointing with the whip to dark sprawling growths ahead.

"You breathe deep up here!" Nancy Belle drank in the light air.

Rife took a sniff, but his blue eyes never ceased to scan the high, black-thatched hill under whose frowning cliff they must pass.

"Soon we can see the Gunstock Mountains," Nancy Belle said.

"And Martin Cross's cabin," Rife nodded. "It's the last water to the Rio Grande."

"He's a nice old man," Nancy Belle ventured casually. "It would be nice to camp by his cabin tonight and talk."

The boy inclined his head. After a few moments he started to whistle softly. At the first cedar Nancy Belle leaped off the moving wagon and climbed back with an evergreen branch. The twig, crushed in her hand, smelled like some store in Santa Fe.

They gained the summit. A breeze was sweeping here from the southwest, and the horses freshened. But Rife had suddenly stopped whistling and Nancy Belle's sprig of cedar lay on her lap. The frowning cliff of the pine-clad hill was still there. But Martin Cross's cabin had turned to a desolate mound of ashes. As they stared, a gust of wind sent wisps of smoke scurrying from the mound, and a red eye opened to watch them from the embers. Nancy Belle felt an uncontrollable twitching in the hair roots at the base of her scalp.

Where Martin Cross's eastbound wheel tracks met the trail, Rife reluctantly halted the horses and wet his air-dried lips.

"The water keg's dry, and the horses. If papa was here, he'd drive over."

"I'm the oldest." Nancy Belle found her voice steady. "I'll ride over. There might be something we can do."

The boy rose quickly. His eyes seemed to remember something his father had said.

"You can drive the wagon over if I wave."

He had thrown her the lines and slipped back through the canvas-covered tunnel of wagon box, picking up Fancy's bridle and the rifle. Barebacked he rode toward the smoldering ashes at the foot of that frowning hill. The chestnut mare's tail and mane streamed like something gold in the wind.

When she looked back to the trail, her eyes were pinioned by a light object in the wheel track ahead of the Bar X horse. It was a long gray feather. Instantly she told herself that it had come from some wild turkey Martin Cross had shot, and yet never had air anywhere become so suddenly horrible and choking as in this canyon.

Rife did not signal her to drive over. She saw him come riding back at full speed. The mare was snorting. As he stopped her at the wagon, her chestnut head kept turning back toward what had once been a cabin. Rife slipped the lead rope about her neck and climbed into the seat with the rifle in his hands.

"The water—you wouldn't want it!" he said thickly. His cheeks, she noticed, were the color of *yeso*.[13]

"Rife"—Nancy Belle touched his arm when she had driven down the canyon—"what did you see at the cabin?"

The boy sat deaf and rigid beside her, eyes staring straight ahead. She saw that his young hands were still tortured around the barrel of his rifle.

Far down on the pitch-dark mesa she stopped the horses in the trail and listened. There were no stars, not a sound but the flapping of the wagon sheet in the wind and the clank of coffeepot and water bucket under the wagon. Half standing on the footboard, she guided the team off the trail in the intense blackness. Her swift hands helped the trembling boy stake out the mare and hobble the team. They did not light a lantern. Rife declined to eat. Nancy Belle chewed a few dry mouthfuls.

The wind came drawing out of the blackness with a great draft. It hissed through the grass, sucked and tore at the wagon sheet, and whistled through the spokes and brake rigging. Rife did not take his bedroll under the wagon tonight. He drew the ends of the wagon sheet together and lay down in the wagon box near his sister. For a long time they were silent. When she heard his heavy breathing, she lifted the rifle from his chest.

The storm grew. Sand began pelting against the canvas and sifted into the wagon box. An invisible cloud of choking dust found its way into eyes, mouth, ears, and lungs. Nancy Belle laid down the rifle a moment to pull a blanket over the face of the boy. He tossed and muttered pitifully, but he slept on.

Magically the rain, when it came, stopped the sand and dust. The girl drank in the clean-washed air. At daylight she slipped out to the ground. The mesa, stretching away in the early light, touched here and there with feathers of mist, would have been beautiful except for a sharp new loneliness. The horses were gone!

At her exclamation, Rife appeared from the wagon box. His shame at having slept through the night was quickly overshadowed by their misfortune.

[13] yeso (yā'sō): gypsum, used to whitewash the walls of pioneer houses in the Southwest.

Together they found where Fancy's stake had been pulled out and dragged. Yards farther on they could tell by Anton Chico's tracks that his hobbles had parted.

Nancy Belle made her brother come back to the wagon and stuff his pockets with cold biscuits and antelope jerky. She said she would have a hot breakfast ready when he returned. The horses, perhaps, were just down in some draw where they had drifted with the wind.

When he had gone with the rifle, she filled the coffeepot from a clearing water hole in the nearest arroyo. She fried potatoes and onions in the long-handled skillet. And when he did not come, she set fresh biscuits in the Dutch oven. Each biscuit held a square of salt side bacon in its top, and as it baked, the fat oozed down and incased it in a kind of glazed tastiness.

At noon she thought she heard a shot. Nowhere could she see him on the endless sweep of mesa. By late afternoon she was still alone. She read her Testament and wondered how many women over the world had read it in hours like this. Sitting in the shadow of the wagon, facing the direction in which he had gone, she looked up every few minutes. But all her eyes could find were cloud shadows racing across the lonely face of the mesa. All she could hear were the desolate cries from the unseen lark sparrows.

Darkness, stillness settled down on the empty land. She climbed back into the wagon and sat on the chuck box, hands rigid on her knees. Again and again she convinced herself that the horses could not have been driven off or she would have seen the drivers' tracks. When wild, sharp barks shattered the stillness and set wires jerking in her limbs, she talked to herself steadily, but a little meaninglessly, of the post—on and on as the darkness was filled with the ringing and counter-ringing of shrill, cracked yappings—not long tones like a dog's, but incredibly short syllables rising, rising in a mad eternal scale and discord.

"I wish Papa had given me two of the chairs," she repeated. "Mamma said they were post oak from Texas. She said they had got white from scrubbing. I liked the laced rawhide seats with the hair left on. It made them soft to sit on. The seats in the parlor were black. And the ones in the kitchen were red. But I liked the brockle[14] one in my room best."

The insane din around the wagon had become terrific. There were only two or three of the animals, Nancy Belle guessed, but they threw their voices and echoes together to make a score.

"When I was little I liked to go in the storage room," her voice went on, scarcely intelligible to her own ears. "It was dark and cool, and smelled of burlap and kerosene and whisky, and sweetish with brown sugar. I can see the fat sacks of green coffee. And the round tins of kerosene had boards on the side. The flour-sacks were printed: 'Rough and Ready' in red letters. Mamma once used to make our underwear out of the sacking. I can smell the salt side bacon in the gunny sacks."

She could tell from the sounds that one of the animals was running insanely back and forth near the wagon tongue. She had never noticed before that they

14 brockle: likely to break; worn or unsteady.

yelped both when breathing in and out. Suddenly came silence. It warned her. Instinctively she felt for the ax.

"Nancy Belle!" a boy's far, anxious voice called from the darkness.

She hallooed and leaned out over the tailboard. Three shadowy forms were coming across the mesa in the starlight. Never had horses looked so good.

"Were you scared?" Rife greeted. "Anything bother you?"

"Nothing," Nancy Belle said. "Just coyotes."

"I had to give Fancy her head after it got dark." He slid wearily to the ground. "She brought us straight back to the wagon."

Nancy Belle had wanted to put her arms around her brother. Now she hugged the mare instead. Rife ate fresh biscuits and a tin plate of cold potatoes. He drank several tin cups of coffee. Nancy Belle had slipped the oats-laden gunny-sack *morrals* over the horses' heads.

"I had to walk halfway to the mountain," Rife said.

"Just help hitch up; then you can sleep all night," she promised.

It rained again heavily toward midnight. Flashes of lightning lit the drenched plain. For minutes at a time, quivering fingers of blue phosphorescence stood on the ears of the toiling horses. At dawn Nancy Belle still held the reins as the mud-splashed wagon crawled through a world bathed in early purple splendor.

Four days they had been crossing a hundred and seventy miles of desolate plain. Now the end waited in sight. To the west lay a land broken and tumbled by a mighty hand. Hill shouldered hill and range peered over range, all indescribably violet except where peaks tipped by the unseen sun were far-off flaming towers of copper.

It was a new land, her promised land, Stephen's land, Nancy Belle told herself, where nobody burned cow chips, but snapping cedar and pine, where cold water ran in the wooded canyons, and the eye, weary of one flat circle the horizon round, had endless geometric designs to refresh the retina.

She sang softly as the wagon lumbered to the edge of a long, shallow valley, brown and uninhabited, running north and south, and desolate except for a winding ribbon that was white with sky and narrowly bordered with green.

"Rife!" Nancy Belle cried. "The Rio Grande!"

An hour afterwards they pulled out of the sun into the shade of the long cottonwood *bosque.* [15] Nancy Belle wasn't singing now. Where she remembered wide sandbars glistening with sky and tracked by waterfowl, a chocolate-red flood rolled. Where had been the island, tops of tule [16] and scrub willow swung to and fro with the current.

Anton Chico and the Bar X horse stopped of their own accord in the trail, ears pricked forward at the swirling brown wash. While Rife turned the three horses loose to graze, Nancy Belle silently fried bacon and made coffee. When she had washed skillet and tin dishes in the river, the boy had wired the wagon box to the brake rigging. Now he was tying securely one end of his rope to the

---

[15] bosque (bōs'kā): a wood or grove.
[16] tule (tōō'lĕ): either of two large bulrushes growing on overflowed land in the southwestern United States.

center of the coupling pole under the wagon. The other end she knew he would fasten to the inadequate upper horn of the side-saddle.

"I wouldn't mind the river if I just had my own saddle," he mourned.

They hitched up the team silently. Rife cinched the side-saddle on Fancy and straddled it, the single stirrup useless to a man. Nancy Belle climbed into the wagon and picked up the lines. The other bank looked as far away as the Espiritu Range from the post. She wanted to say something to her brother—some last word, in case they didn't make it. But all she did was cluck her tongue to the horses.

Gingerly, one slow foot at a time, the team moved down the trail into the water.

"Give 'em their heads!" Rife called from the right rear.

Nancy Belle held a rein in each hand. The red channel water came to the wagon tongue, covered it, reached the horses' bellies. The team wanted to stop. Nancy Belle swung her whip, a stick tipped with a long rawhide lash. The wagon went on. The collars of both horses kept dipping, but never entirely out of sight. Still barely wading, the slow team reached the firmer footing of the island.

Two-thirds of the river still rolled in front of the wagon. The west bank did not seem to have grown much closer, but the east bank behind them had moved far away. The team had to be whipped into the violent current. The water churned white through the wagon wheels. Suddenly both horses appeared to stumble and drop out of sight. Their heads came up wildly, spray blowing from their nostrils. The muddy water hid their legs, but by their bobbing motions Nancy Belle knew that they were swimming.

"Keep 'em pointed up the river!" Rife shouted.

Already she felt the wagon floating. It swung downstream with the current; then Rife's rope from Fancy's saddle snubbed it. The team was snorting with every breath. The Bar X horse swam high in the water, his withers and part of his back out of the chocolate current. But all she could see of Anton Chico were his nose and ears.

Down between her ankles she saw water in the wagon box. She thought of the hemstitched sheets at the bottom of her trunk, the towels and pillowcases crocheted with shell lace. Her blue velvet corduroy dress was probably wet already, and all the cunning print aprons with dust caps to match. River water couldn't hurt the little yellow creamer, sugar bowl, and covered butter dish that had been her mother's. And the gingham dresses could be washed. What worried her were her wedding dress and the keepsake box, especially the tintypes, one of which was Rife in a child's suit edged with black braid, his brand new hat on his knee.

An older Rife was shouting something behind her now. She couldn't catch the words. Then she found what it was. The neck and withers of Anton Chico raised suddenly out of the water and both horses were scrambling up the steep bank below the ford. Only quick work the with lines saved the wagon from turning over. Safe and blowing on the high bank, the dripping horses shook themselves like puppies.

Nancy Belle couldn't go on until she had opened the trunk and appraised the damage. Rife unsaddled Fancy and drove on with the refreshed team. Behind his slight back in the wagon box, the girl changed to her blue velvet corduroy, which was hardly wet at all. Then she combed her hair and rolled into a cranny of her trunk the old felt hat that had been too large for her father.

A half-dozen riders met the wagon some miles down the Gunstock Canyon. All of them, Nancy Belle noticed, carried guns. Stephen wore a new white shirt and a gray hat with curled brim she had not seen before. He stood in his stirrups and swung her down in front of him on the saddle, where he kissed her. She had never felt his lips press into such a straight line.

"Papa couldn't come," she said. "So Rife brought me."

She felt Stephen's rigid arm around her.

"We just got in from the Beaverhead ourselves."

"He means they never get any news out in the Beaverhead or he'd 'a' come further east to meet you!" Uncle Billy Williams put in. He had a lovable, squeaky voice. "The Apaches been breakin' loose again. Funny you didn't hear anything over in your country."

Nancy Belle gave him an inscrutable look with her gray eyes. Uncle Billy pulled out his bandanna and blew his nose.

"They got my old friend Judge Hower and his wife and kid in a buggy on the Upper Espiritu. The man that found what they did to 'em, they say cried like a baby."

"That's all right, Uncle Billy," Stephen said in a gentle voice.

Nancy Belle glanced at Rife. Her brother's face looked gray, the eyes staring as when he had ridden in the late afternoon sunlight from the smoking ashes of Martin Cross's cabin.

Nearly fifty people, gathered in the big parlor upstairs at the hotel, greeted Nancy Belle. An old man whose young black eyes twinkled out of a bearded face said he was glad to see that she had her "hair on straight." Rife stopped with the trunk before driving to the livery, and Stephen's mother showed Nancy Belle to a room to dress.

The guests stopped talking when she came into the parlor in her white wedding dress. Her basque came to a point in the front and back. It fitted like a glove. The silk underskirt came to her instep, and the ruffled overskirt to her knees. She had parted her hair from side to side and brushed the bangs down on her forehead. She felt very light-headed. The wagon still seemed to be jerking under her.

She glimpsed Rife gazing at her, a rapt expression in his reticent blue eyes. She was glad to see that he had brushed his hair. The brass swinging lamp had been lighted and the dark woodwork of the parlor festooned with evergreen branches. White streamers from the wall met in a papier-mâché bell in one corner. She noticed two children peering eagerly from the dark hall.

Stephen came to her, very straight in a long coat and stand-up collar with a black tie. He led her up beneath the papier-mâché bell. In a sibilant, church-like whisper, the Gunstock preacher made sure of her full name. Then he coughed and began the ceremony. He had a deep voice, but Nancy Belle didn't hear all of the service. Her mind kept going back to a tall, grave man in a lonely adobe post on the wide Santa Ana plain. And after she had said: "I do," her lips moved, but she was not praying for Stephen, her husband.

## For Better Reading: The Western Hero

Their legends come down, less by individual names than by examples of individualism. For together, all of the pioneers, settlers, cowboys, and even outlaws created a special kind of legend, the legendary history of the American West.

Western tales and movies have become popular throughout the world because this was a new kind of legend. It required individuals willing to ask for nothing but the right to depend upon fate, the future, and themselves.

In their eyes, the land west of the Mississippi held vast and open spaces, just waiting to be won. For they had to start from the beginning, cross deserts and mountains, as well as face the hostile Indian peoples, whose lands they blindly overran.

What did they have in common that makes their stories fit for legends? Did they know or did they consider that the land was not rightly theirs for the taking? It is important to share and compare focuses in order to reach an understanding of what the legends of the West mean to Americans today.

## Cause and Effect

1. As a post along the El Paso trail, Asa Putman's place served as a (a) secondary fort for the Army cavalry (b) general store selling groceries, yard goods, and hardware (c) post for getting water and fresh horses (d) promising site for settlement.
2. Because Uncle Gideon hadn't arrived, (a) Nancy Belle decided to postpone her wedding (b) the family expressed the fear he'd met with harm (c) Nancy Belle's brother would be best man (d) Asa Putman decided to stay home.
3. Nancy Belle was to be married in Gunstock, about 200 miles away, because it was (a) near the Dewees' ranch (b) halfway between the two families' homes (c) where the newly married couple planned to settle (d) a compromise made to avoid disagreements.

## Questioning the Story

### Part I.
1. At 17, how did Nancy Belle feel about her coming marriage? In what ways does she exhibit qualities of both her father and mother?

2. After saying "Rife's a good slice of a man," how did Nancy Belle's father show confidence in his 15-year-old son? Explain what Asa Putman implied by saying "they's men come to this post no boy can handle"?

3. How did Asa Putman react to Nancy Belle's offer to delay her departure? What were his reasons?

4. What promise to her employer did Ignacita break? What would cause Asa Putman to seek this promise? How did Nancy Belle react to Ignacita's words?

5. After he and Nancy Belle met the family on the trail, why was Rife "relieved that she did not ask what the bearded man had said"? Why didn't Nancy Belle question Rife? Why would both feel the subject should not be mentioned?

6. Explain Nancy Belle's regret that "so soon this boy must bear a man's responsibilities and tell a man's lies," concerning her brother.

**Part II.**

1. What was the first sight greeting brother and sister at Martin Cross's cabin? When Nancy Belle offered to ride there, Rife "seemed to remember something his father had said." What must this have been?

2. Upon returning from the cabin, what did Rife tell his sister? What do you assume he saw? Why wouldn't he say?

3. When they woke in the morning after stopping at Cross's cabin, what new misfortune awaited? After Rife left and darkness fell, what shattered the stillness? How did Nancy Belle try to calm her fears?

4. How does Nancy Belle react when sudden silence follows the "insane din around the wagon"? What does this show about her character?

5. What new threat faces Rife and Nancy Belle at the Rio Grande? How is the river different from Nancy Belle's memory of it? What reason does the story provide for this change?

6. By indicating Nancy Belle's desire "to say something to her brother," what does the author reveal about the crossing? Why didn't Nancy Belle express these thoughts to Rife?

7. At the Gunstock hotel, how did everyone try to make the wedding seem as traditional as possible? Give specific examples. What shows that those in Stephen's party knew of the Apache attacks?

8. During the wedding ceremony, why did Nancy Belle pray for a "tall, grave man in a lonely adobe post" instead of for Stephen, her new husband?

# Looking Deeper

## I. Frontier Dangers

An author who made his home in New Mexico and studied the lives of early settlers, Conrad Richter includes a series of dangers and difficulties faced by pioneers in this short story. List four or more of them, and explain how your picture of early Western life has been changed or confirmed by reading "Early Marriage."

## II. The Need for Individualism

How did the characters in "Early Marriage" show their willingness and ability to depend upon themselves? Give at least three examples. What other positive traits, such as courage, concern for others, thoughtfulness, and pride, did the characters display? Give specific examples of these or other traits.

Concerning Asa Putman, Richter writes, "Nancy Belle knew that her mother's people had never forgiven him." What attitudes do Putman's in-laws represent? What impulses drove people to risk the dangers of going West? Describe your feeling about joining the pioneer movement, if you were living then.

## III. A Better Life

Why did the place where Stephen's family had settled seem like a "promised land" to Nancy Belle, when she compared it with her father's post? In dress and behavior at the wedding, the characters seemed determined to act as though they lived in places apart from the frontier. How and why did this influence their attitude toward the Indians they were displacing?

Did pioneers know or realize that the land was not rightly theirs for the taking? Support your answer from the story. What do many people feel today about the settlement of the West and treatment of Indians? How do you account for this change in attitude?

# Specifications for a Hero

*by Wallace Stegner*

| | |
|---|---|
| ***Born:*** | *Lake Mills, Iowa* |
| ***Early years:*** | *Utah, North Dakota, Washington, Montana, Wyoming, and Saskatchewan* |
| ***Career:*** | *Instructor and professor of English in United States, Canada; novelist, short story writer, and essayist* |

IN OUR TOWN, AS IN most towns, everybody had two names—the one his parents had given him and the one the community chose to call him by. Our nicknames were an expression of the folk culture, and they were more descriptive than honorific. If you were underweight, you were called Skinny or Slim or Sliver; if overweight, Fat or Chubby; if left-handed, Lefty; if spectacled, Four Eyes. If your father was the minister, your name was Preacher Kid, and according to the condition and color of your hair you were Whitey, Blacky, Red, Rusty, Baldy, Fuzzy, or Pinky. If you had a habit of walking girls in the brush after dusk, you were known as Town Bull or T.B. If you were small for your age, as I was, your name was Runt or Peewee. The revelation of your shape at the town swimming hole by the footbridge could tag you for life with the label Birdlegs. The man who for a while ran one of our two grocery stores was universally known as Jew Meyer.

Like the lingo we spoke, our nicknames were at odds with the traditional and educational formalisms; along with them went a set of standard frontier attitudes. What was appropriate for Jimmy Craig in his home or in church or in school would have been shameful to Preacher Kid Craig down at the bare-naked hole. When we were digging a cave in the cutbank back of my house, and someone for a joke climbed up on top and jumped up and down, and the roof caved in on P.K. and he had to be dug out and revived by artificial respiration, even P.K. thought the hullabaloo excessive. He did not blame us, and he did not tattle on anyone. His notions of fortitude and propriety—which were at the other end of the scale from those of his parents—would not have let him.

When we first arrived in Whitemud the Lazy-S was still a working ranch, with corrals, and calves, and a bunkhouse inhabited by heroes named Big Horn, Little

Horn, Slivers, Rusty, and Slippers. There was a Chinese cook named Mah Li, who had been abused in imaginative ways ever since he had arrived back at the turn of the century. In the first district poll for a territorial election, in 1902, someone had taken Mah Li to the polls and enfranchised him on the ground that, having been born in Hong Kong, he could swear that he was a British subject and was not an Indian, and was hence eligible to vote. When I knew him, he was a jabbering, good-natured soul with a pigtail and a loose blue blouse, and I don't suppose a single day of his life went by that he was not victimized somehow. He couldn't pass anybody, indoors or out, without having his pigtail yanked or his shirt tails set on fire. Once I saw the cowboys talk him into licking a frosty doorknob when the temperature was fifteen or twenty below, and I saw the tears in his eyes, too, after he tore himself loose. Another time a couple of Scandinavians tried to get him onto a pair of skis on the North Bench hill. They demonstrated how easy it was, climbed up and came zipping by, and then offered to help his toes into the straps. But Mah Li was too many for them that time. "Sssssssssssss!" he said in scorn. "Walkee half a mile back!" When I was ten or eleven Mah Li was a friend of mine. I gave him suckers I caught in the river, and once he made me a present of a magpie he had taught to talk. The only thing it could say was our laundry mark, the number O Five, but it was more than any other magpie in town could say, and I had a special feeling for Mah Li because of it. Nevertheless I would have been ashamed not to take part in the teasing, baiting, and candy-stealing that made his life miserable after the Lazy-S closed up and Mah Li opened a restaurant. I helped tip over his backhouse on Hallowe'en; I was part of a war party that sneaked to the crest of a knoll and with .22 rifles potted two of his white ducks as they rode a mud puddle near his shack in the east bend.

The folk culture sponsored every sort of crude practical joke, as it permitted the cruelest and ugliest prejudices and persecutions. Any visible difference was enough to get an individual picked on. Impartially and systematically we persecuted Mah Li and his brother Mah Jim, Jew Meyer and his family, any Indians who came down into the valley in their wobble-wheeled buckboards, anyone with a pronounced English accent or fancy clothes or affected manners, any crybaby, any woman who kept a poodle dog and put on airs, any child with glasses, anyone afflicted with crossed eyes, St. Vitus's dance, feeble-mindedness, or a game leg. Systematically the strong bullied the weak, and the weak did their best to persuade their persecutors, by feats of courage or endurance or by picking on someone still weaker, that they were tough and strong.

Immune, because they conformed to what the folk culture valued, were people with Texas or Montana or merely Canadian accents, people who wore overalls and worked with their hands, people who snickered at Englishmen or joined the bedevilment of Chinamen, women who let their children grow up wild and unwashed. Indignation swept the school one fall day when the Carpenter kids were sent home by the new teacher from Ontario. She sent a note along with them saying they had pediculosis and should not return to school until they were cured. Their mother in bewildered alarm brought them in to the doctor, and when she discovered that pediculosis meant only the condition of being lousy, she had to be restrained from going over and pulling the smart-alec teacher's hair out. We sympathized completely. That teacher never did get our confidence, for she had convicted herself of being both over-cleanly and pompous.

Honored and imitated among us were those with special skills, so long as the skills were not too civilized. We admired good shots, good riders, tough fighters, dirty talkers, stoical endurers of pain. My mother won the whole town because once, riding our flighty mare Daisy up Main Street, she got piled hard in front of Christenson's pool hall with half a dozen men watching, and before they could recover from laughing and go to help her, had caught the mare and remounted and ridden off, tightly smiling. The fact that her hair was red did not hurt: among us, red hair was the sign of a sassy temper.

She was one of the immune, and so was my father, for both had been brought up on midwestern farms, had lived on the Dakota frontier, and accepted without question—though my mother would have supplemented it—the code of the stiff upper lip. She had sympathy for anyone's weakness except her own; he went strictly by the code.

I remember one Victoria Day when there was a baseball game between our town and Shaunavon. Alfie Carpenter, from a riverbottom ranch just west of town, was catching for the Whitemud team. He was a boy who had abused me and my kind for years, shoving us off the footbridge, tripping us unexpectedly, giving us the hip, breaking up our hideouts in the brush, stampeding the town herd that was in our charge, and generally making himself lovable. This day I looked up from something just in time to see the batter swing and a foul tip catch Alfie full in the face. For a second he stayed bent over with a hand over his mouth; I saw the blood start in a quick stream through his fingers. My feelings were very badly mixed, for I had dreamed often enough of doing just that to Alfie Carpenter's face, but I was somewhat squeamish about human pain and I couldn't enjoy seeing the dream come true. Moreover I knew with a cold certainty that the ball had hit Alfie at least four times as hard as I had ever imagined hitting him, and there he stood, still on his feet and obviously conscious. A couple of players came up and took his arms and he shook them off, straightened up, spat out a splatter of blood and teeth and picked up his mitt as if to go on with the game. Of course they would not let him—but what a gesture! said my envious and appalled soul. There was a two-tooth hole when Alfie said something; he freed his elbows and swaggered to the side of the field. Watching him, my father broke out in a short, incredulous laugh. "Tough kid!" he said to the man next, and the tone of his voice goose-pimpled me like a breeze on a sweaty skin, for in all my life he had never spoken either to or of me in that voice of approval. Alfie Carpenter, with his broken nose and bloody mouth, was a boy I hated and feared, but most of all I envied his competence to be what his masculine and semi-barbarous world said a man should be.

As for me, I was a crybaby. My circulation was poor and my hands always got blue and white in the cold. I always had a runny nose. I was skinny and small, so that my mother anxiously doctored me with Scott's Emulsion, sulphur and molasses, calomel, and other doses. To compound my frail health, I was always getting hurt. Once I lost both big-toe nails in the same week, and from characteristically incompatible causes. The first one turned black and came off because I had accidentally shot myself through the big toe with a .22 short; the second because, sickly thing that I was, I had dropped a ten-pound bottle of Scott's Emulsion on it.

I grew up hating my weakness and despising my cowardice and trying to pretend that neither existed. The usual result of that kind of condition is bragging. I bragged, and sometimes I got called. Once in Sunday School I said that I was not afraid to jump off the high diving board that the editor of the *Leader* had projected out over the highest cutbank. The editor, who had been a soldier and a hero, was the only person in town who dared use it. It did not matter that the boys who called my bluff would not have dared to jump off it themselves. *I* was the one who had bragged, and so after Sunday School I found myself out on that thing, a mile above the water, with the wind very cold around my knees. The tea-brown whirlpools went spinning slowly around the deep water of the bend, looking as impossible to jump into as if they had been whorls in cement. A half dozen times I sucked in my breath and grabbed my courage with both hands and inched out to the burlap pad on the end of the board. Every time, the vibrations of the board started such sympathetic vibrations in my knees that I had to creep back for fear of falling off. The crowd on the bank got scornful, and then ribald, and then insulting; I could not rouse even the courage to answer back, but went on creeping out, quaking back, creeping out again, until they finally all got tired and left for their Sunday dinners. Then at once I walked out to the end and jumped.

I think I must have come down through thirty or forty feet of air, bent over toward the water, with my eyes out on stems like a lobster's, and I hit the water just so, with my face and chest, a tremendous belly-flopper that drove my eyes out through the back of my head and flattened me out on the water to the thickness of an oil film. The air was full of colored lights; I came to enough to realize I was strangling on weed-tasting river water, and moved my arms and legs feebly toward shore. About four hours and twenty deaths later, I grounded on the mud and lay there gasping and retching, sick for the hero I was not, for the humiliation I had endured, for the mess I had made of the jump when I finally made it—even for the fact that no one had been around to see me, and that I would never be able to convince any of them that I really had, at the risk of drowning, done what I had bragged I would do.

Contempt is a hard thing to bear, especially one's own. Because I was what I was, and because the town went by the code it went by, I was never quite out of sight of self-contempt or the contempt of my father or Alfie Carpenter or some other whose right to contempt I had to grant. School, and success therein, never fully compensated for the lacks I felt in myself. I found early that I could shine in class, and I always had a piece to speak in school entertainments, and teachers found me reliable at cleaning blackboards, but teachers were women, and school was a woman's world, the booby prize for those not capable of being men. The worst of it was that I liked school, and liked a good many things about the womanish world, but I wouldn't have dared admit it, and I could not respect the praise of my teachers any more than I could that of my music teacher or my mother.

"He has the arteestic tempera*ment*," said Madame Dujardin while collecting her pay for my piano lessons. "He's *sensitive*," my mother would tell her friends, afternoons when they sat around drinking coffee and eating Norwegian coffee cake, and I hung around inside, partly for the sake of coffee cake and partly to hear them talk about me. The moment they did talk about me, I was enraged. *Women* speaking up for me, noticing my "sensitivity," observing me with that appraising female stare and remarking that I seemed to like songs such as "Sweet and Low" better than "Men of Harlech," which was *their* sons' favorite—my mother interpolating half with pride and half with worry that sometimes she had to drive me out to play, I'd rather stay in and read Ridpath's *History of the World*. Women giving me the praise I would have liked to get from my father or Slivers or the Assiniboin halfbreed down at the Lazy-S. I wanted to be made of whang leather.

Little as I want to acknowledge them, the effects of those years remain in me like the beach terraces of a dead lake. Having been weak, and having hated my weakness, I am as impatient with the weakness of others as my father ever was. Pity embarrasses me for the person I am pitying, for I know how it feels to be pitied. Incompetence exasperates me, a big show of pain or grief or any other feeling makes me uneasy, affectations still inspire in me a mirth I have grown too mannerly to show. I cannot sympathize with the self-pitiers, for I have been there, or with the braggarts, for I have been there too. I even at times find myself reacting against conversation, that highest test of the civilized man, because where I came from it was unfashionable to be "mouthy."

An inhumane and limited code, the value system of a life more limited and cruder than in fact ours was. We got most of it by inheritance from the harsher frontiers that had preceded ours—got it, I suppose, mainly from our contacts with what was left of the cattle industry....

Read the history of the northern cattle ranges in such an anti-American historian as John Peter Turner and you hear that the "Texas men" who brought the cattle industry to Canada were all bravos, rustlers, murderers, gamblers, thugs, and highwaymen; that their life was divided among monte, poker, six-guns, and dancehall girls; and that their law was the gun-law that they made for themselves and enforced by hand. Allow sixty or seventy per cent of error for patriotic fervor, and Mr. Turner's generalizations may be accepted. But it is likewise true that American cow outfits left their gun-law cheerfully behind them when they found the country north of the Line well policed, that they cheerfully cooperated with the Mounted Police, took out Canadian brands, paid for grazing leases, and generally conformed to the customs of the country. They were indistinguishable from Canadian ranchers, to whom they taught the whole business. Many Canadian ranches, among them the 76, the Matador, the Turkey Track, and the T-Down-Bar, were simply Canadian extensions of cattle empires below the border.

So was the culture, in the anthropological sense, that accompanied the cattle. It was an adaptation to the arid Plains that had begun along the Rio Grande and had spread north, like gas expanding to fill a vacuum, as the buffalo and Indians were destroyed or driven out in the years following the Civil War. Like the patterns of hunting and war that had been adopted by every Plains tribe as soon as it acquired the horse, the cowboy culture made itself at home all the way from the Rio Grande to the North Saskatchewan. The outfit, the costume, the practices, the terminology, the state of mind, came into Canada ready-made, and nothing they encountered on the northern Plains enforced any real modifications. The Texas men made it certain that nobody would ever be thrown from a horse in Saskatchewan; he would be piled. They made it sure that no Canadian steer would ever be angry or stubborn; he would be o'nery or ringy or on the prod. Bull Durham was as native to the Whitemud range as to the Pecos, and it was used for the same purposes: smoking, eating, and spitting in the eye of a ringy steer. The Stetson was as useful north as south, could be used to fan the fire or dip up a drink from a stream, could shade a man's eyes or be clapped over the eyes of a bronc to gentle him down. Boots, bandanna, stock saddle, rope, the ways of busting broncs, the institution of the spring and fall roundup, the bowlegs in batwing or goatskin chaps—they all came north intact. About the only thing that changed was the name for the cowboy's favorite diversion, which down south they would have called a rodeo but which we called a stampede.

It was a nearly womanless culture, nomadic, harsh, dangerous, essentially romantic. It had the same contempt for the dirt-grubbers that Scythian and Cossack had, and Canadian tillers of the soil tended to look upon it with the same suspicion and fear and envy that tillers of the soil have always expressed toward the herdsmen. As we knew it, it had a lot of Confederate prejudices left in it, and it had the callousness and recklessness that a masculine life full of activity and adventure is sure to produce. I got it in my eyes like stardust almost as soon as we arrived in Whitemud, when the town staged its first stampede down in the western bend. Reno Dodds, known as Slivers, won the saddle bronc competition and set me up a model for my life. I would grow up to be about five feet six and weigh about a hundred and thirty pounds. I would be bowlegged and taciturn, with deep creases in my cheeks and a hide like stained saddle leather. I would be the quietest and most dangerous man around, best rider, best shot, the one who couldn't be buffaloed. Men twice my size, beginning some brag or other, would catch my cold eye and begin to wilt, and when I had stared them into impotence I would turn my back contemptuous, hook onto my pony in one bowlegged arc, and ride off. I thought it tremendous that anyone as small and skinny as Slivers could be a top hand and a champion rider. I don't think I could have survived without his example, and he was still on my mind years later when, sixteen years old and six feet tall and weighing a hundred and twenty-five pounds, I went every afternoon to the university gym and worked out on the weights for an hour and ran wind sprints around the track. If I couldn't be big I could be *hard.*

We hung around the Lazy-S corrals a good deal that first year or two, and the cowpunchers, when they had no one else to pester, would egg us into what they called dirt-fights, with green cow manure for snowballs; or they would put a surcingle around a calf and set us aboard. After my try I concluded that I would not do any more of it just at that time, and I limped to the fence and sat on the top rail nursing my sprains and bruises and smiling to keep from bawling out loud. From there I watched Spot Orullian, a Syrian boy a couple of years older than I, ride a wildly pitching whiteface calf clear around the corral and half-way around again, and get piled hard, and come up wiping the cow dung off himself, swearing like a pirate. They cheered him, he was a favorite at once, perhaps all the more because he had a big brown birthmark on his nose and so could be kidded. And I sat on the corral rail hunching my winglike shoulder-blades, smiling and smiling and smiling to conceal the black envy that I knew was just under the skin of my face. It was always boys like Spot Orullian who managed to be and do what I wanted to do and be.

Many things that those cowboys represented I would have done well to get over quickly, or never catch: the prejudice, the callousness, the destructive practical joking, the tendency to judge everyone by the same raw standard. Nevertheless, what they themselves most respected, and what as a boy I most yearned to grow up to, was as noble as it was limited. They honored courage, competence, self-reliance, and they honored them tacitly. They took them for granted. It was their absence, not their presence, that was cause for remark. Practicing comradeship in a rough and dangerous job, they lived a life calculated to make a man careless of everything except the few things he really valued.

## For Better Reading: Remembering a Frontier

Wallace Stegner grew up in Saskatchewan, Canada, on his family's home-stead near the Montana border. He subtitles his book *Wolf River*, "A History, a Story, and a Memory of the Last Plains Frontier."

Stegner writes that he has sometimes been tempted to believe that he grew up on a gun-toting frontier although during his boyhood that time was past. Yet he grew up around cowboys from cattle outfits in both Montana and Texas.

"In the American West men came before law, but in Saskatchewan the law was there before settlers, before even cattlemen, and not merely law but law enforcement," Stegner explains.

Men before law. Consider how that helped create the legends of the American West and form the character of the cowboy heroes who served as models for "Specifications for a Hero."

## Fact or Opinion

Tell which of the following should be accepted as fact and which as opinion.
1. Most of the nicknames Stegner and his friends gave each other were meant to be insulting.

2. Stegner became a braggart to cover his feelings of self-hatred and cowardice.
3. The Texas cowboys are perfect models for true legendary heroes.


## Questioning the Selection

1. After the accident at the cave, Preacher Kid "did not blame" and "did not tattle" on the other boys. What positive qualities was he displaying by this? Why would Stegner decide P.K.'s parents would not approve of P.K.'s "notions" of fortitude and propriety?
2. How did Stegner exhibit a special friendship for the Chinese cook, Mah Li? Why, then, would Stegner "have been ashamed not to take part in the teasing"? How did Mah Li respond to such treatment?
3. In this early "folk culture," the townspeople "picked" on anyone different—for example, those who felt themselves better than the rest, such as someone with an overdone English accent. Consider the various kinds of individuals that Stegner lists as victims of prejudice and persecution, and put them into three main categories, including "For Acting Superior."
4. What categories of people were immune from the persecution of the weak by the strong? What did the weak do in attempts to avoid or escape victimization?
5. In which category from question 3 would you place the "new teacher from Ontario?" Why was she safer from persecution than others?
6. What is the code of the "stiff upper lip"? How did Stegner's mother exhibit it? How did his father and mother differ in regard to their codes of behavior?
7. Why did Stegner "hate and fear" Alfie Carpenter? How did Alfie win the approval of Stegner's father?
8. What made Stegner a likely candidate for abuse? Explain how he attempted to protect himself and why his feat at the swimming hole came to nothing.
9. Name some elements of "cowboy culture," showing how it "made itself at home" across the Canadian border. For instance, the Canadians adopted American slang, using "o'nery" instead of "stubborn" and "piled" instead of "thrown" from a horse. Give two or three additional categories, including examples. In spite of having great influence on Canadian ways, how did the Americans "cheerfully" change their behavior north of the border?
10. What about Reno Dodds, known as Slivers, caused him to become a model to Stegner as a young boy? When Stegner became 16, why could he no longer hope to pattern himself exactly after Dodds?

# Looking Deeper
## I. Cowboy Culture

According to Stegner, the cowboys, with their limited code, honored three qualities: courage, competence, and self-reliance. Explain why each was important to a frontier existence. Considered individually, is each sufficiently valued today? Why or why not?

## II. The Strong vs. the Weak

Looking back as an adult, what bad elements does Stegner see in the frontier, cowboy culture? Have attitudes toward those who are weak or different changed for the better since frontier days? Support your answer with reasons and examples.

What kinds of interest were considered part of the "womanish world" when Stegner was a boy? Why might his liking for these things have contributed to his success as an adult? From the selection, give three examples of how the "weak" exhibited qualities that the cowboys honored.

## III. Life into Legend

Stegner was writing from first-hand knowledge about life on the frontier in the early twentieth century, yet cowboy characters have long been popular in fiction and film.

Based on the legends you've read in this unit, what characteristics would you emphasize and which would you play down or eliminate in order to portray American cowboys as true legendary heroes? If you have seen cowboy movies or read Western novels, such as those by Zane Grey or Louis L'Amour, explain how these compare to the cowboys portrayed by Wallace Stegner.

## REFLECTIONS

What does it take to make a legend? Do events create the legend, or does it take a special kind of individual to stand at a legend's center?

As you look back on the selections in this unit, decide what traits were most outstanding in each.

Can you imagine a folk hero who was a superhuman giant of a man, like Paul Bunyan, but cruel, not fair; dishonest, not honest; greedy, not generous? How are figures like this treated in legends? Why?

Yet even an outlaw like Jesse James can be a folk hero, so long as he's known to "rob the rich and give to the poor," like an earlier folk hero who probably comes to mind.

With the legendary hero and the folk hero, people tell, sing, hear, and read tales—sometimes tall ones—of truly "good guys," those with no flaws to mar their fame. And, though they are clearly too good to be true, do you agree they're needed?

## To Write About or to Discuss

1. Choose one admirable character trait, such as courage, self-reliance, or determination, and explain how it was exhibited by three different heroes or types of hero depicted in this unit.
2. Does everyone need a hero? Why or why not?
3. Movies and television, music, sports—do they present the images of good or bad heroes today? Choose one medium and evaluate its effects.
4. Choose a hero from another land or someone from more recent times, such as Malcolm X or Mother Teresa. Describe him or her briefly, then explain why your choice possesses the qualities of a legendary hero.

# UNIT 4

# A Question of Values

A NATIONWIDE SURVEY* ATTEMPTED TO discover how much Americans value television.

Twenty-three per cent of those polled said they'd agree to give up television permanently if paid $25,000.

A larger number, 46 per cent, declared that, for them, it would take at least $1 million to make them give up watching television.

And, 25 per cent declared they wouldn't give up television, even for a million dollars.

What's watching television worth to you?

Some people act on the belief that everything and everyone has its price. Others believe that there are some things money can't truly buy—such as love, loyalty, and friendship. For, they say, even if someone claims to have purchased another's loyalty, it can't be so. It's only a phony kind of loyalty—always up for sale and ready to be offered to the next, higher bidder.

That means it isn't loyalty at all.

But values concern more than money. What is important in someone's life, and how much is he or she willing to spend or sacrifice for it? Not just money, the cost can include time and effort, self-esteem and the opinion of others, and even one's life. All play a part in the questions of values that Americans in this unit find necessary to face.

* Conducted by *TV Guide* magazine, an AP story in *The Blade* (Toledo, Ohio), Monday, Oct. 5, 1992, p. 1.

# Junkie-Joe Had Some Money

## by Ronald Milner

| | |
|---|---|
| ***Born:*** | *Detroit, Michigan* |
| ***Attended:*** | *Columbia University* |
| ***Career:*** | *Playwright, theater founder and director, short story writer, teacher* |

JUNKIE-JOE HAD SOME MONEY. Nobody thought so—except those two big cats. Everybody thinks he was just a old, poor junkman—everybody but those two big cats, and me.

I mean, I *know* he had some money, I know it, I told them over and over, once—but they didn't believe me, and I'm glad they didn't.

I was just twelve, and asleep kinda', that's why they didn't believe me. When you're twelve nobody believes you know anything. And you don't know too much. You know just about what's good for you and what's not—like green apples and castor oil—and you know just about what's right and what's wrong. Sometimes you don't even know that much, and sometimes even when you know better you just go along with the rest.

I mean, like when the rest of the guys used to run after old Junkie-Joe and holler,

> Oo' JUNKIE-JOE,
>     AIN'T GOT
>         NO DOUGH!
> Oo' JUNKIE-JOE,
>     AIN'T GOT
>         NO PLACE TO GO!
> HE SLEEPS IN
>     A BARN
>         ON A
>             DIRTY
>                 OL'
>                     FLO'!,

I used to run and holler that too.

I mean, I used to go by the barn old Mr. Junkie-Joe lived in when I took a shortcut to my house, and I knew it was real clean on the inside, and I knew he had a bed, and I knew he was a nice old junkman, if you just let him alone. But I used to run and holler that anyway, because the rest of the boys did. And like he would chase you with sticks and things if you followed him hollering that, and that was something to do besides watching the big dudes play ball or something, so the guys used to run after him—me too, even though I knew better. Like I said, when you're twelve you usually go along with the bunch.

Only, there wasn't no bunch that time. I don't know how it happened—I don't remember that part too good—but that time I was by myself. And it was wintertime and snowing so there wasn't even no big studs on the street for me to watch. It was getting dark and cold, and about dinnertime, so I started home.

I took that shortcut I told you about before, through the alleys. And when I got close to Junkie-Joe's barn I saw that it was on fire. I mean, I saw the little window all bright orangey and the long funny moving shadows behind it, and I don't know, I just knew it was on fire inside.

I ran and I hollered, "Hey, Mr. Junkie-Joe! Hey, Mr. Junkie-Joe!" I remember that part good—running and hollering that.

And when I got to his door, it slid open—it was one of those sideways sliding kinds—and the first big cat, the skinny one who had all those dollars in his hand and mean, mean eyes, grabbed me and snatched me inside.

"What the—you doin' aroun' here?" he said, holding my neck too tight, his eyes real mad.

"I saw the fire! I saw the fire," I tried to tell him, but he was holding my neck too tight. I saw the other big cat, the one with the knife, and the blood all over his overcoat, putting Junkie-Joe's blanket over the little window, hurrying up because the fire was climbing all up the back wall and jumping at the ceiling.

"What the—did you have to bring yo' little ass in here for?" The big skinny cat with the mean eyes squeezed my neck so tight I couldn't cry; he pulled me and I bumped hard against his pockets—they were hard with change. He made a fist and gritted his teeth, I felt like I was going to do something on myself, but just then the fire went *whuff* on the ceiling and he looked back at the other big cat. I wanted to cry so bad I could have prayed to cry. He was holding my neck up and I saw the fire moving wild on the ceiling and it was like I was dreaming about Hell. I twisted around and saw the other big cat coming over, and when he stepped over him I saw Junkie-Joe. He was on the floor with his eyes and his mouth open, and blood all over his raggedy shirt, and all over the floor where he was laying—the fire made him look like he wasn't real. And there was blood all over the other big cat's coat. He pushed the skinny cat and grabbed me, it was like the devil had grabbed me, I just wanted to die.

"You had to be nosy, huh? You had to see, huh? Well, you won't see nothing else, little—" it was like his voice was the fire, and I saw the knife move out to the side, and his sleeve was all ugly slimy red, and all the front of his coat was slimy ugly red, and all I could see was the knife and the blood and I knew it was going to hurt, and I opened my mouth—but I couldn't holler to save my soul.

But the skinny cat grabbed him and pushed him. "Naw, man, naw, two of 'em make 'em wonder an' check up!" he hollered.

Then he grabbed me. "You know what'll happen if you tell anybody—anybody! yo' mama, anybody!—We'll cut you up an' burn you—understand!" He bumped me against the door.

My mouth was open, but I couldn't say nothing—he had the meanest eyes in the world—I just shook my head and tried to cry.

"An' if we ever get caught—ever!—our friends'll get you—understand?!" He bumped me on the door again.

"Naw, man, we gotta' do him too—now!" The other big cat pushed him and pulled me up against the sticky wet blood, it was on my face, and the fire was hotter than in Hell, I wanted to just close my eyes and throw up.

"Naw, he knows what'll happen if he tells just one word—one word! to any-body!—don't you?" The skinny cat shook one long finger by one of his mean eyes—I could see the dollars in his hand, the fire was burning my face. I guess I shook my head, because the door slid open, and they pushed me and kicked me in the butt.

I heard the door close, I heard them running away, but I didn't look back, I just ran—God! running never felt so good! And when I got between the houses I stopped and washed the blood off my face with snow—washed it! washed it! washed it! Then I ran home.

I didn't eat much. I didn't want to eat at all, but Mama would have asked questions—Daddy was at work, Mama kept looking at me while I tried to keep my head down and eat. She kept asking me if I felt good; then the fire sirens started and she went to the window. She went to the back door and I scraped my plate in the garbage and covered it up, and told her I was going to bed because I didn't feel too good. She just said okay because she was looking for the fire. I washed up quick and got in the bed. I closed my eyes tight and covered my ears, but I could still see the blood all over his raggedy shirt, and his eyes and mouth wide open, and I could still hear the sirens screaming and hollering, like somebody getting stabbed.

I didn't eat much breakfast the next day either—Mama was telling Daddy all about poor old Junkie-Joe getting burned up in the fire. I just ate a little and ran to school.

I ran home from school too, and then I couldn't be still, I ran back out. I ran all day, all around—I ran whenever I saw my bunch because I knew they would be talking about the fire, and I ran whenever I saw some big cats. I didn't eat much that night either.

And I didn't eat much the next day either; I just ran to school, and back and out again and all around.

I didn't eat much for a long time. I ran all the time, for a long time, all day, every day, in and out, all around, everywhere I could think of. Mama said she was worried about me because I was so fidgety, but Daddy said I was just growing and told me to be still sometimes.

But I couldn't be still, I just ran and ran, and then I'd slow down and walk because I didn't want people to think I was running from them, but I'd be running again before I knew it.

I was running from school one day and I fell down and couldn't get up.

The doctors at the hospital told Mama and Daddy that I had pneumonia. And for a long time I couldn't say nothing at all. But when I started getting a little better I told them over and over that Junkie-Joe had some money, but I was asleep kinda' and they didn't believe me.

I'm glad they didn't believe me, because I'm fourteen now, and those two big cats still look at me funny-like, quiet-like when they see me. And I keep asking my folks to move, and they keep saying that they don't have enough money for a house yet. I just turn away from them when they say that, because I don't care about money and a house, I just want to move away from here—right now! Junkie-Joe had some money, and a house—and you see what happened to him. Hell! I can't even sleep sometimes because he had some money and those two big cats knew it.

## For Better Reading: Inner Conflict

If it's My Side versus Your Side, it's often no problem to choose where you stand. When it's a question of values, the decision becomes far more difficult.

Because stories are about people, readers expect conflict. And, they usually side with the main character, often called the hero, though very far from perfect.

With certain conflicts, there's little question which side to take. It might be Individual vs. Nature, someone trying to conquer a mountain or battle a forest fire. Or, Individual vs. Individual, about a person opposing someone else's cruelty or greed. In such examples, the choice is clear. Go with the hero.

Another kind of conflict is Individual vs. Society. Although outnumbered, the main character takes a stand against the prejudiced or wrong-headed thinking of an entire social group. In fact, it sometimes seems there's only the reader to take the hero's side.

An inner conflict is Individual vs. Self, when a person is caught between conflicting values, interests, beliefs, and emotions. Concerning questions of right and wrong, the 12-year-old hero of this story says, "Sometimes you don't even know that much." So the reader shares the main character's self-doubts and concerns, the fears and hopes that come with questions of values.

To become more actively involved, weigh the reasons for and against the choices open to the main character. Doing so will help you appreciate the struggle arising from a conflict of values.

## Plot Order

Arrange the events in the order in which they actually occur, remembering that the story is told in a flashback.

a. The boy's parents don't believe what he keeps telling them about Junkie-Joe's money.
b. Junkie-Joe is robbed and killed.
c. The boy catches pneumonia.
d. By taking a shortcut, the boy discovers Junkie-Joe is actually nice.
e. The boy is warned to keep quiet.

## Questioning the Story

1. In the opening paragraphs, find proof that the story is being told after Junkie-Joe's murder. When the boy says, "They didn't believe me, and I'm glad . . . ," who is "they" and to what time is he referring?
2. At the beginning of the story, what did the boy do even though he "knew better"? Explain two possible reasons for his going against his own better nature.
3. Concerning the sing-song abuse hollered at Junkie-Joe, what part was incorrect? What true?
4. What portion of the verbal abuse would seem probably true at this time? Why?
5. Why did the boy arrive at the fire before everyone other than those directly involved? Which side of his nature—to do what's right or go along with others—controlled his first response? What proves his intentions?
6. How and why did the two killers differ about what they should do with the boy? What factor determined the final decision?
7. What threat did the killers use to guarantee the boy's silence? What proves this threat needed to be taken seriously? What part might have been bluff?
8. Why didn't the boy's parents immediately realize something was bothering their son terribly? Later, how did the father reply to the mother's concern? How do you explain his reaction?
9. Two years after the murder, what did the boy desire most? Why? How do his parents respond?

## Looking Deeper

### I. Living with Terror

By holding his lonely secret, how was the boy's life changed? If he had told the secret and been believed, what are two possible outcomes? In your opinion, is one possibility more likely, or are both equally probable? Have support for your answer.

## II. Living with a Decision

In the first paragraphs of this story, the author refers to "what's right and what's wrong." What do you believe was right in this situation? Why?

At both the beginning and end, the boy comments, "I'm glad they didn't believe me." Do you believe that he is really glad? Why or why not? Has keeping silent left the boy with a high or low opinion of himself? Use proof from the story in support of your answer. What good values does the boy exhibit throughout the story?

# El Zopilote

## by Alice Marriott

| | |
|---|---|
| **Born:** | *Wilmette, Illinois* |
| **Early life:** | *Moved to Oklahoma City at age 7* |
| **Career:** | *Librarian, Red Cross worker, field representative for US Department of Interior Indian arts and crafts board, author of stories, 20 books* |

THE BOY STOOD IN THE deserted Plaza, directing nonexistent traffic with free, swinging waves of his arms. At one end of the street was the Cathedral; at the other end the theater; and between them was the dime store, its window filled with holy statues of St. Francis, skull in hand. It was before this window that the boy had taken up his position.

In the dull, uncertain light of the moon, the boy's face itself might have been a skull. The great hollows below the cheekbones gave only a suggestion of flesh; the high bulge of the forehead had the white bareness of bone. Clothes hung on his body as if only bones supported them; there was no roundness of flesh beneath the rags that flapped in the wind made by their own waving.

So Father Riley first saw the boy, and so he always remembered him. The priest came from his quarters and crossed the street for the earliest mass. He had a dim awareness of the black-draped old women who were always regular communicants at this hour, but he had come in two months to accept those figures as a part of early winter mornings in a Spanish-American town. The boy was a new feature of the landscape, and in some odd way a frightening one.

Later in the day Father Riley saw the boy again. There had been a funeral; an old man, a member of one of the leading Spanish families, had been buried. As he left the Cathedral in the procession to the cemetery, Father Riley saw from the tail of his eye a skeleton figure of grotesque, ragged movement. With a swirl of arms and coat-tails, the boy swooped upon the funeral procession, establishing himself in a place just behind the bier and the eight men who carried it. There could be no doubt that he took, of deliberate intention, the place usually reserved for the chief mourner. Nor was there anyone in the family of the deceased who was disposed to dispute his possession of that place. Simply, the man's widow and daughters stepped back, and allowed the boy to precede them.

Because the dead man had been both famous and wealthy, the state police had sent an escort to head the procession to the *campo santo*. As a courtesy, they guided the priest's car back to the Cathedral. Father Riley, now without his robes, and with the gilt discharge button* showing on the shoulder of his cassock, found himself saluted by one of the motorcycle officers as he stepped out of the car.

"Where was you, Father?"

"Bataan. At first."

"Yeah. And later?"

"In the Philippines, Camp Sixty-Eight."

"My oldest brother was on Bataan. He died in the hospital there."

The Father nodded.

"Couple of years ago, I'd have said he was the lucky one."

"I miss him yet, though. Just cousins left now, mainly. Good to be back, Father?"

"Yes. Where were you?"

"E.T.O. We had it easy compared to you guys. Name's Garcia, Father. Sergeant Garcia, both places; here, too."

"Is this your home state? You don't speak like most of the people—" Hard to say tactfully, you look Spanish but you don't talk like one.

"I come from Las Cruces, down in the south part of the state. I got cousins up here, though. I went to Agriculture College down there."

"That's why you speak differently."

"Yeah, I guess so. They had a regular police college there, for a while. And I was with the MPs, overseas. We had a lot of northern boys in our outfit; Brooklyn, Boston, all them places. So I guess I learned to talk like them, some. Where you from, Father?"

"Boston, myself. Lots of the boys on Bataan were from New Mexico, though. So I got to know them, and it seems like home, here. They were all right."

"You ought to know, Father. You was with them long enough."

"Yes." An idea came to Father Riley. This man would not laugh at his question. He would accept curiosity as normal, in a fellow veteran. "Wonder if you can tell me something?"

"Try to." The policeman brought a pack of cigarettes from his pocket; hesitated a moment, and then offered them. Father Riley took one; waited for a match, and drew on the tobacco. "What's on your mind, Father?"

"A boy I wondered about. I saw him on the Plaza, this morning—"

"Directing traffic, like?"

"That's the one."

"Yeah." The policeman knocked the ash off his cigarette, carefully careless. "He come to the funeral, too."

"I thought I saw him there."

"Yeah. Well. He's a Spanish boy. Ain't got no father, and his mother died when he was born. His old grandmother brought him up, and then she died a year or

*worn as a sign of military service during World War II

182

so ago. He's got relatives, but he don't have much to do with them. He's kind of not right in the head, and he acts like he's all alone, since his grandma died. Thinks he's got no one to look out for him: He sort of lives on funerals."

"Lives on funerals?"

"Sure. I guess you don't know. A lot of these old-timey Spanish families, when they have a funeral, they have a big feast, too. So everybody comes. Even if the family's poor, and they got to owe the grocer for the next four months, they have a big funeral feast. *Velario,* they call it, like sitting up and watching with the corpse. So this boy, he goes around to the feast and eats, eats. Fills himself up. Seems like he knows, ahead of time. Sometimes even before the person dies, maybe."

"Like a buzzard."

"That's what we say. We call him that. *El Zopilote,* we say. That means buzzard in Spanish."

"But this morning he seemed to be directing traffic."

"Well, he does that, too. Seems to think he's the policeman in charge of the funeral. He's kind of crazy, Father."

"Couldn't he be taken care of? There must be institutions—there are in every state."

The policeman seemed embarrassed.

"He ain't hurting no one, see, Father? He's harmless. And he gets along, with the funerals, and what little help he takes from his people. There's enough funerals in this town to keep him going. And he's kind of a home-town boy, like. He don't bother nobody. What's the good of shutting him up? We keep an eye on him, so he don't get into no trouble, see?"

The priest nodded.

"Yes, I see that. But even if he hurts nobody, maybe it would be better for him to be taken care of."

"He makes out all right. Well, so long, Father. Got to get back on the job. Be seeing you." The man swung his leg over the bar of his motorcycle, kicked backward at the starter, and was gone with a roar and a rush. Father Riley turned indoors.

Being conscious of a man's existence makes you see him, Father Riley thought a week later. First he had become aware of the boy called *El Zopilote*; then of the young policeman. Now it seemed to him that he saw one or the other, or both of them, almost every day. Occasionally he saw them together. Once it was at the funeral of a state official. Garcia was directing traffic, briskly and efficiently, near the Cathedral, and *El Zopilote* stood behind him, following every move that the officer made. Even the blasts of Garcia's whistle brought corresponding puckers of the lips, and shrill toots, from the feeble-minded boy.

Once or twice Garcia came to the Chapter House, asking for Father Riley. The first time he seemed a little embarrassed.

"There's an old lady up on Goat Road, Father. My cousin's wife's been sort of looking after her. Seems like she's dying. Can you come?"

And the policeman was visibly relieved when the priest said, quietly, "Of course. That's my job."

They rode in a police car, formally, that time. But when Garcia came again, to take Father Riley to the scene of an automobile accident, they went on the motorcycle, with the siren screaming.

"He was pinned under when the gas tank blew up. We can't move him." That was all Garcia said then, but later he added, "Thanks, Father. I guess you're used to worse things than that."

Coming back from the wreck, they passed *El Zopilote*, standing at the entrance of the Plaza, swinging his arms. When the boy saw Garcia, he burst into a series of shrill, surprisingly metallic toots, made with his throat and tongue. For a minute Father Riley thought he actually was hearing a police whistle.

After a dozen calls made together, Father Riley began to feel that he knew Garcia's family. The policeman mentioned them occasionally: his cousin, the cousin's wife; their little girl, who seemed to be the center of the whole family. The policeman quoted her; Barbarita had said this or done that; when the child grew up she wanted to teach school and have a big dog; Barbarita had gone wading in the *acequia* behind the house, but had not caught cold. She was a healthy little girl, who didn't seem to get sick easily.

Once, coming back from a sick call, Garcia said,

"My cousin lives right down the street here. Why don't we stop by and drink coffee with them, Father?"

"Will it be all right?" the priest asked. "Won't it put your cousin's wife to too much trouble?"

"Sure not," Garcia said. "She always has the coffee on."

The cousin's wife greeted them with a smile, and a gesture into the room where she stood. She was a young woman, and very pretty; neat and clean as her spotless house. She seated them in a room that seemed to have been furnished from a women's magazine, except for the row of highly-colored plaster saints on the mantel.

"Where's Barbarita?" the policeman asked.

"Out playing in the yard," her mother answered. She stepped to the door and called to the child, who came running in. She was flushed from play; laughing at the sight of her cousin, and solemn when she saw the stranger with him.

"Say howdy to the Father," Garcia said, and the child put out her small hand, and said, "Howdy, Father," in an almost inaudible voice.

"How old is she?" Father Riley asked.

"Almost four," the mother told him.

"She's a big girl. My niece, my brother's child, is a year older, almost five, and she isn't much bigger."

The mother smiled.

"She drinks lots of milk. That's what makes her grow. She goes to the neighbor's every day, when they're milking, with her tin cup, and they fill it for her right from the cow, as many times as she can drink it."

"Some days she drinks five, six cups," Garcia put in.

"My," said Father Riley, impressed, "that's a lot of milk for a little girl."

"Sure it is," said the woman, "but it makes her grow big, like you see."

As summer came on, the priest found himself thinking often of Barbarita. The children of the Spanish seemed to die fast and easily. He was doing a good deal of parochial work; such tasks were often turned over to the younger men of the Chapter by the older fathers, and so it came about that Father Riley was often in families where there were sick or dying children. Sometimes there was a doctor in attendance; sometimes the family had decided against calling a physician, and had enlisted the help of some old neighbor woman who "knew about herbs."

As the weather warmed and the calls to sick children increased in number, Father Riley saw more and more of *El Zopilote*. Sometimes the boy would be hurrying toward a house the priest had just left; sometimes he would appear at a funeral. Often the scarecrow figure stood for hours in the Plaza, directing the summer's influx of out-of-state cars. Sometimes the strange drivers cursed the boy, when they confused his vocal blasts with a real police whistle, but their cursing made no difference to *El Zopilote*. He carried on his self-imposed task with complete seriousness; never stopping, and never speaking to anyone.

One can not feel fear or horror for an indefinite period. Sooner or later its own continuance destroys the emotion. So it was with the priest. The horror he had felt when he first saw *El Zopilote* merged with pity at the sight of the boy's tatters and the bones protruding through them. Father Riley could see the half-wit direct traffic without a shudder; finally without even notice. Only when he met the walking skeleton hurrying to a house he had himself just left, was Father Riley again aware of his first emotion.

Garcia, too, was busy with the out-of-state traffic. He always had time for a nod and a word when Father Riley passed near him, but these days he was always hurried with his greeting.

"Got to keep these damned *turistas* moving," he said once. "Excuse me, Father. But seems like I forget you're a priest sometimes, since I got to know you. Say, thanks for stopping to see old lady Vigil the other day. She sure appreciated it."

"That's all right," said Father Riley. "About the swearing, I mean. The Army makes that sound natural. And I like old lady Vigil. Anyway, I told you before, that's my job. How's Barbarita?"

"Not so good, these last two days," said Garcia. "Hey, you with the Ohio license, get over there! She's been kind of tired, or sick, or something. Didn't want to get up this morning."

"I'd better go by and see her," the priest said.

"Say," said Garcia, his face changing a little, "that'd sure be swell of you. My cousin's wife would appreciate that, all right. You do that if you can make it, Father."

It was late afternoon before Father Riley could. Then he turned in at the gate in the wall that surrounded the house, and knocked on the front door. The cousin's wife opened it, her own face tired and worried.

"Come in, Father," she said. "Barbarita will be glad to see you."

There could be no question that the child was ill. She lay in a crib, moved into the family living room for coolness. Her face was flushed, and her breath came short and quick.

"Have you had a doctor?" Father Riley asked, looking at her.

"Not yet," said the mother. "Do you think we ought to, Father? I've been giving her my grandmother's herb tea. She knew about herbs, my grandmother. She was a good one with them."

"I'd call a doctor," the priest advised her.

"My grandmother was good with herbs," the woman insisted. "I know all her prayers, too, Father. I been saying them at just the right times, when I was mixing and cooking and stirring and all. The herb tea seems to bring her fever down for a while, but then it goes right up again."

"Any hot drink will bring the fever down for a while," said Father Riley. "Hot water would do the same thing, and be better for her. Do you know how she got sick?"

"I don't know," said the woman helplessly. "There's been a lot of sickness around lately. Even the cow died the other day. Barbarita sure does miss her milk. Even as sick as she is, she cries for it when she wakes up. I got her milk from the store, but she don't like it. It don't taste the same. They cook it, someway."

"Pasteurize it," Father Riley said, automatically. "I'll stop by and send the doctor up on my way to the Chapter House, if you like."

"That's sure good of you, Father. We'd appreciate it. And, Father," the woman's fingers held the corner of her apron tightly, "will you pray for her, please, Father?"

"I've been doing that ever since I came in," said Father Riley sternly, and he left. Halfway down the hill he met *El Zopilote*, moving upward with jerky flutters of his rags. The Father walked faster. He wanted to catch the doctor before he left his office.

"Sure, I'll go," said the doctor, when the priest spoke to him. "But from what you tell me, it won't do much good. If the child's been sick from milk from a sick cow for about three days, you know as well as I do that it's more your case than mine, Father. These Spanish are all alike. They're ignorant, and they don't want to be any other way. But I'll go."

"Call me back about her, will you?" Father Riley asked, and the surprised doctor said, "Sure, if you want me to. You a friend of the family?"

"Yes," said Father Riley, slowly, "I guess that's it. A personal friend."

The doctor's call, when it came, was noncommittal.

"She may make it," he said. "Then again, she may not. It's hard to tell, right now. I've given her sulfa, and left more for the mother to give her. She may make it."

"That's good," answered Father Riley. He hesitated, then inquired, as easily as possible, "That half-wit boy, you know the one, was he there?"

"*El Zopilote?*" asked the doctor. "Sure he was. Sitting right outside on the wall, beside the gate. That's why I say she may not make it, too. He knows what's going to happen as often as I do."

It was one-thirty when the laybrother from the door awakened Father Riley. "There's a policeman downstairs asking for you, Father," he said.

"I'm coming," Father Riley told him. He was already feeling for his shoes.

Garcia's big, high-colored face was pale under the unshaded electric light. "She's sick, Father," was all he said. The motorcycle was waiting.

*El Zopilote* sat patiently on the wall in the moonlight. Garcia shivered and crossed himself as they passed the boy, and Father Riley nodded and repeated the gesture.

Inside, the house was a blaze of light. Women sat on the floor, still muffled in their shawls against the night and its sorrows. Every door and window was tightly closed; and in addition to the brightly-glowing chandelier, watchlights burned on the mantel shelf before the row of plaster saints. The crib was gone from the room, replaced by a big bed of curly maple. A man sat on the bed, holding the child in his arms, his legs straight out before him.

"That's my cousin," whispered Garcia.

Beside the bed, the door into the kitchen stood open. There were movements, there, of a dim crowd of men; the sound of their voices; heavier sighings than those of the women; and the clink of bottles against glasses. No one spoke above the murmuring of rosaries, as Father Riley stepped to the bed and bent over the sick child.

"She needs fresh air," he said. "Open the windows."

There was a wordless, protesting cry from the women. No one moved in either room.

"Sergeant!" Father Riley's voice cracked like a whistle cutting through the noise of traffic. "Open the window!"

"Yes, Captain," said Garcia, saluting, and he threw the window wide.

"Now, lay her down on the bed," said the priest, taking the child from her father's arms. Again came the wordless, protesting cry, as he stretched Barbarita on the bed.

"Bring warm water and bathe her," he ordered the mother.

"But she's so hot," the woman argued. "Cold water would cool her."

"Bathe her with warm water," said Father Riley.

"Aren't you going to pray, Father?" a man's voice asked from the kitchen doorway. Father Riley turned to face it.

"Prayer without works is dead," he said. "I'll pray, but someone must care for the child!"

Outside there was the long note of a police whistle, shrilling against the moon.

"Go and send that boy away," said Father Riley to Garcia, and without a word the policeman left the room.

"Now," said the priest to the mother, "you take care of Barbarita. Everybody who wants to pray, come outside with me."

Wordlessly, the crowd followed him out into the moonlight, and knelt as he did facing the open door of the house. Beyond the wall, *El Zopilote* leaped and fluttered in the street, shrilling his policeman's cry, in defiance of Garcia, who spoke fiercely to him.

"Go away," Garcia was saying, in Spanish. "Go away. Never come here again. We don't want you."

The boy drew off to the other side of the street, staring at the group kneeling in the yard. Father Riley began the Rosary of the Sorrows, and the people responded. As their voices rose higher and stronger, the skeleton figure withdrew to the shadows of the houses across the street. Then it melted into the darkness and quite vanished. The mother's figure appeared in the lighted doorway.

"She's alive, Father!" the woman cried. "She's alive, and the fever's gone, and she's sleeping!"

And it was true. Barbarita had turned on her side, tucked her fist under her cheek, and fallen into the honest sleep of any tired child.

Going back to the Chapter House on the motorcycle, neither Garcia nor Father Riley spoke. When they stopped, the priest found words.

"That boy must be sent away," he said. "He can't stay here any longer. He must go to the State Hospital."

"I guess so," Garcia agreed. "I sure hate to see him shut up, though. It's hard on them, and he's harmless."

"He isn't harmless if the sight of him scares people to death," said the priest. "He must go, Sergeant."

"Yes, sir," answered Garcia. "He's got to go. I hate to see him shut up, but I love Barbarita more. You see, Father, he's my little brother."

## For Better Reading: Determining Values

A priest, a policeman, and a crazy young boy.

Too often, the signs of someone's profession—a priest's habit or a police officer's badge—are assumed to automatically reveal the set of values that an individual represents and holds.

In this story, you discover that human doubts about values exist beneath outward appearances. Although one man is a priest and the other a policeman, it's essential to note the similarities, as well as the differences, between men who may seem opposites at first glance.

As you answer the questions, read carefully to discover the clues provided to show you the inner conflicts and values that lie behind the main characters' actions and words.

### Cause and Effect

1. Because he "lives on funerals," the boy is called *El Zopilote,* which in Spanish means (a) vampire (b) undertaker (c) vulture (d) ghoul.
2. At first, Father Riley is surprised that the policeman is Latino because of his (a) being a motorcycle officer (b) reddish brown hair (c) manner of speaking (d) having been to college.

3. Since the death of his grandmother a year earlier, the boy (a) has no close relatives (b) lives by begging from strangers (c) is seen as a danger to himself and others (d) acts crazy but does no real harm.

## Questioning the Story

1. How were the backgrounds of Father Riley and Sergeant Garcia alike? What on the priest's cassock made Garcia aware of this shared experience?
2. When Father Riley first asked about the boy, what feelings caused Garcia to make a "carefully careless" gesture before answering?
3. Instead of saying "he's all alone" and "he's got no one to look out for him," Garcia added the words "he acts like" before the first part and "thinks" before the second. In what way was Garcia carefully telling the truth yet also misleading Riley?
4. What did Father Riley believe should be done to or for *El Zopilote*? How did Garcia feel with regard to the priest's suggestion?
5. Why might Garcia be embarrassed when he first came to ask Father Riley to come with him? Explain the meaning behind the priest's saying, "Of course. That's my job." What is his job, and what does this answer show about his attitude and values?
6. What was Barbarita's relationship to Officer Garcia? Between the time Father Riley met the little girl and his summer visit, what change came over her?
7. After months had passed, how did Father Riley's feelings toward *El Zopilote* change? Why? When the priest meets the boy coming to a house he's leaving, what still affects him?
8. How do Father Riley and Barbarita's mother disagree on the best method for her treatment? How do they agree?
9. What clues lead Father Riley to suspect the cause of Barbarita's illness? What makes the doctor think the Mexican-Americans are ignorant and superstitious? In spite of treating Barbarita with the medicinal drug, sulfa, why did the doctor guess "she may not make it"? What does this show about the doctor himself, and why is it ironic?
10. What steps did Father Riley take to help the sick child, after Garcia came for him at 1:30 in the morning? What action did Garcia take toward *El Zopilote*, and how did the boy respond?

## Looking Deeper
### I. A Clash of Loyalties

For Sergeant Garcia, what were three reasons against having *El Zopilote* put in an institution? What do you feel was the main reason and why? By the end of the story, why did Garcia change his mind?

Why did Father Riley believe the boy responsible for causing harm, even though it was unintentional?

## II. Adding up the Clues

At the beginning of the story, *El Zopilote* is introduced "directing nonexistent traffic." This is just one of the clues to the crazy boy's relationship to his brother. Another is, "he burst into a series of shrill, surprisingly metallic toots" that make Father Riley think he "actually was hearing a police whistle." Find two or three additional examples.

What do these examples reveal about the crazy or feeble-minded boy's feelings towards his older brother? How does this explain the boy's reaction when Garcia "spoke fiercely to him"? Although Garcia said his love for Barbarita was his primary concern, how will other people in the community also be affected by having *El Zopilote* put in an institution? Do you believe that Garcia was right to agree that *El Zopilote* "must be sent away"? Why or why not?

# The Would-Be Emigrant

*Anonymous*

"Since times are so hard, I've thought, my true heart,
Of leaving my oxen, my plough, and my cart,
And away to Wisconsin, a journey we'd go
To double our fortune as other folks do.
While here I must labor each day in the field          5
And the winter consumes all the summer doth yield."

"Oh husband, I've noticed with sorrowful heart
You've neglected your oxen, your plough, and your cart,
Your sheep are disordered; at random they run,
And your new Sunday suit is now every day on.          10
Oh, stay on the farm and you'll suffer no loss,
For the stone that keeps rolling will gather no moss."

"Oh wife, let's go. Oh, don't let us wait.
Oh, I long to be there. Oh, I long to be great!
While you some rich lady—and who knows but I          15
Some governor may be before that I die?
While here I must labor each day in the field,
And winter consumes all the summer doth yield."

"Oh husband, remember that land is to clear,
Which will cost you the labor of many a year,          20
Where horses, sheep, cattle, and hogs are to buy—
And you'll scarcely get settled before you must die.
Oh, stay on your farm and you'll suffer no loss,
For the stone that keeps rolling will gather no moss."

"Oh wife, let's go. Oh, don't let us stay.          25
I will buy me a farm that is cleared by the way,
Where horses, sheep, cattle, and hogs are not dear,
And we'll feast on fat buffalo half of the year.

While here I must labor each day in the field,
And the winter consumes all the summer doth yield." 30

"Oh husband, remember, that land of delight
Is surrounded by Indians who murder by night.
Your house they will plunder and burn to the ground,
While your wife and your children lie murdered around.
Oh, stay on the farm, and you'll suffer no loss, 35
For the stone that keeps rolling will gather no moss."

"Now, wife, you've convinced me. I'll argue no more.
I never had thought of your dying before;
I love my dear children, although they are small,—
But you, my dear wife, are more precious than all. 40
We'll stay on the farm, and suffer no loss
For the stone that keeps rolling will gather no moss."

# For Better Reading: The Folk Ballad

Folk ballads are poems of the people. Like the tales of Paul Bunyan, these ballads were told and retold, often acquiring changes and additions as they were passed from person to person by word of mouth.

As a result, the origins of folk ballads are anonymous, and people's favorites frequently have several versions.

Like many folk ballads, "The Would-Be Emigrant" is told completely in dialogue, with clear clues that alert you to each change of speaker.

Repetition is also a frequent element of folk ballads. Because of their impact, repeated words are a valuable key to the underlying ideas in this American folk ballad, concerning a question of values and a family's future.

## Questioning the Poem

1. Who are the speakers in this poem and in what order do they speak? In the printed version, what are three clues to a change of speaker?
2. Why does the farmer wish to emigrate and move further west? Where does he wish to settle?
3. What change has the wife noticed in her husband's management of the farm? What about his manner of dressing disturbs her? What might this indicate?
4. What hopes does the farmer express for both his wife's and his own future in a new place?
5. According to the wife, in stanza four, what two kinds of "costs" must the farmer pay to build a new farm? How far ahead does she look?

6. How does the farmer answer his wife's objections? Is he being realistic? Support your answer from the poem.
7. What final factor does the wife introduce to convince her husband? To what in his nature does she appeal?

## Looking Deeper

### I. The Power of Repetition

How do the two lines, repeated three times by the farmer, explain his frustration? What clues do they give to the possible location of his present farm, considering his wish to emigrate?

The wife repeats a version of the adage, "A rolling stone gathers no moss." Although you may not be able to interpret it exactly, explain why her husband and his plans make him deserve this comparison?

How does the pattern of repetition change in the final stanza? What does this signify?

### II. Cause and Effect

In her first two efforts to convince her husband, did the wife seem more concerned about his welfare or about her own and the children's? Use details from the stanzas as support.

In the first three stanzas spoken by the farmer, does he seem indifferent to his wife's welfare or not? Support your answer.

By changing his mind, what is the farmer shown to value most? Considering the entire poem and the family's situation, do you agree that he made the right decision? Why or why not? Do you believe the farmer weak for changing his mind or strong for placing his family first? Explain your reasoning.

# The English Lesson

## by Nicholasa Mohr

| | |
|---|---|
| **Born:** | New York, NY |
| **Career:** | Fine arts painter, art instructor, head writer and co-producer of television series, novelist, short story writer and illustrator |
| **Has lived in:** | California, Mexico, Puerto Rico, New Jersey, New Hampshire, and New York |

"**R**EMEMBER OUR ASSIGNMENT FOR TODAY everybody! I'm so confident that you will all do exceptionally well!" Mrs. Susan Hamma smiled enthusiastically at her students. "Everyone is to get up and make a brief statement as to why he or she is taking this course in Basic English. You must state your name, where you originally came from, how long you have been here, and . . . uh . . . a little something about yourself, if you wish. Keep it brief, not too long; remember, there are twenty-eight of us. We have a full class, and everyone must have a chance." Mrs. Hamma waved a forefinger at her students. "This is, after all, a democracy, and we have a democratic class; fairness for all!"

Lali grinned and looked at William, who sat directly next to her. He winked and rolled his eyes toward Mrs. Hamma. This was the third class they had attended together. It had not been easy to persuade Rudi that Lali should learn better English.

"Why is it necessary, eh?" Rudi had protested. "She works here in the store with me. She don't have to talk to nobody. Besides, everybody that comes in speaks Spanish—practically everybody, anyway."

But once William had put the idea to Lali and explained how much easier things would be for her, she kept insisting until Rudi finally agreed. "Go on, you're both driving me nuts. But it can't interfere with business or work—I'm warning you!"

Adult Education offered Basic English, Tuesday evenings from 6:30 to 8:00, at a local public school. Night customers did not usually come into Rudi's Luncheonette until after eight. William and Lali promised that they would leave everything prepared and make up for any inconvenience by working harder and longer than usual, if necessary.

The class admitted twenty-eight students, and because there were only twenty-seven registered, Lali was allowed to take the course even after missing the first two classes. William had assured Mrs. Hamma that he would help Lali catch up; she was glad to have another student to make up the full registration.

Most of the students were Spanish-speaking. The majority were American citizens—Puerto Ricans who had migrated to New York and spoke very little English. The rest were immigrants admitted to the United States as legal aliens. There were several Chinese, two Dominicans, one Sicilian, and one Pole.

Every Tuesday Mrs. Hamma traveled to the Lower East Side from Bayside, Queens, where she lived and was employed as a history teacher in the local junior high school. She was convinced that this small group of people desperately needed her services. Mrs. Hamma reiterated her feelings frequently to just about anyone who would listen. "Why, if these people can make it to class after working all day at those miserable, dreary, uninteresting, and often revolting jobs, well, the least I can do is be there to serve them, making every lesson count toward improving their conditions! My grandparents came here from Germany as poor immigrants, working their way up. I'm not one to forget a thing like that!"

By the time class started most of the students were quite tired. And after the lesson was over, many had to go on to part-time jobs, some even without time for supper. As a result there was always sluggishness and yawning among the students. This never discouraged Mrs. Hamma, whose drive and enthusiasm not only amused the class but often kept everyone awake.

"Now this is the moment we have all been preparing for." Mrs. Hamma stood up, nodded, and blinked knowingly at her students. "Five lessons, I think, are enough to prepare us for our oral statements. You may read from prepared notes, as I said before, but please try not to read every word. We want to hear you speak; conversation is what we're after. When someone asks you about yourself, you cannot take a piece of paper and start reading the answers, now can you? That would be foolish. So ..."

Standing in front of her desk, she put her hands on her hips and spread her feet, giving the impression that she was going to demonstrate calisthenics.

"Shall we begin?"

Mrs. Hamma was a very tall, angular woman with large extremities. She was the tallest person in the room. Her eyes roamed from student to student until they met William's.

"Mr. Colón, will you please begin?"

Nervously William looked around him, hesitating.

"Come on now, we must get the ball rolling. All right now ... did you hear what I said? Listen, 'getting the ball rolling' means getting started. Getting things going, such as—" Mrs. Hamma swiftly lifted her right hand over her head, making a fist, then swung her arm around like a pitcher and, with an underhand curve, forcefully threw an imaginary ball out at her students. Trying to maintain her balance, Mrs. Hamma hopped from one leg to the other. Startled, the students looked at one another. In spite of their efforts to restrain themselves, several people in back began to giggle. Lali and William looked away, avoiding each other's eyes and trying not to laugh out loud. With assured countenance, Mrs. Hamma continued.

"An idiom!" she exclaimed, pleased. "You have just seen me demonstrate the meaning of an idiom. Now I want everyone to jot down this information in his notebook." Going to the blackboard, Mrs. Hamma explained, "It's something which literally says one thing, but actually means another. Idiom . . . idiomatic." Quickly and obediently, everyone began to copy what she wrote. "Has everyone got it? OK, let's GET THE BALL ROLLING, Mr. Colón!"

Uneasily William stood up; he was almost the same height standing as sitting. When speaking to others, especially in a new situation, he always preferred to sit alongside those listening; it gave him a sense of equality with other people. He looked around and cleared his throat; at least everyone else was sitting. Taking a deep breath, William felt better.

"My name is William Horacio Colón," he read from a prepared statement. "I have been here in New York City for five months. I coming from Puerto Rico. My town is located in the mountains in the central part of the island. The name of my town is Aibonito, which means in Spanish 'oh how pretty.' It is name like this because when the Spaniards first seen that place they was very impressed with the beauty of the section and—"

"Make it brief, Mr. Colón," Mrs. Hamma interrupted, "there are others, you know."

William looked at her, unable to continue.

"Go on, go on, Mr. Colón, please!"

"I am working here now, living with my mother and family in Lower East Side of New York City," William spoke rapidly. "I study Basic English por que . . . because my ambition is to learn to speak and read English very good. To get a better job. Y—y también, to help my mother y familia." He shrugged. "Y do better, that's all."

"That's all? Why, that's wonderful! Wonderful! Didn't he do well, class?" Mrs. Hamma bowed slightly toward William and applauded him. The students watched her and slowly each one began to imitate her. Pleased, Mrs. Hamma looked around her; all together they gave William a healthy round of applause.

Next, Mrs. Hamma turned to a Chinese man seated at the other side of the room.

"Mr. Fong, you may go next."

Mr. Fong stood up; he was a man in his late thirties, of medium height and slight build. Cautiously he looked at Mrs. Hamma, and waited.

"Go on, Mr. Fong. Get the ball rolling, remember?"

"All right. Get a ball rolling . . . is idiot!" Mr. Fong smiled.

"No, Mr. Fong, idio*mmmmmm!*" Mrs. Hamma hummed her *m*'s, shaking her head. "Not an—It's idiomatic!"

"What I said!" Mr. Fong responded with self-assurance, looking directly at Mrs. Hamma. "Get a ball rolling, idiomit."

"Never mind." She cleared her throat. "Just go on."

"I said OK?" Mr. Fong waited for an answer.

"Go on, please."

Mr. Fong sighed, "My name is Joseph Fong. I been here in this country United States New York City for most one year." He too read from a prepared statement. "I come from Hong Kong but original born in city of Canton, China. I working delivery food business and live with my brother and his family in Chinatown. I taking the course in Basic English to speak good and improve my position better in this country. Also to be eligible to become American citizen."

Mrs. Hamma selected each student who was to speak from a different part of the room, rather than in the more conventional orderly fashion of row by row, or front to back, or even alphabetical order. This way, she reasoned, no one will know who's next; it will be more spontaneous. Mrs. Hamma enjoyed catching the uncertain looks on the faces of her students. A feeling of control over the situation gave her a pleasing thrill, and she made the most of these moments by looking at several people more than once before making her final choice.

There were more men than women, and Mrs. Hamma called two or three men for each woman. It was her way of maintaining a balance. To her distress, most read from prepared notes, despite her efforts to discourage this. She would interrupt them when she felt they went on too long, then praise them when they finished. Each statement was followed by applause from everyone.

All had similar statements. They had migrated here in search of a better future, were living with relatives, and worked as unskilled laborers. With the exception of Lali, who was childless, every woman gave the ages and sex of her children; most men referred only to their "family." And, among the legal aliens, there was only one who did not want to become an American citizen, Diego Torres, a young man from the Dominican Republic, and he gave his reasons.

" . . . and to improve my economic situation." Diego Torres hesitated, looking around the room. "But is one thing I no want and is to become American citizen"—he pointed to an older man with a dark complexion, seated a few seats away—"like my fellow countryman over there!" The man shook his head disapprovingly at Diego Torres, trying to hide his annoyance. "I no give up my country, Santo Domingo, for nothing," he went on, "nothing in the whole world. OK, man? I come here, pero I cannot help. I got no work at home. There, is political. The United States control most the industry which is sugar and tourismo. Y—you have to know somebody. I tell you, is political to get a job, man! You don't know nobody and you no work, eh? So I come here from necessity, pero this no my country—"

"Mr. Torres," Mrs. Hamma interrupted, "we must be brief, please, there are—"

"I no finish lady!" he snapped. "You wait a minute when I finish!"

There was complete silence as Diego Torres glared at Susan Hamma. No one had ever spoken to her like that, and her confusion was greater than her embarrassment. Without speaking, she lowered her eyes and nodded.

"OK, I prefer live feeling happy in my country, man. Even I don't got too much. I live simple but in my own country I be contento. Pero this is no possible in the situation of Santo Domingo now. Someday we gonna run our own country and be jobs for everybody. My reasons to be here is to make money, man, and go back home buy my house and property. I no be American citizen, no way.

I'm Dominican and proud! That's it. That's all I got to say." Abruptly, Diego Torres sat down.

"All right." Mrs. Hamma had composed herself. "Very good; you can come here and state your views. That is what America is all about! We may not agree with you, but we defend your right to an opinion. And as long as you are in this classroom, Mr. Torres, you are in America. Now, everyone, let us give Mr. Torres the same courtesy as everyone else in this class." Mrs. Hamma applauded with a polite light clap, then turned to find the next speaker.

"Bullshit," whispered Diego Torres.

Practically everyone had spoken. Lali and the two European immigrants were the only ones left. Mrs. Hamma called upon Lali.

"My name is Rogelia Dolores Padillo. I come from Canovanas in Puerto Rico. Is a small village in the mountains near El Yunque Rain Forest. My family is still living there. I marry and live here with my husband working in his business of restaurant. Call Rudi's Luncheonette. I been here New York City Lower East Side since I marry, which is now about one year. I study Basic English to improve my vocabulario and learn more about here. This way I help my husband in his business and I do more also for myself, including to be able to read better in English. Thank you."

Aldo Fabrizi, the Sicilian, spoke next. He was a very short man, barely five feet tall. Usually he was self-conscious about his height, but William's presence relieved him of these feelings. Looking at William, he thought being short was no big thing; he was, after all, normal. He told the class that he was originally from Palermo, the capital of Sicily, and had gone to Milano, in the north of Italy, looking for work. After three years in Milano, he immigrated here six months ago and now lived with his sister. He had a good steady job, he said, working in a copper wire factory with his brother-in-law in Brooklyn. Aldo Fabrizi wanted to become an American citizen and spoke passionately about it, without reading from his notes.

"I be proud to be American citizen. I no come here find work live good and no have responsibility or no be grateful." He turned and looked threateningly at Diego Torres. "Hey? I tell you all one thing, I got my nephew right now fighting in Vietnam for this country!" Diego Torres stretched his hands over his head, yawning, folded his hands, and lowered his eyelids. "I wish I could be citizen to fight for this country. My whole family is citizens—we all Americans and we love America!" His voice was quite loud. "That's how I feel."

"Very good," Mrs. Hamma called, distracting Aldo Fabrizi. "That was well stated. I'm sure you will not only become a citizen, but you will also be a credit to this country."

The last person to be called on was the Pole. He was always neatly dressed in a business suit, with a shirt and tie, and carried a briefcase. His manner was reserved but friendly.

"Good evening fellow students and Madame Teacher." He nodded politely to Mrs. Hamma. "My name is Stephan Paczkowski. I am originally from Poland about four months ago. My background is I was born in capital city of Poland,

Warsaw. Being educated in capital and also graduating from the University with degree of professor of music with specialty in the history of music."

Stephan Paczkowski read from his notes carefully, articulating every word. "I was given appointment of professor of history of music at University of Krakow. I work there for ten years until about year and half ago. At this time the political situation in Poland was so that all Jewish people were requested by the government to leave Poland. My wife who also is being a professor of economics at University of Krakow is of Jewish parents. My wife was told she could not remain in position at University or remain over there. We made arrangements for my wife and daughter who is seven years of age and myself to come here with my wife's cousin who is to be helping us.

"Since four months I am working in large hospital as position of porter in maintenance department. The thing of it is, I wish to take Basic English to improve my knowledge of English language, and be able to return to my position of professor of history of music. Finally, I wish to become a citizen of United States. That is my reasons. I thank you all."

After Stephan Paczkowski sat down, there was a long awkward silence and everyone turned to look at Mrs. Hamma. Even after the confrontation with Diego Torres, she had applauded without hesitation. Now she seemed unable to move.

"Well," she said, almost breathless, "that's admirable! I'm sure, sir, that you will do very well . . . a person of your . . . like yourself, I mean . . . a professor, after all, it's really just admirable." Everyone was listening intently to what she said. "That was well done, class. Now, we have to get to next week's assignment." Mrs. Hamma realized that no one had applauded Stephan Paczkowski. With a slightly pained expression, she began to applaud. "Mustn't forget Mr. Paczkowski; everybody here must be treated equally. This is America!" The class joined her in a round of applause.

As Mrs. Hamma began to write the next week's assignment on the board, some students looked anxiously at their watches and others asked about the time. Then they all quickly copied the information into their notebooks. It was almost eight o'clock. Those who had to get to second jobs did not want to be late; some even hoped to have time for a bite to eat first. Others were just tired and wanted to get home.

Lali looked at William, sighing impatiently. They both hoped Mrs. Hamma would finish quickly. There would be hell to pay with Rudi if the night customers were already at the luncheonette.

"There, that's next week's work, which is very important, by the way. We will be looking at the history of New York City and the different ethnic groups that lived here as far back as the Dutch. I can't tell you how proud I am of the way you all spoke. All of you—I have no favorites, you know."

Mrs. Hamma was interrupted by the long, loud buzzing sound, bringing the lesson to an end. Quickly everyone began to exit.

"Good night, see you all next Tuesday!" Mrs. Hamma called out. "By the way, if any of you here wants extra help, I have a few minutes this evening." Several people bolted past her, excusing themselves. In less than thirty seconds, Mrs. Hamma was standing in an empty classroom.

William and Lali hurried along, struggling against the cold, sharp March wind that whipped across Houston Street, stinging their faces and making their eyes tear.

In a few minutes they would be at Rudi's. So far, they had not been late once.

"You read very well—better than anybody in class. I told you there was nothing to worry about. You caught up in no time."

"Go on. I was so nervous, honestly! But, I'm glad she left me for one of the last. If I had to go first, like you, I don't think I could open my mouth. You were so calm. You started the thing off very well."

"You go on now, I was nervous myself!" He laughed, pleased.

"Mira, Chiquitín," Lali giggled, "I didn't know your name was Horacio. William Horacio. Ave Maria, so imposing!"

"That's right, because you see, my mother was expecting a valiant warrior! Instead, well"—he threw up his hands—"no one warned me either. And what a name for a Chiquitín like me."

Lali smiled, saying nothing. At first she had been very aware of William's dwarfishness. Now it no longer mattered. It was only when she saw others reacting to him for the first time that she was once more momentarily struck with William's physical difference.

"We should really try to speak in English, Lali. It would be good practice for us."

"Dios mío . . . I feel so foolish, and my accent is terrible!"

"But look, we all have to start some place. Besides, what about the Americanos? When they speak Spanish, they sound pretty awful, but we accept it. You know I'm right. And that's how people get ahead, by not being afraid to try."

They walked in silence for a few moments. Since William had begun to work at Rudi's, Lali's life had become less lonely. Lali was shy by nature; making friends was difficult for her. She had grown up in the sheltered environment of a large family living in a tiny mountain village. She was considered quite plain. Until Rudi had asked her parents for permission to court her, she had only gone out with two local boys. She had accepted his marriage proposal expecting great changes in her life. But the age difference between her and Rudi, being in a strange country without friends or relatives, and the long hours of work at the luncheonette confined Lali to a way of life she could not have imagined. Every evening she found herself waiting for William to come in to work, looking forward to his presence.

Lali glanced over at him as they started across the wide busy street. His grip on her elbow was firm but gentle as he led her to the sidewalk.

"There you are, Miss Lali, please to watch your step!" he spoke in English.

His thick golden-blond hair was slightly mussed and fell softly, partially covering his forehead. His wide smile, white teeth, and large shoulders made him appear quite handsome. Lali found herself staring at William. At that moment she wished he could be just like everybody else.

"Lali?" William asked, confused by her silent stare. "Is something wrong?"

"No." Quickly Lali turned her face. She felt herself blushing. "I . . . I was just thinking how to answer in English, that's all."

"But that's it ... don't think! What I mean is, don't go worrying about what to say. Just talk natural. Get used to simple phrases and the rest will come, you'll see."

"All right," Lali said, glad the strange feeling of involvement had passed, and William had taken no notice of it. "It's an interesting class, don't you think so? I mean—like that man, the professor. Bendito! Imagine, they had to leave because they were Jewish. What a terrible thing!"

"I don't believe he's Jewish; it's his wife who is Jewish. She was a professor too. But I guess they don't wanna be separated ... and they have a child."

"Tsk, tsk, los pobres! But, can you imagine, then? A professor from a university doing the job of a porter? My goodness!" Lali sighed. "I never heard of such a thing!"

"But you gotta remember, it's like Mrs. Hamma said, this is America, right? So ... everybody got a chance to clean toilets! Equality, didn't she say that?"

They both laughed loudly, stepping up their pace until they reached Rudi's Luncheonette.

The small luncheonette was almost empty. One customer sat at the counter.

"Just in time," Rudi called out. "Let's get going. People gonna be coming in hungry any minute. I was beginning to worry about you two!"

William ran in the back to change into his workshirt.

Lali slipped into her uniform and soon was busy at the grill.

"Well, did you learn anything tonight?" Rudi asked her.

"Yes."

"What?"

"I don't know," she answered, without interrupting her work. "We just talked a little bit in English."

"A little bit in English—about what?"

Lali busied herself, ignoring him. Rudi waited, then tried once more.

"You remember what you talked about?" He watched her as she moved, working quickly, not looking in his direction.

"No." Her response was barely audible.

Lately Rudi had begun to reflect on his decision to marry such a young woman. Especially a country girl like Lali, who was shy and timid. He had never had children with his first wife and wondered if he lacked the patience needed for the young. They had little in common and certainly seldom spoke about anything but the business. Certainly he could not fault her for being lazy; she was always working without being asked. People would accuse him in jest of overworking his young wife. He assured them there was no need, because she had the endurance of a country mule. After almost one year of marriage, he felt he hardly knew Lali or what he might do to please her.

William began to stack clean glasses behind the counter.

"Chiquitín! How about you and Lali having something to eat? We gotta few minutes yet. There's some fresh rice pudding."

"Later ... I'll have mine a little later, thanks."

"Ask her if she wants some," Rudi whispered, gesturing toward Lali.

William moved close to Lali and spoke softly to her.

"She said no." William continued his work.

"Listen, Chiquitín, I already spoke to Raquel Martinez who lives next door. You know, she's got all them kids? In case you people are late, she can cover for you and Lali. She said it was OK."

"Thanks, Rudi, I appreciate it. But we'll get back on time."

"She's good, you know. She helps me out during the day whenever I need extra help. Off the books, I give her a few bucks. But, mira, I cannot pay you and Raquel both. So if she comes in, you don't get paid. You know that then, OK?"

"Of course. Thanks, Rudi."

"Sure, well, it's a good thing after all. You and Lali improving yourselves. Not that she really needs it, you know. I provide for her. As I said, she's my wife, so she don't gotta worry. If she wants something, I'll buy it for her. I made it clear she didn't have to bother with none of that, but"—Rudi shrugged—"if that's what she wants, I'm not one to interfere."

The door opened. Several men walked in.

"Here they come, kids!"

Orders were taken and quickly filled. Customers came and went steadily until about eleven o'clock, when Rudi announced that it was closing time.

The weeks passed, then the months, and this evening, William and Lali sat with the other students listening to Mrs. Hamma as she taught the last lesson of the Basic English course.

"It's been fifteen long hard weeks for all of you. And I want you to know how proud I am of each and every one here."

William glanced at Lali; he knew she was upset. He felt it too, wishing that this was not the end of the course. It was the only time he and Lali had free to themselves together. Tuesday had become their evening.

Lali had been especially irritable that week, dreading this last session. For her, Tuesday meant leaving the world of Rudi, the luncheonette, that street, everything that she felt imprisoned her. She was accomplishing something all by herself, and without the help of the man she was dependent upon.

Mrs. Hamma finally felt that she had spent enough time assuring her students of her sincere appreciation.

"I hope some of you will stay and have a cup of coffee or tea, and cookies. There's plenty over there." She pointed to a side table where a large electric coffeepot filled with hot water was steaming. The table was set for instant coffee and tea, complete with several boxes of assorted cookies. "I do this every semester for my classes. I think it's nice to have a little informal chat with one another; perhaps discuss our plans for the future and so on. But it must be in English! Especially those of you who are Spanish-speaking. Just because you outnumber the rest of us, don't you think you can get away with it!" Mrs. Hamma lifted her forefinger threateningly but smiled. "Now, it's still early, so there's plenty of time left. Please turn in your books."

Some of the people said good-bye quickly and left, but the majority waited, helping themselves to coffee or tea and cookies. Small clusters formed as people began to chat with one another.

Diego Torres and Aldo Fabrizi were engaged in a friendly but heated debate on the merits of citizenship.

"Hey, you come here a minute, please," Aldo Fabrizi called out to William, who was standing with a few people by the table, helping himself to coffee. William walked over to the two men.

"What's the matter?"

"What do you think of your paisano. He don't wanna be citizen. I say—my opinion—he don't appreciate what he got in this country. This a great country! You the same like him, what do you think?"

"Mira, please tell him we no the same," Diego Torres said with exasperation. "You a citizen, pero not me. Este tipo no comprende, man!"

"Listen, you comprendo ... yo capito! I know what you say. He be born in Puerto Rico. But you see, we got the same thing. I be born in Sicily—that is another part of the country, separate. But I still Italiano, capito?"

"Dios mio!" Diego Torres smacked his forehead with an open palm. "Mira"—he turned to William—"explain to him, por favor."

William swallowed a mouthful of cookies. "He's right. Puerto Rico is part of the United States. And Sicily is part of Italy. But not the Dominican Republic where he been born. There it is not the United States. I was born a citizen, do you see?"

"Sure!" Aldo Fabrizi nodded. "Capito. Hey, but you still no can vote, right?"

"Sure I can vote; I got all the rights. I am a citizen, just like anybody else," William assured him.

"You some lucky guy then. You got it made! You don't gotta worry like the rest of—"

"Bullshit," Diego Torres interrupted. "Why he got it made, man? He force to leave his country. Pendejo, you no capito nothing, man ..."

As the two men continued to argue, William waited for the right moment to slip away and join Lali.

She was with some of the women, who were discussing how sincere and devoted Mrs. Hamma was.

"She's hardworking ..."

"And she's good people ..." an older woman agreed.

Mr. Fong joined them, and they spoke about the weather and how nice and warm the days were.

Slowly people began to leave, shaking hands with their fellow students and Mrs. Hamma, wishing each other luck.

Mrs. Hamma had been hoping to speak to Stephan Paczkowski privately this evening, but he was always with a group. Now he offered his hand.

"I thank you very much for your good teaching. It was a fine semester."

"Oh, do you think so? Oh, I'm so glad to hear you say that. You don't know how much it means. Especially coming from a person of your caliber. I am confident, yes, indeed, that you will soon be back to your profession, which, after all, is your true calling. If there is anything I can do, please ..."

"Thank you, miss. This time I am registering in Hunter College, which is in Manhattan on Sixty-eighth Street in Lexington Avenue, with a course of English Literature for beginners." After a slight bow, he left.

"Good-bye." Mrs. Hamma sighed after him.

Lali, William, and several of the women picked up the paper cups and napkins and tossed them into the trash basket.

"Thank you so much, that's just fine. Luis the porter will do the rest. He takes care of these things. He's a lovely person and very helpful. Thank you."

William shook hands with Mrs. Hamma, then waited for Lali to say good-bye. They were the last ones to leave.

"Both of you have been such good students. What are your plans? I hope you will continue with your English."

"Next term we're taking another course," Lali said, looking at William.

"Yes," William responded, "it's more advance. Over at the Washington Irving High School around Fourteenth Street."

"Wonderful." Mrs. Hamma hesitated. "May I ask you a question before you leave? It's only that I'm a little curious about something."

"Sure, of course." They both nodded.

"Are you two related? I mean, you are always together and yet have different last names, so I was just . . . wondering."

"Oh, we are just friends," Lali answered, blushing.

"I work over in the luncheonette at night, part-time."

"Of course." Mrs. Hamma looked at Lali. "Mrs. Padillo, your husband's place of business. My, that's wonderful, just wonderful! You are all just so ambitious. Very good . . ."

They exchanged farewells.

Outside, the warm June night was sprinkled with the sweetness of the new buds sprouting on the scrawny trees and hedges planted along the sidewalks and in the housing project grounds. A brisk breeze swept over the East River on to Houston Street, providing a freshness in the air.

This time they were early, and Lali and William strolled at a relaxed pace.

"Well," Lali shrugged, "that's that. It's over!"

"Only for a couple of months. In September we'll be taking a more advanced course at the high school."

"I'll probably forget everything I learned by then."

"Come on, Lali, the summer will be over before you know it. Just you wait and see. Besides, we can practice so we don't forget what Mrs. Hamma taught us."

"Sure, what do you like to speak about?" Lali said in English.

William smiled, and clasping his hands, said, "I would like to say to you how wonderful you are, and how you gonna have the most fabulous future . . . after all, you so ambitious!"

When she realized he sounded just like Mrs. Hamma, Lali began to laugh.

"Are you"—Lali tried to keep from giggling, tried to pretend to speak in earnest—"sure there is some hope for me?"

"Oh, heavens, yes! You have shown such ability this"—William was beginning to lose control, laughing loudly—"semester!"

"But I want"—Lali was holding her sides with laughter—"some guarantee of this. I got to know."

"Please, Miss Lali." William was laughing so hard tears were coming to his eyes. "After . . . after all, you now a member in good standing . . . of the promised future!"

William and Lali broke into uncontrollable laughter, swaying and limping, oblivious to the scene they created for the people who stared and pointed at them as they continued on their way to Rudi's.

## For Better Reading: Character Sketches

Can people act from both selfish and unselfish motives at the same time? Do they sometimes have conflicting sets of values that they themselves aren't aware of?

These are some of the questions to consider when reading "The English Lesson." In it, Nicholasa Mohr has created a series of character sketches, introducing members of a Basic English class and their teacher. Although their course of study is the same, their motives and purposes vary widely. By recognizing their individual personalities and comparing their goals and values, you'll realize how much the author reveals about each one.

Mohr most fully develops the characters of Lali, William, and the teacher, Mrs. Hamma. When you discover their values and inner conflicts, you may find yourself wondering what the future holds for Lali and William—and also what choices you'd prefer them to make.

It's up for discussion as a question of values.

## Fact or Opinion

Tell which of the following should be accepted as fact and which as opinion.
1. Mrs. Hamma treats all the members of her class equally.
2. Lali's husband thinks of her only as a worker who is as strong as a country mule and requires no pay.
3. Becoming an American citizen is not the goal of all members of the Mrs. Hamma's class.

## Questioning the Story

1. From her opening speech to her demonstration of "getting the ball rolling," what in Mrs. Hamma's words and actions did members of the

class find humorous? Point out three specific examples and tell why they seem amusing.

2. What motives caused Mrs. Hamma to tell "just about anyone who would listen" about the importance of her Basic English class? How do the attitudes of its members differ from a typical class—yours, for example?

3. While she called on her students to make their statements, "a feeling of control over the situation" gave Mrs. Hamma "a pleasing thrill." What are two ways that Mrs. Hamma kept the class members uncertain and edgy?

4. In making their presentations, what two requests of Mrs. Hamma did a number of students ignore? Explain at least three different reasons they failed to do as she asked.

5. What restrictions did Lali's husband impose before letting her enroll in the class? Although the story includes other character sketches, what makes Lali and William stand out for the reader early in the story?

6. What caused William to feel especially nervous when speaking before the class? What two purposes for studying Basic English did William express? What values do these represent?

7. How did Diego Torres' goals differ from the others'? How did he shock both Mrs. Hamma and the class? How did Mrs. Hamma and the class react when Torres sat down?

8. How does Aldo Fabrizi, the Sicilian, present a contrast to Diego Torres? How is pride involved in both of their attitudes? Why does Mrs. Hamma feel it necessary to distract Fabrizi?

9. How was Stephan Paczkowski's background different from the others'? Why would Mrs. Hamma say his reasons for coming to America were "really just admirable"?

10. Why did Mrs. Hamma remind the class that "everybody here must be treated equally"? Give one or more reasons to explain the class's response. In spite of her reminder, how do her words show that she regarded Mr. Paczkowski as a superior, even to herself?

## Looking Deeper

### I. Two Sides to the Story

When the class is over, the true personalities of William and Lali start to emerge. Why is this true to life?

What makes William's middle name, Horacio,* seem ironic? What are his disadvantages in life? In spite of these, what positive characteristics does he exhibit? Give three or more traits, along with examples.

---

* Roman warrior who, according to legend, stood alone defending the entrance to a bridge in Rome against an enemy army, and there lost an eye.

What difficulties does Lali face after coming to the mainland USA from Puerto Rico? What reasons did she give in class for wishing to study English? What other reasons couldn't she express?

What mixed feelings does Lali's husband, Rudi, have towards his marriage? Does he seem to be basically fair or unfair? Who or what should be blamed for their marital problems? Be sure to use support from the story in your answer.

## II. "Fairness for All"

Even though they did not speak correct English, why were members of the class more knowing and experienced in some ways than their teacher, Mrs. Hamma.

In the opening paragraph, Mrs. Hamma declared, "This is, after all, a democracy, and we have a democratic class; fairness for all." At the end of the final class, how does Mrs. Hamma's attitude and behavior toward Stephan Paczkowski bring out the irony in this claim, by showing she does not consider all of her students as equals? Compare the actions of Paczkowski with those of William, Lali, and several other women after they had refreshments. What does this show about their respective attitudes?

What positive and negative qualities did Mrs. Hamma exhibit as a teacher? Give specific examples.

## III. "The Promised Future"

At the end of the story, William tells Lali, "I would like to say ... how you gonna have the most fabulous future ... after all, you so ambitious!"

What did they find so funny about these words? What, actually, was their main hope for the immediate future?

By repeating the word *future*, the author invites the reader to look past the end of the story. Using what you know of the their pasts, what kinds of future do you think await William and Lali? Although they may not be rich and famous, why does the author lead you expect that their lives might still be good, if not "fabulous"?

# Sermon by a Traveling Preacher

*by Zora Neale Hurston*

| | |
|---|---|
| ***Born:*** | *Eatonville, Florida, 1901* |
| ***Early life:*** | *Left home at age nine as maid for theatrical troupe; finished high school in Baltimore, Maryland; attended college at Howard* |
| ***Famous as:*** | *Novelist, folklorist. Collected folklore through American South and West Indies, participated in a number of voodoo ceremonies* |
| ***Final years:*** | *In county welfare home* |
| ***Background:*** | *To collect the folk tales included in her book* Mules and Men, *Zora Neale Hurston returned to her native Florida after her graduation from college. "Folk-lore is not as easy to collect as it sounds," writes Hurston, who first had to win the confidence of the people she sought.* |
| | *Seeing "a huge smoke stack blowing smut against the sky," Hurston headed for the sawmill camp of the Everglades Cypress Lumber Company in Loughman, Florida, where she stayed at the workmen's quarters and lived in the company boarding house, run by Mrs. Allen. The following took place one evening after the work party came back to camp, and the men returned to their own shacks for supper.* |

B‌ACK IN THE QUARTERS THE sun was setting. Plenty women over the cook-pot scorching up supper. Lots of them were already thru cooking, with the pots shoved to the back of the stove while they put on fresh things and went out in front of the house to see and be seen.

The fishermen began scraping fish and hot grease began to pop in happy houses. All but the Allen's. Mrs. Allen wouldn't have a thing to do with our fish because Mr. Allen and Cliffert had made her mad about the yard. So I fried the fish. She wouldn't touch a bite, but Mr. Allen, Cliffert and I pitched into it. Mr. Allen might have eaten by the rules but Cliffert and I went at it rough-and-tumble with no holds barred.

But we did sit down on the front porch to rest after the fish was eaten.

The men were still coming into the quarters from various parts of the "job." The children played "Shoo-round," and "Chick-mah-Chick" until Mrs. Williams called her four year old Frankie and put her to sleep by rocking her and singing "Mister Frog."

It wasn't black dark, but night was peeping around the corner. The quarters were getting alive. Woofing, threats and brags up and down the line.

Three figures in the dusk-dark detached themselves from the railroad track and came walking into the quarters. A tall black grim-faced man with a rusty black reticule, followed by two women.

Everybody thought he was a bootlegger and yelled orders to him to that effect. He paid no attention, but set down his bag slowly, opened it still slower and took out a dog-eared Bible and opened it. The crowd quieted down. They knew he was a traveling preacher, a "stump-knocker" in the language of the "job."

Some fell silent to listen. Others sucked their teeth and either went back into their houses or went on to the jook.

When he had a reasonable amount of attention he nodded to the woman at his left and she raised "Death Comes a Creepin' " and the crowd helped out. At the end the preacher began:

> You all done been over in Pentecost (got to feeling spiritual by singing) and now we going to talk about de woman that was taken from man. I take my text from Genesis two and twenty-one (Gen. 2:21)

> Behold de Rib!
> Now, my beloved,
> Behold means to look and see.
> Look at dis woman God done made,
> But first thing, ah hah!      5
> Ah wants you to gaze upon God's previous works.
> Almighty and arisen God, hah!
> Peace-giving and prayer-hearing God,

High-riding and strong armded God
Walking acrost his globe creation, hah!                    10
Wid de blue elements for a helmet
And a wall of fire round his feet
He wakes de sun every morning from his fiery bed
Wid de breath of his smile
And commands de moon wid his eyes.                          15
And Oh—
Wid de eye of Faith
I can see him
Standing out on de eaves of ether
Breathing clouds from out his nostrils,                     20
Blowing storms from 'tween his lips
I can see!!
Him seize de mighty axe of his proving power
And smite the stubborn-standing space,
And laid it wide open in a mighty gash—                     25
Making a place to hold de world
I can see him—
Molding de world out of thought and power
And whirling it out on its eternal track,
Ah hah, my strong armded God!                               30
He set de blood red eye of the de sun in de sky
And told it,
Wait, wait! Wait there till Shiloh come
I can see!
Him mold de mighty mountains                                35
And melting de skies into seas.
Oh, Behold, and look and see! hah
We see in de beginning
He made de bestes every one after its kind,
De birds that fly de trackless air,                         40
De fishes dat swim de mighty deep—
Male and fee-male, hah!
Then he took of de dust of de earth
And made man in his own image.
And man was alone,                                          45
Even de lion had a mate
So God shook his head
And a thousand million diamonds
Flew out from his glittering crown
And studded de evening sky and made de stars.               50
So God put Adam into a deep sleep
And took out a bone, ah hah!
And it is said that it was a rib.
Behold de rib!

A bone out of a man's side.                                    55
He put de man to sleep and made wo-man,
And men and women been sleeping together ever since.
Behold de rib!
Brothers, if God
Had taken dat bone out of man's head                           60
He would have meant for woman to rule, hah
If he had taken a bone out of his foot,
He would have meant for us to dominize and rule.
He could have made her out of back-bone
And then she would have been behind us.                        65
But, no, God Amighty, he took de bone out of his side
So dat places de woman beside us;
Hah! God knowed his own mind.
Behold de rib!
And now I leave dis thought wid you,                           70
Let us all go marchin' up to de gates of Glory.
Tramp! tramp! tramp!
In step wid de host dat John saw.
Male and female like God made us
Side by side.                                                  75
Oh, behold the rib!
And less all set down in Glory together
Right round his glorified throne
And praise his name forever.
Amen.                                                          80

At the end of the sermon the woman on the preacher's left raised, "Been a
Listenin' All de Night Long," and the preacher descended from his fiery cloud
and lifted the collection in his hat. The singers switched to, "You Can't Hide,
Sinners, You Can't Hide." The sparse contribution taken, the trio drifted back
into the darkness of the railroad, walking towards Kissimmee.


## For Better Reading: The Mind's Eye

The ability to use the mind's eye is a great advantage to a reader. It
means to picture a place, people, and happenings in your head so that you
feel almost like a first-hand observer.

When you watch television and movies, the scene is entirely pictured
for you. But when you read, using your mind's eye enables you to take an
active part—in fact, so active that seeing a filmed version later might prove
disappointing. It just can't live up to the one you "saw" as you read.

In much the same way, it helps to "hear" the tones and expression of
a speaker's voice in the printed word.

As with film and television, printing and recordings have lessened the need to pass tales and stories by word of mouth—except for jokes, of course.

Writer Zora Neale Hurston traveled the South, gathering folk tales and stories of people's lives and customs. She sought to write them down before the richness of oral traditions was lost forever. Exercise your mind's eye and listen carefully for the rhythms of the voices, as Hurston shares her experience, recorded in her attempt to keep American folk ways alive.

## Inference

1. At supper time, Hurston implies that many women were interested in (a) proving who was the best cook (b) getting the most for their food dollar (c) taking time to socialize (d) making life easier for their husbands.
2. Hurston calls some of the houses "happy" ones because (a) there was enough food on the table for everyone (b) these wives weren't mad at their husbands (c) everyone did an equal share of the work (d) guests were not forced into "rough-and-tumble" behavior.
3. When the traveling preacher first appeared, the people in the quarter showed that they (a) respected his calling (b) were afraid of his power (c) were eager to hear him (d) had not expected him.

## Questioning the Text

1. How does the preacher use the song "Death Comes a Creepin' " to set the mood for his sermon? Why does it seem like a good choice?
2. The preacher takes his text from the book of Genesis, which tells of God's creation of Eve from Adam's rib.

   Although the preacher himself speaks in dialect, how does line 3 show his awareness that his listeners might not comprehend Biblical language?
3. Before dealing with the text, the preacher invites the crowd to "gaze upon" God's previous works. In lines 5–9, which descriptive words offer comfort and which illustrate God's power?
4. In lines 10–22, find four specific words that personify God by giving Him human features. What would be his "blue helmet"? Which of God's actions in these lines make Him seem loving, and which mainly show His might?
5. Lines 23–30 describe the creation of the world. According to the preacher, how does God use "de mighty axe"? Why is this image suited to his listeners? What two ingredients does the preacher name as necessary for "molding de world"?

6. In lines 28–50, what steps of creation does the preacher describe? After God creates man in His own image, what does man lack?
7. In line 54, the preacher repeats, "Behold de rib!" How does he again show his awareness of his listeners' vocabulary?

## Looking Deeper

### I. "Behold de Rib!"

What examples does the preacher give to show the importance of God's choosing a rib in the creation of woman? How do the preacher's ideas compare with current thinking about the relationship between men and women? In lines 71–78, what does the preacher mean by the "gates of Glory"? What final pictures did the preacher wish to leave in his listeners' minds?

### II. Words and Rhythm

In order to capture the sound and spirit of the folk tradition, Hurston spelled words to reflect the preacher's dialect. What are the chief differences from standard written English? Which words, if any, cause difficulties?

According to Hurston, "The 'hah' is a breathing device, done rhythmically to punctuate the lines. The congregation wants to hear the preacher breathing or 'straining.' " Try reading the lines without the word "hah." How does this change the effect? Why does the congregation want the preacher to "strain?" In order to catch and keep the attention of his listeners, how does the preacher also use repetition and short, dramatic phrases?

### III. "Been a listening' . . . "

Hurston uses the expression "descended from his fiery cloud" with regard to the preacher. In what way had he been on a fiery cloud? How did he have to face a "come down" after his efforts? Give some reasons that might account for his listeners' response.

# Inspiration
# (for Indin Artists)

*by Karoniaktatie (Alex Jacobs)*

| | |
|---|---|
| ***Born:*** | *1953* |
| ***Indian tribe:*** | *Mohawk* |
| ***Adult life:*** | *Moved to Kansas City in 1979* |
| ***Noted as:*** | *Poet, graphic artist, painter, and editor* |

Andy Warhol
$ power
fame position
yer teacher
competition bia                                   5
rocknroll alcohol
drugs grades school
yer teachers job
a new car new stereo
live amerikan                                     10
sell amerikan
talk amerikan
die amerikan

sacred pipe    sacred tobacco
sweat lodge    round dance                        15
animal/teachers
plants/medicines
tree of peace
language of dreams
smiles of drum, song, flute                       20
grandparents
children
sundance    kiva    medicine people
prophecies    teachings
earth lodge    skin lodge    wood lodge           25

turn my eyeholes to face the east

## For Better Reading: A Change of Spelling

Whenever a writer uses out-of-the-ordinary spelling, you should stop to ask yourself why.

Unusual punctuation, capital letters, and spacing also tend to put readers on notice that they, too, have a special meaning of their own.

Zora Neale Hurston changed spelling in an attempt to show her readers how to "hear" the sound of the traveling preacher's dialect.

With Karoniaktatie, the reason must be different. The words *American* and *amerikan* would be pronounced quite the same, yet repetition and the missing capital letter signal that it's important. In fact, it looks almost like a foreign language.... Why?

By stopping to ask, you can often figure out the answer for yourself. Karoniaktatie is, of course, the Mohawk name of the poet writing "Inspiration (for Indin Artists)." *Indin* ...?

## Questioning the Poem

1. Why might someone with American Indian blood think of America as a foreign nation?
2. Andy Warhol was a famous American "pop" artist. What do lines 2–3 imply as sources of inspiration?
3. By the way it is written, the poem invites you to make comparisons between words and draw conclusions based on their placement. For example, how might "yer teacher" refer to the items listed in lines 1–4? How might they refer to those in lines 6 and 7? In what ways is "competition" involved in both sets of items?
4. Note the lines before and after "yer teachers job." How is each related to having a teaching job? What are the errors in spelling and in punctuation in line 8? How do these reflect on the job?
5. Considering the way *amerikan* is spelled, what similar reason might account for the misspelled "yer"?
6. What kind of influence are "rocknroll alcohol drugs" for an artist? Give the reasons for your answer.
7. Live ... sell ... talk ... die. As a summary of "amerikan" life, what is the intended effect of these four words? What of value is its outcome?
8. By repeating the word "sacred" in line 14, what contrast does the poet make between the attitudes expressed in stanzas one and two? What do you see as the differences in teachers?

## Looking Deeper
### I. Sources of Inspiration

Compared to the "things" listed in stanza one, what kind of inspiration does the poet list in the second stanza? How does the poem contrast two different ideas of time concerning the past, present, and future? Which source of inspiration do you feel is better? Why?

Although the poem does not explain "bia," it could stand for "Bureau of Indian Affairs." If so, does the poem imply that its influence is positive or negative? Support your answer.

## II. Removing the Limits

Although this poem is titled "Inspiration (for Indin Artists)," do you think its meaning applies to other than Indian artists? Why or why not? How might the poet's use of parentheses help show his intention?

The final line of the poem says, "turn my eyeholes to face the east." What is the eternal and daily occurrence in the east? What, then, might this represent as an inspiration for an artist?

# Mending Wall

*by Robert Frost*

| | |
|---|---|
| ***Born:*** | *California, 1874* |
| ***Early life:*** | *Moved to New Hampshire at age 10 with widowed mother, had two years of college.* |
| ***First attempts:*** | *Tried teaching, editing, farming while seeking recognition as poet* |
| ***First success:*** | *Gained in England, where he lived until age 40, then returned to a New Hampshire farm* |
| ***Famous as:*** | *Pulitzer Prize winner, America's best-loved poet* |

Something there is that doesn't love a wall,
That sends the frozen ground swell under it,
And spills the upper boulders in the sun;
And makes gaps even two can pass abreast.
The work of hunters is another thing:        5
I have come after them and made repair
Where they have left not one stone on a stone,
But they would have the rabbit out of hiding,
To please the yelping dogs. The gaps I mean,
No one has seen them made or heard them made,    10
But at spring mending time we find them there.
I let my neighbor know beyond the hill;
And on a day we meet to walk the line
And set the wall between us once again.
We keep the wall between us as we go.    15
To each the boulders that have fallen to each.
And some are loaves and some so nearly balls
We have to use a spell to make them balance:
"Stay where you are until our backs are turned!"
We wear our fingers rough with handling them.    20

Oh, just another kind of outdoor game,
One on a side. It comes to little more:
There where it is we do not need the wall:
He is all pine and I am apple orchard.
My apple trees will never get across 25
And eat the cones under his pines, I tell him.
He only says, "Good fences make good neighbors."
Spring is the mischief in me, and I wonder
If I could put a notion in his head:
"*Why* do they make good neighbors? Isn't it 30
Where there are cows? But here there are no cows.
Before I built a wall I'd ask to know
What I was walling in or walling out,
And to whom I was like to give offense.
Something there is that doesn't love a wall, 35
That wants it down." I could say "Elves" to him,
But it's not elves exactly, and I'd rather
He said it for himself. I see him there
Bringing a stone grasped firmly by the top
In each hand, like an old stone savage armed. 40
He moves in darkness as it seems to me,
Not of woods only and the shade of trees.
He will not go behind his father's saying,
And he likes having thought of it so well
He says again, "Good fences make good neighbors." 45

## Questioning the Poem

1. Describe the picture the poem asks you to create in your mind's eye:
   a. What time of year is it?
   b. Where are the neighbors as they mend the wall?
   c. What does the task involve?
   d. What is grown on each side of the two properties meeting at the wall?
2. What do lines 2–9 present as two reasonable causes for the fallen boulders and gaps?
3. By using the word "something" in the opening line and mentioning the need for a spell to make the stones balance in line 18, what less reasonable possibility does the poem call to mind? Find one or two additional examples containing this idea.
4. In line 21, the speaker says the task is "just another kind of outdoor game." Point out another line that expresses the same attitude.
5. Which neighbor informed the other that mending time had come?
6. Why doesn't the speaker think that the wall is necessary? What is the neighbor's response to this reasoning?

7. Although not spoken openly, the speaker's private objections to the neighbor's saying are expressed in lines 30–34. Explain them briefly in your own words.

8. The speaker describes the neighbor as looking like "an old stone savage armed." As you "see" him in your mind's eye, describe two or three factors which could make him appear this way. For example, in what way is he "armed" or bearing weapons like a savage? In what other ways do the words "old" and "stone" help you picture him in your imagination?

9. Where did the neighbor get his saying about fences? Why would trying to "put a notion in his head" fail to make the neighbor question this saying?

## Looking Deeper

### I. ". . . The Wall Between Us"

In addition to actual walls, what other kinds of walls can people put between themselves and others? In this poem, in what two ways has the speaker shown that he does not want to "give offense" to his neighbor?

The saying, "Good fences make good neighbors" serves as a "wall" protecting the neighbor, who "moves in darkness" according to the speaker. In what "darkness" does the neighbor "move"? In what way is the neighbor like "an old stone savage armed" in his way of thinking as well as his appearance?

### II. Good Neighbors

Compare the speaker and his neighbor: What positive qualities and values can you see in the speaker, as revealed by his actions and ideas? Have examples to support your conclusions.

What positive qualities are exhibited by the neighbor? What negative ones?

Considering the neighbor's insistence on his saying and the existence of invisible walls separating people, how does the word "something" in lines 1 and 35 go beyond a force that can tear down an actual stone wall? Explain what you feel that "something" might be.

# The Lonely Road to Mora

## by Willa Cather

| | |
|---|---|
| **Born:** | *Virginia, 1873* |
| **Early years:** | *Spent on a ranch near Red Cloud, Nebraska* |
| **Career:** | *Newspaper correspondent, telegraph editor, teacher, writer* |
| **Lived in:** | *Pennsylvania, New York* |

THEY WERE ON THEIR WAY to Mora, the third day out, and they did not know just how far they had still to go. Since morning they had not met a traveler or seen a human habitation. They believed they were on the right trail, for they had seen no other. The first night of their journey they had spent at Santa Cruz, lying in the warm, wide valley of the Rio Grande, where the fields and gardens were already softly colored with early spring. But since they had left the Española country behind them, they had contended first with wind and sandstorms, and now with cold. The Bishop was going to Mora to assist the Padre there in disposing of a crowd of refugees who filled his house. A new settlement in the Conejos valley had lately been raided by Indians; many of the inhabitants were killed, and the survivors, who were originally from Mora, had managed to get back there, utterly destitute.

Before the travelers had crossed the mountain meadows, the rain turned to sleet. Their wet buckskins quickly froze, and the rattle of icy flakes struck them and bounded off. The prospect of a night in the open was not cheering. It was too wet to kindle a fire, their blankets would become soaked on the ground. As they were descending the mountain on the Mora side, the grey daylight seemed already beginning to fail, though it was only four o'clock. Father Latour turned in his saddle and spoke over his shoulder.

"The mules are certainly very tired, Joseph. They ought to be fed."

"Push on," said Father Vaillant. "We will come to shelter of some kind before night sets in." The Vicar had been praying steadfastly while they crossed the meadows, and he felt confident that St. Joseph would not turn a deaf ear. Before the hour was done they did indeed come upon a wretched adobe house, so poor and mean that they might not have seen it had it not lain close beside the trail, on the edge of a steep ravine. The stable looked more habitable than the house, and the priests thought perhaps they could spend the night in it.

As they rode up to the door, a man came out, bare-headed, and they saw to their surprise that he was not a Mexican, but an American, of a very unprepossessing type. He spoke to them in some drawling dialect they could scarcely understand and asked if they wanted to stay the night. During the few words they exchanged with him Father Latour felt a growing reluctance to remain even for a few hours under the roof of this ugly, evil-looking fellow. He was tall, gaunt and ill-formed, with a snake-like neck, terminating in a small, bony head. Under his close-clipped hair this repellent head showed a number of thick ridges, as if the skull joinings were overgrown by layers of superfluous bone. With its small, rudimentary ears, this head had a positively malignant look. The man seemed not more than half human, but he was the only householder on the lonely road to Mora.

The priests dismounted and asked him whether he could put their mules under shelter and give them grain feed.

"As soon as I git my coat on I will. You kin come in."

They followed him into a room where a piñon fire blazed in the corner, and went toward it to warm their stiffened hands. Their host made an angry, snarling sound in the direction of the partition, and a woman came out of the next room. She was a Mexican.

Father Latour and Father Vaillant addressed her courteously in Spanish, greeting her in the name of the Holy Mother, as was customary. She did not open her lips, but stared at them blankly for a moment, then dropped her eyes and cowered as if she were terribly frightened. The priests looked at each other; it struck them both that this man had been abusing her in some way. Suddenly he turned on her.

"Clear off them cheers fur the strangers. They won't eat ye, if they air priests."

She began distractedly snatching rags and wet socks and dirty clothes from the chairs. Her hands were shaking so that she dropped things. She was not old, she might have been very young, but she was probably half witted. There was nothing in her face but blankness and fear.

Her husband put on his coat and boots, went to the door, and stopped with his hand on the latch, throwing over his shoulder a crafty, hateful glance at the bewildered woman.

"Here, you! Come right along, I'll need ye!"

She took her black shawl from a peg and followed him. Just at the door she turned and caught the eyes of the visitors, who were looking after her in compassion and perplexity. Instantly that stupid face became intense, prophetic, full of awful meaning. With her finger she pointed them away, away!—two quick thrusts into the air. Then, with a look of horror beyond anything language could convey, she threw back her head and drew the edge of her palm quickly across her distended throat—and vanished. The doorway was empty; the two priests stood staring at it, speechless. That flash of electric passion had been so swift, the warning it communicated so vivid and definite, that they were struck dumb.

Father Joseph was the first to find his tongue. "There is no doubt of her meaning. Your pistol is loaded, Jean?"

"Yes, but I neglected to keep it dry. No matter."

They hurried out of the house. It was still light enough to see the stable through the grey drive of rain, and they went toward it.

"Señor American," the Bishop called, "will you be good enough to bring out our mules?"

The man came out of the stable. "What do you want?"

"Our mules. We have changed our mind. We will push on to Mora. And here is a dollar for your trouble."

The man took a threatening attitude. As he looked from one to the other his head played from side to side exactly like a snake's. "What's the matter? My house ain't good enough for ye?"

"No explanation is necessary. Go into the barn and get the mules, Father Joseph."

"You dare go into my stable, you—priest!"

The Bishop drew his pistol. "No profanity, Señor. We want nothing from you but to get away from your uncivil tongue. Stand where you are."

The man was unarmed. Father Joseph came out with the mules, which had not been unsaddled. The poor things were each munching a mouthful, but they needed no urging to be gone; they did not like this place. The moment they felt their riders on their backs they trotted quickly along the road, which dropped immediately into the arroyo. While they were descending, Father Joseph remarked that the man would certainly have a gun in the house, and that he had no wish to be shot in the back.

"Nor I. But it is growing too dark for that, unless he should follow us on horseback," said the Bishop. "Were there horses in the stable?"

"Only a burro." Father Vaillant was relying upon the protection of St. Joseph, whose office he had fervently said that morning. The warning given them by that poor woman, with such scant opportunity, seemed evidence that some protecting power was mindful of them.

By the time they had ascended the far side of the arroyo, night had closed down and the rain was pouring harder than ever.

"I am by no means sure that we can keep in the road," said the Bishop. "But at least I am sure we are not being followed. We must trust to these intelligent beasts. Poor woman! He will suspect her and abuse her, I am afraid." He kept seeing her in the darkness as he rode on, her face in the fire-light, and her terrible pantomime.

They reached the town of Mora a little after midnight. The Padre's house was full of refugees, and two of them were put out of a bed in order that the Bishop and his Vicar could get into it.

In the morning a boy came from the stable and reported that he had found a crazy woman lying in the straw, and that she begged to see the two Padres who owned the white mules. She was brought in, her clothing cut to rags, her legs and face and even her hair so plastered with mud that the priests could scarcely recognize the woman who had saved their lives the night before.

She said she had never gone back to the house at all. When the two priests rode away her husband had run to the house to get his gun, and she had plunged down a washout behind the stable into the arroyo, and had been on the way to

Mora all night. She had supposed he would overtake her and kill her, but he had not. She reached the settlement before daybreak, and crept into the stable to warm herself among the animals and wait until the household was awake. Kneeling before the Bishop she began to relate such horrible things that he stopped her and turned to the native priest.

"This is a case for the civil authorities. Is there a magistrate here?"

There was no magistrate, but there was a retired fur trapper who acted as notary and could take evidence. He was sent for, and in the interval Father Latour instructed the refugee women from Conejos to bathe this poor creature and put decent clothes on her, and to care for the cuts and scratches on her legs.

An hour later the woman, whose name was Magdalena, calmed by food and kindness, was ready to tell her story. The notary had brought along his friend, St. Vrain, a Canadian trapper who understood Spanish better than he. The woman was known to St. Vrain, moreover, who confirmed her statement that she was born Magdalena Valdez, at Los Ranchos de Taos, and that she was twenty-four years old. Her husband, Buck Scales, had drifted into Taos with a party of hunters from somewhere in Wyoming. All white men knew him for a dog and a degenerate—but to Mexican girls, marriage with an American meant coming up in the world. She had married him six years ago, and had been living with him ever since in that wretched house on the Mora trail. During that time he had robbed and murdered four travelers who had stopped there for the night. They were all strangers, not known in the country. She had forgot their names, but one was a German boy who spoke very little Spanish and little English; a nice boy with blue eyes, and she had grieved for him more than for the others. They were all buried in the sandy soil behind the stable. She was always afraid their bodies might wash out in a storm. Their horses Buck had ridden off by night and sold to Indians somewhere in the north. Magdalena had borne three children since her marriage, and her husband had killed each of them a few days after birth, by ways so horrible that she could not relate it. After he killed the first baby, she ran away from him, back to her parents at Ranchos. He came after her and made her go home with him by threatening harm to the old people. She was afraid to go anywhere for help, but twice before she had managed to warn travelers away, when her husband happened to be out of the house. This time she had found courage because, when she looked into the faces of these two Padres, she knew they were good men, and she thought if she ran after them they could save her. She could not bear any more killing. She asked nothing better than to die herself, if only she could hide near a church and a priest for a while, to make her soul right with God.

St. Vrain and his friend got together a search party at once. They rode out to Scales's place and found the remains of four men buried under the corral behind the stable, as the woman had said. Scales himself they captured on the road from Taos, where he had gone to look for his wife. They brought him back to Mora, but St. Vrain rode on to Taos to fetch a magistrate.

There was no *calabozo* in Mora, so Scales was put into an empty stable, under guard. This stable was soon surrounded by a crowd of people, who loitered to hear the blood curdling threats the prisoner shouted against his wife. Magdalena was kept in the Padre's house, where she lay on a mat in the corner, begging Father Latour to take her back to Santa Fé, so that her husband could not get at her. Though Scales was bound, the Bishop felt alarmed for her safety. He and the American notary, who had a pistol of the new revolver model, sat in the *sala* and kept watch over her all night.

In the morning the magistrate and his party arrived from Taos. The notary told him the facts of the case in the plaza, where everyone could hear. The Bishop inquired whether there was any place for Magdalena in Taos, as she could not stay on here in such a state of terror.

A man dressed in buckskin hunting clothes stepped out of the crowd and asked to see Magdalena. Father Latour conducted him into the room where she lay on her mat. The stranger went up to her, removing his hat. He bent down and put his hand on her shoulder. Though he was clearly an American, he spoke Spanish in the native manner.

"Magdalena, don't you remember me?"

She looked up at him as out of a dark well; something became alive in her deep, haunted eyes. She caught with both hands at his fringed buckskin knees.

"Christóbal!" she wailed. "Oh, Christóbal!"

"I'll take you home with me, Magdalena, and you can stay with my wife. You wouldn't be afraid in my house, would you?"

"No, no, Christóbal, I would not be afraid with you. I am not a wicked woman."

He smoothed her hair. "You're a good girl, Magdalena—always were. It will be all right. Just leave things to me."

Then he turned to the Bishop. "Señor Vicario, she can come to me. I live near Taos. My wife is a native woman, and she'll be good to her. That varmint won't come about my place, even if he breaks jail. He knows me. My name is Carson."

Father Latour had looked forward to meeting the scout. He had supposed him to be a very large man, of powerful body and commanding presence. This Carson was not so tall as the Bishop himself, was very slight in frame, modest in manner, and he spoke English with a soft Southern drawl. His face was both thoughtful and alert; anxiety had drawn a permanent ridge between his blue eyes. Under his blond moustache his mouth had a singular refinement. The lips were full and delicately modeled. There was something curiously unconscious about his mouth, reflective, a little melancholy,—and something that suggested a capacity for tenderness. The Bishop felt a quick glow of pleasure in looking at the man. As he stood there in his buckskin clothes one felt in him standards, loyalties, a code which is not easily put into words but which is instantly felt when two men who live by it come together by chance. He took the scout's hand. "I have long wanted to meet Kit Carson," he said, "even before I came to New Mexico. I have been hoping you would pay me a visit at Santa Fé."

The other smiled. "I'm right shy, sir, and I'm always afraid of being disappointed. But I guess it will be all right from now on."

This was the beginning of a long friendship.

On their ride back to Carson's ranch, Magdalena was put in Father Vaillant's care, and the Bishop and the scout rode together. Carson said he had become a Catholic merely as a matter of form, as Americans usually did when they married a Mexican girl. His wife was a good woman and very devout; but religion had seemed to him pretty much a woman's affair until his last trip to California. He had been sick out there, and the Fathers at one of the missions took care of him. "I began to see things different, and thought I might some day be a Catholic in earnest. I was brought up to think priests were rascals, and that the nuns were bad women,—all the stuff they talk back in Missouri. A good many of the native priests here bear out that story. Our Padre Martínez at Taos is an old scapegrace, if ever there was one; he's got children and grandchildren in almost every settlement around here. And Padre Lucero at Arroyo Hondo is a miser, takes everything a poor man's got to give him a Christian burial."

The Bishop discussed the needs of his people at length with Carson. He felt great confidence in his judgment. The two men were about the same age, both a little over forty, and both had been sobered and sharpened by wide experience. Carson had been guide in world-renowned explorations, but he was still almost as poor as in the days when he was a beaver trapper. He lived in a little adobe house with his Mexican wife. The great country of desert and mountain ranges between Santa Fé and the Pacific coast was not yet mapped or chartered; the most reliable map of it was in Kit Carson's brain. This Missourian, whose eye was so quick to read a landscape or a human face, could not read a printed page. He could at that time barely write his own name. Yet one felt in him a quick and discriminating intelligence. That he was illiterate was an accident; he had got ahead of books, gone where the printing-press could not follow him. Out of the hardships of his boyhood—from fourteen to twenty picking up a bare living as cook or mule-driver for wagon trains, often in the service of brutal and desperate characters—he had preserved a clean sense of honor and a compassionate heart. In talking to the Bishop of poor Magdalena he said sadly: "I used to see her in Taos when she was such a pretty girl. Ain't it a pity?"

The degenerate murderer, Buck Scales, was hanged after a short trial. Early in April the Bishop left Santa Fé on horseback and rode to St. Louis, on his way to attend the Provincial Council at Baltimore. When he returned in September, he brought back with him five courageous nuns, Sisters of Loretto, to found a school for girls in letterless Santa Fé. He sent at once for Magdalena and took her into the service of the Sisters. She became housekeeper and manager of the Sisters' kitchen. She was devoted to the nuns, and so happy in the service of the Church that when the Bishop visited the school he used to enter by the kitchen-garden in order to see her serene and handsome face. For she became beautiful, as Carson said she had been as a girl. After the blight of her horrible youth was over, she seemed to bloom again in the household of God.

# For Better Reading: A Matter of Character

When you are reading a short story or novel, there's a great difference between being able to identify a character and identifying *with* her or him.

To get the most from your reading, it's not enough to identify the names, background, and action. When you identify with a character, you yourself become caught up in the conflict, and you share the emotions and tension aroused by the forces that test his or her values and beliefs.

That means asking yourself how you would feel and act if placed in the same situation, faced with the same limitations and difficulties. In this way, reading allows you to test your own feelings and reactions in a wide range of experiences.

## Important Details

1. On their third day out, the two missionary priests found themselves (a) not knowing which trail to take (b) in a warm, wide valley of the Rio Grande (c) facing a two days' journey through the desert (d) in the sleet and cold of a mountainous terrain.
2. Father Latour and Father Vaillant were going to Mora in order to (a) inaugurate a new cathedral (b) help survivors of an Indian raid (c) establish a new mission outpost (d) solemnize the governor's wedding.
3. When the priests first met the owner of the adobe house, they were (a) relieved he spoke English (b) given a warm welcome (c) reluctant to stay (d) told they had to leave at dawn.

## Questioning the Story

1. What was the priests' first impression of the owner's wife? What caused them to feel this way about her?
2. How did the woman startle the priests? Mentally or actually try to duplicate her gestures. Then describe and interpret them.
3. How did the owner react to the priests' leaving? What was ironic about the priests' "show of force"?
4. As they were descending toward Mora, what fears did each of the priests express for themselves and Magdalena?
5. When the boy found the "crazy woman lying in the straw," how was his assessment of her similar to the priests' original opinion? How had her appearance changed for the worse? Why?
6. Why had Magdalena Valdez married Buck Scales? Why had she left him after the birth of her first baby? What caused her to go back to him?
7. What was the probable fate of a stranger stopping at Scales' place for the night? What was the conflict facing Magdalena with regard to her

husband's deeds? What did she finally decide was the best she could hope for?

8. How did St. Vrain, the Canadian trapper, and his search party prove Magdalena's story true? Even after Scales was captured, why did the Bishop, Father Latour, feel that Magdalena was still in danger?

9. Why is Kit Carson's offer the perfect, immediate solution to Magdalena's problems? Give at least three reasons.

# Looking Deeper

## I. Humanizing a Legend

Toward the end of the story, the author introduces Kit Carson, a frontier scout who's become one of the legendary figures of America's past. Considering his fame and his feats, what surprises the Bishop about his appearance?

According to the Bishop, Carson's face looked both "thoughtful and alert." Something about his mouth suggested a "capacity for tenderness," and the Bishop "felt in him" high standards. Give examples to show how his behavior matches this assessment.

How do you account for the fact that Carson's world-wide fame had not made him rich? Explain why the fact that he was illiterate is called just an "accident." Why would the Bishop consider him educated?

## II. A Change of Fortunes

Speaking of Magdalena after meeting her in Mora, Kit Carson says, "I used to see her in Taos when she was such a pretty girl. Ain't it a pity?"

What are the changes that take place in Magdalena's appearance in the course of the story? Does the story show her to be a true victim of circumstances or in some ways responsible for the "blight of her horrible youth"? Have thoughtful reasons to support your viewpoint.

This story, "The Lonely Road to Mora," is part of Willa Cather's historical novel about early New Mexico, *Death Comes for the Archbishop.*

Explain whether or not you feel the characters and their reactions seem true-to-life or overly dramatic, considering the time period, situations, and individual limitations. Include supporting evidence and reasons.

# The Kind of Light That Shines on Texas

## by Reginald McKnight

| | |
|---|---|
| **Born:** | *Furstenfeldbruck, Germany, Fablen Air Force base* |
| **Childhood:** | *Spent partly in father's homestate, Texas, and partly in mother's homestate, Alabama* |
| **Career:** | *Teacher at University of Pittsburgh, author* |

I NEVER LIKED MARVIN PRUITT. Never liked him, never knew him, even though there were only three of us in the class. Three black kids. In our school there were fourteen classrooms of thirty-odd white kids (in '66, they considered Chicanos provisionally white) and three or four black kids. Primary school in primary colors. Neat division. Alphabetized. They didn't stick us in the back, or arrange us by degrees of hue, apartheidlike. This was real integration, a ten-to-one ratio as tidy as upper-class landscaping. If it all worked, you could have ten white kids all to yourself. They could talk to you, get the feel of you, scrutinize you bone deep if they wanted to. They seldom wanted to, and that was fine with me for two reasons. The first was that their scrutiny was irritating. How do you comb your hair—why do you comb your hair—may I please touch your hair—were the kinds of questions they asked. This is no way to feel at home. The second reason was Marvin. He embarrassed me. He smelled bad, was at least two grades behind, was hostile, dark skinned, homely, close-mouthed. I feared him for his size, pitied him for his dress, watched him all the time. Marveled at him, mystified, astonished, uneasy.

He had the habit of spitting on his right arm, juicing it down till it would glisten. He would start in immediately after taking his seat when we'd finished with the Pledge of Allegiance, "The Yellow Rose of Texas," "The Eyes of Texas Are upon You," and "Mistress Shady." Marvin would rub his spit-flecked arm with his left hand, rub and roll as if polishing an ebony pool cue. Then he would rest his head in the crook of his arm, sniffing, huffing deep like blackjacket boys huff bagsful of acrylics. After ten minutes or so, his eyes would close, heavy. He would sleep till recess. Mrs. Wickham would let him.

There was one other black kid in our class, a girl they called Ah-so. I never learned what she did to earn this name. There was nothing Asian about this big-shouldered girl. She was the tallest, heaviest kid in school. She was quiet, but I don't think any one of us was subtle or sophisticated enough to nickname our classmates according to any but physical attributes. Fat kids were called Porky or Butterball; skinny ones were called Stick or Ichabod. Ah-so was big, thick, and African. She would impassively sit, sullen, silent as Marvin. She wore the same dark blue pleated skirt every day, the same ruffled white blouse every day. Her skin always shone as if worked by Marvin's palms and fingers. I never spoke one word to her, nor she to me.

Of the three of us, Mrs. Wickham called only on Ah-so and me. Ah-so never answered one question, correctly or incorrectly, so far as I can recall. She wasn't stupid. When asked to read aloud she read well, seldom stumbling over long words, reading with humor and expression. But when Wickham asked her about Farmer Brown and how many cows, or the capital of Vermont, or the date of this war or that, Ah-so never spoke. Not one word. But you always felt she could have answered those questions if she'd wanted to. I sensed no tension, embarrassment, or anger in Ah-so's reticence. She simply refused to speak. There was something unshakable about her, some core so impenetrably solid, you got the feeling that if you stood too close to her she could eat your thoughts like a black star eats light. I didn't despise Ah-so as I despised Marvin. There was nothing malevolent about her. She sat like a great icon in the back of the class-room, tranquil, guarded, sealed up, watchful. She was close to sixteen, and it was my guess she'd given up on school. Perhaps she was just obliging the wishes of her family, sticking it out till the law could no longer reach her.

There were at least half a dozen older kids in our class. Besides Marvin and Ah-so there was Oakley, who sat behind me, whispering threats into my ear; Varna Willard with the large breasts; Eddie Limon, who played bass for a high school rock band; and Lawrence Ridderbeck, who everyone said had a kid and a wife. You couldn't expect me to know anything about Texan educational prac-tices of the 1960s, so I never knew why there were so many older kids in my sixth grade class. After all, I was just a boy and had transferred into the school around midyear. My father, an air force sergeant, had been sent to Viet Nam. The air force sent my mother, my sister Claire, and me to Connolly Air Force Base, which during the war housed "unaccompanied wives." I'd been to so many different schools in my short life that I ceased wondering about their differences. All I knew about the Texas schools is that they weren't afraid to flunk you.

Yet though I was only twelve then, I had a good idea why Wickham never once called on Marvin, why she let him snooze in the crook of his polished arm. I knew why she would press her lips together, and narrow her eyes at me whenever I correctly answered a question, rare as that was. I knew why she badgered Ah-so with questions everyone knew Ah-so would never even consider answering. Wickham didn't like us. She wasn't gross about it, but it was clear she didn't want us around. She would prove her dislike day after day with little stories and jokes. "I just want to share with you all," she would say, "a little riddle my daughter told me at the supper table th'other day. Now, where do you go when you injure your knee?" Then one, two, or all three of her pets would say for the rest of us, "We don't know, Miz Wickham," in that skin-chilling way suckasses speak, "where?" "Why, to Africa," Wickham would say, "where the knee grows."

The thirty-odd white kids would laugh, and I would look across the room at Marvin. He'd be asleep. I would glance back at Ah-so. She'd be sitting still as a projected image, staring down at her desk. I, myself, would smile at Wickham's stupid jokes, sometimes fake a laugh. I tried to show her that at least one of us was alive and alert, even though her jokes hurt. I sucked ass, too, I suppose. But I wanted her to understand more than anything that I was not like her other nigra children, that I was worthy of more than the nonattention and the negative attention she paid Marvin and Ah-so. I hated her, but never showed it. No one could safely contradict that woman. She knew all kinds of tricks to demean, control, and punish you. And she could swing her two-foot paddle as fluidly as a big league slugger swings a bat. You didn't speak in Wickham's class unless she spoke to you first. You didn't chew gum, or wear "hood" hair. You didn't drag your feet, curse, pass notes, hold hands with the opposite sex. Most especially, you didn't say anything bad about the Aggies, Governor Connolly, LBJ, Sam Houston, or Waco. You did the forbidden and she would get you. It was that simple.

She never got me, though. Never gave her reason to. But she could have invented reasons. She did a lot of that. I can't be sure, but I used to think she pitied me because my father was in Viet Nam and my uncle A.J. had recently died there. Whenever she would tell one of her racist jokes, she would always glance at me, preface the joke with, "Now don't you nigra children take offense. This is all in fun, you know. I just want to share with you all something Coach Gilchrest told me th'other day." She would tell her joke, and glance at me again. I'd giggle, feeling a little queasy. "I'm half Irish," she would chuckle, "and you should hear some of those Irish jokes." She never told any, and I never really expected her to. I just did my Tom-thing. I kept my shoes shined, my desk neat, answered her questions as best I could, never brought gum to school, never cursed, never slept in class. I wanted to show her we were not all the same.

I tried to show them all, all thirty-odd, that I was different. It worked to some degree, but not very well. When some article was stolen from someone's locker or desk, Marvin, not I, was the first accused. I'd be second. Neither Marvin nor Ah-so nor I were ever chosen for certain classroom honors—"Pledge leader," "flag holder," "noise monitor," "paper passer outer"—but Mrs. Wickham once let me be "eraser duster." I was proud. I didn't even care about the cracks my fellow students made about my finally having turned the right color. I had done something that Marvin, in the deeps of his never-ending sleep, couldn't even dream of doing. Jack Preston, a kid who sat in front of me, asked me one day at recess whether I was embarrassed about Marvin. "Can you believe that guy?" I said. "He's like a pig or something. Makes me sick."

"Does it make you ashamed to be colored?"

"No," I said, but I meant yes. Yes, if you insist on thinking us all the same. Yes, if his faults are mine, his weaknesses inherent in me.

"I'd be," said Jack.

I made no reply. I was ashamed. Ashamed for not defending Marvin and ashamed that Marvin even existed. But if it had occurred to me, I would have asked Jack whether he was ashamed of being white because of Oakley. Oakley, "Oak Tree," Kelvin "Oak Tree" Oakley. He was sixteen and proud of it. He made it clear to everyone, including Wickham, that his life's ambition was to stay in school one more year, till he'd be old enough to enlist in the army. "Them slopes got my brother," he would say. "I'mna sign up and git me a few slopes. Gonna kill them dead." Oakley, so far as anyone knew, was and always had been the oldest kid in his family. But no one contradicted him. He would, as anyone would tell you, "snap yer neck jest as soon as look at you." Not a boy in class, excepting Marvin and myself, had been able to avoid Oakley's pink bellies, Texas titty twisters, Moon Pie punches, or worse. He didn't bother Marvin, I suppose, because Marvin was closer to his size and age, and because Marvin spent five-sixths of the school day asleep. Marvin probably never crossed Oakley's mind. And to say that Oakley hadn't bothered me is not to say he had no intention of ever doing so. In fact, this haphazard sketch of hairy fingers, slash of eyebrow, explosion of acne, elbows, and crooked teeth, swore almost daily that he'd like to kill me.

Naturally, I feared him. Though we were about the same height, he outweighed me by no less than forty pounds. He talked, stood, smoked, and swore like a man. No one, except for Mrs. Wickham, the principal, and the coach, ever laid a finger on him. And even Wickham knew that the hot lines she laid on him merely amused him. He would smile out at the classroom, goofy and bashful, as she laid down the two, five, or maximum ten strokes on him. Often he would wink, or surreptitiously flash us the thumb as Wickham worked on him. When she was finished, Oakley would walk so cool back to his seat you'd think he was on wheels. He'd slide into his chair, sniff the air, and say, "Somethin's burnin. Do y'all smell smoke? I swanee, I smell smoke and fahr back here." If he had made these cracks and never threatened me, I might have grown to admire Oakley, even liked him a little. But he hated me, and took every opportunity during the six-hour school day to make me aware of this. "Some Sambo's gittin his ass broke open one of these days," he'd mumble. "I wanna fight somebody. Need to keep in shape till I git to Nam."

I never said anything to him for the longest time. I pretended not to hear him, pretended not to notice his sour breath on my neck and ear. "Yep," he'd whisper. "Coonies keep ya in good shape for slope killin." Day in, day out, that's the kind of thing I'd pretend not to hear. But one day when the rain dropped down like lead balls, and the cold air made your skin look plucked, Oakley whispered to me, "My brother tells me it rains like this in Nam. Maybe I oughta go out at recess and break your ass open today. Nice and cool so you don't sweat. Nice and wet to clean up the blood." I said nothing for at least half a minute, then I turned half right and said, "Thought you said your brother was dead." Oakley, silent himself, for a time, poked me in the back with his pencil and hissed, "*Yer* dead." Wickham cut her eyes our way, and it was over.

It was hardest avoiding him in gym class. Especially when we played murderball. Oakley always aimed his throws at me. He threw with unblinking intensity, his teeth gritting, his neck veining, his face flushing, his black hair sweeping over one eye. He could throw hard, but the balls were squishy and harmless. In fact, I found his misses more intimidating than his hits. The balls would whizz by, thunder against the folded bleachers. They rattled as though a locomotive were passing through them. I would duck, dodge, leap as if he were throwing grenades. But he always hit me, sooner or later. And after a while I noticed that the other boys would avoid throwing at me, as if I belonged to Oakley.

One day, however, I was surprised to see that Oakley was throwing at everyone else but me. He was uncommonly accurate, too; kids were falling like tin cans. Since no one was throwing at me, I spent most of the game watching Oakley cut this one and that one down. Finally, he and I were the only ones left on the court. Try as he would, he couldn't hit me, nor I him. Coach Gilchrest blew his whistle and told Oakley and me to bring the red rubber balls to the equipment locker. I was relieved I'd escaped Oakley's stinging throws for once. I was feeling triumphant, full of myself. As Oakley and I approached Gilchrest, I thought about saying something friendly to Oakley: Good game, Oak Tree, I would say. Before I could speak, though, Gilchrest said, "All right, boys, there's five minutes left in the period. Y'all are so good, looks like, you're gonna have to play like men. No boundaries, no catch outs, and you gotta hit your opponent three times in order to win. Got me?"

We nodded.

"And you're gonna use these," said Gilchrest, pointing to three volleyballs at his feet. "And you better believe they're pumped full. Oates, you start at the end of the court. Oak Tree, you're at th'other end. Just like usual, I'll set the balls at mid-court, and when I blow my whistle I want y'all to haul your cheeks to the middle and th'ow for all you're worth. Got me?" Gilchrest nodded at our nods, then added, "Remember, no boundaries, right?"

I at my end, Oakley at his, Gilchrest blew his whistle. I was faster than Oakley and scooped up a ball before he'd covered three quarters of his side. I aimed, threw, and popped him right on the knee. "One-zip!" I heard Gilchrest shout. The ball bounced off his knee and shot right back into my hands. I hurried my throw and missed. Oakley bent down, clutched the two remaining balls. I remember being amazed that he could palm each ball, run full out and throw left-handed or right-handed without a shade of awkwardness. I spun, ran, but one of Oakley's throws glanced off the back of my head. "One-one!" hollered Gilchrest. I fell and spun on my ass as the other ball came sailing at me. I caught it. "He's out!" I yelled. Gilchrest's voice boomed, "No catch outs. Three hits. Three hits." I leapt to my feet as Oakley scrambled across the floor for another ball. I chased him down, leapt, and heaved the ball hard as he drew himself erect. The ball hit him dead in the face, and he went down flat. He rolled around, cupping his hands over his nose. Gilchrest sped to his side, helped him to his feet, asked him whether he was OK. Blood flowed from Oakley's nose, dripped in startlingly bright spots on the floor, his shoes, Gilchrest's shirt. The coach removed Oakley's T-shirt and pressed it against the big kid's nose to stanch the bleeding. As they walked past me toward the office I mumbled an apology to

Oakley, but couldn't catch his reply. "You watch your filthy mouth, boy," said Gilchrest to Oakley.

The locker room was unnaturally quiet as I stepped into its steamy atmosphere. Eyes clicked in my direction, looked away. After I was out of my shorts, had my towel wrapped around me, my shower kit in hand, Jack Preston and Brian Nailor approached me. Preston's hair was combed slick and plastic looking. Nailor's stood up like frozen flames. Nailor smiled at me with his big teeth and pale eyes. He poked my arm with a finger. "You screwed up," he said.

"I tried to apologize."

"Won't do you no good," said Preston.

"I swanee," said Nailor.

"It's part of the game," I said. "It was an accident. Wasn't my idea to use volleyballs."

"Don't matter," Preston said. "He's jest lookin for an excuse to fight you."

"I never done nothing to him."

"Don't matter," said Nailor. "He don't like you."

"Brian's right, Clint. He'd jest as soon kill you as look at you."

"I never done nothing to him."

"Look," said Preston, "I know him pretty good. And jest between you and me, it's cause you're a city boy—"

"Whadda you mean? I've never—"

"He don't like your clothes—"

"And he don't like the fancy way you talk in class."

"What fancy—"

"I'm tellin him, if you don't mind, Brian."

"Tell him then."

"He don't like the way you say 'tennis shoes' instead of sneakers. He don't like coloreds. A whole bunch a things, really."

"I never done nothing to him. He's got no reason—"

"*And*," said Nailor, grinning, "*and*, he says you're a stuck-up rich kid." Nailor's eyes had crow's-feet, bags beneath them. They were a man's eyes.

"My dad's a sergeant," I said.

"You chicken to fight him?" said Nailor.

"Yeah, Clint, don't be chicken. Jest go on and git it over with. He's whupped pert near ever'body else in the class. It ain't so bad."

"Might as well, Oates."

"Yeah, yer pretty skinny, but yer jest about his height. Jest git im in a headlock and don't let go."

"Goddamn," I said, "he's got no reason to—"

Their eyes shot right and I looked over my shoulder. Oakley stood at his locker, turning its tumblers. From where I stood I could see that a piece of cotton was wedged up one of his nostrils, and he already had the makings of a good shiner. His acne burned red like a fresh abrasion. He snapped the locker open and kicked his shoes off without sitting. Then he pulled off his shorts, revealing two paddle stripes on his ass. They were fresh red bars speckled with white, the white speckles being the reverse impression of the paddle's suction holes. He must not have watched his filthy mouth while in Gilchrest's presence. Behind me, I heard Preston and Nailor pad to their lockers.

Oakley spoke without turning around. "Somebody's gonna git his skinny black ass kicked, right today, right after school." He said it softly. He slipped his jock off, turned around. I looked away. Out the corner of my eye I saw him stride off, his hairy nakedness a weapon clearing the younger boys from his path. Just before he rounded the corner of the shower stalls, I threw my toilet kit to the floor and stammered, "I—I never did nothing to you, Oakley." He stopped, turned, stepped closer to me, wrapping his towel around himself. Sweat streamed down my rib cage. It felt like ice water. "You wanna go at it right now, boy?"

"I never did nothing to you." I felt tears in my eyes. I couldn't stop them even though I was blinking like mad. "Never."

He laughed. "You busted my nose, asshole."

"What about before? What'd I ever do to you?"

"See you after school, Coonie." Then he turned away, flashing his acne-spotted back like a semaphore. "Why?" I shouted. "Why you wanna fight me?" Oakley stopped and turned, folded his arms, leaned against a toilet stall. "Why you wanna fight *me*, Oakley?" I stepped over the bench. "What'd I do? Why me?" And then unconsciously, as if scratching, as if breathing, I walked toward Marvin, who stood a few feet from Oakley, combing his hair at the mirror. "Why not him?" I said. "How come you're after *me* and not *him*?" The room froze. Froze for a moment that was both evanescent and eternal, somewhere between an eye blink and a week in hell. No one moved, nothing happened; there was no sound at all. And then it was as if all of us at the same moment looked at Marvin. He just stood there, combing away, the only body in motion, I think. He combed his hair and combed it, as if seeing only his image, hearing only his comb scraping his scalp. I knew he'd heard me. There's no way he could not have heard me. But all he did was slide the comb into his pocket and walk out the door.

"I got no quarrel with Marvin," I heard Oakley say. I turned toward his voice, but he was already in the shower.

I was able to avoid Oakley at the end of the school day. I made my escape by asking Mrs. Wickham if I could go to the restroom.

" 'Restroom,' " Oakley mumbled. "It's a damn toilet, sissy."

"Clinton," said Mrs. Wickham. "Can you *not* wait till the bell rings? It's almost three o'clock."

"No, ma'am," I said. "I won't make it."

"Well, I should make you wait just to teach you to be more mindful about ... hygiene ... uh things." She sucked in her cheeks, squinted. "But I'm feeling charitable today. You may go." I immediately left the building, and got on the bus. "Ain't you a little early?" said the bus driver, swinging the door shut. "Just left the office," I said. The driver nodded, apparently not giving me a second thought. I had no idea why I'd told her I'd come from the office, or why she found it a satisfactory answer. Two minutes later the bus filled, rolled and shook its way to Connolly Air Base.

When I got home, my mother was sitting in the living room, smoking her

Slims, watching her soap opera. She absently asked me how my day had gone and I told her fine. "Hear from Dad?" I said.

"No, but I'm sure he's fine." She always said that when we hadn't heard from him in a while. I suppose she thought I was worried about him, or that I felt vulnerable without him. It was neither. I just wanted to discuss something with my mother that we both cared about. If I spoke with her about things that happened at school, or on my weekends, she'd listen with half an ear, say something like, "Is that so?" or "You don't say?" I couldn't stand that sort of thing. But when I mentioned my father, she treated me a bit more like an adult, or at least someone who was worth listening to. I didn't want to feel like a boy that afternoon. As I turned from my mother and walked down the hall I thought about the day my father left for Viet Nam. Sharp in his uniform, sure behind his aviator specs, he slipped a cigar from his pocket and stuck it in mine. "Not till I get back," he said. "We'll have us one when we go fishing. Just you and me, out on the lake all day, smoking and casting and sitting. Don't let Mamma see it. Put it in y'back pocket." He hugged me, shook my hand, and told me I was the man of the house now. He told me he was depending on me to take good care of my mother and sister. "Don't you let me down, now, hear?" And he tapped his thick finger on my chest. "You almost as big as me. Boy, you something else." I believed him when he told me those things. My heart swelled big enough to swallow my father, my mother, Claire. I loved, feared, and respected myself, my manhood. That day I could have put all of Waco, Texas, in my heart. And it wasn't till about three months later that I discovered I really wasn't the man of the house, that my mother and sister, as they always had, were taking care of me.

For a brief moment I considered telling my mother about what had happened at school that day, but for one thing, she was deep down in the halls of "General Hospital," and never paid you much mind till it was over. For another thing, I just wasn't the kind of person—I'm still not, really—to discuss my problems with anyone. Like my father I kept things to myself, talked about my problems only in retrospect. Since my father wasn't around, I consciously wanted to be like him, doubly like him, I could say. I wanted to be the man of the house in some respect, even if it had to be in an inward way. I went to my room, changed my clothes, and laid out my homework. I couldn't focus on it. I thought about Marvin, what I'd said about him or done to him—I couldn't tell which. I'd done something to him, said something about him; said something about and done something to myself. *How come you're after me and not him?* I kept trying to tell myself I hadn't meant it that way. *That* way. I thought about approaching Marvin, telling him what I really meant was that he was more Oakley's age and weight than I. I would tell him I meant I was no match for Oakley. *See, Marvin, what I meant was that he wants to fight a colored guy, but is afraid to fight you cause you could beat him.* But try as I did, I couldn't for a moment convince myself that Marvin would believe me. I meant it *that* way and no other. Everybody heard. Everybody knew. That afternoon I forced myself to confront the notion that tomorrow I would probably have to fight both Oakley and Marvin. I'd have to be two men.

I rose from my desk and walked to the window. The light made my skin look orange, and I started thinking about what Wickham had told us once about light. She said that oranges and apples, leaves and flowers, the whole multicolored world, was not what it appeared to be. The colors we see, she said, look like they do only because of the light or ray that shines on them. "The color of the thing isn't what you see, but the light that's reflected off it." Then she shut out the lights and shone a white light lamp on a prism. We watched the pale splay of colors on the projector screen; some people ooohed and aaahed. Suddenly, she switched on a black light and the color of everything changed. The prism colors vanished, Wickham's arms were purple, the buttons of her dress were as orange as hot coals, rather than the blue they had been only seconds before. We were all very quiet. "Nothing," she said after a while, "is really what it appears to be." I didn't really understand then. But as I stood at the window, gazing at my orange skin, I wondered what kind of light I could shine on Marvin, Oakley, and me that would reveal us as the same.

I sat down and stared at my arms. They were dark brown again. I worked up a bit of saliva under my tongue and spat on my left arm. I spat again, then rubbed the spittle into it, polishing, working till my arm grew warm. As I spat, and rubbed, I wondered why Marvin did this weird, nasty thing to himself, day after day. Was he trying to rub away the black, or deepen it, doll it up? And if he did this weird nasty thing for a hundred years, would he spit-shine himself invisible, rolling away the eggplant skin, revealing the scarlet muscle, blue vein, pink and yellow tendon, white bone? Then disappear? Seen through, all colors, no colors. Spitting and rubbing. Is this the way you do it? I leaned forward, sniffed the arm. It smelled vaguely of mayonnaise. After an hour or so, I fell asleep.

I saw Oakley the second I stepped off the bus the next morning. He stood outside the gym in his usual black penny loafers, white socks, high-water jeans, T-shirt and black jacket. Nailor stood with him, his big teeth spread across his bottom lip like playing cards. If there was anyone I felt like fighting, that day, it was Nailor. But I wanted to put off fighting for as long as I could. I stepped toward the gymnasium, thinking that I shouldn't run, but if I hurried I could beat Oakley to the door and secure myself near Gilchrest's office. But the moment I stepped into the gym, I felt Oakley's broad palm clap down on my shoulder. "Might as well stay out here, Coonie," he said. "I need me a little target practice." I turned to face him and he slapped me, one-two, with the back, then the palm of his hand, as I'd seen Bogart do to Peter Lorre in *The Maltese Falcon*. My heart went wild. I could scarcely breathe. I couldn't swallow.

"Call me a nigger," I said. I have no idea what made me say this. All I know is that it kept me from crying. "Call me a nigger, Oakley."

He slapped me again, scratching my eye. "I don't do what coonies tell me."

"Call me a nigger."

"Outside, Coonie."

"Call me one. Go ahead."

He lifted his hand to slap me again, but before his arm could swing my way, Marvin Pruitt came from behind me and calmly pushed me aside. "Git out my way, boy," he said. And he slugged Oakley on the side of his head. Oakley stumbled back, stiff-legged. His eyes were big. Marvin hit him twice more, once again to the side of the head, once to the nose. Oakley went down and stayed down. Though blood was drawn, whistles blowing, fingers pointing, kids hollering, Marvin just stood there, staring at me with cool eyes. He spat on the ground, licked his lips, and just stared at me, till Coach Gilchrest and Mr. Calderon tackled him and violently carried him away. He never struggled, never took his eyes off me.

Nailor and Mrs. Wickham helped Oakley to his feet. His already fattened nose bled and swelled so that I had to look away. He looked around, bemused, wall-eyed, maybe scared. It was apparent he had no idea how bad he was hurt. He didn't even touch his nose. He didn't look like he knew much of anything. He looked at me, looked me dead in the eye in fact, but didn't seem to recognize me.

That morning, like all other mornings, we said the Pledge of Allegiance, sang "The Yellow Rose of Texas," "The Eyes of Texas Are upon You," and "Mistress Shady." The room stood strangely empty without Oakley, and without Marvin, but at the same time you could feel their presence more intensely somehow. I felt like I did when I'd walk into my mother's room and could smell my father's cigars, or cologne. He was more palpable, in certain respects, than when there in actual flesh. For some reason, I turned to look at Ah-so, and just this once I let my eyes linger on her face. She had a very gentle-looking face, really. That surprised me. She must have felt my eyes on her because she glanced up at me for a second and smiled, white teeth, downcast eyes. Such a pretty smile. That surprised me too. She held it for a few seconds, then let it fade. She looked down at her desk, and sat still as a photograph.

## For Better Reading: Strength Vs. Weakness

"Despising my weakness ... I bragged."
"Sometimes even when you know better you just go along ..."
These two quotations, one by author Wallace Stegner and one by the main character of "Junkie-Joe Had Some Money," are examples of some-one's willingness to admit a personal failing.

When you read, it's important to know whether or not you can trust the word of a non-fiction writer or first-person narrator of a story or novel.

How do you decide?

Owning up to a weakness is hard. When someone admits a shortcoming, you can generally assume that person values truthfulness, not just on a personal basis but also in dealing with others.

In this way, someone often shows a positive quality by confessing to a weak point. Yet such openness can be misleading. By not looking deeply enough, a reader may see only the flaw and miss the high standards that another person holds and is striving to attain.

In "The Kind of Light That Shines on Texas," the ability of Clint Oates to judge his own mistakes and weaknesses invites recognition as a positive trait.

## Cause and Effect

1. Clint Oates, the narrator, wanted to be a model student because he thought (a) this would cause Mrs. Wickham to pass him (b) it would make his mother happy (c) he felt he was being misjudged (d) it protected him from Oakley's insults.
2. Clint guessed that Ah-so refused to speak because she (a) had given up (b) was bored (c) had a speech impediment (d) was overweight and embarrassed.
3. When he got home from school, Clint's first question was "Hear from Dad?" because (a) he wanted to avoid telling his mother about school (b) it was the one topic both he and his mother cared about (c) he felt worried and vulnerable with his father gone from home (d) they had not heard from his father in over three months.

## Questioning the Story

1. What admission does Clint Oates make about his classmate Marvin Pruitt in the first paragraph? Why would Marvin cause him to have each of the following feelings: embarrassment, pity, uneasiness.
2. Why was Clint new to the school and therefore unfamiliar with "Texan educational practices of the 1960s"? According to Clint, what was the only thing he knew about Texas schools?
3. What did Clint find distasteful about his own behavior towards Mrs. Wickham? Why did he act this way?
4. What about Oakley would cause the narrator to say, "I might have grown to admire him"? How did he actually feel and why?
5. What did Clint say that made Oakley tell him, "*Yer* dead"? In effect, of what had Clint accused him?
6. After threatening Clint, how did Oakley start "going after" him during gym class ? In their games of murderball, how did the other boys first show their feelings that Clint "belonged to Oakley"?
7. When playing "murderball" one day, why were Oakley and Clint left as the only players? How did the coach change the rules for the final five minutes of class? What "excuse" did the one-on-one contest give Oakley for fighting Clint?
8. What are two ways that Clint tried to escape from fighting Oakley? Why did he feel "I'd have to be two men"?
9. After the fight, how did the school day begin as usual? How did Clint feel about the absence of both Oakley and Marvin? In what two ways did Ah-so surprise Clint?

# Looking Deeper

## I. Beyond the Obvious

In what ways did Oakley's hatred of Clint go beyond his being black? When a boy in the locker room told Clint, "Jest go on and git it over with," why would they be able to share some of Clint's feelings? How might this have affected their playing in gym class?

What reasons did Clint have for feeling different and all alone, both at school and at home? After first telling Oakley to fight Marvin instead of himself, Clint thought, "I'd done something to him ... done something to myself"? Why does he feel this way concerning Marvin? Even though he won the fight, in what ways has Marvin "lost"? What did Clint feel he had done to himself?

In what respects does Clint want to be like his father? What positive values does Clint either exhibit or wish to possess? Give at least three examples and supporting illustrations.

## II. "The Light That Shines . . ."

What did Clint wonder about Marvin's "nasty habit" of polishing his skin? Before the fight, Marvin "calmly" pushed Clint aside, saying "Git out of my way, boy," and afterward, just stood there, "staring ... with cool eyes." Why do you think he fought in place of Clint? Why was he so "calm" and "cool"?

Wallace Stegner wrote, "Despising my weakness ... I bragged." In what way might these words apply to Oakley? What difference did Clint briefly see in Ah-so the morning after the fight? What does her smile seem to indicate?

While in his room, Clint thought of a lesson in which Mrs. Wickham told the class, "The color of the thing isn't what you see, but the light that's reflected off it." How might this idea apply to prejudice?

# Assignment: Gang Warfare

## by Gordon Parks

**Born:** *Fort Scott, Kansas*
**Early life:** *Became homeless at 15, took jobs as busboy, waiter, piano player, janitor*
**Adult life:** *Widely-traveled as photographer, correspondent*
**Famous as:** *Writer/photographer, novelist, composer, poet, painter*

MOST BLACKS WERE WEIGHTED WITH the denial of opportunity but I had been fortunate to be able to shove aside those restrictive boundaries. Now what I wanted was what so many photographers, black and white, found almost impossible to get; a staff job at *Life* magazine. That publication wasn't exactly trumpeting the black man's cause, but it would be a prestigious base for me to work from since it was so well known and reached millions of readers throughout the world. So one morning I took my portfolio to Wilson Hicks, the magazine's picture editor, and asked for a job. Miraculously he decided to give me a try.

Wilson Hicks later explained his decision to me: "There was a scarcity of documentary photographers on the staff, and none with fashion experience, and we sorely needed someone to cover the Paris collections. It was that simple."

But even later I learned it *wasn't* that simple. Hicks had to be cajoled into my acceptance by two senior editors, John Dille and Sally Kirkland, who ran the fashion department. I could serve both their needs. He wanted a powerful documentary story for an upcoming issue, and she was frantically preparing for the French collections.

Eyeing me with skepticism, Hicks had thrown out a question that caught me off guard: "Have you something in mind that you'd like to do?"

"Yes I do," I lied, never expecting things would get so far so quickly. "A gang war is taking place up in Harlem, and I'd like to cover it." Then hurriedly I concocted a deeper reason. "Such a story might help black kids realize the folly in murdering one another."

Hicks wasn't impressed. It would be easier to freeze snowballs in hell, he replied dryly. But after a terribly long moment he caved in. "Okay, I'll go along with that idea, but I can only offer you five hundred dollars."

"So little?" I was astounded.

Dille cut in quickly. "Take it—just take it. Everything will work out." Reluctantly I agreed to the price. It was an opening. Once outside Hicks's office Dille assured me that I would work with an unlimited expense account. This made *very* good sense. It had been a tense session, but both Sally and John were contented, and I was secretly ecstatic—yet apprehensive as well. It was indeed a tough assignment, and I was now struck with the impossibility of pulling it off.

The next morning I drove up to Harlem in the Buick Roadmaster I had bought—against Stryker's advice—in search of a gang leader. It was like searching for a bubble in the sea. For a week I drove around up there, with Hicks's doubts overlapping my own. Why would any sensible gang leader, having just blown away somebody, want his face spread over the pages of *Life* magazine? And why should he take me, a stranger, into his confidence? Doggedly I kept on with the search.

I was at the 125th Street police precinct one morning talking with a detective friend, Jimmie Morrow, when luck arrived in the person of a sixteen-year-old, freckle-faced boy with a prizefighter's build and demeanor. The obscenities he was hurling at the desk sergeant were strong enough to get his head cracked, but the sergeant sat quietly, red-faced.

Amazed, I turned and looked at Jimmie questioningly. He smiled. "That's your man if you can talk him into it."

Red Jackson was *the* Harlem gang leader. Now the crown prince of the Midtowners, he was cursing out the desk sergeant for failing to give his gang the protection it had been promised—not from the police, but from a rival gang that had killed a Midtowner the day before. The police, recognizing him as the most powerful leader in the slaughter that was taking place, had asked him to pull back and help cool things off. Now, having lost one of his gang, he was giving vent to his anger.

I followed him into the street. "Hi, Red."

He turned on me with a look of hostility. "Who are you, man, a cop or a stoolie?"

"Neither. I'm just a friend of Jimmie Morrow's."

"He's a cop."

"Yeh, I know. He told me who you are."

"So?"

"I've got a problem I'd like to talk with you about."

He looked at me from head to foot. "What's your problem?"

"I'm a photographer with *Life* magazine and I would like to hang out with you and your gang."

"You ain't got a problem, man. You've got a death wish."

His answer was chilling, but it had merit. "I'm willing to take the chance. How about it?"

"You must take me for a real patsy. Why would I do something stupid as that?"

"Jimmie Morrow was telling me about your problems with the desk sergeant. Maybe I could be some help to you in some way."

His eyes narrowed. "The only help you can give me is by kicking that sergeant in the head for lying to me. Later, man." He started walking off.

"Can I give you a lift somewhere?"

"I've got carfare."

I opened the door of the Roadmaster. "Come on, I'll take you where you're going."

"That your rod?" Evidently he liked what he saw.

"Yeh, it's mine."

"Okay. I'll let you drop me at 116th Street." He got in, and as I drove along slowly he patted the upholstery admiringly. "Man, this rod must have cost you some big bread. How long you had it?"

"About four months. Do you like it?"

He rubbed the dashboard. "It's a gas. How fast will it go?"

"Over a hundred on a straightaway."

"You ever let it out all the way?"

"Never had any cause to."

We stopped at a red light. "What's this about *Life* magazine?"

I thought deeply and then took a chance on the validity of those thoughts. "I'm going to come clean with you, Red. This story I want to do is a big one and an important one."

"What makes it so important?"

"You—and a lot of other black kids are knocking one another off for some stupid reasons. Think of yourself as brothers, then you'll see that it doesn't make any sense."

The light changed and we drove off. "That sounds like some of that sergeant's bull we fell for. Tells me to lay back. Said he'd take care of things. Then wham, a Midtowner's pulled out of the river with four slugs in his head. I know who did it and their asses belong to the Midtowners, man."

"So you go on killing one another?"

"You have to kill to live in this place, man. Don't you understand?"

"I'd hate to find out tomorrow that you'd got it."

"I would, too, but you have to expect to take the lumps."

We were approaching 116th Street and time was running out. "I want to help you get rid of those lumps."

"How? How're you going to do that?"

"With your help. Look, Red, you can't like facing death every day. Nobody does, not even your enemies. If I get a good story that appeals to all of the gangs, then things might really cool off."

He laughed derisively. "Hell, man, those cats won't even see your magazine, let alone read it. They don't even read anything. I don't."

"They'll read it if they see your picture."

"My picture?"

"Yeh, and the rest of the Midtowners."

We turned into 116th Street. It was teeming with black people, and it was a hot day. Fire hydrants, turned on by the Midtowners, were flooding the streets and cooling off the neighborhood kids. He pointed at a squalid tenement. "This is where I get off." He got out and slammed the door shut. "Thanks for the lift."

I made one more try. "How about it, Red?"

His eyes had shifted to a second-story window where a scantily clad girl leaned on the sill. "I'll talk to my war lords about it. Pick me up here about this time tomorrow. I'll let you know what they say. Later," he said as he headed for the second floor. I didn't feel as though I had made any sort of an impression, but I expected that my new Roadmaster had, and I drove back downtown with my hopes pinned upon it.

Red wasn't easy to find the next day. No one, it appeared, had even heard of Red Jackson. Obviously I was being taken for a detective, and I felt deceived. After hanging around outside his building on 116th Street for two hours I was driving off when a younger replica of Red came up to the car. "You the cat who brought my brother home yesterday?"

"That's me." I felt relieved.

He turned, cupped his hands around his mouth and hollered, "Red!" After a few seconds the window on the second floor went up and Red stuck his head out. His torso was bare. "Yeh!"

"Your man's down here!"

The girl came to his side and he put his arms around her naked shoulders. "I'll be down in a few minutes. Tell him to cool it!"

The few minutes lasted for another hour. By the time he arrived my car was surrounded by Midtowners. The four war lords had bunched themselves together in the back seat. The front seat was left for Red. Obviously he had spread the word, and it looked as though the Midtowners had agreed to take on a chauffeur with a big new Roadmaster. No other gang in Harlem could make such an extravagant boast. Red got in and nodded toward his henchmen in the back of the car. "They're Herbie, Joey, Butch and Jimmy. Fellows, this is Mr. Parks."

"Hi—fellows. Good to meet you." Silence. "Well, Red, where to?"

"Just cruise around. Want'a look the turf over."

The turf, spreading between the Harlem and the Hudson Rivers, and that space between 116th Street and 135th Street, was inhabited by more people than a lot of small American towns with a mayor. And it was a long, nervous cruise that lasted until four in the morning—interlaced with hotdogs and soft drinks I gladly supplied.

A week had passed before Red asked me when I was going to start using my camera. It was a small one and in my jacket pocket. I smiled and patted it. "Whenever something happens." With his Humphrey Bogart look, Red lit a cigarette, took a long drag and blew out the smoke. "You know, Mr. Parks, we like you—but we don't like double-crossers."

"I dig you, Red," I replied coolly but uncomfortably, with the thought that there might be a very thin line between betrayal and honest reporting. It was not the time to discuss the delicacy of that difference. "Always remember this, Red—you can trust me, and I hope to trust you."

"You're on," he replied, and we slapped hands.

That trust was cemented by two incidents that took place shortly after that. I had casually mentioned that my exposure meter was suddenly missing.

"That little black thing with a needle and numbers?"

"Yeh. The guys were playing around with it the other day."

The following morning Herbie handed me the meter—with a great big apology. Then one afternoon the police burst into the basement of the Midtowners' headquarters. Someone had reported a rumble in progress. When I pulled out my *Life* magazine credentials and convinced them that I was doing a "social study" on Harlem youth, they left immediately. Red was flabbergasted. "The flatfoots would'a cracked our heads if you hadn't been here, man."

In the weeks to follow I found how indifferent death could be in this warring place, where honor meant spilling blood over the most trivial thing—an accidental bump on the shoulder; a dispute over a stolen bicycle; an invasion of the wrong territory; a girl's innocent wink; or a game of stickball. Teenagers, talking death, took blood oaths to die together. Mothers feared a knock at the door; afraid it was the police to say that a son was dead. All the Midtowners had knife or bullet wounds, and they wore them with bravura. They were like badges of courage. Such passionate allegiance, Red explained, had good reason.

"It's for protection. You wise up fast here in Harlem. You join up with somebody or keep getting your ass kicked. They say, 'You belong to a gang, cat?' 'No.' 'You got some loot?' 'No, I ain't got none.' Then—bop! Bop! Bop! 'Next time you better have some!' If you've got some the next time they take it and you get bopped anyway. If you're a Midtowner, they think twice before starting anything, 'cause they know they'll have to rumble."

As the Midtowners moved toward the first rumble I experienced with them, it was drizzling. Dusk had fallen and there was an ominous feel in the air. As we rode along Red calmly told me how he became boss of the Midtowners.

"Cappy was our leader then, and I was right beside him. The Harlem Dukes had us outnumbered, and they was coming at us hot and heavy. Pow! Pow! Pow! Cappy went down and blood was popping out of his head and I knew he was gone. I grabbed his .38 and started shooting with two guns, shooting and running. Pow! Pow! And two of their cats fell. Then the bastards turned tail while I kept banging away at their asses. Next day I was made the head man."

Now the Midtowners were about to settle matters with the same Harlem Dukes. One had called Red's sister a bitch and spit on her shoe. She didn't know his name; no matter, that was reason enough for a rumble. The point of encounter was on Eighth Avenue near 135th Street, less than two blocks from the 135th police precinct. We left the car at 125th Street, met twelve other Midtowners and started walking. Red, wearing dark glasses and an old trench coat I had given him, looked every bit the leader. The others, packing revolvers, zip guns and chains, moved along stealthily. Red had given orders two hours before, and they were ready. A police car passed, slowed, then went on.

I was carrying a small camera the *Life* technicians had rigged up. The infrared flash, they told me, would hardly be discernible—just a small flicker of light in the darkness. My feelings were split. Those of the reporter pulsed for action. Yet, in human terms I worried about the possible consequences. Swiftly and silently the Midtowners walked into rival territory. Then Red's hand shot up, signaling us to stop. He gave a quick nod of his head, and three of the most powerful of them slammed their weight against a basement door. My nerves were scrambling as we broke into the Dukes' den, taking them by surprise.

Tiger Johnson, the rival leader, leaped to his feet, but before he could grab a lead pipe, Red knocked him to the floor with a brutal right. The Midtowners aimed their weapons, and seven of the Dukes stood motionless as Red put a switchblade to Tiger's throat. "Which one of you bastards spit on my sister?" Tiger's eyes snapped toward a boy crouching beside him. "I'm sorry, man," the boy mumbled.

"Get to your feet, punk!" Red ordered. The boy rose slowly with fear in his eyes, and fear was bolting through me as well. "Open your shirt, punk!" The boy opened the buttons at his chest. When Red placed the point of the blade just above his heart I snapped the shutter and froze. "Say it again, punk, and make it loud."

"I'm sorry, man!" Sweat was rolling down his face and chest. Red flicked the blade upward for about a quarter of an inch. The boy moaned as a thin trickle of blood came, and I felt like turning away. "You're lucky I don't cut out your heart and make you eat it!" Inwardly I sighed a sigh of relief. He spat on the boy's chest and dropped him with a terrible right. "Frisk these other punks!" That was done quickly with expertise, then we backed out of the place—with the Midtowners' arsenal swelled by four pistols, five knives and six zip guns. Then we were out of the block as swiftly and silently as we had come.

Three weeks later Joey, a Midtowners war lord, was knifed to death by the Sabers, another gang. On the third day Red and Herbie, his chief war counselor, went to the funeral home where Joey's body lay. "You had better travel light," Red had warned me. "We may have to do some running." I went as lightly burdened as possible, wearing a pair of sneakers. Only Red and Herbie went in to see the body. The others waited outside to stand guard in case the Sabers showed up.

The funeral home attendant came to stand beside us as we viewed Joey's body. "Would you mind leaving us alone with our friend, man?" Red's request was more like an order, and the attendant obeyed it. I cringed as Red lifted his war lord's head and examined the cuts on the neck and skull, then placed it back in position. "They did a good job on him," he mumbled. "They gonna get the same treatment. Let's go."

A few minutes later we *were* running from an attempted Saber ambush, and people were hurrying for shelter as we fled to an empty second-story hideout to escape the Sabers. Once there, Red knocked out a window, reached for his .38 and prepared to start firing. From a dark corner I photographed him. It was that photograph that made him known throughout the world. Further violence was avoided when two police cars from the 135th Street precinct careened into the block.

Twelve days later a Saber was killed, but a Midtowner's stomach was badly slashed during that rumble. Since the police would be searching the hospitals, two of the Midtowners stitched the gaping wound together with needle and thread. I had seen enough bloodshed to last me for a lifetime, and I believed I had the story I had come for. Two weeks later the Red Jackson story was on the stands.

There had been some contention between the editors and myself during the layout of the story. They had wanted to show Red on the cover with a smoking gun in his hand. I fought against it, even destroyed the negative to be sure it wasn't used for such a purpose. After the story was published I brought the Midtowners to my house in White Plains to spend a day with my two sons, hoping that among the trees, fields and horses, they would lean toward a better kind of existence. They were, for that Saturday, just kids eating hotdogs and swilling down soft drinks and riding my sons' horses. It was a good day for them, for my family, and for me. I remember sitting by Red as he tossed pebbles into a stream. "Why'd you bring us up here, Mr. Parks?" (It was never Gordon as I had once suggested.) "My family wanted you to come. Wouldn't you like to get out of Harlem someday, away from all the violence?" I asked.

He had smiled sadly. "Oh, I'd like to, but not a chance—not a chance." Then he asked a favor of me. "Why don't you let your son Gordon spend a weekend in Harlem with us? You won't have to worry. We'll take good care of him."

"I'm sure you will, but you'll have to promise—no rumbles."

"No rumbles," he promised, and we slapped hands. Gordon did go to spend a weekend with Red. And a promise made was a promise kept. "Dad, I had a hell of a good time," my son reported when he returned.

The most disturbing thing about that assignment was the double edge it presented; if a war did break out boys would die; without the uncommon violence they indulged in, the story itself would have died.

As things went, another Midtowner died when gunfire cut through the noise of Harlem two months later. While reading about it I seemed to be there, but observing safely from behind a steel curtain, devastated, knowing there was nothing I might have done to prevent the tragedy. I had tried to lay the horror of gang war before the nation, hoping that somehow a way could be found to end it. Perhaps someone paid attention; the following year passed with just a few Harlem gang murders. For the time being it seemed that youth's killing of youth was slowly coming to a halt.

Now, forty years later, hard drugs have become the rainbow, and again youthful gangs roam city streets killing one another—protecting their little kingdoms of heroin and crack. Gunfire erupts nightly, and unfortunately black teenagers are caught dead-center of the catastrophe. Despair settles in and they try burning it out with alcohol and hard drugs. In a short time they fade into mere shadows of themselves; into nothingness, then early death. Spun from the loom of such disaster is a remarkably cold statistic. The average black male in Harlem is fortunate to live past the age of forty. Pausing now to look back, I see myself in the distance—leaving there with a sigh of thankfulness.

Red Jackson's fate was less final than it had seemed when I found him leading the Midtowners in Harlem back in 1948. After almost forty years a letter came assuring me that, for him, time had beneficently wielded its power. With learned humility he wrote:

"Dear Gordon, I saw my picture in *Life* again the other day, and it brought back some bad memories. That story was a big ego trip for me. At fifty-six, I've been through the mill, and along the way I've met dozens of ghetto kids that wound up the same way I did. Now, with your help, I would like to reach some of them and tell them how quickly glory faded from me, and that there's a much better way to go. I might wind up saving some of them. Even one would be worth it. I would like to help a few Harlem kids to get an education. That's the key: Education! Would you believe that at my age I'm preparing to take the test for my High School Equivalency Diploma? I love it! And I'd love to hear from you again. Yours truly, Red Jackson."

A door from Red's sordid past had finally opened up, and he had chosen to walk through it to a better kind of life. Time had deceived both of us. Now I could firmly believe he would make it—something that I had for so long doubted. The letter had been dated January 5, 1987. He had taken a long step from his old unhappiness.

## For Better Reading: *Voices in the Mirror*

The possibility of hearing "voices in the mirror" shouldn't sound strange or crazy to most people. Everyone sees others' faces more often than his or her own. And sometimes in a mirror, one's own face looks like a stranger—who might have something important to say, if given the chance to speak.

*Voices in the Mirror* is the title of Gordon Parks' autobiography, from which the foregoing chapter was taken. In his book, Parks describes a morning when he was a young man. Looking into the mirror while shaving, he asked himself some bothersome questions and got some straight answers back.

Here are a few:

"You're approaching manhood and you dislike yourself . . . [*Well, make up your mind to do something about it.*] . . . The softest criticism rubs you raw. [*Accept criticism, man. It can't hurt, and it could be helpful.*] . . . Envy of others' success hangs around your neck like a rope. [*That's stupid. Use their success to give you inspiration.*] . . ."

As you think about Parks' experiences starting out as a reporter for *Life* magazine, decide how well he listened to those "voices in the mirror" . . . or benefited from his own advice!

## Important Details

1. When Parks first meets Red Jackson, the Harlem gang leader (a) has just been brought in for questioning (b) is accusing the desk sergeant

of breaking a promise (c) has come to seek protection from a rival gang (d) is eager to sell his story for ready cash.

2. After meeting Parks, Red seems most impressed with (a) his offer of payment and protection (b) his acceptance of Red's viewpoints (c) the opportunity to "be somebody" (d) the chance to ride in Parks' car.

3. Parks shows his confidence in Red and the Midtowners by (a) lending them money (b) letting his son spend a weekend with them (c) writing a recommendation for Red (d) accepting their account of Joey's injuries.

## Questioning the Selection

1. How does Parks' versatility as a photographer get him a chance on the *Life* staff? How does an impulsive answer determine his first assignment?

2. What beneficial purpose does he "concoct" for doing the story? Why does it at first seem impossible to pull off?

3. Parks told Red, ". . . You can't like facing death every day. Nobody does . . ." Although he sneered at these words, how does Red's comment "You have to kill to live" help confirm Parks' belief? Using examples from the entire selection, give other ways that Red's words, attitude, and actions help prove Parks right.

4. What two incidents cement the trust between Parks and the Midtowners?

5. How had Red become leader of the Midtowners? What starts the first rumble Parks experiences? Why was or wasn't this typical?

6. What conflicting feelings does Parks have as the fight begins? Why did Parks feel relieved by the outcome?

7. Why did Parks argue with the *Life* editors about the cover photo of Red Jackson? How did Parks make sure of getting his way? What was Parks risking by going against his editors?

8. Why does Parks feel he has "seen enough bloodshed" in 1948? Almost 40 years later, what are his feelings about present day gangs? What hope does the selection offer in Red Jackson's example?

# Looking Deeper

## I. Backward Glances

On a personal level, does Parks seem to have listened to his "voices in the mirror"? Although he said he "lied" in saying he had the gang warfare story in mind, did he show himself sincere about hoping to "help black kids realize the folly in murdering one another"? Why might this have been, especially for Parks, a topic already on his mind? Support your answers with valid proof.

## II. " . . . A Better Way to Go"

What positive qualities did Red and his gang exhibit, even at the height of their gang days? In what ways are the gangs of the Midtowners' time similar to and different from those of today?

─────────────────── **REFLECTIONS** ───────────────────

Unlike the "stuff of legends," almost all of the selections in this unit are about people trying to "measure up" to the standards and values they've set for themselves—their individual codes of ethics.

It's often not easy, as you've seen. It may be courage overwhelmed by impossible odds, honesty gripped by fear, or loyalties divided that hold a person back.

Yet, though it's not always possible to live up to the ideal, that doesn't make values unimportant. As these selections show, the opinion that matters most is not someone else's. What counts is the person looking back from the mirror—who knows you from the inside, as well as the outside.

Americans have a record of expecting a lot from themselves, as well as from their country. And falling short is often a sign of how high someone has been aiming.

### To Write About or to Discuss

1. The selections in this unit are mostly examples of realism, or writing about ordinary people and their problems as they really are. Choose one example and explain why you find it true to life.
2. Courage, honesty, thoughtfulness. Compare two characters in the light of one of these three character traits. How closely did they come to their own ideal, and what were the forces working for and against them?
3. A voice in the mirror. Imagine yourself a character in one of the selections or make up a character of your own. Then, write a dialogue between that person and his or her reflection.

# UNIT 5

# The American Dream

"I HAVE A DREAM ..."

"We hold these truths to be self-evident: that all men are created equal; that they are endowed by their creator with certain unalienable rights; that among these are life, liberty, and the pursuit of happiness."

" ... Our fathers brought forth on this continent a new nation, conceived in liberty and dedicated to the proposition that all men are created equal."

Words, words, words—from speeches, documents, and even advertising—words become slogans, beliefs, and ideas that Americans choose to live by.

"I still have a dream," said Martin Luther King, Jr. "It is a dream deeply rooted in the American Dream."

> Equality, human rights, the pursuit of happiness
> Success, popularity, power
> Money, love, fame
> Some may express the dream as symbols:
> $  ♡  ☆

And others sum up "what's good" about American life by naming ordinary things with popular appeal like "baseball, hot dogs and apple pie," symbols in themselves.

To find America, you must hear the constant echoes of the American Dream, which still calls people the world over to share in America's promise.

In this unit, you'll meet individual Americans engaged in their own "pursuit of happiness." As you read, look for ways that the deeper beliefs of the American Dream—found in the words of Jefferson, Lincoln, and King—color everyday ideas, words, and deeds.

# The Electrical Wizard

## *by John Dos Passos*

| | |
|---|---|
| ***Born:*** | *Chicago, Illinois, 1896* |
| ***Family:*** | *Portuguese descent on father's side* |
| ***Early life:*** | *Harvard graduate, ambulance driver and medical corpsman in Europe in World War I* |
| ***Famous as:*** | *Author of trilogy U.S.A.* |

EDISON WAS BORN IN MILAN, Ohio, in eighteen-fortyseven;

Milan was a little town on the Huron River that for a while was the wheatshipping port for the whole Western Reserve; the railroads took away the carrying trade, the Edison family went up to Port Huron in Michigan to grow up with the country;

his father was a shinglemaker who puttered round with various small speculations; he dealt in grain and feed and lumber and built a wooden tower a hundred feet high; tourists and excursionists paid a quarter each to go up the tower and look at the view over Lake Huron and the St. Clair River and Sam Edison became a solid and respected citizen of Port Huron.

Thomas Edison went to school for only three months because the teacher thought he wasn't right bright. His mother taught him what she knew at home and read eighteenth-century writers with him, Gibbon and Hume and Newton, and let him rig up a laboratory in the cellar.

Whenever he read about anything he went down cellar and tried it out.

When he was twelve he needed money to buy books and chemicals; he got a concession as newsbutcher on the daily train from Detroit to Port Huron. In Detroit there was a public library and he read it.

He rigged up a laboratory on the train and whenever he read about anything he tried it out. He rigged up a printing press and printed a paper called *The Herald,* when the Civil War broke out he organized a newsservice and cashed in on the big battles. Then he dropped a stick of phosphorus and set the car on fire and was thrown off the train.

By that time he had considerable fame in the country as the boy editor of the first newspaper to be published on a moving train. The London *Times* wrote him up.

He learned telegraphy and got a job as night operator at Stratford Junction in Canada, but one day he let a freight-train get past a switch and had to move on.

(During the Civil War a man that knew telegraphy could get a job anywhere.)

Edison traveled round the country taking jobs and dropping them and moving on, reading all the books he could lay his hands on; whenever he read about a scientific experiment he tried it out, whenever he could get near an engine he'd tinker with it, whenever they left him alone in a telegraph office he'd do tricks with the wires. That often lost him the job and he had to move on.

He was tramp operator through the whole Middle West: Detroit, Cincinnati, Indianapolis, Louisville, New Orleans, always broke, his clothes stained with chemicals, always trying tricks with the telegraph.

He worked for the Western Union in Boston.

In Boston he doped out the model of his first patent, an automatic vote recorder for use in Congress, but they didn't want an automatic voterecorder in Congress, so Edison had the trip to Washington and made some debts and that was all he got out of that; he worked out a stockticker and burglar alarms and burned all the skin off his face with nitric acid.

But New York was already the big market for stocks and ideas and gold and greenbacks.

*(This part is written by Horatio Alger:)*

When Edison got to New York he was stony broke and had debts in Boston and Rochester. This was when gold was at a premium and Jay Gould was trying to corner the gold market. Wall Street was crazy. A man named Law had rigged up an electric indicator (Callahan's invention) that indicated the price of gold in brokers' offices. Edison, looking for a job, broke and with no place to go, had been hanging round the central office passing the time of day with the operators when the general transmitter stopped with a crash in the middle of a rush day of nervous trading; everybody in the office lost his head. Edison stepped up and fixed the machine and landed a job at three hundred dollars a month.

In sixtynine, the year of Black Friday, he started an electrical engineering firm with a man named Pope.

From then on he was on his own; he invented a stock ticker and it sold. He had a machineshop and a laboratory; whenever he thought of a device he tried it out. He made forty thousand dollars out of the Universal Stock Ticker.

He rented a shop in Newark and worked on an automatic telegraph and on devices for sending two and four messages at the same time over the same wire.

In Newark he tinkered with Sholes on the first typewriter, and invented the mimeograph, the carbon rheostat, the microtasimeter, and first made paraffin paper.

Something he called etheric force worried him; he puzzled a lot about etheric force but it was Marconi who cashed in on the Hertzian waves. Radio was to smash the ancient universe. Radio was to kill the old Euclidian God, but Edison was never a man to worry about philosophical concepts;

he worked all day and all night tinkering with cogwheels and bits of copperwire and chemicals in bottles; whenever he thought of a device he tried it out. He made things work. He wasn't a mathematician. I can hire mathematicians but mathematicians can't hire me, he said.

In eighteen-seventysix he moved to Menlo Park where he invented the carbon transmitter that made the telephone a commercial proposition, that made the microphone possible

he worked all day and all night and produced

the phonograph

the incandescent electric lamp

and systems of generation, distribution, regulation and measurement of electric current, sockets, switches, insulators, manholes. Edison worked out the first system of electric light using the direct current and small unit lamps and the multiple arc that were installed in London Paris New York and Sunbury Pennsylvania,

the threewire system,

the magnetic ore separator,

an electric railway.

He kept them busy at the Patent Office filing patents and caveats.

To find a filament for his electric lamp that would work, that would be a sound commercial proposition, he tried all kinds of paper and cloth, thread, fishline, fibre, celluloid, boxwood, coconutshells, spruce, hickory, bay, mapleshavings, rosewood, punk, cork, flax, bamboo, and the hair out of a redheaded Scotchman's beard;

whenever he got a hunch he tried it out.

In eighteen-eightyseven he moved to the huge laboratories at West Orange.

He invented rockcrushers and the fluoroscope and the reeled film for movie cameras and the alkaline storage battery and the long kiln for burning out portland cement and the kinetophone that was the first talking movie and the poured cement house that is to furnish cheap artistic identical sanitary homes for workers in the electrical age.

Thomas A. Edison at eightytwo worked sixteen hours a day;

he never worried about mathematics or the social system or generalized philosophical concepts;

in collaboration with Henry Ford and Harvey Firestone who never worried about mathematics or the social system or generalized philosophical concepts;

he worked sixteen hours a day trying to find a substitute for rubber: whenever he read about anything he tried it out: whenever he got a hunch he went to the laboratory and tried it out.

# For Better Reading: Rags to Riches

John Dos Passos notes, "This part is written by Horatio Alger" before the second half of "The Electrical Wizard." Inventor Thomas Edison, poet Maya Angelou, and several American Presidents all have this in common: their lives contain elements of a Horatio Alger story.

To some, Horatio Alger's version of the American Dream is just too good to be true. It holds the possibility of going from rags to riches with the right combination of "pluck"—courage in the face of difficulties—plus luck.

In his first novel, *Ragged Dick*, Alger told the tale of a homeless shoeshine boy, who lived in a "Box Hotel," a small packing crate with bed of straw. Published over 100 years ago and subtitled "Street Life in New York," the book was immediately popular.

Going from a homeless bootblack to "a young gentleman on the way to fame and fortune," Ragged Dick became the model for the Alger books that would follow and for anyone compared to an Alger hero today.

Yet Alger writes, "Our ragged hero wasn't a model boy ... I'm afraid he swore sometimes and now and then he played tricks upon unsophisticated boys from the country.... Another of Dick's faults was his extravagance.... However much he managed to earn during the day, all was generally spent before morning." At age fourteen, he had "formed the habit of smoking" and sometimes "strayed in" a gambling house "and played with the rest" of the young men crowded there.

Not a model boy, but "he was above doing anything mean or dishonorable. He would not steal, or cheat ... was frank and straight-forward ... and self-reliant." For Alger, the riches and luck were the reward of hard work and an honest nature.

As you read about Thomas Edison, Eugene Debs, and other Americans who have "made it," you may wish to use the Horatio Alger model as a yardstick to measure how closely they fit.

## Cause and Effect

1. Edison's mother taught him at home because (a) the family was too poor to afford proper clothing (b) Edison's parents objected to public school textbooks (c) his teacher thought Edison short on intelligence (d) Edison was expelled for playing hooky.
2. At 12, Edison worked as a newsbutcher or newsboy to (a) get away from small town life (b) buy books and chemicals (c) have spending money for snacks and shows (d) prove he could live on his own.
3. One reason Edison lost jobs as a telegrapher was that he (a) forgot to send important messages (b) played tricks with the telegraph wires (c) became a victim of economic slowdowns (d) used company lines for his newsservice.

## Questioning the Selection

1. During his early years, why doesn't Edison's family background fit the "rags to riches" model?
2. As a newsboy on the Milan-Detroit train, how does Edison show both intellectual curiosity and initiative? What does Dos Passos mean by stating Edison "cashed in on the big battles" of the Civil War?
3. In the years before going to New York, Edison in some ways seemed like his "own worst enemy." Give examples showing how his interest in reading might have led to carelessness on the job and how intellectual curiosity may have made him seem a troublemaker.
4. What were the results from Edison's first patented invention? Why is each of the following, "stocks . . . ideas . . . gold and greenbacks," a factor that would help attract Edison to New York?
5. When first in New York, how does Edison fit the profile of an Alger's "rags to riches" character? What part does luck play in his landing a job?
6. In addition to luck, how were both hard work and the willingness to fail also parts of Edison's success?
7. When searching for an electric filament, how did Edison show stick-to-itiveness? Give one or more additional examples from elsewhere in the selection.
8. Explain three areas in which Edison's inventions changed and benefited people's lives.

## Looking Deeper

### I. ". . . Written by Horatio Alger"

John Dos Passos introduces the second part of "The Electrical Wizard" as "written by Horatio Alger." Did Alger actually write it, or does Edison's life fit so perfectly that it almost seems that way?

Before answering, compare the two halves of the selection and their use of the following: slangy words like "rigged up"; words run together like "fortyseven" and "newsservice"; lists of items that seem to pile up Edison's accomplishments. Give examples from each half to illustrate your findings.

Consider that Edison's electrical engineering firm started in 1869, two years after the publication of Alger's book, *Rags to Riches*. How does this affect the probability of Alger's writing Edison's biography?

Explain your reasons for concluding whether or not "This part is written by Horatio Alger."

### II. "The Old Euclidian God"

The Greek mathematician Euclid, 300 BC, is known as the father of plane geometry. The German physicist Hertz in 1887 proved the existence of radio waves. The Italian Marconi in 1895 sent the first long-wave signals, and the "etheric force" refers to the ancient belief that a specific kind of substance or material must exist in the upper space through which radio waves travel.

Considering the definition of "etheric force," how did "Radio ... smash the ancient universe"?

Philosophy is sometimes called "thinking about thought." Edison was more interested in the practical side of life. How does this explain his attitude toward mathematics and mathematicians? In what ways are Henry Ford and Harvey Firestone similarly associated with practical results?

Although Edison, Ford, and Firestone "never worried" about their efforts' justice or injustice, how do you evaluate their effects on American society? You may need research to help in answering.

# Lover of Mankind

*by John Dos Passos*

---

DEBS WAS A RAILROADMAN, BORN in a weatherboarded shack at Terre Haute.

He was one of ten children.

His father had come to America in a sailingship in '49,

an Alsatian from Colmar; not much of a moneymaker, fond of music and reading,

he gave his children a chance to finish public school and that was about all he could do.

At fifteen Gene Debs was already working as a machinist on the Indianapolis and Terre Haute Railway.

He worked as a locomotive fireman,

clerked in a store

joined the local of the Brotherhood of Locomotive Firemen, was elected secretary, traveled all over the country as organizer.

He was a tall shamblefooted man, had a sort of gusty rhetoric that set on fire the railroad workers in their pineboarded halls

made them want the world he wanted,

a world brothers might own

where everybody would split even:

*I am not a labor leader. I don't want you to follow me or anyone else. If you are looking for a Moses to lead you out of the capitalist wilderness you will stay right where you are. I would not lead you into this promised land if I could, because if I could lead you in, someone else would lead you out.*

That was how he talked to freighthandlers and gandywalkers, to firemen and switchmen and engineers, telling them it wasn't enough to organize the railroadmen, that all workers must be organized, that all workers must be organized in the workers' co-operative commonwealth.

Locomotive fireman on many a long night's run,

under the smoke a fire burned him up, burned in gusty words that beat in pineboarded halls; he wanted his brothers to be free men.

That was what he saw in the crowd that met him at the old Wells Street Depot when he came out of jail after the Pullman strike, those were the men that chalked up nine hundred thousand votes for him in nineteen-twelve and scared the frockcoats and the tophats and diamonded hostesses at Saratoga Springs, Bar Harbor, Lake Geneva with the bogy of a Socialist president.

But where were Gene Debs's brothers in nineteen eighteen when Woodrow Wilson had him locked up in Atlanta for speaking against war,

where were the big men fond of whiskey and fond of each other, gentle rambling tellers of stories over bars in small towns in the Middle West,

quiet men who wanted a house with a porch to putter around and a fat wife to cook for them, a few drinks and cigars, a garden to dig in, cronies to chew the rag with

and wanted to work for it

and others to work for it;

where were the locomotive firemen and engineers when they hustled him off to Atlanta Penitentiary?

And they brought him back to die in Terre Haute

to sit on his porch in a rocker with a cigar in his mouth,

beside him American Beauty roses his wife fixed in a bowl;

and the people of Terre Haute and the people in Indiana and the people of the Middle West were fond of him and afraid of him and thought of him as an old kindly uncle who loved them, and wanted to be with him and to have him give them candy,

but they were afraid of him as if he had contracted a social disease, syphilis or leprosy, and thought it was too bad,

but on account of the flag

and prosperity

and making the world safe for democracy,

they were afraid to be with him,

or to think much about him for fear they might believe him;

for he said:

*While there is a lower class I am of it, while there is a criminal class I am of it, while there is a soul in prison I am not free.*


## For Better Reading: Propaganda

Who was Eugene Victor Debs? Should he be called a hero or villain, a success or failure, a friend of society or its enemy? It all depends who's telling his story.

Eugene Debs was the perfect target for attack by propaganda—ideas or information purposely spread to promote or injure someone or something. Propaganda may consist of outright lies and exaggeration. It often contains half-truths, such as "America is a violent country," ignoring the fact that America is also dedicated to seeking peace. Or it may depend on words so slanted that one speaker's "hearty snack" is the same product as another's "empty calories." Political campaigns are full of propaganda. Advertising, too.

Before making a judgment about propaganda, you need to search out the truth beneath the surface and seek the reason for its spread.

Eugene Debs was born in Terre Haute, Indiana, in 1855. After 1900, he ran five times for U.S. President as candidate of the American Socialist Party, which urged community-wide ownership and control of industry, commerce, and property. He was a labor leader who supported unions and a pacifist who rejected violence. Debs was first imprisoned for going against a legal order during a railroad strike. He was again jailed for violating the Espionage Act, at a time when many American Socialists were suspected of being Communist agents because of Russia's revolution.

Consider this information, adapted from an encyclopedia, as you question the selection. Use it to compare how a single set of facts can be slanted or colored to make the same man seem like a "Lover of Mankind"—or its opposite.

## Words in Context

1. As a labor organizer, Debs "had a sort of *gusty rhetoric* that set on fire the railroad workers in their pineboarded halls." "Gusty rhetoric" refers to his (a) tendency to "blast away" at friends and foes alike (b) breezy and casual kind of openness (c) forceful, inspiring style of speaking (d) gentlemanly appearance and shocking beliefs.
2. By winning 900,000 Presidential votes, Debs "scared . . . the tophats and diamonded hostesses at Saratoga Springs, Bar Harbor, Lake Geneva with the *bogy* of a Socialist president." The word *bogy* compares Debs to a (a) hobgoblin or evil spirit (b) missed chance or opportunity (c) thief or criminal (d) fake or counterfeit bill.
3. "The tophats" must stand for the (a) locomotive firemen (b) entire slate of Presidential candidates (c) foreign supporters of Debs (d) wealthy employers and financiers.

## Questioning the Selection

1. Give three details from Debs' family background that fit the "rags to riches" model.
2. How does Debs show the ability to become an Alger type of success?
3. Debs said, "I don't want you to follow me or anyone else." How does this fit a socialistic viewpoint? What must a "commonwealth of workers" mean?
4. How did Debs' fellow workers react when he was released from jail after the Pullman strike? What did he "see" or want for them?
5. According to the encyclopedia, Debs was "jailed from 1918–1921 for

violating the Espionage Act." What reason does Dos Passos give for this second imprisonment?

6. How did Debs' fellow workers react when he went to the Atlanta Penitentiary in 1918? "On account of" what three reasons had people become afraid of Debs? How could support of Debs affect each?

7. According to the encyclopedia, Debs was "widely revered as a martyr to his principles." Why can Debs be considered someone who suffered and sacrificed himself for his beliefs?

## Looking Deeper

### I. "Lover of Mankind"

In this selection, even the title indicates Dos Passos's purpose to present Debs favorably as a "lover of mankind." List three details that support his right to this title. If you were against Eugene Debs, how could you use the same details to create negative propaganda?

If he had not sided with the workers and "lower class," do you think Debs could have been successful as a businessman or politician? Give evidence to support your opinion.

### II. Who Was Eugene Victor Debs?

Hero or villain, success or failure, friend of society or its enemy—which is closer to the truth? Discuss your conclusions about Debs, including the reasons that back your opinions. You may wish to do additional research.

# Mammon and the Archer

*by O. Henry*

| | |
|---|---|
| ***Born:*** | *North Carolina* |
| ***Name:*** | *William Sydney Porter* |
| ***Early life:*** | *Raised by grandmother and aunt; left school at age 15* |
| ***Early jobs:*** | *Texas ranch worker, pharmacist's assistant, bookkeeper, draftsman, newspaperman, bank teller; once imprisoned for embezzlement* |
| ***Famous as:*** | *Master of the surprise ending in short stories* |

O LD ANTHONY ROCKWALL, RETIRED MANUFACTURER and proprietor of Rockwall's Eureka Soap, looked out the library window of his Fifth Avenue mansion and grinned. His neighbor to the right—the aristocratic clubman, G. Van Schuylight Suffolk-Jones—came out to his waiting motor-car, wrinkling a contumelious nostril, as usual, at the Italian renaissance sculpture of the soap palace's front elevation.

"Stuck-up old statuette of nothing doing!" commented the ex-Soap King. "The Eden Museée'll get that old frozen Nesselrode yet if he don't watch out. I'll have this house painted red, white, and blue next summer and see if that'll make his Dutch nose turn up any higher."

And then Anthony Rockwall, who never cared for bells, went to the door of his library and shouted "Mike!" in the same voice that had once chipped off pieces of the welkin on the Kansas prairies.

"Tell my son," said Anthony to the answering menial, "to come in here before he leaves the house."

When young Rockwall entered the library the old man laid aside his newspaper, looked at him with a kindly grimness on his big, smooth, ruddy countenance, rumpled his mop of white hair with one hand and rattled the keys in his pocket with the other.

"Richard," said Anthony Rockwall, "what do you pay for the soap that you use?"

Richard, only six months home from college, was startled a little. He had not yet taken the measure of this sire of his, who was as full of unexpectedness as a girl at her first party.

"Six dollars a dozen, I think, dad."

"And your clothes?"

"I suppose about sixty dollars, as a rule."

"You're a gentleman," said Anthony, decidedly. "I've heard of these young bloods spending $24 a dozen for soap, and going over the hundred mark for clothes. You've got as much money to waste as any of 'em, and yet you stick to what's decent and moderate. Now I use the old Eureka—not only for sentiment, but it's the purest soap made. Whenever you pay more than 10 cents a cake for soap you buy bad perfumes and labels. But 50 cents is doing very well for a young man in your generation, position and condition. As I said, you're a gentleman. They say it takes three generations to make one. They're off. Money'll do it as slick as soap grease. It's made you one. By hokey! it's almost made one of me. I'm nearly as impolite and disagreeable and ill-mannered as these two old knickerbocker gents on each side of me that can't sleep of nights because I bought in between'em."

"There are some things that money can't accomplish," remarked young Rockwall, rather gloomily.

"Now, don't say that," said old Anthony, shocked. "I bet my money on money every time. I've been through the encyclopedia down to Y looking for something you can't buy with it; and I expect to have to take up the appendix next week. I'm for money against the field. Tell me something money won't buy."

"For one thing," answered Richard, rankling a little, "it won't buy one into the exclusive circles of society."

"Oho! won't it?" thundered the champion of the root of evil. "You tell me where your exclusive circles would be if the first Astor hadn't had the money to pay for his steerage passage over?"

Richard sighed.

"And that's what I was coming to," said the old man, less boisterously. "That's why I asked you to come in. There's something going wrong with you, boy. I've been noticing it for two weeks. Out with it. I guess I could lay my hands on eleven millions within twenty-four hours, besides the real estate. If it's your liver, there's the *Rambler* down in the bay, coaled, and ready to steam down to the Bahamas in two days."

"Not a bad guess, dad; you haven't missed it far."

"Ah," said Anthony, keenly; "what's her name?"

Richard began to walk up and down the library floor. There was enough comradeship and sympathy in this crude old father of his to draw his confidence.

"Why don't you ask her?" demanded old Anthony. "She'll jump at you. You've got the money and the looks, and you're a decent boy. Your hands are clean. You've got no Eureka soap on 'em. You've been to college, but she'll overlook that."

"I haven't had a chance," said Richard.

"Make one," said Anthony. "Take her for a walk in the park, or a straw ride, or walk home with her from church. Chance! Pshaw!"

"You don't know the social mill, dad. She's part of the stream that turns it. Every hour and minute of her time is arranged for days in advance. I must have that girl, dad, or this town is a blackjack swamp forevermore. And I can't write it—I can't do that."

"Tut!" said the old man. "Do you mean to tell me that with all the money I've got you can't get an hour or two of a girl's time for yourself?"

"I've put it off too late. She's going to sail for Europe at noon day after to-morrow for a two years' stay. I'm to see her alone tomorrow evening for a few minutes. She's at Larchmont now at her aunt's. I can't go there. But I'm allowed to meet her with a cab at the Grand Central Station tomorrow evening at the 8:30 train. We drive down Broadway to Wallack's at a gallop, where her mother and a box party will be waiting for us in the lobby. Do you think she would listen to a declaration from me during that six or eight minutes under those circumstances? No. And what chance would I have in the theatre or afterward? None. No, dad, this is one tangle that your money can't unravel. We can't buy one minute of time with cash; if we could, rich people would live longer. There's no hope of getting a talk with Miss Lantry before she sails."

"All right, Richard, my boy," said old Anthony, cheerfully. "You may run along down to your club now. I'm glad it ain't your liver. But don't forget to burn a few punk sticks in the joss house to the great god Mazuma from time to time. You say money won't buy time? Well, of course, you can't order eternity wrapped up and delivered at your residence for a price, but I've seen Father Time get pretty bad stone bruises on his heels when he walked through the gold diggings."

That night came Aunt Ellen, gentle, sentimental, wrinkled, sighing, oppressed by wealth, in to Brother Anthony at his evening paper, and began discourse on the subject of lovers' woes.

"He told me all about it," said Brother Anthony, yawning. "I told him my bank account was at his service. And then he began to knock money. Said money couldn't help. Said the rules of society couldn't be bucked for a yard by a team of ten-millionaires."

"Oh, Anthony," sighed Aunt Ellen, "I wish you would not think so much of money. Wealth is nothing where a true affection is concerned. Love is all-powerful. If he only had spoken earlier! She could not have refused our Richard. But now I fear it is too late. He will have no opportunity to address her. All your gold cannot bring happiness to your son."

At eight o'clock the next evening Aunt Ellen took a quaint old gold ring from a moth-eaten case and gave it to Richard.

"Wear it tonight, nephew," she begged. "Your mother gave it to me. Good luck in love she said it brought. She asked me to give it to you when you had found the one you loved."

Young Rockwall took the ring reverently and tried it on his smallest finger. It slipped as far as the second joint and stopped. He took it off and stuffed it into his vest pocket, after the manner of man. And then he 'phoned for his cab.

At the station he captured Miss Lantry out of the gabbing mob at eight thirty-two.

"We mustn't keep mamma and the others waiting," said she.

"To Wallack's Theatre as fast as you can drive!" said Richard, loyally.

They whirled up Forty-second to Broadway, and then down the white-starred lane that leads from the soft meadows of sunset to the rocky hills of morning.

At Thirty-fourth Street young Richard quickly thrust up the trap and ordered the cabman to stop.

"I've dropped a ring," he apologized, as he climbed out. "It was my mother's, and I'd hate to lose it. I won't detain you a minute—I saw where it fell."

In less than a minute he was back in the cab with the ring.

But within that minute a crosstown car had stopped directly in front of the cab. The cab-man tried to pass to the left, but a heavy express wagon cut him off. He tried the right and had to back away from a furniture van that had no business to be there. He tried to back out, but dropped his reins and swore dutifully. He was blockaded in a tangled mess of vehicles and horses.

One of those street blockades had occurred that sometimes tie up commerce and movement quite suddenly in the big city.

"Why don't you drive on?" said Miss Lantry impatiently. "We'll be late."

Richard stood up in the cab and looked around. He saw a congested flood of wagons, trucks, cabs, vans and street cars filling the vast space where Broadway, Sixth Avenue, and Thirty-fourth Street cross one another as a twenty-six inch maiden fills her twenty-two inch girdle. And still from all the cross streets they were hurrying and rattling toward the converging point at full speed, and hurling themselves into the straggling mass, locking wheels and adding their drivers' imprecations to the clamor. The entire traffic of Manhattan seemed to have jammed itself around them. The oldest New Yorker among the thousands of spectators that lined the sidewalks had not witnessed a street blockade of the proportions of this one.

"I'm very sorry," said Richard, as he resumed his seat, "but it looks as if we are stuck. They won't get this jumble loosened up in an hour. It was my fault. If I hadn't dropped the ring we—"

"Let me see the ring," said Miss Lantry. "Now that it can't be helped, I don't care. I think theatres are stupid, anyway."

At 11 o'clock that night somebody tapped lightly on Anthony Rockwall's door.

"Come in," shouted Anthony, who was in a red dressing-gown, reading a book of piratical adventures.

Somebody was Aunt Ellen, looking like a gray-haired angel that had been left on earth by mistake.

"They're engaged, Anthony," she said, softly. "She has promised to marry our Richard. On their way to the theatre there was a street blockade, and it was two hours before their cab could get out of it.

"And oh, Brother Anthony, don't ever boast of the power of money again. A little emblem of true love—a little ring that symbolized unending and unmercenary affection—was the cause of our Richard finding his happiness. He dropped it in the street, and got out to recover it. And before they could continue the blockade occurred. He spoke to his love and won her there while the cab was hemmed in. Money is dross compared with true love, Anthony."

"All right," said old Anthony. "I'm glad the boy has got what he wanted. I told him I wouldn't spare any expense in the matter if—"

"But, Brother Anthony, what good could your money have done?"

"Sister," said Anthony Rockwall. "I've got my pirate in a devil of a scrape. His ship has just been scuttled, and he's too good a judge of the value of money to let drown. I wish you would let me go on with this chapter."

The story should end here. I wish it would as heartily as you who read it wish it did. But we must go to the bottom of the well for truth.

The next day a person with red hands and a blue polka-dot necktie, who called himself Kelly, called at Anthony Rockwall's house, and was at once received in the library.

"Well," said Anthony, reaching for his check-book, "it was a good bilin' of soap. Let's see—you had $5,000 in cash."

"I paid out $300 more of my own," said Kelly. "I had to go a little above the estimate. I got the express wagons and cabs mostly for $5; but the trucks and two-horse teams mostly raised me to $10. The motormen wanted $10, and some of the loaded teams $20. The cops struck me hardest—$50 I paid two, and the rest $20 and $25. But didn't it work beautiful, Mr. Rockwall? I'm glad William A. Brady wasn't onto that little outdoor vehicle mob scene. I wouldn't want William to break his heart with jealousy. And never a rehearsal, either! The boys was on time to the fraction of a second. It was two hours before a snake could get below Greeley's statue."

"Thirteen hundred—there you are, Kelly," said Anthony, tearing off a check. "Your thousand, and the $300 you were out. You don't despise money, do you, Kelly?"

"Me?" said Kelly. "I can lick the man that invented poverty."

Anthony called Kelly when he was at the door.

"You didn't notice," said he, "anywhere in the tie-up, a kind of a fat boy without any clothes on shooting arrows around with a bow, did you?"

"Why, no," said Kelly, mystified. "I didn't. If he was like you say, maybe the cops pinched him before I got there."

"I thought the little rascal wouldn't be on hand," chuckled Anthony. "Good-by, Kelly."

# For Better Reading: Preparing for a Surprise

> *Mammon:* An evil spirit or false god worshipped as the personification of money or material wealth
>
> *The Archer:* Usually pictured as a winged, chubby baby carrying a bow and arrow. Could it be Cupid?

You may know all three of these sayings: Money is the root of all evil (or, better: love of money is the root of all evil). Some things money can't buy. And, love conquers all.

In this story, O. Henry has taken these sayings and turned them upside-down. Although its details should surprise you, O. Henry makes millionaire Anthony Rockwall a man of uncommon ideas and extraordinary means so his final plan seems right in character. As you question the story, you'll see how the "Master of the surprise ending" puts an original slant on what money can and can't buy, making you wonder if Mammon is really so bad, after all.

## Inference

1. People called Anthony Rockwall's Fifth Avenue mansion the "soap palace" because of (a) its smooth, white marble exterior (b) the source of his inherited wealth (c) his belief in clean living (d) the product he had manufactured.
2. When Rockwall said, "I'll have this house painted red, white, and blue next summer," he was thinking of ways to (a) annoy his snobbish neighbor (b) celebrate the Fourth of July (c) escape the "soap palace" image (d) get free newspaper publicity.
3. By yelling instead of ringing for his servant, Rockwall shows that he's (a) heartless and lazy (b) fond of playing practical jokes (c) natural and down-to-earth (d) generous and kind.

## Questioning the Story

1. How does Anthony feel inherited wealth affects the personality and manners of those like his next door neighbors? By what two standards is Anthony "almost" a gentleman himself?
2. Although Anthony believes ten cents enough to pay for soap, why does he feel his son sticks to "what's decent and moderate" considering his condition?
3. How do Richard and his father differ about what money can buy? Give the example each uses to illustrate his views.

4. Even before learning Richard's problem, how did Anthony show both his sensitivity and generous impulses towards him?
5. What are two reasons Richard felt hopeless about finding time to tell Miss Lantry his feelings?
6. How did Aunt Ellen feel about Anthony's attitude toward money? About love? What did she give to her nephew and why?
7. On the way to Wallack's Theatre, why did Richard first ask the cabman to stop? What prevented him and Miss Lantry from driving on?
8. Why did Aunt Ellen credit "the Archer" for the happy ending? What does a man called Kelly, visiting at Rockwall's library, reveal about the part played by "Mammon?"

## Looking Deeper
### I. "Your Hands Are Clean."

According to Richard's father, "they" claim it takes three generations to "make" a gentleman. In other words, the first generation earns money; the next inherits it and "earns" acceptance into exclusive social circles for his children.

Considering this, what did Anthony mean by saying Richard had "no Eureka soap" on his hands? Why was this an advantage? Why does Anthony feel that college is not an advantage for a gentleman? En route to the theater, how did Miss Lantry show the "social whirl" did not entirely please her?

### II. For Love or Money?

How does Anthony Rockwall differ from those for whom "love of money" is the "root of evil?" What is his real reason for not answering his sister's question, "What good could your money have done?" Give one or more examples proving that love and concern for his family come before money in Anthony Rockwall's version of the American Dream.

Why can't O. Henry's surprise ending be taken as a worthwhile moral "lesson"? How does it also poke fun at common attitudes about money and love?

# Money

## by Dana Gioia

| | |
|---|---|
| **Born:** | *Los Angeles, California, 1950* |
| **Career:** | *Business executive, foods corporation* |
| **Literary accomplishments:** | *Poet, translator of Italian poetry* |

> *Money is a kind of poetry.*
> —Wallace Stevens

Money, the long green,
cash, stash, rhino, jack
or just plain dough.

Chock it up, fork it over,
shell it out. Watch it                              5
burn holes through pockets.

To be made of it! To have it
to burn! Greenbacks, double eagles,
megabucks and Ginnie Maes.

It greases the palm, feathers a nest,              10
holds heads above water,
makes both ends meet.

Money breeds money.
Gathering interest, compounding daily.
Always in circulation.                             15

Money. You don't know where it's been,
but you put it where your mouth is.
And it talks.

# For Better Reading: Just an Everyday Metaphor

It's easy to turn away from poetry, printed line for line in a textbook, yet meet and enjoy poetic language every day without realizing it. For a metaphor is merely a name or comparison that brings you a fresh way of looking at something familiar. A good metaphor is colorful, sharp, and lively—to make you think again about the item compared.

To an auto maker, a car is not a car. It's a Safari or Skylark, Wrangler or Banshee. All go beyond identification of brand by giving each model a name, actually a metaphor, that expresses the car's "spirit": ruggedly adventurous or carefree, tough as a workhorse or eager for daredevil excitement.

Reread "Money" and notice the creative use of words, not invented but collected in the poem. For these are everyday metaphors inspired by this sought-after but frustrating goal of many Americans' dreams.

## Questioning the Poem

1. In the first stanza, the poet lists six synonyms or slang terms for money. Choose three with which you are familiar, and explain the differing attitudes each expresses. Name other similar examples if you can.
2. What is the difference between "forking" money over and "shelling" it out? When can money seem to "burn holes through pockets"?
3. Explain the difference between someone's being "made of money" and "having it to burn." Which better describes Anthony Rockwall's relation to money, and why?
4. "Double eagles" are $20 gold pieces and "Ginnie Macs," a type of investment. Why do the four metaphors in lines 8–9 fit better here than in stanza one?
5. Explain the literal sense or meaning of each of the four phrases about money in lines 10–12.
6. How does money "breed" money? How might the expression "put your money where your mouth is" apply to someone who brags or boasts?

## Looking Deeper

## I. Speaking About Money

In this poem, Dana Gioia concentrates on the way words reveal people's feelings about money.

Name at least four attitudes or feelings, such as hardboiled or envious, that money inspires, and list metaphors from the poem indicating each. Does the poem make money seem an attractive goal? Why or why not?

## II. More Everyday Metaphors

For cars, perfumes, brands of soap and clothing, as well as everyday items like money—everywhere you look are metaphors to bring out a special quality or create a definite impression.

Choose one type of item—perhaps more models of cars—and list at least four model-names or everyday metaphors for it, plus the attitude each attempts to express.

 **Prologue**

**from *Friday Night Lights***

*H. G. Bissinger*

**Born in:** *New York*
**Career:** *Journalist, editor, investigative reporter, and editor*
*Newpaperman for:* Norfolk, Va. Ledger-Star, *St. Paul, Minn.*, Pioneer Press Dispatch, *Philadelphia (Pa.)* Inquirer, *Chicago (Ill.)* Tribune
**Awards:** *Pulitzer Prize, National Headliner Award*

IF THE SEASON COULD EVER have any salvation, if it could ever make sense again, it would have to come tonight under a flood of stars on the flatiron plains, before thousands of fans who had once anointed him the chosen son but now mostly thought of him as just another nigger.

He felt good when he woke up in the little room that was his, with the poster of Michael Jordan taped to the wall. He felt good as he ate breakfast and talked to his uncle, L.V., who had rescued him from a foster home when he had been a little boy, who had been the one to teach him the game and had shown him how to cut for the corner and swivel his hips and use the stiff arm.

L.V. still had inescapable visions of his nephew—Boobie Miles as the best running back in the history of Permian High School, Boobie as the best high school running back in the whole damn state of Texas, Boobie as belle of the ball at Nebraska or Texas A & M or one of those other fantastic college casinos, Boobie as winner of the Heisman. He couldn't get those dreams out of his head, couldn't let go of them. And neither, of course, could Boobie.

There were still some questions about the knee, about how ready Boobie was after the injury two months earlier that had required arthroscopic surgery (they had a tape of it that L.V., who was out of work because of the slump in the oil field, sometimes watched in the afternoon darkness of the living room, just as he sometimes watched other pivotal moments of his nephew's football career).

The Cooper Cougars had thrashed Boobie pretty badly the previous week down in Abilene, headhunting for him to the point that he had to be restrained from getting into a fistfight. But he had held up under the physical punishment, two or three or four tacklers driving into him on many of the plays, the risk always there that they would take a sweet shot at his knee, smash into that still-tender mass of cartilage and ligament with all their might and see how tough the great Boobie Miles really was, see how quickly he got up off the ground after a jolting *thwack* that sounded like a head-on car collision, see how much he liked the game of football now as fear laced through him and the knee began to feel as tender to the touch as the cheek of a baby, see how the future winner of the Heisman felt as he lay there on the clumpy sod with those Cooper Cougars taunting through the slits in their helmets.

He had made it through, he had survived, although it was clear to everyone that he wasn't the same runner of the year before, the instinct and the streak of meanness replaced by an almost sad tentativeness, a groping for feeling and moments and movements that before had always come as naturally as the muscles that rippled through his upper torso.

But there was a fire in his belly this morning, an intensity and sense of purpose. This game wasn't against a bunch of goody-two-shoes hacks from Abilene, the buckle of the West Texas Bible Belt. It was against Midland Lee—Permian's arch-rivals—the Rebels, those no-good bastard Rebels—under the Friday night lights for the district championship before a crowd of fifteen thousand. If Permian won, it was guaranteed a trip to the most exciting sporting event in the entire world, the Texas high school football playoffs, and a chance to make it all the way, to go to State. Anybody who had ever been there knew what a magic feeling that was, how it forever ranked up there with the handful of other magic feelings you might be lucky enough to have in your life, like getting married or having your first child.

After tonight, Boobie knew the fans would be back in his corner extolling him once again, the young kids who were counting off the years until their own sun-kissed moment excitedly whispering to one another as he walked down the street or through the mall. *There he is! That's Boobie! There he is!* The bigtime college recruiters would come charging back as well, the boys from Nebraska and Texas A & M and Arkansas and all the others who before the injury had come on to him as shamelessly as a street whore supporting a drug habit, telling him in letter after letter *what a fine-looking thing* he was with that six-foot, two-hundred-pound frame of his and that 4.6 speed in the forty and how sweet he would look in a uniform in Norman or College Station or Fayetteville and how he should just *stick with me, sugar, I'll take good care of you.* They would all be there pleading for him, just as they had before the knee injury, before his dreams had so horribly unraveled.

He felt good when he left the little white house that he lived in, where a green pickup truck sat in the bare, litter-strewn yard like a wrecked boat washed up on the shore. He felt good as he made his way out of the Southside part of town, the place where the low-income blacks and Mexicans lived, and crossed the railroad tracks as he headed for Permian over on the northeast side of town, the fancy side of town, the white side of town.

He felt good as he walked into the locker room of the Permian field house that morning and pulled on his jersey with the number 35 on it. He felt good at the pep rally as he and his teammates sat at the front of the gym in little metal chairs that were adorned with dozens of black and white balloons, the decorations making them look like little boys attending a gigantic birthday party. The wild cheering of the entire student body, two thousand strong, above him in the bleachers, the sweet hiss of the pom-poms from the cheerleaders, the sexy preening of the majorettes in their glittery black costumes with hair as intricately laced as frozen drizzles of ice and their tender Marilyn Monroe smiles, the way the lights dimmed during the playing of the alma mater, the little gifts of cookies and candy and cakes from the Pepettes, the pandemonium that broke loose when defensive back Coddi Dean gave the last lines of his verse—

*The moral is obvious, it's plain to see*
*Tonight at Ratliff Stadium, we're gonna stomp on Lee!*

—all these things only energized Boobie Miles even more. The feeling came back to him now, the cockiness, the "attitude" as his teammates liked to call it, the self-confidence that had caused him to gain 1,385 yards the previous season and knock vaunted linebackers semi-unconscious. As he sat there, surrounded by all that pulsating frenzy, he could envision sitting in this very same spot a week from now, acknowledging the cheers of the crowd as he picked up the Superstar of the Week award from one of the local television stations for his outstanding performance against the Rebels.

*"A person like me can't be stopped. If I put it in my mind,*
*they can't stop me . . . ain't gonna stop me.*
*"See if I can get a first down. Keep pumping my legs up, spin out*
*of it, go for a touchdown, go as far as I can."*

That's right. That's how it would feel again, getting that ball, tucking it under his arm, and going forever like someone in the euphoria of flight. Nothing in the world could ever be like it. No other thing could ever compare, running down that field in the glow of those Friday night lights with your legs pumping so high they seemed to touch the sky and thousands on their feet cheering wildly as the gap between you and everyone else just got wider and wider and wider.

After the pep rally he went to class, but it was impossible to concentrate. He sat there in a daze, the messages of algebra and biology and English lost to him. Like most of his other teammates on game day, he couldn't be bothered with classes. They were irrelevant, a sidelight to the true purpose of going to Permian High School: to play football for the Panthers. Only one thought crossed his mind as he sat in those antiseptic, whitewashed classrooms until the middle of the afternoon, and it didn't have anything to do with schoolwork. He desperately wanted to perform well against Midland Lee, to break tackle after tackle, to be Boobie once again.

He didn't seem like a high school football player at all, but an aging prizefighter who knew that if he didn't get a knockout tonight, if he didn't turn his opponent's face into a bloody pulp, if he didn't sting and jab and show the old footwork, he was done, washed up, haunted forever by the promise of what could have been. Could he regain his former footing as a star? Or at the age of eighteen, was he already a has-been?

He felt good as he left class for the day and had a few hours to kill before it was time to go to the field house to suit up.

He felt good.

After classes ended, Jerrod McDougal walked out of school into the parking lot. It didn't take him long to find his black Chevy pickup, perhaps the tallest object in all of Odessa with the thirty-three-inch Desert Dueler treads that made it hard to get into without a stepladder. He climbed inside the cab amid the clutter of cassettes and paper cups. He found what he was looking for and did the same thing he did every Friday afternoon in those lousy waning hours before game time.

The pounding of the drums came on first, then the scream of "Hey!", then the sound of a guitar like that of ten-inch fingernails sliding up and down a blackboard, then explosive sounds moving back and forth between the speakers. There were more guttural yells, more screeching snippets of guitar, then the sudden, ominous wail of an organ that kept building and building and made his heart beat a little faster.

The guitars dug into his ears and the lyrics poured into his veins like liquid fire, the louder the better, the angrier the better, every sound aimed to strike right at the top of the skull and just rattle up there for a little while, get trapped in there, like a ball bouncing repeatedly off a wall:

> *Lay your hands on me*
> *Lay your hands on me*
> *Lay your hands on me*
> *Lay your hands on me*
> *Lay your hands on me*

Thank God for Bon Jovi.

McDougal closed the tiny eyes of his face and leaned his head against the back of the seat. He waited to see if the feeling would be there, as it had been a couple of weeks ago when Permian had beaten the hell out of the Bulldogs, had taught them a thing or two about having the nerve to step on the same field with the Panthers, the Boys in Black. And it was, yes it was, a series of chills shooting down his back straight to his spine like lightning splitting a tree, a tingling feeling that both reassured and excited him. And at that moment, at that very moment, he knew there was no way that Permian could lose to Midland Lee tonight, no way, not as long as he was alive.

It was all that mattered to him, not because it was a ticket to anything or a way out of this town that held as many secrets as the back of his hand. Long before, when he had stopped growing at five nine, he had put away all lofty dreams of playing for the University of Texas, or anywhere else for that matter. He knew that all he was, when you got to the core of it, was an offensive tackle with a lot of heart but little natural ability.

After the season there would be plenty of time to think about college and careers and all that other stuff that a high school senior might want to start thinking about. But not now, not when the most important moment of his life was about to take place. Friday night is what he lived for, bled for, worked so hard for. It sure as hell wasn't school, where he shuffled from one creampuff course to another. It wasn't the prospect of going into the oil business either, where he had watched his father's company, built with sweat and tears, slide through the continued depression in oil prices.

> *I'm a fighter, I'm a poet*
> *I'm a preacher*
> *I've been to school and*
> *Baby, I've been the teacher*
> *If you show me how to get*
> *Up off the ground*
> *I can show you*
> *How to fly and never*
> *Ever come back down*

Thank God for Bon Jovi.

The tingling sensation stayed with him, and he knew that when he stepped on the field tonight he wouldn't feel like a football player at all but like someone much more powerful entering a glittering, barbaric arena.

"It's like the gladiators" was the way he once described it. "It's like the Christians and the lions, like Caesar standing up there and saying yea or nay. There's nineteen thousand fans in the stands and they can't do what you're doing, and they're all cheering for one thing, they're cheering for you. Man, that's a high no drug or booze or woman can give you."

He pulled back into the school parking lot. He left his pickup and entered the locker room of the field house where everything had been laid out the night before with the meticulousness of a Christmas display window, the shoes and the shoulder pads and the socks and the pants all in their proper places, the helmets fresh and gleaming from the weekly hand cleaning by one of the student trainers.

Mike Winchell hated these moments in the field house, wandering around in his uniform as the minutes dripped away with excruciating slowness. Secretly he wished that he could be knocked out and not wake up until five minutes before game time when there was no longer any time to dwell on it. He was the quarterback and that gave him a certain status, because just about everybody in town knew who the quarterback was and the novelty of having his picture in the local paper had worn off long ago. But with all the responsibilities—learning the audible calls and the three-play packages, not getting fooled by that overshifted defense the Rebels liked to run—it was hard not to feel overwhelmed.

He awoke early that day, in the darkness of the shabby house on Texas Avenue that shamed him so much he wouldn't even let his girlfriend enter it. In silence he had carefully wrapped up some toast and bacon in paper towels so he would have something to eat when he got to school. Then he got his mother up so she could drive him there since, unlike most kids at Permian High School, he didn't have his own car. They barely said anything to each other, because he hated questions about the game. When she dropped him off she whispered, "Good luck," and then left.

Once he got to school he had to go to the pep rally, where his long, angular face, framed by balloons, had a look of delicate sadness as haunting as a Diane Arbus photograph. It was a fascinating face, Huck Finnish, high-cheekboned, yet somehow devoid of expression, the eyes flat and deadened against the roar and tumult that surrounded him, impervious to it, unable to react.

He welcomed going to class afterward, finding relief in the equations spread across the blackboard in algebra II, glad to have something else filling his head besides the thousand and one things that were expected of him. But outside class the pressure intensified again, the Lee game hovering over him like a thundercloud, the incessant questions of the students as he walked through the halls driving him crazy and offering him no escape.

Everyone seemed uptight to him, even the teachers who always dressed up in black on game day. When he walked through the halls of school during the season it wasn't as a proud gladiator, but instead he seemed enveloped in an almost painful shyness, his head ducked to the side and his eyes shifting furtively, fending off questions with one-word answers, especially hating it when people came up to him and asked, "Do y'all think you're gonna win?"

He had first started as a junior, and back then he had been so nervous that the butterflies started on Tuesdays. In the huddle his hands shook. Teammates looked at him and wondered if he was going to make it. But this season he was leading the district in passing and had cut his interceptions down to almost none. A big game against the Rebels would be further vindication, further proof that he had what it took to be a college quarterback in the Southwest Conference.

There could have been other options for him. During the season he had gotten a letter from Brown expressing interest in him because he was not only a decent quarterback but a good student. But for Winchell, who had never been east of the Texas-Louisiana border, the mere idea scared him to death. Rhode Island? Where in God's name was *Rhode Island*? He looked on a map and there it was, halfway across the earth, so tiny it could move into West Texas overnight and no one would ever know it, taking its anonymous place beside Wink and Kermit and Notrees and Mentone.

"Hell, Brown, that might as well have been in India" was the way he put it. He had read about the Ivy League in the sports pages and seen a few of those games on ESPN where the caliber of play wasn't too bad but it sure as heck wasn't football the way he had grown up to understand football. He also got a nibble of interest from Yale, but when he tried to imagine what these schools were like, all he could think of was people standing around in goofy sweaters with little *Y*'s on the fronts yelling, "Go Yale, beat Brown."

A series of meetings was held in the field house, the five Permian coaches trying to pound in the game plan against Lee one more time. Afterward, as part of a long-standing tradition, all the lights were turned off. Some of the players lay on the floor or slumped against concrete posts. Some listened to music, the tinny sound from their headphones like violent whispering in a serious domestic spat. Winchell, who had gone over the audible calls in his mind yet again, agonized over the wait. It was the worst part of all, the very worst. After several minutes the lights came back on and he and his teammates boarded the yellow school buses waiting outside.

With the flashers of a police escort leading the way so there wouldn't be any wait at the traffic lights, the caravan made its way to Ratliff Stadium like a presidential motorcade.

The sound of vomiting echoed through the dressing room of the stadium, the retching, the physical embodiment of the ambivalence Ivory Christian felt about what he was doing and why he was there. Droplets of sweat trickled down his face as he lay in front of the porcelain. None of the other players paid much notice. They had heard it before and gave little half-smiles. It was just Ivory.

There was so much about football he hated—the practices, the conditioning, the expectations that because he was a captain he had to be Joe Rah-Rah. He wasn't sure if he cared about beating Midland Lee. He wasn't sure if he cared about winning the district championship and getting into the playoffs. Let other players dream their foolish dreams about getting recruited by a big-time school. It wasn't going to happen to him and he figured that after the year was over he would enlist in the Marines or something, maybe buy a Winnebago so he could get out of this place and drive around the country without a care in the world, where no one could get to him.

But the game had a funny hold on him. The elemental savagery of it appealed to him and he was good at it, damn good, strong, fast, quick, a gifted middle linebacker with a future potential he didn't begin to fathom. Severing from it, letting it go, was not going to be as easy as he thought it would be, particularly in Odessa, where if you were big and strong and fast and black it was difficult not to feel as if the whole world expected you to do one thing and one thing only and that was play football. And despite the grim detachment with which he seemed to approach almost everything, he seemed scared to death at the thought of failing at it. He loved it and he hated it and he hated it and he loved it.

After he had finished vomiting, he reappeared in the dressing room with a relieved smile on his face. He had gone through the catharsis. He had gotten it out of his system, the ambivalence, the fear.

Now he was ready to play.

Every sound in the dressing room in the final minutes seemed amplified a thousand times—the jagged, repeated rips of athletic tape, the clip of cleats on the concrete floor like that of tap shoes, the tumble of aspirin and Tylenol spilling from plastic bottles like the shaking of bones to ward off evil spirits. The faces of the players were young, but the perfection of their equipment, the gleaming shoes and helmets and the immaculate pants and jerseys, the solemn ritual that was attached to almost everything, made them seem like boys going off to fight a war for the benefit of someone else, unwitting sacrifices to a strange and powerful god.

In the far corner of the dressing room Boobie Miles sat on a bench with his eyes closed, his face a mixture of seriousness and sadness, showing no trace of what this pivotal night would hold for him. Jerrod McDougal, pacing back and forth, went to the bathroom to wipe his face with paper towels. Staring into the mirror, he checked to make sure his shirt was tucked in and the sleeves were taped. He straightened his neck roll and then put on his gloves to protect his hands, the last touches of gladiatorial splendor. It looked good. It looked damn good. In the distance he could hear the Midland Lee band playing "Dixie," and it enraged him. He hated that song and the way those cocky bastards from Lee swaggered to it. His face became like that of an impulse killer, slitty-eyed, filled with anger. Mike Winchell lay on the floor, seduced by its coldness and how good it felt. His eyes closed, but the eyelids still fluttered and you could feel the nervousness churning inside him.

In the silence of that locker room it was hard not to admire these boys as well as fear for them, hard not to get caught up in the intoxicating craziness of it, hard not to whisper "My God!" at how important the game had become, not only to them, but to a town whose spirits crested and fell with each win and each loss. You wished for something to break that tension, a joke, a sigh, a burst of laughter, a simple phrase to convince them that if they lost to the Rebels tonight it wasn't the end of the world, that life would go on as it always had.

Gary Gaines, the coach of Permian, called the team to gather around him. He was a strikingly handsome man with a soft smile and rows of pearly white teeth somehow unstained, as if by divine intervention, from the toxic-looking thumbfuls of tobacco snuff that he snuck between front lip and gum when his wife wasn't around to catch him. He had beautiful eyes, not quite gray, not quite blue, filled with softness and reassurance. His message was short and sincere.

"Nobody rest a play, men. Don't coast on any play. You're on that field, you give it everything you got."

Across the field, in the visitor's dressing room, Earl Miller, the coach of the Rebels, gave similar advice in his thick Texas twang that made every syllable seem as long as a sentence.

"First time you step out on that field, you go down there as hard as you can and bust somebody."

Brian Chavez's eyes bulged as he made his way to the coin toss with the other captains. On one side was Ivory Christian, belching and hiccuping and trying to stop himself from retching again. On the other was Mike Winchell, lost in a trance of intensity. The three of them held hands as they walked down a ramp and then turned a corner to catch the first glimpse of a sheet of fans dressed in black that seemed to stretch forever into the desert night. The farther they moved into the stadium field, the more it felt as if they were entering a fantastic world, a world unlike any other.

The metamorphosis began to take hold of Chavez. When the game began and he took the field, his body would be vibrating and his heart would be beating fast and every muscle in his body would become taut. He knew he would try to hit his opponent as hard as he possibly could from his tight end position, to hurt him, to scare him with his 215-pound frame that was the strongest on the team, to make him think twice about getting back up again.

It was the whole reason he played football, for those hits, for those acts of physical violence that made him tingle and feel wonderful, for those quintessential shots that made him smile from ear to ear and earned him claps on the back from his teammates when he drove some defensive lineman to the sidelines and pinned him right on his butt. He knew he was an asshole when he played, but he figured it was better to be, as he saw it, an "asshole playin' football rather than in real life."

He had no other expectations beyond the physical thrill of it. He didn't have to rely on it or draw all his identity from it. "I played because I like it," he once said. "Others played because it was Permian football. It was their ticket to popularity. It was just a game to me, a high school game."

As the number-one student in his class, his aspirations extended far beyond the glimmer of expectation that a Texas school, any Texas school, might be willing to give him a football scholarship. He had set his sights differently, zeroing in on a target that seemed incomprehensible to his family, his friends, just about everyone. He wanted to go to Harvard.

When he tried to imagine it, he thought it would be like stepping into a different world, a world that was steeped in history and breathtaking and so utterly different from the finite world of Odessa, which spread over the endless horizon like the unshaven stubble of a beard. When he visited it his senior year, he sat by the window of his hotel and watched the rowers along the Charles with their seemingly effortless grace, the strokes of their oars so delicate and perfectly timed as they skimmed along the water past the white domes and the red brick buildings and all those beautiful trees. It didn't seem real to him when he gazed out that window, but more like a painting, beautiful, unfathomable, unattainable.

But now he wasn't thinking about Harvard. Every bone in his body was focused on beating Midland Lee, and he felt so absolutely confident that he had already ordered a DISTRICT CHAMPS patch for his letter jacket. As the coin was being thrown into the air by one of the officials he stared across at Quincy White, Lee's bruising fullback. At that moment Brian felt hatred toward the Rebels, absolute hatred, and he wanted to prove he was the best there was on the damn field, the very best.

The team left the dressing room and gathered behind a huge banner that had been painstakingly made by the cheerleaders. It took up almost half the end zone and was fortified by the Pepettes with pieces of rope like in some scene of war from the Middle Ages. It became a curtain. The players congregated behind it in the liquid, fading light, yelling, screaming, pounding each other on the shoulder pads and the helmets, furious to be finally set loose onto the field, to revel in the thrilling roar of the crowd.

The fans couldn't see the players yet, but they could hear them bellowing behind that banner and they could see their arms and knees and helmets push against it and make it stretch. The buildup was infectious, making one's heart beat faster and faster. Suddenly, like a fantastic present coming unwrapped, the players burst through the sign, ripping it to shreds, little pieces of it floating into the air. They poured out in a steady stream, and the crowd rose to its feet.

The stillness was ruptured by a thousand different sounds smashing into each other in wonderful chaos—deep-throated yells, violent exhortations, giddy screams, hoarse whoops. The people in the stands lost all sight of who they were and what they were supposed to be like, all dignity and restraint thrown aside because of these high school boys in front of them, *their* boys, *their* heroes, upon whom they rested all their vicarious thrills, all their dreams. No connection in all of sports was more intimate than this one, the one between town and high school.

*"MO-JO! MO-JO! MO-JO! MO-JO!"*

Chants of the Permian monicker, which was taken from the title of an old Wilson Pickett song and stuck to the team after a bunch of drunken alumni had yelled the word for no apparent reason during a game in the late sixties, passed through the home side. The visitor's side answered back with equal ferocity:

*"REB-ELS! REB-ELS! REB-ELS!"*

Each wave of a Confederate flag by a Lee fan was answered by the waving of a white handkerchief by a Permian fan. Each rousing stanza of "Dixie" by the Lee band was answered by an equally rousing stanza of "Grandioso" by the Permian band, each cheer from the Rebelettes matched by one from the Pepettes. Nothing in the world made a difference on this October night except this game illuminating the plains like a three-hour Broadway finale.

Permian took the opening kickoff and moved down the field with the methodical precision that had made it a legend throughout the state of Texas. An easy touchdown, a quick and bloodless 7–0 lead. But Lee, a twenty-one-point underdog, came back with a touchdown of its own to tie the game. Early in the second quarter, a field goal gave the Rebels a 10–7 lead.

Permian responded with a seventy-seven-yard drive to make it 14–10. Chris Comer, the new great black hope who had replaced Boobie Miles in the backfield, carried the ball seven of nine plays and went over a thousand yards for the season.

Earlier in the season, Boobie had cheered on Comer's accomplishments with a proud smile. As the season progressed and Comer became a star while Boobie languished, the cheers stopped.

He made no acknowledgment of Comer's score. He sat on the bench, his eyes staring straight ahead, burning with a mixture of misery and anger as it became clear to him that the coaches had no intention of playing him tonight, that they were willing to test his knee out in meaningless runaways but not in games that counted. His helmet was off and he wore a black stocking cap over his head.

The arm pads he liked still dangled from his jersey. The towel bearing the legend "TERMINATOR X" from the name of one of the members of the rap group Public Enemy, hung from his waist, spotless and unsullied. The stadium was lit up like a dance floor, its green surface shimmering and shining in the lights, and his uniform appeared like a glittering tuxedo loaded down with every conceivable extra. But it made him look silly, like one of those kids dressed to the nines to conceal the fact that they were unpopular and couldn't dance a lick. He sat on the bench and felt a coldness swirl through him, as if something sacred inside him was dying, as if every dream in his life was fleeing from him and all he could do was sit there and watch it disappear amid all those roars that had once been for him.

With 2:27 left in the half, Winchell threw the finest pass of his life, a sixty-yard bomb to Lloyd Hill, to make the score 21–10. But then, with less than ten seconds left, Lee scored after connecting on a forty-nine-yard Hail Mary pass that unfolded like a Rube Goldberg drawing, the ball fluttering off the hands and helmets and shoulder pads of several Permian defenders before somehow settling into the hands of a receiver who had never caught a varsity pass in his life. Lee's try for a two-point conversion failed.

The score was 21–16 at halftime.

The Permian players came off the field exhausted, in for a fight they had never quite expected. The gray shirts they wore underneath their jerseys were soaked. Winchell, who had taken a massive hit in the first half, felt dizzy and disoriented. They grabbed red cups of Coke and sat in front of their locker stalls trying to get their breath, the strange Lee touchdown at the end of the half a weird and scary omen. There was hardly a sound, hardly a movement. The players seemed more shell-shocked than frantic, and few even noticed when Boobie flung his shoulder pads against the wall.

In a furious rage he threw his equipment into a travel bag and started to walk out the door. He had had it. He was quitting at halftime of the biggest game of the year. He couldn't bear to watch it anymore, to be humiliated in those lights where everyone in the world could stare at him and know that he wasn't a star anymore, just some two-bit substitute who might get a chance to play if someone got hurt.

None of the varsity coaches made a move to stop him; it was clear that Boobie had become an expendable property. If he wanted to quit, let him go and good riddance. But Nate Hearne, a black junior varsity football coach whose primary responsibility was to handle the black players on the team, herded him into the trainer's room to try to calm him down, to somehow salvage what little of his psyche hadn't already been destroyed.

Boobie stood in the corner of the darkened room with his arms folded and his head turned down toward the floor, as if protecting himself from any more pain. "I quit, coach, they got a good season goin'," he said, his tone filled with the quiet hurt of a child who can't process the shame of what has happened except to run from it.

"Come on, man, don't do this."

"Why'd Gaines play me the last weekend and the weekend before that?"

"I know how hard it is. Don't quit now. Come on."

"That's why I'm gonna quit. They can do it without me."

"Everything's gonna be all right. Everybody knows how it feels to be on the sidelines when he should be out there."

"Could have hurt my knee last week, could have hurt it the week before. He didn't think about it then."

"You'll be all right. Just hang tough for now. The team needs you. You know we need you. Use your head. Don't let one night destroy everything."

"Why not just quit?"

"This is one game. We got six games down the line."

"Six games to sit on the sidelines."

"We're almost there and now you want to do this, don't do this."

"Next week it ain't gonna be a new story because I ain't gonna play. Just leave me alone, and I'll get out of here."

"You can't walk off now, in the middle of a game. You just can't walk off in the middle of a game."

"I'm just gonna leave because I ain't gonna sit on the sidelines for no one. I see what it's all about.

"What's it all about?"

"I'm a guinea pig."

It went on a little longer, Hearne's heartfelt understanding in contrast to the attitude of most of the other members of the Permian football staff who derided Boobie, who had grown weary of his emotional outbursts and privately called him lazy, and stupid, and shiftless, and selfish, and casually described him as just another "dumb nigger" if he couldn't carry a football under his arm.

Reluctantly, Boobie left the trainer's room and walked back out to the dressing room. Without emotion, he put on his hip pads and shoulder pads. Carefully, meticulously, he tucked his TERMINATOR X towel into the belt of his pants and put that ridiculous costume back on again because that's what it was now, a costume, a Halloween outfit. He went back out on the field, but it no longer had any promise. When players tried to talk to him, he said nothing. The Rebels scored early in the fourth quarter on a one-yard run to take a one-point lead, 22–21. The Lee band broke into "Dixie" and the taunting chant, now stronger than ever, resumed:

*"REB-ELS! REB-ELS! REB-ELS!"*

With about six minutes left Permian moved to a first and ten at the Lee 18, but the drive stalled and a thirty-yard field goal was blocked.

Permian got the ball back at its own 26 with 2:55 left in the game, but instead of confidence in the huddle there was fear. Chavez could see it in the eyes of the offensive linemen. He tapped them on the helmet and said, "Com'on, let's get it, this is it." But he could tell they weren't listening. The game was slipping away.

They were going to lose. They were going to lose and everything they had worked for for the past six years of their lives, everything they cared about, was about to be ruined.

Winchell, after the glorious touchdown pass he had thrown, now seemed hunted by failure. His face was etched in agony, the passes coming off his hand in a tentative, jerky motion, thrown desperately without rhythm. The Lee fans were on their feet. There was the incessant beat of the drums from the band. Both sides were screaming their hearts out.

"*REB-ELS! REB-ELS!*"

"*MO-JO! MO-JO!*"

How could a seventeen-year-old kid concentrate at a moment like this amid the frenzy of fifteen thousand fans? How could he possibly keep his poise?

With a third and ten at the Lee 41, flanker Robert Brown broke free down the left sideline after his defender fell down, but the ball was thrown way out of bounds.

"Winchell!" screamed starting linebacker Chad Payne from the sidelines as the ball fluttered helplessly beyond Brown's grasp. With a fourth and ten, another pass fell incomplete.

It wasn't even close.


Jerrod McDougal watched as the Lee players fell all over each other on the field like kittens. He watched as they spit comtemptuously on the field, *his* field, defiling it, disgracing it, and never in his life had he felt such humiliation. Some gladiator he was, some heroic gladiator. In the dressing room he started to cry, his right hand draped tenderly around the bowed head of linebacker Greg Sweatt, who was sobbing also. With his other hand he punched a wall. Chavez and Winchell sat in silence, and Ivory Christian felt that creeping numbness. With a three-way tie for first and only one game left in the regular season, now Permian might not get into the state playoffs. But that wasn't potentially devastating to Ivory. There had to be something else in life, if only he could figure out what it was.

Boobie officially quit the team two days later. But no one paid much attention. There were a lot more important things to worry about than that pain-in-the-ass prima donna with a bad knee who couldn't cut worth a crap anymore anyway. There were plenty more on the Southside where he came from.

The loss to Lee sent Odessa into a tailspin, so unthinkable, so catastrophic was it. As in a civil war, goodwill and love disintegrated and members of the town turned on each other.

Gaines himself was distraught, a year's worth of work wasted, the chorus against him only growing stronger that he was a very nice man who wasn't a very good coach when it counted. When he got back to the field house he stayed in the coaches' office long past midnight, still mulling over what had happened and why the eighteen-hour days he had spent preparing for the Rebels had not paid off. The idea of a team with this kind of talent not making the playoffs seemed impossible, but now it might happen. And if it did, he had to wonder if he would be in the same job next year.

When he went home late that night, several FOR SALE signs had been punched into his lawn, a not-so-subtle hint that maybe it would be best for everyone if he just got the hell out of town. He took them and dumped them in the garage along with the other ones he had already collected. He wasn't surprised by them.

After all, he was a high school football coach, and after all, this was Odessa, where Bob Rutherford, an affable realtor in town, might as well have been speaking for thousands when he casually said one day as if talking about the need for a rainstorm to settle the dust, "Life really wouldn't be worth livin' if you didn't have a high school football team to support."

## For Better Reading: Beyond the Label

It's called nonfiction. To write of the attraction and effect of sports on American life, H.G. Bissinger took a leave from his newspaper job and moved to Odessa, Texas, with his wife and five-year-old twin sons.

There he lived for a year in a town where high school football "went to the very core of life." Bissinger spent time with Permian Panthers team members at practices and games, at school and home, in church and on rattlesnake hunts. He talked with hundreds of people to discover what football meant, not only to the Panthers players and coaches, but to everyone in town.

Although labeled nonfiction, *Friday Night Lights* uses techniques of fiction, interpreting players' thoughts as well as reporting what they did and quoting what they said.

### Important Details

1. Boobie Miles did not start the game against Midland Lee because of (a) a failing grade in biology (b) an injury to his knee (c) being ejected for brawling (d) trouble with the law.
2. For Jerrod McDougal, the most important thing in life was (a) winning a scholarship (b) getting away from home (c) making his father proud (d) playing Panthers football.
3. Mike Winchell, the quarterback, (a) welcomed algebra after the pep rally (b) wanted to attend an Ivy League college (c) was promised a car by a wealthy fan (d) cut class to escape the pregame pressure.

### Questioning the Selection

1. Why was the game against the Midland Lee Rebels so important to the Permian Panthers?
2. What "inescapable visions" did Boobie Miles' uncle have for his nephew? Why did a special closeness exist between the two?
3. Since gaining 1,385 yards the previous season, how and why does Boobie no longer seem like the same runner? What are two things he dreams of happening once more when he is "Boobie once again"?

4. Explain Ivory Christian's "love/hate" feelings towards football. Does his pregame reaction seem natural or unnatural to you? Explain why.
5. Minutes before the game, the boys are like "unwitting sacrifices to a strange and powerful god." List at least two preceding phrases in this paragraph that relate to this same notion.
6. What was Brian Chavez's only reason for playing football? What made his high goals "seem incomprehensible" to "just about everyone" on the team? What makes his dream seem possible?
7. When the score became 14–10, what realization made Boobie Miles feel "every dream in his life was fleeing from him"?
8. How does an attempt to escape humiliation lie behind Boobie's explosion at half time? How did Nate Hearne react differently from the other coaches?
9. Why did Boobie feel his uniform was a "ridiculous costume . . . Halloween costume" when he went back on the field? What is your reaction to Boobie's decision to stay? Explain your reasons.
10. Describe three different ways players reacted to the game's outcome after reaching the dressing room. What are two indications that the coach had personal reasons to worry, as a further result of losing the game?

## Looking Deeper

### I. Football Fever

Speaking of high school athletics, a parent said, "It creates this make-believe world where normal rules don't apply. We build this false atmosphere. When it's over and the harsh reality sets in, that's the real joke we play on people . . ."

Discuss this statement with relation to one or more players in the selection, or to someone you know. Do you agree athletics is a world of make-believe? Do some players become "victims" of high school, college, and professional athletics? Give examples and reasons to support your opinion.

### II. The Quality of a Dream

Throughout the prologue, Bissinger refers to the players' dreams. For example, both Boobie and his uncle L.V. "couldn't let go" of their dreams for Boobie, even after his injury. Jerrod McDougal "put away all lofty dreams," while still in high school. Ivory Christian decided to "let other players dream their foolish dreams," while Brian Chavez "set his sights differently."

In what ways are the players' dreams related to the greater, American Dream? Do you believe with Ivory that some players' dreams are foolish or misguided? Why or why not? Have reasons or examples to support your statements.

 # Watching Football on TV

## by Howard Nemerov

| | |
|---|---|
| ***Born:*** | *New York City* |
| ***Educated:*** | *Harvard University* |
| ***Military service:*** | *Joined Royal Canadian Air Force at outbreak of World War II; became a First Lieutenant, U.S. Army Air Force* |
| ***Member of faculty:*** | *Universities and colleges in New York, Minnesota, Massachusetts, Missouri, Vermont* |
| ***Famous as:*** | *Poet, novelist, editor, essayist; American Poet Laureate* |

I
It used to be only Sunday afternoons,
But people have got more devoted now
And maybe three four times a week retire
To their gloomy living room to sit before
The polished box alive with silver light      5
And moving shadows, that incessantly
Gives voice, even when pausing for messages.
The colored shadows made of moving light,
The voice that ritually recites the sense
Of what they do, enter a myriad minds.      10
Down on the field, massed bands perform the anthem
Sung by a soprano invisible elsewhere;
Sometimes a somewhat neutral public prayer—
For in the locker rooms already both
Sides have prayed God to give them victory.      15

## II

Totemic scarabs, exoskeletal,
Nipped in at the thorax, bulky above and below,
With turreted hard heads and jutting masks
And emblems of the lightning or the beast;
About the size of beetles in our sight,                    20
Save for the closeup and the distant view,
Yet these are men, our representatives
More formidable than ourselves in speed and strength
And preparation, and more injured too;
Bandage and cast exhibit breakages                         25
Incurred in wars before us played before;
Hard plaster makes a weapon of an arm,
A calf becomes a club. Now solemnly
They take up their positions in the light,
And soon their agon will begin again.                      30

## III

To all this there are rules. The players must
Remember that in the good society
Grabbing at anybody's mask will be
A personal foul and incur a penalty.
So too will pushing, tripping, interfering                 35
In any manner with someone else's pass.
Fighting is looked on with particular
Severity; though little harm can come
To people so plated at shoulder, head and thigh,
The most conspicuous offenders are                         40
Ejected from the game and even fined.
That's one side of the coin, the other one
Will bear the picture of a charging bull
Or some such image imprecating fear,
And for its legend have the one word: *Kill.*               45

## IV

Priam on one side sending forth eleven
Of many sons, and Agamemnon on
The other doing much the same; is it
The Game of Troy again? the noble youth
Fiery with emulation, maneuvering                          50
Toward power and preeminence? Well no,
It's not. Money is the name of the game
From the board room to the beers and souvenirs.
The players are mean and always want more money.
The owners are mean and always have more money             55

And mean to keep it while the players go
Out there to make them more; they call themselves
Sportsmen, they own, are and carry a club.
Remember this when watching the quarterback's
Suppliant hands under the center's butt.                    60

V
We watch all afternoon, we are enthralled
To what? some drama of the body and
The intellectual soul? of strategy
In its rare triumphs and frequent pratfalls?
The lucid playbook in the memory                            65
Wound up in a spaghetti of arms and legs
Waving above a clump of trunks and rumps
That slowly sorts itself out into men?
That happens many times. But now and then
The runner breaks into the clear and goes,                  70
The calm parabola of a pass completes
Itself like destiny, giving delight
Not only at skill but also at the sight
Of men who imitate necessity
By more than meeting its immense demands.                   75

VI
Passing and catching overcome the world,
The hard condition of the world, they do
Human intention honor in the world.
A football wants to wobble, that's its shape
And nature, and to make it spiral true                      80
's a triumph in itself, to make it hit
The patterning receiver on the hands
The instant he looks back, well, that's to be
For the time being in a state of grace,
And move the viewers in their living rooms                  85
To lost nostalgic visions of themselves
As in an earlier, other world where grim
Fate in the form of gravity may be
Not merely overcome, but overcome
Casually and with style, and that is grace.                 90

VII
Each year brings rookies and makes veterans,
They have their dead by now, their wounded as well,
They have Immortals in a Hall of Fame,
They have the stories of the tribe, the plays

And instant replays many times replayed.                              95
But even fame will tire of its fame,
And Immortality itself will fall asleep.
It's taken many years, but yet in time,
To old men crouched before the ikon's changes,
Changes become reminders, all the games                             100
Are blended in one vast remembered game
Of similar images simultaneous
And superposed; nothing surprises us
Nor can delight, though we see the tight end
Stagger into the end zone again again.                              105

# For Better Reading: The Need for a Background

On television, in movies, and in everyday life, as well as in reading—the
more you learn and grow, the more you'll become aware of *allusions*.

An allusion makes a reference to a person, thing, or event that the reader
or listener is expected to know.

For example, a politician might say, "There must never be another Pearl
Harbor." And, the hearer would recognize a call for military preparedness.

When you were younger, it's likely that most allusions passed by unnoticed. Even Saturday morning cartoons contain allusions that smaller kids
don't "catch."

When you're older, allusions are harder to ignore and often frustrating
if you realize their purpose, but not their sense. Yet it's a matter of growth,
not intelligence. As your store of knowledge grows, so will your ease in
understanding allusions, as well.

Although the subject is football on TV, poet Howard Nemerov makes
many allusions that link modern football to ancient times. "Catching" them
adds a necessary dimension to his poem.

*Scarab:*      An image of a beetle, considered sacred by the an-
               cient Egyptians and used as a symbol, seal, charm,
               or jewelry. In this way the scarab was *totemic*, a
               natural or living thing serving as the emblem of a
               group.

*Trojan War:*  A ten-year war waged against the Trojan king Priam
               to avenge the abduction of Helen, wife of the king
               of Sparta, by Priam's son, Paris. The attacking
               Greeks were led by Agamemnon, king of Mycenae.

## Questioning the Poem

1. In lines 3–6 what are two contrasts existing between the living room
   and picture on TV?

2. The mention of locker room prayers in lines 14 and 15 makes the coming contest seem more than "just a game." In the first stanza, find at least three additional examples of words that can relate to religion or a religious ceremony.

3. *Exoskeletal* refers to a shell or outer covering; *thorax* is the human body between neck and abdomen. How does the bulk of a football player's body resemble a scarab or beetle? Why does TV also make them seem beetle-size?

4. What are the "emblems of the lightning or the beast"? Name one or more teams whose mascots fit this description.

5. Line 26 introduces the comparison of football games to wars. How do players' "weapons" seem better-fitted to ancient wars than modern ones? In Greek, the word *agon* means struggle or contest and is also the root of the English word *agony.* How do both Greek and English senses fit the poem?

6. In part III what are the "two sides of the coin" concerning fighting and violence in football?

7. Why does the number of Priam's sons make the allusion seem more fitting? What was the aim of the "noble youth" fighting at Troy? What is the "name of the game" in football? Why are both owners and players "mean" with respect to this goal?

8. In line 58 who are the "sportsmen"? In what sense do they "carry a club"?

9. In part V what are two word choices that make football's "drama" seem more like comedy? What word or words relate football to the "intellectual soul"?

10. Concerning line 74, why do the players merely "imitate necessity"? Although not "necessity," what does a football game show about the power of human will or intention?

11. Because of its shape, why does a football impose a "hard condition" on players?

12. Name two ways that football, like ancient Greek mythology, now seems to have its own "immortals." By *ikon,* Nemerov means the TV set, which he compares to an icon or sacred image. How will "old men crouched before the ikon's changes" respond differently after the passage of time?

## Looking Deeper

### "A State of Grace"

In the poem, the word *grace* is used in two senses: 1. beauty of form, manner, or motion, and 2. the condition of being favored by God. Find examples of how football's "state of grace" involves both.

Throughout the poem, allusions such as "immortality" and "grace" show it not only concerns a game. Discuss how each of the following also touches on destiny and religious belief:

1. "The voice that ritually recites the sense of what they do ..." (Lines 9–10)

2. "Now solemnly they take up their positions in the light ..." (Lines 28–29)

3. "An earlier, other world where grim fate ... may be not merely overcome, but overcome ... with style. (Lines 87–90)

List and explain any other, similar allusions you find.

Why do professional sports have such impact on Americans and their dreams? How does Nemerov's poem illustrate both the negative and positive sides of using professional sports as a way of fulfilling one's dream? Include at least two examples, pro and con.

# A Couple

*by Carl Sandburg*

He was in Cincinnati, she in Burlington.
He was in a gang of Postal Telegraph linemen.
She was a pot rassler in a boarding house.
"The crying is lonely," she wrote him.
"The same here," he answered.                                      5
The winter went by and he came back and they married
And he went away again where rainstorms knocked
     down telegraph poles and wires dropped with frozen
     sleet.
And again she wrote him, "The crying is lonely."
And again he answered, "The same here."
Their five children are in the public schools.                     10
He votes the Republican ticket and is a taxpayer.
They are known among those who know them
As honest American citizens living honest lives.
Many things that bother other people never bother them.
They have their five children and they are a couple,               15
A pair of birds that call to each other and satisfy.
As sure as he goes away she writes him, "The crying is
     lonely"
And he flashes back the same old answer, "The same
     here."
It is a long time since he was a gang lineman at
     Cincinnati
And she was a pot rassler in a Burlington boarding
     house;                                                    20
Yet they never get tired of each other; they are a couple.

# For Better Reading: A Step Back

To many, love is the vital part of the American Dream: love, marriage, family—"having it all."

Yet statistics suggest that something's going more and more wrong—and no one knows why.

An advantage of reading is that it lets you step back and look at life, not through your eyes but someone else's. This opportunity to share another's vision can sharpen you perception and help you become more objective.

In the foregoing poem and the two following, three American poets take different slants on love and marriage. One poet focuses on the strengths that influence a good marriage; the other two are concerned with the problems and the misunderstandings that shadow the romantic dream that's an American ideal.

## Questioning the Poem

1. The poem doesn't say specifically, yet judging from their jobs, where and why did "he" and "she" meet?
2. Calling her a "pot rassler" is obviously slang. What would be the work of someone "wrestling pots" in a boarding house?
3. Explain the reason given in the poem for their marriage.
4. Lines 8 and 9 state "And again she wrote him . . . and again he answered . . ." What does the repetition show about their feelings?
5. What about their lives makes them seem like ordinary, rather dull American citizens? Give at least three examples.
6. "Pair of birds" in line 16 invites a connection to love birds. In lines 17 and 18, what words repeated in their letters show that the couple's feelings remain strong, even after many years of marriage? Do they seem like love birds? Why or why not? Why else might they fittingly be compared to "a pair of birds"?

## Looking Deeper
### "A Couple"

What qualities in both wife and husband have made their marriage last? What reasons found in the poem account for the fact they "never get tired of each other"?

# Divorced, Husband Demolishes House

## —*News Item*

*by John Ciardi*

It is time to break a house.
What shall I say to you
but torn tin and the shriek
of nails pulled orange
from the ridge pole? Rip it                                     5
and throw it away. Beam
by beam. Sill, step, and lintel.
Crack it and knock it down.
Brick by brick. (I breathe
the dust of openings. My tongue                                 10
is thick with plaster. What can I
say to you? The sky has come
through our rafters. Our windows
are flung wide and the wind's
here. There are no doors                                        15
in or out.) Tug it
and let it crash. Haul it.
Bulldoze it over. What can I say
to you except that nothing
must be left of the nothing                                     20
I cannot say to you? It's
done with. Let it come down.

# For Better Reading: An Extended Metaphor

Although John Ciardi based this poem on a newspaper headline, he has thought far beyond its few brief words.

In fact, he compares the marriage to the house itself.

By accepting this comparison or metaphor as the poem's foundation, you will discover how Ciardi extends or carries it throughout the poem.

As divorce is the act of destroying a marriage, so the husband's demolishing the house is parallel to the divorce. While questioning the poem, picture the literal acts of destruction the poem describes and think of their relation to destroying a marriage. Through the use of extended metaphor, Ciardi attempts to write of a failed marriage on a scale that makes its impact more forcefully felt.

## Questioning the Poem

1. In relation to the marriage, what must be the simple and direct meaning that lies behind the statement in line 1?
2. Who do you assume are the "I" and "you," the speaker and person addressed by him?
3. A "ridge pole" is the horizontal timber running across the top of a roof. What must happen to the house when this is ripped out and thrown away?
4. If the house represents marriage, what words in lines 3–5 show that this causes the speaker pain?
5. A "lintel" is the horizontal support over windows and doors. Although the speaker says, "Crack it and knock it down," what phrases in lines 6–9 make the process seem slow and difficult?
6. In lines 9 and 10, "the dust of openings" must come from the house's ripped-apart wood and plaster. As part of the extended metaphor, what kind of "openings" would be torn in the marriage? How would the speaker also seem to "breathe" these?
7. For the first time in line 13, the man uses the word "our" in speaking of "our" rafters and "our" windows. What has he realized about the house and the effects of its destruction in relationship to himself, as well as his wife?
8. Between lines 1–13, the man has twice said, "What shall (or can) I say to you." What in the marriage might compare to the "dust of openings," making his tongue "thick with plaster," preventing his speaking?
9. Why might there be no "doors in or out" of the house or of the marriage? Why might it be best for both if "nothing . . . be left"?

# Looking Deeper

## I. Words Unsaid

Often people have thoughts and feelings that are too difficult or deep to put into words. In this poem, John Ciardi looks into those feelings and attempts to express them through an extended metaphor.

Judging merely by the headline, "Divorced, Husband Demolishes House," what is your natural reaction towards the man and why? By first asking "What shall I say . . ." and then "What can I say . . . ," the speaker reveals a change of intentions. Explain what he might have liked to say. What awareness prevents his saying it?

## II. A Feeling for Words

In lines 19 and 20, the poem repeats the word "nothing" twice in almost the same position, calling attention to its multiple senses. Although divorce may mean that nothing is legally left of a marriage, what often remains? Is it possible that "nothing be left" of a failed marriage? Why or why not?

With whom do you sympathize: the husband? the wife? both? neither? Have reasons based in the poem to support your answer.

# Dolls

### for Charmaine

## by Allison Joseph

**Background:**   Written while a member of
Indiana University Graduate
Writing Program

Don't know where you are now,
whether you have children

of your own, whether you wake
at night with a start, still

remembering your handsome,                    5
virile father, a man who loved

new cars, sharp suits,
whose money bought you clothes,

the jungle gym behind your house
where we spent entire days                     10

swinging and seesawing, playing
tag in the yard's lush grass.

I thought you were lucky—
you had games and toys, dolls

we crouched to play with,                       15
combing their hair until

bald patches appeared
on their plastic scalps.

They looked nothing like us—
small-nosed, thin-waisted,                                    20

figures with blond hair,
long legs. In your room,

door closed, we'd huddle
on the floor with them,

transform all we scrounged                                    25
into furniture for their lives—

the cap from a tube of Colgate
became a cup, a tissue box

a bed. We worked hard,
created women whose bodies                                    30

were wanted by the blank
plastic flesh of the male doll—

dressing them with ribbons
and bits of lace, painting

their faces with watercolors.                                 35
Not knowing how life came,

we banged male and female
together, while outside the door

your mother and father screamed,
voices hot with accusations,                                  40

his strong black hands throwing
plate after plate at her,

at her small, terrified body.
We played while the screams

went on, while your parents                                   45
shook in their anger, china

smashing on the kitchen floor.
All I know is you moved away,

fleeing with your mother, leaving
that house I thought was beautiful,                           50

your handsome father alone,
the swing set out back

undisturbed, rusting without
us, our quick, eager, play.

## Questioning the Poem

1. What was the relationship between the speaker and the person addressed as "you" in the poem?
2. About how much time has passed since the speaker last saw her? Use clues from the poem as evidence.
3. From lines 5–14 list three things that caused the speaker to feel envy. How does the object of the father's "love" relate to the family's problem and his feelings for his daughter?
4. In line 19, the speaker says their dolls "looked nothing like us." Considering the dolls' blondness and slim figures, give two reasons why this is so.
5. As they played, how do the objects transformed into "furniture for their lives" show the girls' capacity for make-believe? How did dreams of romance affect their play?
6. What contrast between the dream and the reality is introduced in lines 36–40?
7. In line 48, the speaker says, "All I know is you moved away." Fill in the details that cause the other girl to go.
8. How do the last four words in the poem contrast with the speaker's present mood?

## Looking Deeper

### I. Aftereffects

In lines 3–4, the speaker wonders "whether you wake at night with a start." After reading the poem, why do you see this worry is justified? How does the poem show a twisted version of the American dream?

The speaker states "I thought you were lucky" in line 13 and the "house I thought was beautiful" in line 50. What realization does she have as she speaks?

### II. Questions, Not Answers

Each of these three poems invites the reader to step back and think about the question of marriage in the United States—yet none offers advice or solutions. Do you believe each expresses a valid viewpoint or situation? Why or why not?

# "The Work of One Day Is Gazed Upon for One Thousand Days"

## *Chinese Proverb*

### by Jade Snow Wong

| | |
|---|---|
| **Born:** | *San Francisco, California* |
| **Early jobs:** | *Housekeeper, office worker* |
| **Later career:** | *Potter and enamelist, travel agent, lecturer, and writer about life in a Chinese-American community* |

JADE SNOW TRUDGED THE FAMILIAR paths of Chinatown, looking for a store location where she could make and sell her pottery. She didn't know any of the owners, but instead of following the traditional, established custom of the Chinese, who handle such transactions through a middleman who knows the people and can bargain over a cup of tea, she explored every store along Grant Avenue herself.

As there was no unleased vacant store in those days, she was forced to abandon her first wish to have her own store. Instead, she considered subrenting a portion of an art-goods store. She started with the best corner locations. Some wanted too much rent; some just shook their heads; others seemed interested and asked her to return, only to report that co-owners or stockholders disapproved. All were amazed but interested in what she wanted to do; some almost wouldn't believe her.

It was a discouraging round, in which hope alternated with disappointment. Jade Snow became less particular about the choice of location, and began to work on the smaller establishments. Still without luck, she came to almost the only store she hadn't approached. The China Bazaar near Clay Street was a neat little place, and she had looked into it a number of times. But the proprietor, who sat at his cash register at the back and only waited on customers if he felt like it, always with an air of dignity and stoicism, had been altogether too formidable a figure for her to face. Now, driven by desperation, she made herself enter and tell the proprietor what she had in mind.

He said, "I notice everything and everyone who passes by my store, and I have seen you look in several times before now. You don't look like an American-Chinese to me, with two braids on your head instead of a permanent wave."

"I was born here," Jade Snow replied. "Our family head is named Wong Hong. Do you know him?"

"Yes, I have heard of him, and I know that he is an honest Christian."

Jade Snow waited, with hope beginning to rise again.

"Now, I am not a Christian," he added. "I wouldn't move out of my way to do a good deed. But if a good deed comes to my front door and asks to be done, I have very little choice. A man can go through life minding his own business only until someone comes along who desperately needs his help. A middleman I could have said 'No' to, but you make it difficult to refuse you personally."

Jade Snow assured him, "Everyone has refused me but you. This is my life purpose. All I am asking is to get a start until I can find a permanent location."

"But you can see that I have very little room and a very narrow store. I like to keep it exactly my way. I wouldn't mind displaying your finished things, but there would be no room for you to work in."

"Oh, I must work too, for as my stock is sold I shall have to be ready with more things. I can't have a hired staff yet, and I must both make and sell the pottery."

They both thought hard. Jade Snow got an idea. "Would you let me use one of your two store windows to install my wheel? Then the clay splatter will be confined to a small area, and perhaps my working there would attract people to your store to buy your own wares."

The proprietor was doubtful. "I have only the two windows."

Jade Snow implored him. "Please, try it. If it isn't good for your business, we'll make other arrangements."

They discussed terms. The proprietor said, "Now to be frank with you, I'll never be able to make much money off you. Suppose we just decide on a percentage commission on the total amount you sell. If I am going to try to help you, we might as well be fair about it. My commission will cover what you use in space and utilities. You don't know yet how much you will sell. The plan is new for both of us."

Jade Snow mulled over that proposition. "You don't quite believe what I say, do you?" the man questioned. "Go home and ask your father; he is a fair business man."

So Jade Snow told her family, all of whom were surprised that she had at last found something. Until now, they had thought she was taking the wrong means to a silly objective which she would have to give up eventually. In true Wong family fashion, they weren't preventing her from having her own way, nor helping.

"Daddy, I have today found a store which offers the greatest possibilities to date." And she described her experience in detail.

Daddy agreed that the proprietor's proposal was fair. "Now, it is right for me to go and thank this gentleman for his courtesy and generosity, and to make his acquaintance."

The next few weeks were busy ones. With the help of Jade Precious Stone and a former Navy co-worker, Jade Snow bustled around, ordering supplies, price-marking the pottery, getting announcements printed and sent out, and caring for all the details of starting a business, no matter how small. Her former architect-boss went over the store-window foundation for her, to determine what additional bracing was required in order to support the weight of the potter's wheel. He designed and drew up plans for a set of redwood shelves and cases with concealed lights, so that in the little six-by-five-foot floor space there was room to work, store drying pottery, and display a few finished items. The window floor was paved with bricks laid in a basket pattern. Altogether, the use of natural materials in keeping with the look of pottery made an attractive whole which was certainly unlike any other store window in Chinatown.

With materials scarce, it took Jade Snow days of hunting to find even the bricks for the floor. A Chinese carpenter, a fellow Wong and Daddy's old friend, was the only person who would consent to build the shelves and bracing for her, and he could hardly understand the architectural notations on the detailed drawings. Jade Snow's shipyard training in getting things done stood her in good stead.

At last everything was completed and she was ready to set up the window. Prosperity, who had been most interested in all the bustle, went with her to the store and helped lay bricks. The shelves fitted in exactly. The wheel was set in place, and a stack of plaster bats, molded in pie tins and used to support pottery while being made, was placed near by. A beautiful large philodendron plant curled up gracefully along one corner of the window, gift of Mama and Daddy in honor of the new enterprise.

Even while the brick flooring was being laid, curious passers-by stopped. Jade Snow discovered that one had only to get into a window to attract spectators. As they worked, Jade Snow saw a few insects crawling around; they looked like white ants, and she called the proprietor.

"That is indeed a good omen," he declared excitedly. "White ants do not appear except on very rare occasions. When they appear for a new business, it means that the business is blessed and will prosper."

"Oh, come now; haven't you seen white ants here before when you dressed the windows?"

The proprietor shook his head solemnly, "No, never!"

Soon the curious spectators began to murmur aloud, conjecturing as to the nature of the equipment in the elevated display.

"She must be planning to make bricks for the housing project in Chinatown."

"No, look at those white pies; she is setting up a model kitchen."

"You are both wrong; this is a rice-threshing machine. See the stick across it? I have seen them in China!"

"Oh, look, and it is a China girl too. Look, she has no permanent wave. Her braids are the way they wear them in Shanghai. Here is a Shanghai girl!"

Prosperity listened in curiosity and mounting indignation. At last he ran out to the street and announced: "You are all wrong. This is my Honey's pottery machine, and she is going to stir mud on it."

The onlookers laughed. "Listen to the child; he doesn't know what he's talking about!"

There was little chance for other spectators not to know what Jade Snow was doing in the days which followed. From the time she first threw down a ball of clay on the wheel, the street was packed. There were even people on the balconies across the street, and clinging to the telephone pole. Passing automobiles on narrow Grant Avenue stopped and held up traffic while the drivers watched. The first day, policemen came because they thought there might be a riot. Jade Snow could have an audience any time of the day or night on that busy street.

The morning paper carried a picture and two-column story of the new enterprise. Jade Snow had become a wonder in the eyes of the Western world. They declared that she had invented a new mousetrap.

Chinatown was agog. A woman in the window, her legs astride a potter's wheel, her hair in braids, her hands perpetually messy with sticky California clay, her finished products such things as coolies used in China, the daughter of a conservative family, running a business alone—such a combination was sure to fail!

When Jade Snow went around Chinatown, many storekeepers laughed at her. "Look, here comes the mud-stirring maiden. Sold a pot today? Ha! Ha!" Strangers turned to stare long and curiously.

Caucasians came from far and near to see her work, and Jade Snow sold all the pottery she could make. Even before it had been fired, the first piece was eagerly spoken for by the man who had kindly found her bricks for the window. But the Chinese did not come to buy one piece from her.

Then those who had laughed hardest stopped. After two months, the mud-stirring maiden was still in business! After three months, she was driving the first postwar automobile in Chinatown. The skeptics knitted their brows. It must be those crazy foreigners, who didn't know any better. Some Chinese approached the proprietor for information. Was it because her clay came from China? Was it because she had invented a new chemical process to make pottery?

The proprietor would smile politely. "Ask her," he would say.

But no one ever asked her. Chinese and Americans alike acted as if they thought she were deaf or dumb or couldn't understand their language. She learned a very curious thing about human beings: they would wonder, guess, speculate, but never question the person who could give them the direct answers.

One day two high-ranking Caucasian Army officers wandered into the store. They stood and watched her patiently putting a handle on a pitcher while she sat at the wheel. Since the wheel was being used for a table it was motionless.

"I wonder how that wheel operates?" one officer asked another.

"Oh, she sits there and kicks it with her feet," the other replied. Jade Snow, not two feet from them, heard them plainly, and was amused that apparently they did not observe the one-third horsepower motor which Daddy had installed on the wheel, hung almost at their eye level.

"That seems to me unnecessarily primitive," returned the first man. "But that's just the trouble, you can't teach the Chinese anything new!"

And they went off without further investigation, nodding their heads in self-satisfaction.

The reaction of her friends and family was different. Friends and fellow guild members sent flowers. Later they sometimes dropped in for tea, which she brewed in the back kitchen. And they told their friends about the new enterprise. Dr. Reinhardt never failed to call whenever she was near the neighborhood.

But it was Mama who epitomized the family's change of heart. Where there was formerly only tolerance toward their peculiar fifth daughter whom no one could understand, the tolerance was now tinged by an attitude of respect. Mama, who would not look at the potter's wheel at home, now came to the store to see what everyone was talking about.

Daddy, typically, touched her heart in another way. First, he was critical of her daring in assuming a position in the window above her spectators' heads. But when he saw that she was getting the prices and the market she wished, he ventured a suggestion. "Perhaps you should drape printed percale around your wheel, so that people will not see how crude a piece of equipment you use to make fine things."

Then one afternoon driving home, he sat beside her, lost in reverie. When they were parked in front of their house, he told her a story: "I told you once that your grandfather would have been glad to see that you had learned a handicraft. I can add now that he would have been happier to see that you have established your own business alone, even though you must begin modestly for lack of capital. Grandfather used to brush characters on a small red poster, whenever he wished to impress us with words of great importance or wisdom. This poster would be mounted inside the glass door of a big American grandfather's clock, so that whenever we observed the time, we would also be reminded of the words. I remember that after failure in his first business venture, he posted these bitterly learned words, 'Remember carefully! Remember carefully! With one penny of capital, buy eight bags of peanuts to resell, but do not seek a partner to begin a business.' "

The narrative, unusual in nature and length, was continued, "When I first came to America, my cousin wrote me from China and asked me to return. That was before I can even tell you where you were. But I still have the carbon copy of the letter I wrote him in reply. I said, 'You do not realize the shameful and degraded position into which the Chinese culture has pushed its women. Here in America, the Christian concept allows women their freedom and individuality. I wish my daughters to have this Christian opportunity. I am hoping that some day I may be able to claim that by my stand I have washed away the former disgraces suffered by the women of our family.' "

Then Daddy turned and looked at her kindly, "And who would have thought that you, my Fifth Daughter Jade Snow, would prove today that my words of many years ago were words of true prophecy?"

As for Jade Snow, she knew that she still had before her a hard upward climb, but for the first time in her life, she felt contentment. She could stop searching for that niche that would be hers alone. She had found herself and struck her speed. And when she came home now, it was to see Mama and Daddy look up from their work, and smile at her, and say, "It is good to have you home again!"

## For Better Reading: Something's Peculiar

When something's called *peculiar*, it's usually the same as saying it's "not quite right."

Although it's not strange or different enough to be thought "eccentric," something or someone peculiar has a quality or qualities unlike the rest of its kind.

At first, you might find something peculiar about the way Jade Snow Wong chooses to tell her own story. Most autobiographies are written in the first person, but Jade Snow Wong doesn't call herself "I." Instead, she speaks of herself by name and uses the pronoun "she."

This is the traditional Chinese literary form for autobiography and is an example of the "disregard for the individual" within the Chinese culture, she has explained.

Wong writes, "Even written in English, an 'I' book by a Chinese would seem outrageously immodest" to anyone raised with a sense of proper Chinese behavior.

As you question the selection, consider how the difference between traditional Chinese and typical American views of the individual led to this young Chinese-American being labeled as the family's "peculiar" fifth Chinese daughter.

Note: Prosperity is Wong's youngest brother, named Prosperity in Heaven to reflect the family's joy at having another male heir.

During World War II, Wong worked in a shipyard office, which was supervised by the War Production Board in Washington, D.C.

## Important Details

1. While hunting a store location, Jade Snow (a) had to be accompanied by a brother (b) demanded a corner location (c) insisted on room to make pottery (d) required the services of a middleman.
2. The proprietor of the China Bazaar thought Jade Wong was different from most Chinese-American girls because (a) she spoke perfect Chinese (b) her hair was braided, not curled (c) she approached him timidly and respectfully (d) her hands were stained with clay.
3. Before making final business arrangements, the China Bazaar proprietor

told Jade Snow (a) she should talk with her father (b) she must sign a lease (c) he must consult his lawyer (d) he needed approval of his stockholders.

## Questioning the Selection

1. Why hadn't Jade Snow entered the China Bazaar until "driven by desperation"?
2. Why did the China Bazaar proprietor believe that he had "little choice" about agreeing to Jade Snow's request?
3. In her search for a store location, in what ways did Jade Snow act like an independent young woman? In what ways did she exhibit traditional and family values? Give at least two examples for each.
4. Until she reported that she "at last found something," how had her family behaved "in true Wong family fashion" toward Jade Snow's ambition?
5. When she reported the offer to her father, what action did he say he planned to take? How did both parents show pride in their daughter's new enterprise when it was ready to open?
6. What did the shop proprietor take as an "omen" about Jade Snow's business future and why?
7. To the people of Chinatown, what combination of factors meant Jade Snow's business "was sure to fail"? In their opinion, why was each important?
8. What seems ironic about the people of Chinatown thinking of Caucasians (white Americans) as foreigners? How did Chinese-Americans react to the fact that only Caucasians bought Jade Snow's pottery? Give two examples.
9. Why did two high-ranking white army officers believe that Jade Snow's method of making pottery was "unnecessarily primitive"? What conclusion did they draw as a result? What obvious factor did they overlook?
10. As her business prospered, how did both Jade Snow's mother and father show a "change of heart" regarding their "peculiar fifth daughter"? Give an example for each. Why would Jade Snow say that "for the first time in her life, she felt contentment"?

## Looking Deeper

### I. Deaf, Dumb, or Simply Different?

From her experiences in the shop, Jade Snow decided people "never question the person who could give them the direct answers." What were the reasons that the people of Chinatown and the Caucasian officers thought Jade Snow "peculiar"? Do you feel that treating someone "peculiar" as if also deaf and dumb is typical or not typical? Explain your reasoning.

## II. "Words of True Prophecy"

When he first came to America, how had Jade Snow's father shown his hope to wash away "the former disgraces suffered by the women of our family"? Considering his belief in "freedom and individuality," do you feel he did enough to help and encourage Jade Snow to have her own shop? Why or why not? Do you see any benefits in the Chinese belief in the submergence of the individual: can individuality be encouraged too much? Explain the reasons underlying your opinion.

# The Person of the Moment

### from *I Know Why the Caged Bird Sings*

*by Maya Angelou*

| | |
|---|---|
| ***Born:*** | *St. Louis, Missouri* |
| ***Childhood:*** | *Sent to Stamps, Arkansas, at age 3 to live with paternal grandmother she called "Momma"* |
| ***Youth:*** | *Missouri and California* |
| ***Career:*** | *Actress, singer, dancer, playwright, director, producer, professor, poet, author* |
| ***Honor:*** | *Presented original poem at President Clinton's inauguration* |

THE CHILDREN IN STAMPS TREMBLED visibly with anticipation. Some adults were excited too, but to be certain the whole young population had come down with graduation epidemic. Large classes were graduating from both the grammar school and the high school. Even those who were years removed from their own day of glorious release were anxious to help with preparations as a kind of dry run. The junior students who were moving into the vacating classes' chairs were tradition-bound to show their talents for leadership and management. They strutted through the school and around the campus exerting pressure on the lower grades. Their authority was so new that occasionally if they pressed a little too hard it had to be overlooked. After all, next term was coming, and it never hurt a sixth grader to have a play sister in the eighth grade, or a tenth-year student to be able to call a twelfth grader Bubba. So all was endured in a spirit of shared understanding. But the graduating classes themselves were the nobility. Like travelers with exotic destinations on their minds, the graduates were remarkably forgetful. They came to school without their books, or tablets or even pencils. Volunteers fell over themselves to secure replacements for the missing equipment. When accepted, the willing workers might or might not be thanked, and it was of no importance to the pregraduation rites. Even teachers were respectful of the now quiet and aging seniors, and tended to speak to them, if not as equals, as beings only slightly lower than themselves. After tests were returned and grades given, the student body, which acted like an extended family, knew who did well, who excelled, and what piteous ones had failed.

Unlike the white high school, Lafayette County Training School distinguished itself by having neither lawn, nor hedges, nor tennis court, nor climbing ivy. Its two buildings (main classrooms, the grade school and home economics) were set on a dirt hill with no fence to limit either its boundaries or those of bordering farms. There was a large expanse to the left of the school which was used alternately as a baseball diamond or a basketball court. Rusty hoops on the swaying poles represented the permanent recreational equipment, although bats and balls could be borrowed from the P. E. teacher if the borrower was qualified and if the diamond wasn't occupied.

Over this rocky area relieved by a few shady tall persimmon trees the graduating class walked. The girls often held hands and no longer bothered to speak to the lower students. There was a sadness about them, as if this old world was not their home and they were bound for higher ground. The boys, on the other hand, had become more friendly, more outgoing. A decided change from the closed attitude they projected while studying for finals. Now they seemed not ready to give up the old school, the familiar paths and classrooms. Only a small percentage would be continuing on to college—one of the South's A & M (agricultural and mechanical) schools, which trained Negro youths to be carpenters, farmers, handymen, masons, maids, cooks and baby nurses. Their future rode heavily on their shoulders, and blinded them to the collective joy that had pervaded the lives of the boys and girls in the grammar school graduating class.

Parents who could afford it had ordered new shoes and ready-made clothes for themselves from Sears and Roebuck or Montgomery Ward. They also engaged the best seamstresses to make the floating graduating dresses and to cut down secondhand pants which would be pressed to a military slickness for the important event.

Oh, it was important, all right. Whitefolks would attend the ceremony, and two or three would speak of God and home, and the Southern way of life, and Mrs. Parsons, the principal's wife, would play the graduation march while the lower-grade graduates paraded down the aisles and took their seats below the platform. The high school seniors would wait in empty classrooms to make their dramatic entrance.


In the Store I was the person of the moment. The birthday girl. The center. Bailey had graduated the year before, although to do so he had had to forfeit all pleasures to make up for his time lost in Baton Rouge.

My class was wearing butter-yellow piqué dresses, and Momma launched out on mine. She smocked the yoke into tiny crisscrossing puckers, then shirred the rest of the bodice. Her dark fingers ducked in and out of the lemony cloth as she embroidered raised daisies around the hem. Before she considered herself finished she had added a crocheted cuff on the puff sleeves, and a pointy crocheted collar.

I was going to be lovely. A walking model of all the various styles of fine hand sewing and it didn't worry me that I was only twelve years old and merely graduating from the eighth grade. Besides, many teachers in Arkansas Negro schools had only that diploma and were licensed to impart wisdom.

The days had become longer and more noticeable. The faded beige of former times had been replaced with strong and sure colors. I began to see my classmates' clothes, their skin tones, and the dust that waved off pussy willows. Clouds that lazed across the sky were objects of great concern to me. Their shiftier shapes might have held a message that in my new happiness and with a little bit of time I'd soon decipher. During that period I looked at the arch of heaven so religiously my neck kept a steady ache. I had taken to smiling more often, and my jaws hurt from the unaccustomed activity. Between the two physical sore spots, I suppose I could have been uncomfortable, but that was not the case. As a member of the winning team (the graduating class of 1940) I had outdistanced unpleasant sensations by miles. I was headed for the freedom of open fields.

Youth and social approval allied themselves with me and we trammeled memories of slights and insults. The wind of our swift passage remodeled my features. Lost tears were pounded to mud and then to dust. Years of withdrawal were brushed aside and left behind, as hanging ropes of parasitic moss.

My work alone had awarded me a top place and I was going to be one of the first called in the graduating ceremonies. On the classroom blackboard, as well as on the bulletin board in the auditorium, there were blue stars and white stars and red stars. No absences, no tardinesses, and my academic work was among the best of the year. I could say the preamble to the Constitution even faster than Bailey. We timed ourselves often: "WethepeopleoftheUnitedStatesinordertoformamoreperfectunion ..." I had memorized the Presidents of the United States from Washington to Roosevelt in chronological as well as alphabetical order.

My hair pleased me too. Gradually the black mass had lengthened and thickened, so that it kept at last to its braided pattern, and I didn't have to yank my scalp off when I tried to comb it.

Louise and I had rehearsed the exercises until we tired out ourselves. Henry Reed was class valedictorian. He was a small, very black boy with hooded eyes, a long, broad nose and an oddly shaped head. I had admired him for years because each term he and I vied for the best grades in our class. Most often he bested me, but instead of being disappointed I was pleased that we shared top places between us. Like many Southern Black children, he lived with his grandmother, who was as strict as Momma and as kind as she knew how to be. He was courteous, respectful and soft-spoken to elders, but on the playground he chose to play the roughest games. I admired him. Anyone, I reckoned, sufficiently afraid or sufficiently dull could be polite. But to be able to operate at a top level with both adults and children was admirable.

His valedictory speech was entitled "To Be or Not to Be." The rigid tenth-grade teacher had helped him write it. He'd been working on the dramatic stresses for months.

The weeks until graduation were filled with heady activities. A group of small children were to be presented in a play about buttercups and daisies and bunny rabbits. They could be heard throughout the building practicing their hops and their little songs that sounded like silver bells. The older girls (nongraduates, of course) were assigned the task of making refreshments for the night's festivities. A tangy scent of ginger, cinnamon, nutmeg and chocolate wafted around the home economics building as the budding cooks made samples for themselves and their teachers.

In every corner of the workshop, axes and saws split fresh timber as the woodshop boys made sets and stage scenery. Only the graduates were left out of the general bustle. We were free to sit in the library at the back of the building or look in quite detachedly, naturally, on the measures being taken for our event.

Even the minister preached on graduation the Sunday before. His subject was, "Let your light so shine that men will see your good works and praise your Father, Who is in Heaven." Although the sermon was purported to be addressed to us, he used the occasion to speak to backsliders, gamblers and general ne'er-do-wells. But since he had called our names at the beginning of the service we were mollified.

Among Negroes the tradition was to give presents to children going only from one grade to another. How much more important this was when the person was graduating at the top of the class. Uncle Willie and Momma had sent away for a Mickey Mouse watch like Bailey's. Louise gave me four embroidered handkerchiefs. (I gave her three crocheted doilies.) Mrs. Sneed, the minister's wife, made me an underskirt to wear for graduation, and nearly every customer gave me a nickel or maybe even a dime with the instruction "Keep on moving to higher ground," or some such encouragement.

Amazingly the great day finally dawned and I was out of bed before I knew it. I threw open the back door to see it more clearly, but Momma said, "Sister, come away from that door and put your robe on."

I hoped the memory of that morning would never leave me. Sunlight was itself still young, and the day had none of the insistence maturity would bring it in a few hours. In my robe and barefoot in the backyard, under cover of going to see about my new beans, I gave myself up to the gentle warmth and thanked God that no matter what evil I had done in my life He had allowed me to live to see this day. Somewhere in my fatalism I had expected to die, accidentally, and never have the chance to walk up the stairs in the auditorium and gracefully receive my hard-earned diploma. Out of God's merciful bosom I had won reprieve.

Bailey came out in his robe and gave me a box wrapped in Christmas paper. He said he had saved his money for months to pay for it. It felt like a box of chocolates, but I knew Bailey wouldn't save money to buy candy when we had all we could want under our noses.

He was as proud of the gift as I. It was a soft-leatherbound copy of a collection of poems by Edgar Allan Poe, or, as Bailey and I called him, "Eap." I turned to "Annabel Lee" and we walked up and down the garden rows, the cool dirt between our toes, reciting the beautifully sad lines.

Momma made a Sunday breakfast although it was only Friday. After we finished the blessing, I opened my eyes to find the watch on my plate. It was a dream of a day. Everything went smoothly and to my credit. I didn't have to be reminded or scolded for anything. Near evening I was too jittery to attend to chores, so Bailey volunteered to do all before his bath.

Days before, we had made a sign for the Store, and as we turned out the lights Momma hung the cardboard over the doorknob. It read clearly: CLOSED. GRADUATION.

My dress fitted perfectly and everyone said that I looked like a sunbeam in it. On the hill, going toward the school, Bailey walked behind with Uncle Willie, who muttered, "Go on, Ju." He wanted him to walk ahead with us because it embarrassed him to have to walk so slowly. Bailey said he'd let the ladies walk together, and the men would bring up the rear. We all laughed, nicely.

Little children dashed by out of the dark like fireflies. Their crepe-paper dresses and butterfly wings were not made for running and we heard more than one rip, dryly, and the regretful "uh uh" that followed.

The school blazed without gaiety. The windows seemed cold and unfriendly from the lower hill. A sense of ill-fated timing crept over me, and if Momma hadn't reached for my hand I would have drifted back to Bailey and Uncle Willie, and possibly beyond. She made a few slow jokes about my feet getting cold, and tugged me along to the now-strange building.

Around the front steps, assurance came back. There were my fellow "greats," the graduating class. Hair brushed back, legs oiled, new dresses and pressed pleats, fresh pocket handkerchiefs and little handbags, all homesewn. Oh, we were up to snuff, all right. I joined my comrades and didn't even see my family go in to find seats in the crowded auditorium.

The school band struck up a march and all classes filed in as had been rehearsed. We stood in front of our seats, as assigned, and on a signal from the choir director, we sat. No sooner had this been accomplished than the band started to play the national anthem. We rose again and sang the song, after which we recited the pledge of allegiance. We remained standing for a brief minute before the choir director and the principal signaled to us, rather desperately I thought, to take our seats. The command was so unusual that our carefully rehearsed and smooth-running machine was thrown off. For a full minute we fumbled for our chairs and bumped into each other awkwardly. Habits change or solidify under pressure, so in our state of nervous tension we had been ready to follow our usual assembly pattern: the American national anthem, then the pledge of allegiance, then the song every Black person I knew called the Negro National Anthem. All done in the same key, with the same passion and most often standing on the same foot.

Finding my seat at last, I was overcome with a presentiment of worse things to come. Something unrehearsed, unplanned, was going to happen, and we were going to be made to look bad. I distinctly remember being explicit in the choice of pronoun. It was "we," the graduating class, the unit, that concerned me then.

The principal welcomed "parents and friends" and asked the Baptist minister to lead us in prayer. His invocation was brief and punchy, and for a second I thought we were getting back on the high road to right action. When the principal came back to the dais, however, his voice had changed. Sounds always affected me profoundly and the principal's voice was one of my favorites. During assembly it melted and lowed weakly into the audience. It had not been in my plan to listen to him, but my curiosity was piqued and I straightened up to give him my attention.

He was talking about Booker T. Washington, our "late great leader," who said we can be as close as the fingers on the hand, etc. . . . Then he said a few vague things about friendship and the friendship of kindly people to those less fortunate than themselves. With that his voice nearly faded, thin, away. Like a river diminishing to a stream and then to a trickle. But he cleared his throat and said, "Our speaker tonight, who is also our friend, came from Texarkana to deliver the commencement address, but due to the irregularity of the train schedule, he's going to, as they say, 'speak and run.'" He said that we understood and wanted the man to know that we were most grateful for the time he was able to give us and then something about how we were willing always to adjust to another's program, and without more ado—"I give you Mr. Edward Donleavy."

Not one but two white men came through the door offstage. The shorter one walked to the speaker's platform, and the tall one moved over to the center seat and sat down. But that was our principal's seat, and already occupied. The dislodged gentleman bounced around for a long breath or two before the Baptist minister gave him his chair, then with more dignity than the situation deserved, the minister walked off the stage.

Donleavy looked at the audience once (on reflection, I'm sure that he wanted only to reassure himself that we were really there), adjusted his glasses and began to read from a sheaf of papers.

He was glad "to be here and to see the work going on just as it was in the other schools."

At the first "Amen" from the audience I willed the offender to immediate death by choking on the word. But Amens and Yes, sir's began to fall around the room like rain through a ragged umbrella.

He told us of the wonderful changes we children in Stamps had in store. The Central School (naturally, the white school was Central) had already been granted improvements that would be in use in the fall. A well-known artist was coming from Little Rock to teach art to them. They were going to have the newest microscopes and chemistry equipment for their laboratory. Mr. Donleavy didn't leave us long in the dark over who made these improvements available to Central High. Nor were we to be ignored in the general betterment scheme he had in mind.

He said that he had pointed out to people at a very high level that one of the first-line football tacklers at Arkansas Agricultural and Mechanical College had graduated from good old Lafayette County Training School. Here fewer Amen's were heard. Those few that did break through lay dully in the air with the heaviness of habit.

He went on to praise us. He went on to say how he had bragged that "one of the best basketball players at Fisk sank his first ball right here at Lafayette County Training School."

The white kids were going to have a chance to become Galileos and Madame Curies and Edisons and Gauguins, and our boys (the girls weren't even in on it) would try to be Jesse Owenses and Joe Louises.

Owens and the Brown Bomber were great heroes in our world, but what school official in the white-goddom of Little Rock had the right to decide that those two men must be our only heroes? Who decided that for Henry Reed to become a scientist he had to work like George Washington Carver, as a boot-black, to buy a lousy microscope? Bailey was obviously always going to be too small to be an athlete, so which concrete angel glued to what country seat had decided that if my brother wanted to become a lawyer he had to first pay penance for his skin by picking cotton and hoeing corn and studying correspondence books at night for twenty years?

The man's dead words fell like bricks around the auditorium and too many settled in my belly. Constrained by hard-learned manners I couldn't look behind me, but to my left and right the proud graduating class of 1940 had dropped their heads. Every girl in my row had found something new to do with her handkerchief. Some folded the tiny squares into love knots, some into triangles, but most were wadding them, then pressing them flat on their yellow laps.

On the dais, the ancient tragedy was being replayed. Professor Parsons sat, a sculptor's reject, rigid. His large, heavy body seemed devoid of will or willing-ness, and his eyes said he was no longer with us. The other teachers examined the flag (which was draped stage right) or their notes, or the windows which opened on our now-famous playing diamond.

Graduation, the hush-hush magic time of frills and gifts and congratulations and diplomas, was finished for me before my name was called. The accomplish-ment was nothing. The meticulous maps, drawn in three colors of ink, learning and spelling decasyllabic words, memorizing the whole of *The Rape of Lu-crece*—it was for nothing. Donleavy had exposed us.

We were maids and farmers, handymen and washerwomen, and anything higher that we aspired to was farcical and presumptuous.

Then I wished that Gabriel Prosser and Nat Turner had killed all whitefolks in their beds and that Abraham Lincoln had been assassinated before the signing of the Emancipation Proclamation, and that Harriet Tubman had been killed by that blow on her head and Christopher Columbus had drowned in the *Santa Maria*.

It was awful to be Negro and have no control over my life. It was brutal to be young and already trained to sit quietly and listen to charges brought against my color with no chance of defense. We should all be dead. I thought I should like to see us all dead, one on top of the other. A pyramid of flesh with the whitefolks on the bottom, as the broad base, then the Indians with their silly

316 ————————————————————————————————————————

tomahawks and teepees and wigwams and treaties, the Negroes with their mops and recipes and cotton sacks and spirituals sticking out of their mouths. The Dutch children should all stumble in their wooden shoes and break their necks. The French should choke to death on the Louisiana Purchase (1803) while silk-worms ate all the Chinese with their stupid pigtails. As a species, we were an abomination. All of us.

Donleavy was running for election, and assured our parents that if he won we could count on having the only colored paved playing field in that part of Arkansas. Also—he never looked up to acknowledge the grunts of accep-tance—also, we were bound to get some new equipment for the home economics building and the workshop.

He finished, and since there was no need to give any more than the most perfunctory thank-you's, he nodded to the men on the stage, and the tall white man who was never introduced joined him at the door. They left with the attitude that now they were off to something really important. (The graduation ceremon-ies at Lafayette County Training School had been a mere preliminary.)

The ugliness they left was palpable. An uninvited guest who wouldn't leave. The choir was summoned and sang a modern arrangement of "Onward, Christian Soldiers," with new words pertaining to graduates seeking their place in the world. But it didn't work. Elouise, the daughter of the Baptist minister, recited "Invictus," and I could have cried at the impertinence of "I am the master of my fate, I am the captain of my soul."

My name had lost its ring of familiarity and I had to be nudged to go and receive my diploma. All my preparations had fled. I neither marched up to the stage like a conquering Amazon, nor did I look in the audience for Bailey's nod of approval. Marguerite Johnson, I heard the name again, my honors were read, there were noises in the audience of appreciation, and I took my place on the stage as rehearsed.

I thought about colors I hated: ecru, puce, lavender, beige and black.

There was shuffling and rustling around me, then Henry Reed was giving his valedictory address, "To Be or Not to Be." Hadn't he heard the whitefolks? We couldn't *be*, so the question was a waste of time. Henry's voice came out clear and strong. I feared to look at him. Hadn't he got the message? There was no "nobler in the mind" for Negroes because the world didn't think we had minds, and they let us know it. "Outrageous fortune"? Now, that was a joke. When the ceremony was over I had to tell Henry Reed some things. That is, if I still cared. Not "rub," Henry, "erase." "Ah, there's the erase." Us.

Henry had been a good student in elocution. His voice rose on tides of promise and fell on waves of warnings. The English teacher had helped him to create a sermon winging through Hamlet's soliloquy. To be a man, a doer, a builder, a leader, or to be a tool, an unfunny joke, a crusher of funky toadstools. I marveled that Henry could go through with the speech as if we had a choice.

I had been listening and silently rebutting each sentence with my eyes closed; then there was a hush, which in an audience warns that something unplanned is happening. I looked up and saw Henry Reed, the conservative, the proper, the A student, turn his back to the audience and turn to us (the proud graduating class of 1940) and sing, nearly speaking,

> "Lift ev'ry voice and sing
> Till earth and heaven ring
> Ring with the harmonies of Liberty . . . "*

It was the poem written by James Weldon Johnson. It was the music composed by J. Rosamond Johnson. It was the Negro national anthem. Out of habit we were singing it.

Our mothers and fathers stood in the dark hall and joined the hymn of encouragement. A kindergarten teacher led the small children onto the stage and the buttercups and daisies and bunny rabbits marked time and tried to follow:

> "Stony the road we trod
> Bitter the chastening rod
> Felt in the days when hope, unborn, had died.
> Yet with a steady beat
> Have not our weary feet
> Come to the place for which our fathers sighed?"

Every child I knew had learned that song with his ABC's and along with "Jesus Loves Me This I Know." But I personally had never heard it before. Never heard the words, despite the thousands of times I had sung them. Never thought they had anything to do with me.

On the other hand, the words of Patrick Henry had made such an impression on me that I had been able to stretch myself tall and trembling and say, "I know not what course others may take, but as for me, give me liberty or give me death."

And now I heard, really for the first time:

> "We have come over a way that with tears
> has been watered,
> We have come, treading our path through
> the blood of the slaughtered."

While echoes of the song shivered in the air, Henry Reed bowed his head, said "Thank you," and returned to his place in the line. The tears that slipped down many faces were not wiped away in shame.

We were on top again. As always, again. We survived. The depths had been icy and dark, but now a bright sun spoke to our souls. I was no longer simply a member of the proud graduating class of 1940; I was a proud member of the wonderful, beautiful Negro race.

Oh, Black known and unknown poets, how often have your auctioned pains sustained us? Who will compute the lonely nights made less lonely by your songs, or by the empty pots made less tragic by your tales?

If we were a people much given to revealing secrets, we might raise monuments and sacrifice to the memories of our poets, but slavery cured us of that weakness. It may be enough, however, to have it said that we survive in exact relationship to the dedication of our poets (include preachers, musicians and blues singers).

## For Better Reading: Compare and . . .

Making comparisons is a vital part of becoming a good reader. In fact, you've already been asked to make them at least six times before in this chapter alone.

Yet, there is more than one reason to make comparisons. A common reason is to help you make a choice—whether it's ordering from a menu or deciding about your future.

Some people "always pick the same brand," whether it's cars or candidates. That can be because their comparisons aren't thorough enough. By basing their choices on just one factor, they use comparison as their way of putting people, things, and ideas into tidy groups and rigid categories. To some, it becomes an easy way to avoid the need for thinking.

When making comparisons, good readers train themselves to look beyond surface differences to the important likenesses—and past outward sameness to inner differences, as well. In this way, comparisons are essential steps in critical thinking, giving you the basis for thoughtful judgments as you read.

## Fact or Falsehood

Have proof from the selection to support your answers.
1. Lafayette Country Training School had fewer refinements than the white high school.
2. The majority of graduating seniors were overjoyed because they were done with school for the rest of their lives.
3. With graduation fever raging, the teachers had difficulty keeping the students under control.

## Questioning the Selection

1. How does Maya's "butter-yellow piqué dress" show the importance of 8th grade graduation in the black community? Give at least two reasons.

2. Although "merely" an 8th grade graduation, why did this represent considerable education in Arkansas black schools of the 1930's?
3. As one of her class's top students, what are three accomplishments Maya could take pride in?
4. Compare Henry Reed's and Maya's family backgrounds and school records, and name at least three factors that were alike or different. Why did Maya admire him?
5. What special preparations were each of the following assigned for graduation: the small children, the older girls who were not graduating, and the workshop boys?
6. How was graduation also brought into the church service? How did her grandmother's owning a general store make Maya seem especially lucky?
7. In what two ways did Maya's brother Bailey help make it a "dream of a day"?
8. Angelou states, "The school blazed without gaiety," as she and her family approached. What are three additional indications that Maya sensed something would go wrong at the graduation ceremony?
9. What change in the opening ceremony upset the "carefully rehearsed and smooth-running machine"? Why was the commencement speaker guilty for the confusion? As a result, how was the entire community wrongly "made to look bad" in the speaker's eyes?
10. Compare the principal's words with the change Maya heard in his voice. Describe the emotions he probably felt.
11. How did the second, unexpected white man show apparent lack of consideration? How was the situation smoothed over? What attitude is reinforced by the fact that the speaker "never introduced" the man who accompanied him?
12. Although the speaker failed to realize it, Maya and the rest of the audience were making mental comparisons as he spoke. In the light of this, explain why the words "Amen" and "Yes, sir" were difficult to say.
13. Explain how Henry Reed and Maya's brother Bailey are both examples of the kind of difficulties black students faced.
14. Why was Maya at first shocked and disgusted by Henry's commencement speech? How did Henry surprise Maya and enable her to say, "We were on top again"?

## Looking Deeper

### I. "Trained to Sit Quietly"

Describe how Professor Parsons, the other teachers, and the other girls in Maya's row behaved during Donleavy's speech. What did these variations of behavior all have in common?

What was unfair about Donleavy's campaign promises to the people of Stamps? What in the past and their current situation explains why the audience members would just "sit quietly and listen," not object or protest to the words of the white speaker?

## II. Dreaming the Dream

Based on the entire selection, compare Maya Angelou's schooling as an 8th grader with your own. List at least three factors that are different, and explain how you account for them.

In what ways did Maya's learning seem mainly rooted in a patriotic version of the American dream? What chances of fulfilling the American dream did those in the commencement audience have? Explain the reason behind your answer.

Describe at least three extremes of emotion felt by Maya at age 12 on graduation day, and explain the cause of each. What were the "ancient tragedy" and present unfairness that caused her emotions to explode and Maya to feel, "It was awful to be Negro"?

## III. " . . . the Dedication of Our Poets"

Until her 8th grade graduation, Maya had never really "heard" the Negro National Anthem but knew Patrick Henry's words by heart. Compare the white American patriot's words with the first and last section by the black American poet. How are they alike and different? What special elements in James Weldon Johnson's poem make it a fit choice as the Negro National Anthem?

"We were on top again. As always, again. We survived." Considering the "days when hope, unborn, had died," why were "poets (include preachers, musicians, and blues singers)" among the few who were not prevented from sustaining hope of freedom from slavery and being a "bright sun" that "spoke to our souls"?

# Lifelong Dreamer—Vietnam Boat Person

*by Mary-Beth McLaughlin*

***Career:*** *Newspaper writer, Toledo, Ohio,* Blade

---

**N**ANCY PHAM SAYS THAT SHE has been a dreamer most of her life.

Her dreams have taken her from a crowded refugee boat in the choppy seas off war-torn South Vietnam to the quiet confines of a former church in suburban Toledo where she's opened her own beauty salon.

She's still navigating choppy seas—any entrepreneur trying to launch a new business in tough economic times knows the going isn't easy. But she exudes a quiet confidence.

"I'm already a success, because I've already done what I wanted to do," said the owner of the Fifth Avenue beauty salon, which opened three months ago at the corner of Sylvania and McCord Roads.

Such confidence is born from a lifetime of beating the odds, starting at age 13, when the Vietnam war came to the city of Saigon where she lived with her family.

Confidence also comes from having survived a 15-day boat trip with her husband and two small children, one of whom was so sick, she feared she would have to bury the child by tossing her into the sea.

And still more confidence comes from having survived ending up in Oak Harbor, OH., with no job or money, not speaking English, and not even being sure of the size of the United States.

Speaking in soft, accented English, Mrs. Pham retold her story quietly. Only the long pauses and heavy sighs gave away the pain of surviving during wartime.

From 1963 on, there were sandbags in the living room where the family ran during bombings that occurred every night.

"I was not afraid of it. Sometimes, I would just sleep in my bed and you could feel the whole house shake. It was really, really noisy," she said. "And then I would get up in the morning and I was not scared. I would feel wonderful I'm alive. And I would walk around the neighborhood and check and see who is alive and who is dead."

But life went on, and Mrs. Pham did the "normal" things: graduating from high school; learning shorthand, typing, and English, and getting a job as a secretary at Macvee II, a company associated with the U.S. Army.

She met and married Chinh, a man 11 years her elder, who was in the Navy. They had two children, Huy (renamed William) and Trang (renamed Jenny). After Jenny was born in 1973, Mrs. Pham quit Macvee to become a full-time mother.

Although it was nerve-wracking to ride on buses or go to hotels where Americans stayed—both were prime targets for bombs—the South Vietnamese people loved the Americans and Saigon thrived with their presence, she said.

But in 1972, the Americans started their withdrawal, and things began to change. By 1975, with Saigon on the verge of falling, all former and current Macvee employees were promised safe passage to the U.S. if they wanted.

Mrs. Pham's sister, still a Macvee employee, typed up the forms for the whole family to leave.

Their mother, who did not speak English, but already had moved once to escape Communism, was determined to leave. But Mrs. Pham hesitated.

"I worry, what will I do over [in the U.S.]? We have money, and a business, and house, and I thought, I never did anything to the Communists, they won't do anything to me. So I don't go," she said.

So while her sister, mother, and remaining family members headed for a ship in the harbor, Mrs. Pham stayed with her two small children—until her husband arrived the next day and demanded to know why they hadn't left.

Brushing aside her arguments, he loaded the kids in the car with clothes and borrowed milk, told neighbors they would return the next day after a visit to her aunt, and set off for the harbor.

Mr. Pham ignored the restrictions on service personnel leaving the country and boarded the boat with his family.

On April 29, 1975, the ship pulled out of the harbor as the radio blared news that Ho Chi Minh was now in charge of Saigon.

Pausing while lost deep in memories, Mrs. Pham whispered, "It seems like yesterday."

They had no idea where they were going or how long it would take to get there, she said.

There was no roof, no room to move, and canned Army rations included raw fish with a worm inside. And there was no milk for 10-month-old Jenny, so they fed her sugar and water. But as days went by, Jenny became weak until she all but stopped moving, and her mother thought she had died.

"I don't know where I'm at. Even if there had been a coconut floating by, I would have had some idea. My husband was crying and I was running from one room to another but there was no medicine," she said. "We were just hoping they would stop somewhere."

"I kept thinking, 'If she dies in the ship, we'd have to throw her in the ocean,' " Mrs. Pham said.

But in the first of what she called "miracles," the ship carrying the Phams stopped at Subic Bay, The Philippines, after 15 days at sea.

Jenny was given a shot, and in three days she was better, Mrs. Pham said. Jenny now is a student at Sylvania Northview High School.

The family boarded another ship to Guam, and eventually was sent to a camp in Pennsylvania, where they waited for a family or church to sponsor them.

Many families requested sponsors located in sunnier climates like Florida or California, but Mrs. Pham couldn't wait.

"I did not know how big the U.S. is and I was worrying about everything. I wanted to get out and see what outside world is, and so I tell my husband we have to get out and make a living," she said.

Her mother moved to New Jersey, her sister to California, and the Pham family was sponsored by St. John Lutheran Church, in Rocky Ridge, near Oak Harbor. On July 16, 1975, the Pham family boarded a plane for Ohio.

Nancy said she was anxious, having been told Ohio was full of snow and ice and cold.

"I'm such a worrier, that I looked down, picturing snow and ice and no living thing," she said. "I look down and everything was so green and there were mountains and rivers. I feel so happy. I feel like I'm a bird, like I'm a fish. Everything is so beautiful and I think, 'I can make a living.'"

The Phams stayed with an Oak Harbor family for two weeks, then moved when the church found a house for them to rent.

Chinh found a job at Glasstech, Inc., within two weeks, while Nancy took English lessons. But Nancy said she quickly knew that life in a rural community wasn't for her, and started urging her husband to move the family closer to Toledo.

Eventually, Mrs. Pham borrowed money from her brother and the family bought a small house in east Toledo.

She sewed clothes for a next door neighbor, made and sold egg rolls, cleaned people's houses, and worked as a lunchtime waitress. Along the way, she had Thomas, now 10.

But always, always she was dreaming.

"There was a lot of things I want to do, but I have no money and I can't stand it," she said.

"I've always had my dreams. I dream all the time and I think I can do anything," she says.

While working as a waitress she said she dreamed of someday being her own boss.

She became a student at Ma Chere Hair Style Academy, and later a manicurist, renting space at Paul & Co.

Louise Hedge, owner of Ma Chere, said she never had any doubt that Nancy Pham would someday have her own shop.

"I'm not surprised because that was her goal. She really wanted it and kept telling me that," Miss Hedge said. "She was an excellent student because she had a lot of personality. I don't mind having them when they really want it."

Mrs. Pham remembers having difficulty with the language, and over-compensating by taping lectures and memorizing them while she made egg rolls. When it came time to take her state exam in Columbus, Mrs. Pham memorized the book.

She spent most of the 1980s working at Paul & Co., but always dreaming of her own shop.

"I like to be my own boss and I want to treat employees fair and equal. I like take and give. I don't want people who only take and don't give," she said.

This year, Mrs. Pham got to be her own boss when her husband noticed that the church at the corner of McCord and Sylvania roads was up for sale.

He wanted to open a restaurant in the old church, but after Mrs. Pham convinced him that would be too much work, she broached the idea of a beauty salon.

Donna Pollex, an agent with Loss Realty Co. who handled the deal, had nothing but praise for the Phams.

"They are fantastic people. They're very dedicated and very honest and try to please people and I wish them lots of success," she said. "They just brought themselves up from nothing and I know they will be successful. The hours she puts in are incredible and it's really a family affair. The husband does the yard and the daughter handles appointments and both sons also help out.

"They are very, very hard working people," she said.

With the help of workers, the church was remodeled into a beauty salon which opened about three months ago.

Mrs. Pham said she doesn't worry about whether her business will be a success.

"What you want to do, you should do. You may lose money, but you do not lose what you want to do," she said. "I don't worry about being famous or about being rich. I . . . want to have a beauty salon for everyone."

It is an attitude that sits well with her eight employees.

Madonna Fong, a hair stylist at Fifth Avenue, said she has been in the beauty business for 16 years and has worked at a lot of salons that have been "temples to egos."

"[Nancy] is very kind, very caring," she said. "And she has such a great sense of peace in herself."

Mrs. Pham said if she seems peaceful, it's only because she still has dreams.

"If I stopped dreaming, that means I already died," she said.

# For Better Reading: Just the Facts

It's a newspaper reporter's duty to be factual: to tell the reader what happened and what those involved did and said. It's called being *objective*.

A good reporter avoids taking a *subjective* stand. In writing "straight" news, he or she does not express personal opinions, even staying away from such opinionated words as "good," "pretty," and "admirable." And, since reporters can never know what a person they interview truly thinks or believes, they only report what someone *says* he or she is thinking.

That's why McLaughlin, writing about her interview with Nancy Pham, adds "she said" to her statement that "the South Vietnamese people loved the Americans."

Yet, since McLaughlin has her by-line on this article, she is somewhat more free to express her own thoughts, such as commenting that Nancy Pham "exudes a quiet confidence."

Just as with reporting, there's more to being a good newspaper reader than is evident at first glance. For it's the news writers' job to report what they saw and heard as accurately and objectively as possible. It's the readers' job to see beyond the "what happened and how" to make necessary judgments and decisions for themselves.

## Words in Context

1. "Any *entrepreneur* trying to launch a new business ... knows the going isn't easy." *Entrepreneur* means (a) dreamer or idealist (b) inexperienced person (c) foreigner (d) operator or manager.
2. "By 1975, with Saigon on the *verge* of falling ..." *Verge* means (a) edge (b) question (c) certainty (d) depths.
3. Mrs. Pham was "overcompensating for" her language difficulties by "memorizing the book." To *overcompensate* means to (a) worry about (b) make up for (c) pay no attention to (d) do more than necessary.
4. "She *broached* the idea of a beauty salon." To *broach* means to (a) pin one's hopes on (b) first suggest (c) debate with oneself about (d) dread.

## Questioning the Selection

1. When she arrived in Ohio, what are three problems Nancy Pham needed to overcome to survive?
2. In wartime Saigon, how did war affect everyday life, and what "went on" in "normal" fashion? List three examples of each.
3. In some cases, Mrs. Pham—with McLaughlin as an objective reporter—seems to understate the wartime terror. Find at least two examples, and explain how and why you imagine their being worse.

4. As Mrs. Pham retold her story, how did McLaughlin interpret her "long pauses and heavy sighs"? Why wouldn't Mrs. Pham wish to express her feelings more fully?

5. When the Americans began withdrawing from South Vietnam, why was Mrs. Pham promised safe passage to the United States? How did her attitude toward this differ from her family's and why?

6. Describe three major difficulties the Phams faced on the 15-day boat trip from Vietnam to the Philippine Islands.

7. Once in the United States, what reasons lay behind the family's coming first to Ohio and then to Toledo?

8. The article quotes Mrs. Pham as saying, "I think I can do anything." Find at least two examples in the article that show why she has such confidence.

9. What qualities of the Phams does the real estate agent credit for their success? Give three examples.

10. Find three examples of Mary-Beth McLaughlin's "coloring" Nancy Pham's story with her own conclusions and reactions, and explain whether you think they add to an understanding of the article.

## Looking Deeper

### I. A Horatio Alger Story?

When she arrived in the United States, how did Nancy Pham seem to fit the model for a Horatio Alger hero? Why was her situation different?

Does Pham's story contain an Alger-like combination of "pluck"—or courage in the face of difficulties—and luck? Include supporting evidence to back your opinion.

According to Alger's description, his hero "was frank and straight-forward ... and self-reliant," as well as hard working and honest. Which of these qualities does Nancy Pham possess? Provide specific examples for each.

How might Nancy Pham's story to some people "fall short" of Alger's "Rags to Riches" tale?

### II. "I'm Already a Success"

Explain why you agree or disagree with Nancy Pham's feeling that she is already successful.

Although she was born in Vietnam, do you feel that Nancy Pham has a good understanding of the American dream? Explain why or why not.

After saying she doesn't want riches or fame, Mrs. Pham states, "If I stopped dreaming, that means I already died." Explain your interpretation of this statement and its effect as the article's final quote.

―――――――――――――――――――― **REFLECTIONS** ――――――――――――――――――――

There's a universal sense of something special about being American and sharing in the American dream.

Is it the hope of gaining wealth? America has long been thought the richest country in the world—richest in dollars and natural resources and standard of living. This is not necessarily true, for other countries rank higher when quantity is the measure.

Yet, Americans still feel themselves the richest—in the promises and possibilities of the American dream.

There are as many versions and shadings to the American Dream as there are Americans. In this unit, you've read of those who have seemingly "arrived" and others who feel shut out. Some imagine dreaming by itself should bring "happiness ever after," while others strive to live up to their dreams. As you think back on these selections, consider what version of the America dream is revealed in each and what elements you want to emphasize in your own life.

## To Write About or Discuss

1. Are there Horatio Alger's stories in real life? Research the life of someone who seems to fit the "rags to riches" model, such as Henry Ford, Maya Angelou, a U.S. President, or other prominent American of the past or present, and draw a comparison to determine your answer.
2. What is the best "measure of success"? Choose two selections from this unit and explain why you do or do not admire the versions of the American dream held by someone in each.
3. Do advertising, television, and movies lead to false expectations with regard to American dreams of happiness? Base your answer on the selections you've read and your own observations.

# Search for the Spirit

"... AMERICA DIDN'T INHERIT A NATION—it invented one that was supposed to be better than everything that had gone before.... And, because we expected more, we know more about disillusion."

Alistair Cooke's *America*

That's the spirit!

"The Spirit of '76"

... the American spirit!

The American spirit is made up of many different elements. It's the attitude and mood that Americans have toward themselves and the world around them. It's the combination of impulses that inspires them to act and the energy that's their essence, what Americans are "really like."

"That's the spirit!" It's encouragement Americans give someone whose actions they think are right.

Is there a single, unified spirit that all Americans share? Of course not. With more than 200,000,000 Americans, that just isn't possible. Yet since its beginnings, people both here and abroad have tried to describe what makes Americans "different."

The American spirit is outgoing, good-humored, determined to be fair, loaded with energy. "Full of bounce and bluster." (Samuel Eliot Morison) Weak on manners but warm at heart. Can you sum up the American spirit? Based on ideals yet rooted in reality, Americans created a code differing from Old World models and still evolving ... a spirit recognizably American as this chapter shows.

# The Dentist

*by Charles Kuralt*

| | |
|---|---|
| ***Born:*** | *North Carolina* |
| ***Family descent:*** | *Norse, Celtic, Bavarian, Scotch-Irish, Slovenian* |
| ***First jobs:*** | *Student news editor, general reporter, TV writer* |
| ***Famous as:*** | *Author, TV broadcaster* |

**I** WENT BACK TO THE SOVIET UNION in May 1988. Sometimes—once in a great while—a story on television actually brings people together, and touches them, and helps make their lives whole. I watched this happen that spring. The man who made it happen was a retired Russian dentist.

I carry around in my head memories of hundreds of people I have met in these years of wandering. The memory of this one man haunts me. Hardly a day goes by that I don't think of Nikita Zakaravich Aseyev.

He was a stocky old bulldog of a man who barged into the hotel where I was staying in Moscow while I helped out with coverage of the Reagan-Gorbachev summit meeting. The hotel, the gigantic Rossiya which looms behind Red Square, was closed to Soviet citizens that week. All comings and goings were regulated by KGB men at the doors wearing red armbands inscribed "I am here to help you." "Pals," the wry Muscovites call these grim-faced guards. Those of us who had rooms and temporary offices in the hotel—mostly American and Western European reporters—wore credentials on chains around our necks to get us into the building past the Pals. Dr. Aseyev got in on his medals.

He wore his World War II medals on the lapels of his suit coat, as do many old soldiers in the Soviet Union. When the KGB men stopped him at the front door of the Rossiya, an acquaintance of mine happened to be there watching. He reported that the old man erupted in indignation.

He thundered, "What do you mean I cannot enter? You children, you pups! You have the gall to tell a veteran of the Great Patriotic War he cannot pass into a common hotel lobby?"

He slapped the place over his heart where his medals hung.

"Where were you?" he demanded of the young chief of the guard detail, who had come striding over to see what the shouting was about. "Where were *you* when I received these honors for helping repel the fascist hordes from our precious motherland?"

His voice rose even louder as he theatrically answered his own question. "Cowering in a safe corner, a child who never heard the guns!" he roared. "Or suckling at your mother's breast!"

The KGB men looked at one another with resignation. The chief of the detail started to speak, but the old man interrupted him.

"Where were *you* when the Gestapo gave me *this?*" he shouted, pointing dramatically to a deep scar in his skull over his right eye.

A little crowd of Western reporters was beginning to gather. The raving old man poked the KGB chief in the chest with a stubby finger.

"Where were *you?*" he roared at the top of his lungs. He jutted out his old square chin and paused for a reply.

The KGB man shrugged. Without a word, he unhooked the chain that barred the door and stood aside.

The old man marched into the lobby of the Rossiya Hotel looking satisfied, his medals swinging from his chest.

He approached the first person in his path and demanded to see a representative of American television. "CBS, third floor," he was told.

Minutes later, he showed up in the CBS News offices, a chunky, obviously unofficial character ranting in Russian, insisting that he be heard. As it happened, everybody in the place was busily preoccupied, preparing for coverage of what seemed more important at the time: the final meeting of the week between the President of the United States and the General Secretary of the Communist Party of the Soviet Union. A young assistant, a Russian-speaking foreign student at Moscow's Pushkin Institute who had been hired by CBS for the week of summit duty, took the old man into a vacant room in order to get him out of the hall, calm him down and get rid of him. The student listened to a few minutes of what seemed to be a carefully rehearsed speech, explained that everybody was too busy to hear his story at the moment, walked the old man back down to the hotel lobby and sent him home in a CBS-hired taxi—but only after making a solemn promise that a reporter from CBS News would see him next morning.

And that is how it happened that the next morning, I went for a walk in a park with Dr. Nikita Zakaravich Aseyev.

He wore his medals. He carried a walking stick in one hand and a worn shopping bag in the other. The tail of his sport shirt hung out over his trousers, which did not match his suit coat. We were accompanied by an interpreter, but Dr. Aseyev kept forgetting to wait for his words to be put into English. He was in a great rush to say what he had to say.

"You have to help me," he said. "You are my hope. Everybody lives in hope, you know, and I am no different. For more than forty years, I have waited for this chance, and now it has come."

He shifted his cane to the hand that held the shopping bag and grasped my arm.

"You can speak to America, is this not true?" he asked, and went on before I could answer. "You must help me find some Americans I knew during the war.

I have to thank them for saving my life and the lives of many other Russian soldiers."

We sat down on a park bench. He pointed to the scar in his forehead.

"A memory of the Gestapo," he said. "Not a very happy memory. I have another in the side of my body."

He cleared his throat and began:

"We were all prisoners of the Germans at a big concentration camp at Fürstenberg on the Oder River. There were eight thousand American soldiers there, captured in North Africa. The camp was laid out this way."

With his cane, he drew a map on the ground in front of the bench.

"Here the town ... here the river and the railroad tracks ... here the camp, Stalag 3-B. The Gestapo barracks were here, near the gate," he said, "here the French prisoners, the Polish, the Yugoslav, the partisans." He indicated each compound by drawing large rectangles in the dirt. "Here," he said, drawing the largest enclosure of all, "the Russians. And next to us," he said, finishing his map, "just across the wire fence—the Americans.

"Nearly every Friday, the Americans each received a five-kilo food parcel from the Red Cross. But the Germans gave us only one liter of turnip soup per day, and one liter of water. It wasn't enough to keep us alive. We were dying by the tens, and then by the hundreds. The Americans could see this. Twenty-five thousand men died in that concentration camp...."

His eyes looked past me for a moment, into the distance.

"I could tell you many stories about those who died," he said softly. He paused, still looking away. Then, abruptly, returning to me, "But that is not what I am here to do. It's the Americans I want to talk about, you see.

"In all the camp, I was the only dentist. Every living person, can, of course get sick, and the Germans permitted me to treat the Americans. There was no dental surgery. I just accepted patients in an ordinary chair, even when I had to perform complicated operations. I treated hundreds of American soldiers, and I believe there were never any complications afterwards, even in such conditions as perhaps you can imagine. I was the only Russian permitted any contact with the Americans, and the Americans respected me. All eight thousand of them knew me, or had heard about me, and understood that I was a very good specialist, and they held me in respect.

"One day, after I had been there about a year, two American brothers named Wowczuk, Michael and Peter, and a third American whose name I forget, spoke to me about conditions in the Russian compound. These brothers I knew by now. They were from Chicago, workers in the stockyards, and I understood already that they were very good people. We were alone in the room that was the dental clinic. This was the beginning of the thing I want to tell you. The brothers Wowczuk and this other, whose name I cannot remember, proposed a plot by which the Americans would smuggle food to the Russians. They told me that not only the three of them, but many others of the Americans were willing to participate. I instantly agreed. That is how it all started."

"Wasn't this dangerous?" I asked.

Dr. Aseyev threw up his hands. "Oh, of course!" he exclaimed. "We would have been shot if they had caught us. Merely to be found outside the barracks at night was a shooting offense, and many men were executed in that camp for much less!"

"How did the Americans get the food to you?"

The old man smiled to remember. "They waited until the sentry had passed at night and threw the parcels over the fence," he said. "The fence was only eight meters high. Those Americans were strong! They could have thrown those things a hundred meters!" He laughed.

"I organized a group on our side to rush out to the fence and retrieve the packages. In one night, we received 1,350 parcels in this way."

Dr. Aseyev took my arm again and gripped it tightly.

"Do you realize what I am saying?" he asked me. "This was nearly seven thousand kilos of food in one night! Do you understand what this food meant on our side of the wire, where men were dying every night of starvation?"

He released my arm. "This went on," he said, "at least one night a week for many months. At least one night a week, the Americans, many different ones, risked their lives to collect food parcels and dash out at night to throw them to us. Not one parcel ever failed to make it across the wire. Not one ever was wasted."

"Why do you think the Americans did this?" I asked.

"Because we were allies," Dr. Aseyev answered. "And because they were good men."

He reached for the old plastic shopping bag lying beside him on the bench and brought out a fuzzy photograph.

"This was a good man, too," he said. "This was a German corporal, one of the guard detail. He stumbled into knowledge of what we were doing almost from the first night. He turned his back and let us continue. He was a soldier of the Wehrmacht, but he did not like seeing enemy soldiers starve. After the war, I wrote to his family and they sent me this portrait of him." He handed the photograph to me. "I had a copy made yesterday," Dr. Aseyev said. "It is for you to take home to America. With perfect assurance, you may tell people that Corporal Alfred Jung was an exceptional member of the human race."

"What happened to him?" I asked, looking at the unfocused image of a young man in a German Army uniform.

"The day the plot was finally discovered," Dr. Aseyev said, "they took him out and guillotined him."

He set the shopping bag back on the bench.

"What else do you have there?" I asked.

"I will show you presently," Dr. Aseyev said. "But now I want to tell you about the behavior of the Americans when the plot was discovered.

"All eight thousand American prisoners were assembled on the parade ground in a great semicircle. This was late in May 1944. It was a hot day. Four SS officers went down the line of them saying to each one, 'Give us the name of the Russian who organized this plot.' For three hours in the sun, with nothing to drink, the Americans stood in absolute silence. They stood there with clenched lips. The German officers threatened them with severe reprisal. They stood in silence.

Not one word was spoken. Not one American gave the name of the Russian Dr. Aseyev.

"Finally, to bring the thing to an end, the brothers Wowczuk, Peter and Michael, stepped forward. 'We did it,' they said. 'The whole thing was our idea.' A squad of German guards seized them, and the two brothers were driven out of the camp in a closed truck. Later, I learned that they were taken to another camp, a place for special punishment, where they were questioned every day for four months by the Gestapo—and the Gestapo was the Gestapo, you know! I was afraid for them, but I had no fear for myself. I knew that Michael and Peter would never reveal my name, and they did not."

Dr. Aseyev smiled and lowered his voice. "Later, we were all moved to a different camp," he said, "and do you know—I found Michael and Peter there. And within a few days, we had organized the plot all over again!"

He beamed triumphantly, and started rummaging around again in his shopping bag.

"After the war," he said, "I wrote down the names of those Americans so I could never forget them." He showed me a carbon copy of a document of several pages, typed in Cyrillic characters and dated September 1, 1949.

"This is for you," he said. "It is the only extra copy, so do not lose it. It tells the names of the Americans and what I remember about them. For now, I will tell you the names only."

Gravely, he began to read.

"Wowczuk, Michael.

"Wowczuk, Peter.

"Oh," he said, "Bennett! I just thought of Bennett. He isn't on the list. He was on his deathbed and I did an operation on him. I don't know his first name.

"Jarema, William. He was from New York.

"Harold Symmonds. He was from Mississippi. He lived on that famous river of yours.

"Walhaug, Lloyd. He was a farmer from Illinois.

"Emil Vierling, thirty years old, also a farmer.

"Gut. He was a medic.

"Gasprich. How I loved Gasprich!"

He looked up from the paper in his hand to say emotionally, "What good men they were! What good men they all were!"

He took out a handkerchief and wiped his eyes. "I loved these guys," he said. He continued reading:

"Brockman. Doctor. Captain. I will tell you more about Brockman. . . .

"Dr. Hughes. He was a good friend.

"Dr. Amrich."

I sat on a park bench in Moscow listening to these American names pronounced in a Russian accent. I knew I was hearing a roll call of heroes.

"There were others not written down here," Dr. Aseyev said. "They all took part in smuggling food. I remember Rossbridge, Tossi, Snow—from California, I think—Mangelomani, Audeni . . ."

He leaned forward and said to me, "There were four of us Russian doctors in the camp who took an oath one night that after the war we would find a way to thank these Americans. You see, I am getting old now. This is my chance.

"Now, now because of you," he said, "if these guys are still alive they will know I remember—this dentist who loved them, and whom they did not betray."

He stopped. He exhaled deeply, handed me the list of names and slumped back on the bench. After forty-three years, Nikita Zakaravich Aseyev had just fulfilled an oath.

I invited him to lunch at the Rossiya Hotel. The KGB men stood aside as we entered, not wishing to tangle with him again. At the lunch table, where we were joined by CBS News producer Peter Schweitzer and others, Dr. Aseyev produced more keepsakes from his shopping bag.

"Oh," he said, "oh . . . These are my darlings, my treasures!"

There were photographs of the abandoned camp, clipped from a Soviet newspaper after the war. There were snapshots of the Russian medical doctors who had survived the ordeal of Stalag 3-B with him. There were more medals, wrapped in tissue. Finally, there was a crude cigarette case made of hammered tin.

"Late in the war," said Dr. Aseyev, "Dr. Brockman, who was a gentleman, and with whom I had many long and searching conversations, left the camp. He and some others learned they had been exchanged for German prisoners. Before he left, he came to me and gave me this. It was the only thing he had to give me."

Into the top of the case was scratched the inscription "To N. Z. Aseyev from Sidney Brockman, Captain, U.S. Army."

After lunch, I walked Dr. Aseyev to the taxi that would take him home.

"I know you will not fail me," he said.

I extended my hand, but he didn't take it. Instead, he gave me a vigorous military salute, stepped into the taxi with his cane and shopping bag, and shut the door. As he was driven away, he looked back, and I said good-bye to him in the only way that was now possible. I stood at attention in my best imitation of the form I learned once in the Army Reserve, and returned his salute.

The next morning, June 4, I left Moscow for London by Aeroflot jet, carrying in my hand an orange CBS News shipping bag with the word "URGENT" printed on it in red capital letters. The bag contained the videotape cassettes of Dr. Aseyev's story. All our news shipments are labelled "URGENT." This one, I felt, really was. On arrival in London, I went straight to the CBS News offices in Knightsbridge, where Al Balisky was waiting for me in an editing room. As we sat with the door closed screening the cassettes, I noticed Al's eyes growing moist.

"Imagine," he said gruffly. "The old guy remembered all these years."

Then, without saying anything more, he began the hard job of editing Dr. Aseyev's story into a form that would fit the stringent time requirements of that night's *Evening News*. Once more, on tape, Dr. Aseyev recalled the names.

"Wowczuk . . . Symmonds . . . Jarema . . . Brockman . . ."

"Listen to these names back there in America," I said. "If your name is on this list, an old soldier is saying thank you."

Watching the news that night, William Jarema, retired New York City police detective, felt tears spring to his eyes. "It was a different kind of weeping," he explained a few days later, still unable to speak without choking up. "These are tears of joy. We were like brothers. I thought he was dead."

Dr. Sidney Brockman, retired from the San Antonio, Texas, Health Department, also wept that night. "We were all very close to Dr. Aseyev," he explained later. "We all had tremendous respect for the man, because we knew the Russian prisoners were having things mighty rough.

"In the wintertime, when the Russian prisoners died in their barracks, their comrades did not report their death to the Germans. They brought them out and stood them up for roll call so that their bodies would be counted for rations."

He took out a handkerchief, just as Dr. Aseyev had done on the park bench, and dabbed at his eyes.

"How could we not try to help them?" he asked.

But to risk his own life for them?

"It was part of the game," Dr. Brockman said. "We had all risked our lives to begin with or we wouldn't have been in that place. What was one more risk?"

He said, "Look, I have not believed in being a professional prisoner of war. What happened is done with. I want to forget it if I can." Against his will, he started to weep again.

"But I can't," he said. He paused for a while to collect himself.

"I appreciate Dr. Aseyev remembering me. I have never forgotten him. I will never forget him. What more can I say?"

He got up, went to a cedar chest in a hall closet, and after a time found what he was looking for. "I keep it in here where it's safe and where I don't have to look at it very often," he said. "I took it with me when I left the camp. It's about the only thing I've kept from the war."

It was a cigarette case fashioned of scrap wood, patiently handmade. He opened the case and shook a small metal plaque into his hand.

The plaque read: "To Sidney Brockman from N. Z. Aseyev."

The typewritten pages Dr. Aseyev entrusted to me on the park bench, when translated, give further details of the sacrifice and heroism that ennobled a miserable place once known as Stalag 3-B. When he wrote these notes in 1949, they were meant only as a memorandum to himself, insurance against forgetting some men he had vowed never to forget. But as I read his unadorned recital of bravery and brotherhood in a dark time, I could not help thinking of his notes as a message to the world.

I did my best to deliver Dr. Aseyev's message of gratitude and remembrance to all those on his list. I found that some have died, among them the brave brothers Wowczuk. One or two find the memory of Stalag 3-B so painful that they refuse to discuss it, even now, even on the telephone. In spite of a diligent search by the Military Field Branch of the Department of Defense and by the Center of Military History in Washington, several remain unaccounted for. By recent act of Congress, World War II prisoners of war have been awarded decorations, years after their imprisonment. So far as I know, none of the heroes of Stalag 3-B has ever been honored for what he did there, except in the memory of an aging Russian dentist.

"It was a terrific operation," William Jarema said. "Terrific. We were repaid many times by our feeling of satisfaction, knowing we helped people in need.

"See, when you're starving, it is an awful feeling, your stomach tightens up on you. People don't know how it feels. If you've ever been starving yourself, you can't just walk away from a person who's starving. We were all in trouble in that camp, and we did everything we could to help one another."

He thought about it for a minute and said, "There ought to be more of that in the world today."

## For Better Reading: Setting the Stage

The heart of Charles Kuralt's story concerns American and Russian soldiers in a German prison camp during World War II.

Yet he begins over forty years later, in 1988 while on a television assignment in Moscow, then capital of the Communist-controlled Soviet Union.

In literary terms, it's called *exposition*, laying out background information essential for understanding. You can also think of it as setting the stage. But, just as stage decorations sometimes distract from the action, details in an exposition can mislead or confuse an inattentive reader.

That's true in this selection, "The Dentist," about "a stocky old bulldog" and "raving old man" everyone sees as foolish and crazy. At first, Nikita Zakaravich Aseyev doesn't seem newsworthy.

Yet the alert reader catches Kuralt's comment, "The memory of this one man haunts me" and notes how the author repeatedly calls attention to Dr. Aseyev's medals. It's the way that exposition builds to action—and an understanding why such ideas, more than details, are vital in setting the stage.

### Fact or Opinion

Have supporting evidence from the selection to back your decision.
1. Dr. Aseyev made a fool of himself because of his efforts to gain admission to the hotel and CBS offices.
2. Charles Kuralt wanted the assignment to interview Aseyev because he specialized in human interest stories.
3. The young assistant at CBS was sincere about his promise to have Aseyev interviewed the following day.

### Questioning the Selection

1. When Aseyev first arrived at the CBS office in Moscow, what seemed "more important at the time" than an old man's story?
2. For what chance had Aseyev waited more than 40 years? How does this explain his attitude and behavior the first day?
3. What was the largest compound in the German prisoner-of-war camp, Stalag 3-B? What physical reminders did Dr. Aseyev have of his experiences with the Gestapo?

4. Why were American prisoners better fed than Russian ones? What supports the literal truth of the doctor's statement that "Americans could see" Russian prisoners starving by "the tens, and then by the hundreds"?

5. Why was Aseyev the only Russian permitted contact with Americans? Why did he deserve to be proud that "there were never any complications"?

6. Describe how the Americans "smuggled" food to the Russian prisoners. What punishment did they risk? What two reasons did Aseyev give for risking it?

7. Why did Aseyev call the German Corporal Alfred Jung "an exceptional member of the human race"? What became of him?

8. After the plot's exposure, what debt did Aseyev feel he owed to all 8000 American prisoners—and why? What "special punishment" was given the Wowczuk brothers—and why?
What did Aseyev mean by saying "and the Gestapo was the Gestapo, you know," in relation to the Wowczuks' punishment?

9. How did the Wowczuks and other American prisoners prove, later, that German threats and punishment had not broken their spirit?

10. Why was Aseyev so intent on getting his message to America? Give at least two reasons. What souvenirs of "long and searching conversations" had both Drs. Brockman and Aseyev kept for years?

## Looking Deeper
### I. "Part of the Game . . ."

In what sense was it "part of the game" for the Americans to risk their lives helping the Russian prisoners of war? Why does the means of "delivering" the food packages seem typically American? Although Dr. Brockman called it a game, what proves his feelings were genuine and deep? Give at least two reasons.

By calling it a "game," Dr. Brockman underplayed the ideas of bravery, heroism, and sacrifice. Do you believe such understatement is typically American? Explain why or why not.

### II. "There Ought to Be More . . ."

In one night, the Americans smuggled 1,350 parcels or over 14,000 pounds of food to the Russians.

About their deeds, a retired New York City police detective, William Jarema, said, "You just can't walk away. . . . We were all in trouble." Is this still the attitude of America as a nation today? Of individual Americans? Give reasons and examples supporting your views.

Do you agree that "there ought to be more" of this spirit in American life today? Why or why not?

# The Chief Research Chemist of the Metaplast Corporation

## from *"Surely You're Joking, Mr. Feynman!"*

### by Richard P. Feynman

| | |
|---|---|
| **Born:** | Far Rockaway (New York City), NY, 1918 |
| **Winner:** | Nobel Prize in physics |
| **Graduate:** | MIT (Massachusetts Institute of Technology) |
| **Military:** | Disqualified from WWII for failing psychiatric exam |
| **Research:** | On nuclear energy during WWII at Los Alamos, New Mexico; theoretical physics in California |

AFTER I FINISHED AT MIT I wanted to get a summer job. I had applied two or three times to the Bell Labs, and had gone out a few times to visit. Bill Shockley, who knew me from the lab at MIT, would show me around each time, and I enjoyed those visits terrifically, but I never got a job there.

I had letters from some of my professors to two specific companies. One was to the Bausch and Lomb Company for tracing rays through lenses; the other was to Electrical Testing Labs in New York. At that time nobody knew what a physicist even was, and there weren't any positions in industry for physicists. Engineers, OK; but physicists—nobody knew how to use them. It's interesting that very soon, after the war, it was the exact opposite: people wanted physicists everywhere. So I wasn't getting anywhere as a physicist looking for a job late in the Depression.

About that time I met an old friend of mine on the beach at our home town of Far Rockaway, where we grew up together. We had gone to school together when we were about eleven or twelve, and were very good friends. We were both scientifically minded. He had a "laboratory," and I had a "laboratory." We often played together, and discussed things together.

We used to put on magic shows—chemistry magic—for the kids on the block. My friend was a pretty good showman, and I kind of liked that too. We did our tricks on a little table, with Bunsen burners at each end going all the time. On the burners we had watch glass plates (flat glass discs) with iodine on them, which made a beautiful purple vapor that went up on each side of the table while the show went on. It was great! We did a lot of tricks, such as turning "wine" into water, and other chemical color changes. For our finale, we did a trick that used something which we had discovered. I would put my hands (secretly) first into a sink of water, and then into benzine. Then I would "accidentally" brush by one of the Bunsen burners, and one hand would light up. I'd clap my hands, and both hands would then be burning. (It doesn't hurt because it burns fast and the water keeps it cool.) Then I'd wave my hands, running around yelling, "FIRE! FIRE!" and everybody would get all excited. They'd run out of the room, and that was the end of the show!

Later on I told this story at college to my fraternity brothers and they said, "Nonsense! You can't *do* that!"

(I often had this problem of demonstrating to these fellas something that they didn't believe—like the time we got into an argument as to whether urine just ran out of you by gravity, and I had to demonstrate that that wasn't the case by showing them that you can pee standing on your head. Or the time when somebody claimed that if you took aspirin and Coca-Cola you'd fall over in a dead faint directly. I told them I thought it was a lot of baloney, and offered to take aspirin and Coca-Cola together. Then they got into an argument whether you should have the aspirin before the Coke, just after the Coke, or mixed in the Coke. So I had six aspirin and three Cokes, one right after the other. First, I took aspirins and then a Coke, then we dissolved two aspirins in a Coke and I took that, and then I took a Coke and two aspirins. Each time the idiots who believed it were standing around me, waiting to catch me when I fainted. But nothing happened. I do remember that I didn't sleep very well that night, so I got up and did a lot of figuring, and worked out some of the formulas for what is called the Riemann-Zeta function.)

"All right, guys," I said. "Let's go out and get some benzine."

They got the benzine ready, I stuck my hand in the water in the sink and then into the benzine and lit it . . . and it hurt like hell! You see, in the meantime I had grown *hairs* on the back of my hand, which acted like wicks and held the benzine in place while it burned, whereas when I had done it earlier I had no hairs on the back of my hand. After I *did* the experiment for my fraternity brothers, I didn't have any hairs on the back of my hands either.

Well, my pal and I met on the beach, and he told me that he had a process for metal-plating plastics. I said that was impossible, because there's no conductivity; you can't attach a wire. But he said he could metal-plate anything, and I still remember him picking up a peach pit that was in the sand, and saying he could metal-plate *that*—trying to impress me.

What was nice was that he offered me a job at his little company, which was on the top floor of a building in New York. There were only about four people in the company. His father was the one who was getting the money together and was, I think, the "president." He was the "vice-president," along with another fella who was a salesman. I was the "chief research chemist," and my friend's brother, who was not very clever, was the bottle-washer. We had six metal-plating baths.

They had this process for metal-plating plastics, and the scheme was: First, deposit silver on the object by precipitating silver from a silver nitrate bath with a reducing agent (like you make mirrors); then stick the object, with silver on it as a conductor, into an electroplating bath, and the silver gets plated.

The problem was, does the silver stick to the object?

It doesn't. It peels off easily. So there was a step in between, to make the silver stick better to the object. It depended on the material. For things like Bakelite, which was an important plastic in those days, my friend had found that if he sandblasted it first, and then soaked it for many hours in stannous hydroxide, which got into the pores of the Bakelite, the silver would hold onto the surface very nicely.

But it worked only on a few plastics, and new kinds of plastics were coming out all the time, such as methyl methacrylate (which we call plexiglass, now), that we couldn't plate directly, at first. And cellulose acetate, which was very cheap, was another one we couldn't plate at first, though we finally discovered that putting it in sodium hydroxide for a little while before using the stannous chloride made it plate very well.

I was pretty successful as a "chemist" in the company. My advantage was that my pal had done no chemistry at all; he had done no experiments; he just knew how to do something once. I set to work putting lots of different knobs in bottles, and putting all kinds of chemicals in. By trying everything and keeping track of everything I found ways of plating a wider range of plastics than he had done before.

I was also able to simplify his process. From looking in books I changed the reducing agent from glucose to formaldehyde, and was able to recover 100 percent of the silver immediately, instead of having to recover the silver left in solution at a later time.

I also got the stannous hydroxide to dissolve in water by adding a little bit of hydrochloric acid—something I remembered from a college chemistry course—so a step that used to take *hours* now took about five minutes.

My experiments were always being interrupted by the salesman, who would come back with some plastic from a prospective customer. I'd have all these bottles lined up, with everything marked, when all of a sudden, "You gotta stop the experiment to do a 'super job' for the sales department!" So, a lot of experiments had to be started more than once.

One time we got into one hell of a lot of trouble. There was some artist who was trying to make a picture for the cover of a magazine about automobiles. He had very carefully built a wheel out of plastic, and somehow or other this salesman had told him we could plate anything, so the artist wanted us to metal-plate the hub, so it would be a shiny, silver hub. The wheel was made of a new plastic that we didn't know very well how to plate—the fact is, the salesman never knew what we could plate, so he was always promising things—and it didn't work the first time. So, to fix it up we had to get the old silver off, and we couldn't get it off easily. I decided to use concentrated nitric acid on it, which took the silver off all right, but also made pits and holes in the plastic. We were really in hot water that time! In fact, we had lots of "hot water" experiments.

The other fellas in the company decided we should run advertisements in *Modern Plastics* magazine. A few things we metal-plated were very pretty. They looked good in the advertisements. We also had a few things out in a showcase in front, for prospective customers to look at, but nobody could pick up the things in the advertisements or in the showcase to see how well the plating stayed on. Perhaps some of them were, in fact, pretty good jobs. But they were made specially; they were not regular products.

Right after I left the company at the end of the summer to go to Princeton, they got a good offer from somebody who wanted to metal-plate plastic pens. Now people could have silver pens that were light, and easy, and cheap. The pens immediately sold, all over, and it was rather exciting to see people walking around everywhere with these pens—and you knew where they came from.

But the company hadn't had much experience with the material—or perhaps with the filler that was used in the plastic (most plastics aren't pure; they have a "filler," which in those days wasn't very well controlled)—and the darn things would develop a blister. When you have something in your hand that has a little blister that starts to peel, you can't help fiddling with it. So everybody was fiddling with all the peelings coming off the pens.

Now the company had this *emergency* problem to fix the pens, and my pal decided he needed a big microscope, and so on. He didn't know what he was going to look at, or why, and it cost his company a lot of money for this fake research. The result was, they had trouble: They never solved the problem, and the company failed, because their first big job was such a failure.

A few years later I was in Los Alamos, where there was a man named Frederic de Hoffman, who was a sort of scientist; but more, he was also very good at administrating. Not highly trained, he liked mathematics, and worked very hard; he compensated for his lack of training by hard work. Later he became the president or vice president of General Atomics and he was a big industrial character after that. But at the time he was just a very energetic, open-eyed, enthusiastic boy, helping along with the Project as best he could.

One day we were eating at the Fuller Lodge, and he told me he had been working in England before coming to Los Alamos.

"What kind of work were you doing there?" I asked.

"I was working on a process for metal-plating plastics. I was one of the guys in the laboratory."

"How did it go?"

"It was going along pretty well, but we had our problems."

"Oh?"

"Just as we were beginning to develop our process, there was a company in New York ..."

"*What* company in New York?"

"It was called the Metaplast Corporation. They were developing further than we were."

"How could you tell?"

"They were advertising all the time in *Modern Plastics* with full-page advertisements showing all the things they could plate, and we realized that they were further along than we were."

"Did you have any stuff from them?"

"No, but you could tell from the advertisements that they were way ahead of what we could do. Our process was pretty good, but it was no use trying to compete with an American process like that."

"How many chemists did you have working in the lab?"

"We had six chemists working."

"How many chemists do you think the Metaplast Corporation had?"

"Oh! They must have had a *real* chemistry department!"

"Would you describe for me what you think the chief research chemist at the Metaplast Corporation might look like, and how his laboratory might work?"

"I would guess they must have twenty-five or fifty chemists, and the chief research chemist has his own office—special, with glass. You know, like they have in the movies—guys coming in all the time with research projects that they're doing, getting his advice, and rushing off to do more research, people coming in and out all the time. With twenty-five or fifty chemists, how the hell could we compete with them?"

"You'll be interested and amused to know that you are now talking to the chief research chemist of the Metaplast Corporation, whose staff consisted of one bottle-washer!"


## For Better Reading: The Scientific Approach

Even though you speak only English, you probably know more than one kind of language.

The slang that each generation adopts for its own is one way of creating a "private" language within the broader language that most Americans share. Computer language is another example of a specialized form of English that can seem impossible to understand to someone not "in the know." Others are the "legalese" of law and the differing vocabularies of every sport from basketball to soccer.

The language of science and the breeziness of slang at first seem worlds apart. So it might seem surprising how freely Richard P. Feynman, a Nobel Prize-winning scientist, uses both. Yet, knowing both languages, Feynman does not hesitate to use the words he thinks fit best.

Becoming a better reader means learning how to approach specialized vocabularies—whether of science or slang. First, decide if the subject is meant to be technical—and requires using the dictionary for precise definitions of words you don't know. If it's not for experts, you often find that approximating the meaning in context is the better approach.

## Words in Context

1. "I would put my hands (secretly) first into a sink of water, and then into *benzine*." *Benzine* must be (a) fireproof gloves (b) a flammable liquid (c) a protective ointment (d) the by-product of Bunsen burners.
2. "First, deposit silver on the object by *precipitating* silver from a silver nitrate bath." *Precipitating* must mean by (a) separating in solid form (b) acting without thinking (c) slowing the flow from (d) increasing the proportion of.
3. The word *metaplast* most likely is a (a) meaningless, imaginary word (b) part of the Riemann-Zeta function (c) shortened version of the scientific term, metaphasiaplastachloric acid (d) word-blend combining *metal* and *plastic*.

## Questioning the Selection

1. After graduating from the Massachusetts Institute of Technology, why did Feynman have difficulty finding a summer job? Give two reasons.
2. Explain two ways that Feynman and his friend showed their interest in science at age 11 or 12.
3. Give an example of Feynman's using the scientific approach to win arguments with his college fraternity brothers. In such cases, why would Feynman call those who differed with him "idiots"?
4. While proving the benzine trick wasn't "nonsense," what had Feynman failed to realize?
5. What was the main difficulty in perfecting the process for metal-plating plastics? Why did Feynman feel his friend was at a disadvantage in accomplishing this goal?
6. Although Feynman uses slang to write of putting "lots of" different knobs in bottles and adding "all kinds of" chemicals, how are these key steps of the scientific method? What other steps did he take to insure his experiments were valid?
7. What did Feynman mean by "hot water" experiments? Describe at least one example.
8. Why did Feynman think his pal's decision to buy a big microscope meant spending money on "fake research"?
9. When both were working at Los Alamos, what similar experience did Feynman and de Hoffman discover in their backgrounds?
10. How had de Hoffman first learned of the Metaplast Corporation? What are two faulty conclusions drawn by de Hoffman and his fellow chemists? What was the truth in each case?

## Looking Deeper

### Think Big

Feynman thought that de Hoffman would be "interested and amused" to know the truth about the Metaplast Corporation. Do you think he was genuinely amused? Why or why not?

In what ways was the operation of the Metaplast Corporation similar to Feynman and his pal's boyhood shows? Do you feel Feynman's friend purposely deceived his customers—or was he "thinking big" and hoping for the best? Use solid reasoning to support your opinion.

Does Feynman's pal reflect a typically American attitude? Explain why or why not.

# Americans Playing Slow-Pitch Softball at an Airbase near Kunsan, South Korea*

## by Halvard Johnson

**Born:**      *Newburgh, New York*
**Career:**    *Teacher, instructor, poet, guest editor*
**Lived in:**  *Illinois, Texas, Puerto Rico, Maryland*

—Early September

The first game of
the evening begins
about five-thirty.

The men (not that
only men play—                                              5
one team has

a female catcher)
finish their work
on whatever they

work on—                                                    10
correspondence,
water mains, Phantoms*—

get out of one uniform,
into another, and come
out to the ballpark.                                         15

The lights go on early.
By eight here it's totally
dark. Half an hour earlier

Note: The poem concerns the conflict between North and South Korea, during which American and other United Nations forces fought in support of the South. A *Phantom* is a type of American jet fighter.

the sky was a tangle
of rose, magenta,                                    20
lavender, as the sun

went down in China,
beyond the Yellow Sea.
Brisk wind tonight—

raises the infield dirt,                              25
whips it into narrowed eyes
of batter, catcher, umpire,

the three or four spectators
in the bleachers behind them.
A regulation seven-inning                            30

game is played, unless one
team is so far out in front
that the ten-run rule

is invoked, ending
the game after five. A ball                          35
the size of a small

grapefruit is lofted
into the air, a slight
backspin making it

seem to drift and float                              40
down toward the plate.
No easy hit. The batter

has to apply his own
muscle to put it anywhere.
This batsman clips the top                           45

and bounces to the third
baseman, who fires to first
for an easy out. He shrugs

and jogs to the dugout.
The next batter flies out,                           50
and the game ends 15-zip

after five full innings.
Another two teams take the field.
Some of the players stand

by to watch the second game,                                55
but most wander off,
concerned with other things.

The bleachers are fuller now—
a rowdier crowd, raring for action.
Crisp evening air. Korean girlfriends                       60

cuddle close for warmth. An airman
pops open a beer. Behind their
backs a pair of Phantoms

roar into the sky, their afterburners
glowing as they lift from the runway,                       65
vanish into black clouds. Uncertain

weather tonight, a stiff wind, high
scudding clouds. A tricky weather
system reaching north to

the DMZ, east to the Sea of Japan,                          70
south to the East China Sea.
Typhoon Orchid approaches Okinawa,

far to the southeast. Possibly
this is all a part of that. Inning
after inning goes by, vanishing                             75

into a past that exists only on paper.
Hits, runs, and errors go down
in the league's record book,

but screw the past, we're having
fun tonight. Neither the pitcher,                           80
the fliers, nor the Korean

women in the stands
remember or care about a war
that happened thirty years ago.

It's the girls' fathers who have                                   85
the bad dreams, wake in terror in
the night. Their grandfathers, too.

They'll all support General Chun
and pray he'll protect them
from devils. A friend of mine                                      90

in Europe once wrote a poem
about memory and the historical
imagination, which ended

with these lines:
"Our assignment is to remember,                                    95
to deliver blows."

No American could have written that.
We live our lives inning by inning,
season by season, war by war.

I'll end this in an American way—                                  100
with the words of the great black,
American pitcher, Satchel Paige:

"Don't look back.
Something may be
gaining on you."                                                   105

## For Better Reading: Echoes

Some things just don't seem to fit. The dual subjects of this poem—war and softball—are prime examples.

They seem totally different at first. War is violent reality, full of ugliness, terror, and death. Ballgames are all in sport, played by the rules, full of healthy exercise, and fun.

Totally different—yet when brought together in this poem, each serves to echo the other.

As you read, these echoes should act as constant reminders that the young ballplayers are also airmen, whose lives involve both sport and the potential for being called to engage actively in war. The poem concerns the peacetime presence of American forces in South Korea, some thirty years after the end of hostilities between it and North Korea.

Although the Korean conflict was only a matter of history to the young airmen, the possibility of war is a constant presence in this poem. As an active reader, keep alert to the echoes of war in the background of the game—and the importance of sport in a situation shadowed by wartime reminders.

## Questioning the Poem

1. How has the poet created a visual sense of order and calm with respect to stanzas and line length?
2. Notice that ends of stanzas do not necessarily end a thought. How does this affect your reading of the poem?
3. According to lines 8–10, team members have finished their "work on whatever they work on." As peace-keeping forces, for what purpose are they stationed in South Korea? Regardless of their individual duties, how is this different from ordinary "work"? What is meant by "work ... on Phantoms"?
4. In lines 14–15, what relative importance is given the two types of uniform? How does this differ from the usual view?
5. Lines 19–21 describe the sky as being "rose, magenta, lavender." Explain how the poet would have changed the effect by choosing such words as "blood red, purple, and flame."
6. Explain the "ten-run rule." What does this show about the players' ideas concerning good sportsmanship?
7. Lines 36–51 contain a number of words and phrases that create an easy-going, commonplace effect. For example, the ball is like a "grapefruit" and "is lofted." Find at least three examples more.
8. In the same lines, find at least three words or phrases indicating the teams are playing good ball.
9. How do mood and atmosphere change in lines 58–74? List at least three examples, and explain how each brings the echo of war closer.
10. Line 76 speaks of a "past that exists only on paper." Why is this true, both of past wars and ballgames? Why might "a war that happened thirty years ago" seem unreal to the girls, fliers, and players at the game? Why might the girls' fathers and grandfathers "wake in terror" from dreams of this same war?

# Looking Deeper

## I. Protection From the Devils

According to line 88, South Korean adults and old men support General Chun as leader. Who must the "devils" be? How is this use of "devils" related to their waking "in terror" from dreams?

A European wrote, "Our assignment is to remember, to deliver blows."

Does his attitude toward war seem predominately businesslike or emotional? Why? How does the European attitude differ from the South Korean one?

## II. The American Way

Explain how Americans, by living their lives "war by war," have a different attitude from both the Europeans and South Koreans. Give at least two examples of past wars that illustrate this American attitude. How does the ten-run rule also symbolize an American attitude toward war?

At the end, how does the quotation by Satchel Paige express both a serious and humorous attitude toward winning and losing? Is this typical of the American spirit? Why or why not?

# Lingo

## from *Good Morning, America*

*by Carl Sandburg*

| | |
|---|---|
| **Born:** | *Illinois in 1878, son of Swedish immigrants* |
| **Background:** | *Had little formal schooling, roamed US as hobo* |
| **Gained fame as:** | *Poetry writer and reader, guitarist and folksinger* |

A code arrives; language; lingo; slang;
behold the proverbs of a people, a nation:
Give 'em the works. Fix it, there's always
a way. Be hard boiled. The good die young.

Be a square shooter. Be good; if you can't          5
be good be careful. When they put you in
that six foot bungalow, that wooden kimono,
you're through and that's that.

Sell'em sell'em. Make 'em eat it. What
if we gyp 'em? It'll be good for 'em. Get their          10
names on the dotted line and give 'em the haha.

The higher they go the farther they drop.
The fewer the sooner. Tell 'em. Tell 'em.
Make 'em listen. They got to listen when
they know who you are. Don't let 'em know          15
what you got on your hip. Hit 'em where
they ain't. It's good for whatever ails
you and if nothing ails you it's good for
that. Where was you raised—in a barn?

They're a lot of muckers, tin horns; show          20

those slobs where they get off at. Tell 'em
you're going to open a keg of nails. Beat 'em
to a fare-thee-well. Hand 'em the razz-berries.
Clean 'em and then give 'em carfare home.
Maybe all you'll get from 'em you can put in 25
your ear, anyhow.

They got a fat nerve to try to tie a can
on you. Send 'em to the cleaners. Put the
kibosh on 'em so they'll never come back.
You don't seem to know four out of five 30
have pyorrhea in Peoria.

Your head ain't screwed on wrong, I trust.
Use your noodle, your nut, your think tank,
your skypiece. God meant for you to use it.
If they offer to let you in on the ground 35
floor take the elevator.

Put up a sign: Don't worry; it won't last;
nothing does. Put up a sign: In God we
trust, all others pay cash. Put up a sign:
Be brief, we have our living to make. Put 40
up a sign: Keep off the grass.

Aye, behold the proverbs of a people:
The big word is Service.
Service—first, last, and always.
Business is business. 45
What you don't know won't hurt you.
Courtesy pays.
Fair enough.
The voice with a smile.
Say it with flowers. 50
Let one hand wash the other.
The customer is always right.
Who's your boy friend?
Who's your girl friend?
O very well. 55
God reigns and the government at Washington lives.
Let it go at that.
There are lies, dam lies and statistics.
Figures don't lie but liars can figure.
There's more truth than poetry in that. 60
You don't know the half of it, dearie.

It's the roving bee that gathers the honey.[1]
A big man is a big man whether he's a president or a
    prizefighter.[2]
Name your poison.
Take a little interest.          65
Look the part.
It pays to look well.
Be yourself.
Speak softly and carry a big stick.[3]
War is hell.          70
Honesty is the best policy.
It's all in the way you look at it.
Get the money—honestly if you can.
It's hell to be poor.
Well, money isn't everything.          75
Well, life is what you make it.
Speed and curves—what more do you want?
I'd rather fly than eat.[4]
There must be pioneers and some of them get killed.[4]
The grass is longer in the backyard.[5]          80
Give me enough Swedes and snuff and I'll build a
    railroad to hell.[6]
How much did he leave? All of it.[7]
Can you unscramble eggs?[8]
Early to bed and early to rise and you never meet any
    prominent people.[9]
Let's go. Watch our smoke. Excuse our dust.          85
Keep your shirt on.


First come the pioneers, lean, hungry, fierce, dirty.
They wrangle and battle with the elements.
They gamble on crops, chills, ague, rheumatism.
They fight wars and put a nation on the map.          90
They battle with blizzards, lice, wolves.

---

[1]On hearing from his father "A rolling stone gathers no moss," John L. Sullivan won one of his important early fights and telegraphed this reply.
[2]John L. Sullivan's greeting spoken to President Theodore Roosevelt in the White House.
[3]A Spanish proverb first Americanized by Theodore Roosevelt.
[4]Charles A. Lindbergh.
[5]Based on a Republican campaign story in 1892 alleging that a man on all fours eating grass on the White House lawn told President Grover Cleveland, "I'm hungry," and was advised, "The grass is longer in the backyard."
[6]A saying that took rise from James J. (Jim) Hill.
[7]A folk tale in Chicago chronicles two ditch diggers on the morning after Marshall Field I died, leaving an estate of $150,000,000, as having this dialogue.
[8]J. Pierpont Morgan's query as to court decrees dissolving an inevitable industrial combination.
[9]George Ade.

They go on a fighting trail
To break sod for unnumbered millions to come.

Then the fat years arrive when the fat drips.
Then come the rich men baffled by their riches,                    95
Bewildered by the silence of their tall possessions.
Then come the criers of the ancient desperate taunt:
    Stuff your guts
    and strut your stuff,
    strut it high and handsome;                         100
    when you die you're dead
    and there's no comeback
    and not even the winds
    will say your name—
    feed, oh pigs, feed, oh swine.                       105

Old timer, dust of the earth so kindly,
Old timer, dirt of our feet and days.
Old time gravel and gumbo of the earth,
Take them back kindly,
These pigs, these swine.                                           110
The bones of them and their brothers blanch to the
    same yellow of the years.

# For Better Reading: Language as Code

A language is usually intended to enable people to communicate with each other. It can also be a kind of code, a way of keeping communication secret from someone not "in the know."

If you know Pig Latin, you've probably had the fun of feeling superior to someone who hasn't learned its secret.

"Lingo" is a word that describes a kind of "fast talk" or unfamiliar version of what can even be your own language. It's another way of saying it's strange and peculiar.

In this excerpt from *Good Morning, America*, Carl Sandburg crams over seventy-five examples of American lingo. Taken together, they illustrate why a historian has described the American spirit as "full of bounce and bluster."*

Even though some words and expressions in "Lingo" seem unfamiliar and strange, enjoy the sounds of America's past, and discover "proverbs" and feelings still part of America's spirit today.

* Samuel Eliot Morison, *The Oxford History of the American People*, Vol. 2, p. 216. The New American Library, New York, 1972.

## Questioning the Poem

1. In lines 3–12, what are three examples of "bluster"? How is "Fix it ..." an example of "bounce," high spirits and optimism?
2. From stanzas three and four, list at least three sayings that seem to contradict "Be a square shooter," the advice in line 5.
3. By the frequent use of " 'em" instead of "them," what attitude does this set of sayings seem to create towards "the other person"? What do they fail to acknowledge?
4. "Pyorrhea in Peoria" may be either a catchy advertising slogan or merely nonsense. Of what does the speaker accuse "you" for not finding it familiar? Is this accusation fair? Why or why not?
5. Lines 32–41 illustrate an American tendency to mix seriousness and humor. Choose one example from each stanza, and explain how it contains both attitudes.
6. By introducing them, "Aye, behold the proverbs of a people," Sandburg makes the sayings in lines 42–65 seem weighty and deep. Find at least three examples that express each of the following: (1) concern for others, (2) putting oneself first, (3) a sense of humor. Use each example only once.
7. How do lines 66–86 echo elements of the American Dream? Give at least three examples.

# Looking Deeper

## I. "The People, Yes"

Carl Sandburg had little formal schooling. As a young man, he roamed the United States as a hobo and worked many jobs, such as brickyard helper, hotel dishwasher, and harvest hand. He was a champion of the common people, and one of his most famous poems is "The People, Yes."

How is Sandburg's love of ordinary people reflected in "Lingo"?

What elements of the American spirit are expressed by the saying, "A big man is a big man whether he's a president or a prizefighter"?

## II. Contradictions

Some of the sayings in "Lingo" support the idea that "It's all in the way you look at it." Explain why the following pairs of familiar sayings seem to express opposite viewpoints.

"Look the part," and "Be yourself."

"Honesty is the best policy," and "Get the money—honestly if you can."

"Let's go. Watch our smoke. Excuse our dust," and "Keep your shirt on."

What qualities in the American dream and spirit cause these contradictions to be a natural part of an American make-up?

# The First Piano in a Mining Camp

## by Sam Davis

**Background:**   *Reporter, San Francisco* Argonaut;
editor, *Carson City (Nevada)*
Appeal

IN 1858—IT MIGHT HAVE been five years earlier or later; this is not the history for the public schools—there was a little camp about ten miles from Pioche, occupied by upwards of three hundred miners, every one of whom might have packed his prospecting implements and left for more inviting fields any time before sunset. When the day was over, these men did not rest from their labors, like the honest New England agriculturist, but sang, danced, gambled, and shot each other, as the mood seized them.

One evening the report spread along the main street (which was the only street) that three men had been killed at Silver Reef, and that the bodies were coming in. Presently a lumbering old conveyance labored up the hill, drawn by a couple of horses, well worn out with their pull. The cart contained a good-sized box, and no sooner did its outlines become visible, through the glimmer of a stray light here and there, than it began to affect the idlers. Death always enforces respect, and even though no one had caught sight of the remains, the crowd gradually became subdued, and when the horses came to a standstill, the cart was immediately surrounded. The driver, however, was not in the least impressed with the solemnity of his commission.

"All there?" asked one.

"Haven't examined. Guess so."

The driver filled his pipe, and lit it as he continued:

"Wish the bones and load had gone over the grade!"

A man who had been looking on stepped up to the man at once.

"I don't know who you have in that box, but if they happen to be any friends of mine, I'll lay you alongside."

"We can mighty soon see," said the teamster, coolly. "Just burst the lid off, and if they happen to be the men you want, I'm here."

The two looked at each other for a moment, and then the crowd gathered a little closer, anticipating trouble.

"I believe that dead men are entitled to good treatment, and when you talk about hoping to see corpses go over a bank, all I have to say is, that it will be better for you if the late lamented ain't my friends."

"We'll open the box. I don't take back what I've said, and if my language don't suit your ways of thinking, I guess I can stand it."

With these words the teamster began to pry up the lid. He got a board off, and then pulled out some old rags. A strip of something dark, like rosewood; presented itself.

"Eastern coffins, by thunder!" said several, and the crowd looked quite astonished.

Some more boards flew up, and the man who was ready to defend his friend's memory shifted his weapon a little. The cool manner of the teamster had so irritated him that he had made up his mind to pull his weapon at the first sight of the dead, even if the deceased was his worst and oldest enemy. Presently the whole of the box cover was off, and the teamster, clearing away the packing revealed to the astonished group the top of something which puzzled all alike.

"Boys," said he, "this is a pianner."

A general shout of laughter went up, and the man who had been so anxious to enforce respect for the dead, muttered something about feeling dry, and the keeper of the nearest bar was several ounces better off by the time the boys had given the joke all the attention it called for.

Had a dozen dead men been in the box, their presence in the camp could not have occasioned half the excitement that the arrival of that lonely piano caused. By the next morning it was known that the instrument was to grace a hurdy-gurdy saloon, owned by Tom Goskin, the leading gambler in the place. It took nearly a week to get this wonder on its legs, and the owner was the proudest individual in the State. It rose gradually from a recumbent to an upright position amid a confusion of tongues, after the manner of the tower of Babel.

Of course everybody knew just how such an instrument should be put up. One knew where the "off hind leg" should go, and another was posted on the "front piece."

Scores of men came to the place every day to assist.

"I'll put the bones in good order."

"If you want the wires tuned up, I'm the boy."

"I've got music to feed it for a month."

Another brought a pair of blankets for a cover, and all took the liveliest interest in it. It was at last in a condition for business.

"It's been showin' its teeth all the week. We'd like to have it spit out something."

Alas! there wasn't a man to be found who could play upon the instrument. Goskin began to realize that he had a losing speculation on his hands. He had a fiddler, and a Mexican who thrummed a guitar. A pianist would have made his orchestra complete. One day a three-card monte player told a friend confidentially that he could "knock any amount of music out of the piano, if he only had it alone a few hours, to get his hand in." This report spread about the camp, but on being questioned he vowed that he didn't know a note of music. It was noted, however, as a suspicious circumstance, that he often hung about the instrument, and looked upon it longingly, like a hungry man gloating over a beefsteak in a restaurant window. There was no doubt but that this man had music in his soul, perhaps in his fingers'-ends, but did not dare to make trial of his strength after the rules of harmony had suffered so many years of neglect. So the fiddler kept on with his jigs, and the greasy Mexican pawed his discordant guitar, but no man had the nerve to touch the piano. There were, doubtless, scores of men in the camp who would have given ten ounces of gold dust to have been half an hour alone with it, but every man's nerve shrank from the jeers which the crowd would shower upon him should his first attempt prove a failure. It got to be generally understood that the hand which first essayed to draw music from the keys must not slouch its work.

*   *   *   *   *   *   *   *

It was Christmas Eve, and Goskin, according to his custom, had decorated his gambling hall with sprigs of mountain cedar, and a shrub whose crimson berries did not seem a bad imitation of English holly. The piano was covered with evergreens, and all that was wanting to completely fill the cup of Goskin's contentment was a man to play the instrument.

"Christmas night, and no piano-pounder," he said. "This is a nice country for a Christian to live in."

Getting a piece of paper, he scrawled the words:

$20 Reward
To a compitant Pianer Player.

This he stuck up on the music-rack, and, though the inscription glared at the frequenters of the room until midnight, it failed to draw any musician from his shell.

So the merry-making went on; the hilarity grew apace. Men danced and sang to the music of the squeaky fiddle and worn-out guitar, as the jolly crowd within tried to drown the howling of the storm without. Suddenly they became aware of the presence of a white-haired man, crouching near the fire-place. His garments—such as were left—were wet with melting snow, and he had a half-starved, half-crazed expression. He held his thin, trembling hands toward the fire, and the light of the blazing wood made them almost transparent. He looked about him once in a while, as if in search of something, and his presence cast such a chill over the place that gradually the sound of the revelry was hushed, and it seemed that this waif of the storm had brought in with it all of the gloom and coldness of the warring elements. Goskin, mixing up a cup of hot egg-nogg, advanced and remarked cheerily:

"Here, stranger, brace up! This is the real stuff."

The man drained the cup, smacked his lips, and seemed more at home.

"Been prospecting, eh? Out in the mountains—caught in the storm? Lively night, this!"

"Pretty bad," said the man.

"Must feel pretty dry?"

The man looked at his streaming clothes and laughed, as if Goskin's remark was a sarcasm.

"How long out?"

"Four days."

"Hungry?"

The man rose up, and walking over to the lunch counter, fell to work upon some roast bear, devouring it like any wild animal would have done. As meat and drink and warmth began to permeate the stranger, he seemed to expand and lighten up. His features lost their pallor, and he grew more and more content with the idea that he was not in the grave. As he underwent these changes, the people about him got merrier and happier, and threw off the temporary feeling of depression which he had laid upon them.

"Do you always have your place decorated like this?" he finally asked of Goskin.

"This is Christmas Eve," was the reply.

The stranger was startled.

"December twenty-fourth, sure enough."

"That's the way I put it up, pard."

"When I was in England I always kept Christmas. But I had forgotten that this was the night. I've been wandering about in the mountains until I've lost track of the feasts of the church."

Presently his eye fell upon the piano.

"Where's the player?" he asked.

"Never had any," said Goskin, blushing at the expression.

"I used to play when I was young."

Goskin almost fainted at the admission.

"Stranger, do tackle it, and give us a tune! Nary man in this camp ever had the nerve to wrestle with that music-box." His pulse beat faster, for he feared that the man would refuse.

"I'll do the best I can," he said.

There was no stool, but seizing a candle-box, he drew it up and seated himself before the instrument. It only required a few seconds for a hush to come over the room.

"That old coon is going to give the thing a rattle."

The sight of a man at the piano was something so unusual that even the faro-dealer, who was about to take in a fifty-dollar bet on the trey, paused and did not reach for the money. Men stopped drinking, with the glasses at their lips. Conversation appeared to have been struck with a sort of paralysis, and cards were no longer shuffled.

The old man brushed back his long white locks, looked up to the ceiling, half closed his eyes, and in a mystic sort of reverie passed his fingers over the keys. He touched but a single note, yet the sound thrilled the room. It was the key to his improvisation, and as he wove his chords together the music laid its spell upon every ear and heart. He felt his way along the keys, like a man treading uncertain paths; but he gained confidence as he progressed, and presently bent to his work like a master. The instrument was not in exact tune, but the ears of his audience, through long disuse, did not detect anything radically wrong. They heard a succession of grand chords, a suggestion of paradise, melodies here and there, and it was enough.

"See him counter with his left!" said an old rough, enraptured.

"He calls the turn every time on the upper end of the board," responded a man with a stack of chips in his hand.

The player wandered off into the old ballads they had heard at home. All the sad and melancholy and touching songs, that came up like dreams of childhood, this unknown player drew from the keys. His hands kneaded their hearts like dough, and squeezed out tears as from a wet sponge. As the strains flowed one upon the other, they saw their homes of the long ago reared again; they were playing once more where the apple blossoms sank through the soft air to join the violets on the green turf of the old New England States; they saw the glories of the Wisconsin maples and the haze of the Indian summer blending their hues together; they recalled the heather of Scottish hills, the white cliffs of Britain, and heard the sullen roar of the sea, as it beat upon their memories, vaguely. Then came all the old Christmas carols, such as they had sung in church thirty years before; the subtle music that brings up the glimmer of wax tapers, the solemn shrines, the evergreen, holly, misletoe, and surpliced choirs. Then the remorseless performer planted his final stab in every heart with "Home, Sweet Home."

When the player ceased, the crowd slunk away from him. There was no more revelry and devilment left in his audience. Each man wanted to sneak off to his cabin and write the old folks a letter. The day was breaking as the last man left the place, and the player, laying his head down on the piano, fell asleep.

"I say, pard," said Goskin, "don't you want a little rest?"

"I feel tired," the old man said. "Perhaps you'll let me rest here for the matter of a day or so."

He walked behind the bar, where some old blankets were lying, and stretched himself upon them.

"I feel pretty sick. I guess I won't last long. I've got a brother down in the ravine—his name's Driscoll. He don't know I'm here. Can you get him before morning. I'd like to see his face once before I die."

Goskin started up at the mention of the name. He knew Driscoll well.

"He your brother? I'll have him here in half an hour."

As he dashed out into the storm the musician pressed his hand to his side and groaned. Goskin heard the word "Hurry!" and sped down the ravine to Driscoll's cabin. It was quite light in the room when the two men returned. Driscoll was pale as death.

"My God! I hope he's alive! I wronged him when we lived in England, twenty years ago."

They saw the old man had drawn the blankets over his face. The two stood a moment, awed by the thought that he might be dead. Goskin lifted the blanket, and pulled it down astonished. There was no one there!

"Gone!" cried Driscoll, wildly.

"Gone!" echoed Goskin, pulling out his cash-drawer. "Ten thousand dollars in the sack, and the Lord knows how much loose change in the drawer!"

The next day the boys got out, followed a horse's tracks through the snow, and lost them in the trail leading towards Pioche.

There was a man missing from the camp. It was the three-card monte man, who used to deny point-blank that he could play the scale. One day they found a wig of white hair, and called to mind when the "stranger" had pushed those locks back when he looked toward the ceiling for inspiration, on the night of December 24, 1858.

## For Better Reading: Levels of Humor

It's safe to say almost everyone likes a good laugh although not everyone finds the same things funny.

There are many different levels of humor. It can be high or low, clean or dirty, gentle or cruel. Some people delight in "putting something over" on someone else—their favorite humor is practical jokes and dirty tricks. Others prefer to poke gentle fun at themselves and the amusing traits almost everyone shares.

Humor may lie in a tall tale or a brief punch line. Humor sometimes counts on shock value—hurling insults, breaking social and language taboos, or daring to outrage some people to make others laugh.

Humor can be both physical and intellectual. Not always meant to be comical or wildly funny, humor is often intended to amuse or make you chuckle, nod in agreement, and even think.

One of the highest forms of humor is wit—displaying a keen imagination, a flair for word play, and a fondness for linking ideas in an amusing way.

As you assess Sam Davis's "The First Piano in a Mining Camp," decide which kinds of humor the story contains and also which humorous techniques, such as incongruity, exaggeration (or understatement), ridiculous situations, surprise, and irony.

## Inference

1. By stating "this is not the history for the public schools," the author prepares the reader (a) for a burst of propaganda (b) to doubt its accuracy (c) for an up-to-the-minute report (d) to expect criticism of educational methods.
2. In noting every one of the miners might have "left for more inviting fields any time before sunset," the author implies most of the miners (a) had already made their fortunes (b) disapproved of the wildness at the camp (c) envied the security of New England farmers (d) stayed because they wanted to.

3. From the man in the crowd's saying "I'll lay you alongside," and the teamster's replying, "I'm here," the reader should infer the first wanted to (a) hire the other (b) fight the other (c) question the other (d) offer the other lodgings.

## Questioning the Selection

1. How does the "report spread along the main street" result in a faulty conclusion? Compare the attitudes of the teamster and the crowd regarding the cart's supposed cargo "of bones." What accounts for the differences?
2. What was the real reason the man "so anxious to enforce respect" suddenly "felt dry" and left? How would "the boys" go about giving the matter "all the attention it called for"?
3. The piano created more excitement than "a dozen dead men." Explain what this reveals about the level of law and order at the mining camp. Find other examples for added support.
4. In trying to get "this wonder on its legs," the miners showed more familiarity with horses than "pianners." List at least three additional examples of the miners' humorous way of describing the piano and its parts as if it were a horse.
5. Although quick to fight, why did "no man have the nerve to touch the piano?" What peculiarity of human nature does this make fun of?
6. Find at least two examples of the author's use of overstatement in describing Christmas Eve at Tom Goskin's saloon.
7. What is ironic about Goskin's saying, "This is a nice country for a Christian to live in"?
8. What change came over the miners when they first noticed the "white-haired man . . . near the fireplace"?
9. After offering the stranger eggnog, what did Goskin mean by asking, "Must feel pretty dry?" How did the stranger mistake Goskin's words as sarcasm? What proves Goskin was serious, not sarcastic?
10. How did the stranger explain his unawareness of its being Christmas? When the stranger stopped playing, why was "no more revelry and devilment left in his audience"?
11. Why did Goskin go to Driscoll's cabin? How did Driscoll's comments about his brother seem to back up the stranger's story? What are two discoveries Goskin made upon returning to the saloon?
12. Ridiculous situations, exaggeration, and incongruity are three techniques of humor found in this story. List one or more examples of each.

# Looking Deeper

## I. Foreshadowing a Surprise

Looking back at the story, you'll see the careful groundwork laid for its surprise ending. What details prepare for the three-card monte player's being the piano-playing "stranger"? How might his not really being a stranger have enabled him to prepare for claiming the false identity?

In what two ways does the story "set the stage" for his being left all alone in the saloon? How does the first paragraph prepare for the monte player's ability to "pick up and leave" without suspicion?

Did Sam Davis succeed in surprising and amusing you? Explain why or why not.

## II. True to Human Nature

Although the story is humorous and overdrawn, its characters have traits common to almost everyone. Why did seeing the "old man" depress the miners at first? How is this similar to their first reaction to the cart's supposed cargo?

What thoughts and memories overcame the miners while the "stranger" played? What was "remorseless" or pitiless about his choosing such songs? What feelings did Driscoll have about seeing his brother again?

The miners' attitude toward the piano and the sentimental music showed them not as tough as they pretended to be. Do you think it "typically American" to cover up deep feelings? Explain why or why not. What other elements of the American spirit does this story contain? Give examples to support your choices.

# Health Card

## by Frank Yerby

| | |
|---|---|
| ***Born:*** | *Augusta, Georgia, 1916* |
| ***Early job:*** | *Assembly line worker at Ford factory in Michigan* |
| ***Later career:*** | *English instructor in Florida, Louisiana; laboratory technician, product inspector* |
| ***Also resided:*** | *France, Spain* |
| ***Famous as:*** | *Writer of historical romances, short stories* |

**J**OHNNY STOOD UNDER ONE OF the street lights on the corner and tried to read the letter. The street lights down in the Bottom were so dim that he couldn't make out half the words, but he didn't need to: he knew them all by heart anyway.

"Sugar," he read, "it took a long time but I done it. I got the money to come to see you. I waited and waited for them to give you a furlough, but it look like they don't mean to. Sugar, I can't wait no longer. I got to see you. I got to. Find a nice place for me to stay—where we can be happy together. You know what I mean. With all my love, Lily."

Johnny folded the letter up and put it back in his pocket. Then he walked swiftly down the street past all the juke joints with the music blaring out and the G.I. brogans pounding. He turned down a side street, scuffing up a cloud of dust as he did so. None of the streets down in Black Bottom was paved, and there were four inches of fine white powder over everything. When it rained the mud would come up over the tops of his army shoes, but it hadn't rained in nearly three months. There were no juke joints on this street, and the Negro shanties were neatly whitewashed. Johnny kept on walking until he came to the end of the street. On the corner stood the little whitewashed Baptist Church, and next to it was the neat, well-kept home of the pastor.

Johnny went up on the porch and hesitated. He thrust his hand in his pocket and the paper crinkled. He took his hand out and knocked on the door.

"Who's that?" a voice called.

"It's me," Johnny answered; "it's a sodjer."

The door opened a crack and a woman peered out. She was middle-aged and fat. Looking down, Johnny could see that her feet were bare.

"Whatcha want, sodjer?"

Johnny took off his cap.

"Please, ma'am, lemme come in. I kin explain it t' yuh better settin' down."

She studied his face for a minute in the darkness.

"Aw right," she said; "you kin come in, son."

Johnny entered the room stiffly and sat down on a cornshuck-bottomed chair.

"It's this way, ma'am," he said. "I got a wife up Nawth. I been tryin' an' tryin' t' git a furlough so I could go t' see huh. But they always put me off. So now she done worked an' saved enuff money t' come an' see me. I wants t' ax you t' rent me a room, ma'am. I doan' know nowheres t' ax."

"This ain't no hotel, son."

"I know it ain't. I cain't take Lily t' no hotel, not lak hotels in this heah town."

"Lily yo wife?"

"Yes'm. She my sho' nuff, honest t' Gawd wife. Married in th' Baptist Church in Deetroit."

The fat woman sat back, and her thick lips widened into a smile.

"She a good girl, ain't she? An' you doan' wanta take her t' one o' these heah ho'houses they calls hotels."

"That's it, ma'am."

"Sho' you kin bring huh heah, son. Be glad t' have huh. Reveren' be glad t' have huh too. What yo' name, son?"

"Johnny. Johnny Green. Ma'am—"

"Yas, son?"

"You understands that I wants t' come heah too?"

The fat woman rocked back in her chair and gurgled with laughter.

"Bless yo' heart, chile, I ain't always been a ole woman! And I ain't always been th' preacher's wife neither!"

"Thank you, ma'am. I gotta go now. Time fur me t' be gettin' back t' camp."

"When you bring Lily?"

"Be Monday night, ma'am. Pays you now if you wants it."

"Monday be aw right. Talk it over with th' Reveren', so he make it light fur yuh. Know sodjer boys ain't got much money."

"No, ma'am, sho' Lawd ain't. G'night, ma'am."

When he turned back into the main street of the Negro section the doors of the joints were all open and the soldiers were coming out. The girls were clinging onto their arms all the way to the bus stop. Johnny looked at the dresses that stopped halfway between the pelvis and the knee and hugged the backside so that every muscle showed when they walked. He saw the purple lipstick smeared across the wide full lips, and the short hair stiffened with smelly grease so that it covered their heads like a black lacquered cap. They went on down to the bus stop arm in arm, their knotty bare calves bunching with each step as they walked. Johnny thought about Lily. He walked past them very fast without turning his head.

But just as he reached the bus stop he heard the whistles. When he turned around he saw the four M.P.s and the civilian policeman stopping the crowd. He turned around again and walked back until he was standing just behind the white men.

"Aw right," the M.P.s were saying, "you gals git your health cards out."

Some of the girls started digging in their handbags. Johnny could see them dragging out small yellow cardboard squares. But the others just stood there with blank expressions on their faces. The soldiers started muttering, a dark, deep-throated sound. The M.P.s started pushing their way through the crowd, looking at each girl's card as they passed. When they came to a girl who didn't have a card they called out to the civilian policemen:

"Aw right, mister, take A'nt Jemima for a little ride."

Then the city policemen would lead the girl away and put her in the Black Maria.

They kept this up until they had examined every girl except one. She hung back beside her soldier, and the first time the M.P.s didn't see her. When they came back through, one of them caught her by the arm.

"Lemme see your card, Mandy," he said.

The girl looked at him, her little eyes narrowing into slits in her black face.

"Tek yo' hands offen me, white man," she said.

The M.P.'s face crimsoned, so that Johnny could see it, even in the darkness.

"Listen, black girl," he said, "I told you to lemme see your card."

"An' I tole you t' tek yo' han' offen me, white man!"

"You better do like I tell you!"

Johnny didn't see very clearly what happened after that. There was a sudden explosion of motion, and then the M.P. was trying to jerk his hand back, but he couldn't, for the little old black girl had it between her teeth and was biting it to the bone. He drew his other hand back and slapped her across the face so hard that it sounded like a pistol shot. She went over backwards and her tight skirt split, so that when she got up Johnny could see that she didn't have anything on under it. She came forward like a cat, her nails bared, straight for the M.P.'s eyes. He slapped her down again, but the soldiers surged forward all at once. The M.P.'s fell back and drew their guns and one of them blew a whistle.

Johnny, who was behind them, decided it was time for him to get out of there and he did; but not before he saw the squads of white M.P.s hurling around the corner and going to work on the Negroes with their clubs. He reached the bus stop and swung on board. The minute after he had pushed his way to the back behind all the white soldiers he heard the shots. The bus driver put the bus in gear and they roared off toward the camp.

It was after one o'clock when all the soldiers straggled in. Those of them who could still walk. Eight of them came in on the meat wagon, three with gunshot wounds. The colonel declared the town out of bounds for all Negro soldiers for a month.

"Dammit," Johnny said, "I gotta go meet Lily, I gotta. I cain't stay heah. I cain't!"

"Whatcha gonna do," Little Willie asked, "go A.W.O.L.?"

Johnny looked at him, his brow furrowed into a frown.

"Naw," he said, "I'm gonna go see th' colonel!"

"Whut! Man, you crazy! Colonel kick yo' black ass out fo' you gits yo' mouf open."

"I take a chanct on that."

He walked over to the little half mirror on the wall of the barracks. Carefully he readjusted his cap. He pulled his tie out of his shirt front and drew the knot tighter around his throat. Then he tucked the ends back in at just the right fraction of an inch between the correct pair of buttons. He bent down and dusted his shoes again, although they were already spotless.

"Man," Little Willie said, "you sho' is a fool!"

"Reckon I am," Johnny said; then he went out of the door and down the short wooden steps.

When he got to the road that divided the colored and white sections of the camp his steps faltered. He stood still a minute, drew in a deep breath, and marched very stiffly and erect across the road. The white soldiers gazed at him curiously, but none of them said anything. If a black soldier came over into their section it was because somebody sent him, so they let him alone.

In front of the colonel's headquarters he stopped. He knew what he had to say, but his breath was very short in his throat and he was going to have a hard time saying it.

"Whatcha want, soldier?" the sentry demanded.

"I wants t' see th' colonel."

"Who sent you?"

Johnny drew his breath in sharply.

"I ain't at liberty t' say," he declared, his breath coming out very fast behind the words.

"You ain't at liberty t' say," the sentry mimicked. "Well I'll be damned! If you ain't at liberty t' say, then I ain't at liberty t' let you see the colonel! Git tha hell outa here, nigger, before I pump some lead in you!"

Johnny didn't move.

The sentry started toward him, lifting his rifle butt, but another soldier, a sergeant, came around the corner of the building.

"Hold on there," he called. "What tha hell is th' trouble here?"

"This here nigger says he want t' see tha colonel an' when I ast him who sent him he says he ain't at liberty t' say!"

The sergeant turned to Johnny.

Johnny came to attention and saluted him. You aren't supposed to salute N.C.O.s, but sometimes it helps.

"What you got t' say fur yourself, boy?" the sergeant said, not unkindly. Johnny's breath evened.

"I got uh message fur th' colonel, suh," he said; "I ain't s'posed t' give it t' nobody else but him. I ain't even s'posed t' tell who sont it, suh."

The sergeant peered at him sharply.

"You tellin' tha truth, boy?"

"Yassuh!"

"Aw right. Wait here a minute."

He went into H.Q. After a couple of minutes he came back.

"Aw right, soldier, you kin go on in."

Johnny mounted the steps and went into the colonel's office. The colonel was a lean, white-haired soldier with a face tanned to the color of saddle leather. He was reading a letter through a pair of horn-rimmed glasses which had only one earhook left, so that he had to hold them up to his eyes with one hand. He put them down and looked up. Johnny saw that his eyes were pale blue, so pale that he felt as if he were looking into the eyes of an eagle or some other fierce bird of prey.

"Well?" he said, and Johnny stiffened into a salute. The colonel half smiled.

"At ease, soldier," he said. Then: "The sergeant tells me that you have a very important message for me."

Johnny gulped in the air.

"Beggin' th' sergeant's pardon, suh," he said, "but that ain't so."

"What!"

"Yassuh," Johnny rushed on, "nobody sent me. I come on m' own hook. I had t' talk t' yuh, Colonel, suh! You kin sen' me t' th' guardhouse afterwards, but please, suh, lissen t' me fur jes' a minute!"

The colonel relaxed slowly. Something very like a smile was playing around the corners of his mouth. He looked at his watch.

"All right, soldier," he said. "You've got five minutes."

"Thank yuh, thank yuh, suh!"

"Speak your piece, soldier; you're wasting time!"

"It's about Lily, suh. She my wife. She done worked an' slaved fur nigh onto six months t' git the money t' come an' see me. An' now you give th' order that none of th' cullud boys kin go t' town. Beggin' yo' pahdon, suh, I wasn't in none of that trouble. I ain't neber been in no trouble. You kin ax my cap'n, if you wants to. All I wants is permission to go into town fur one week, an' I'll stay outa town fur two months if yuh wants me to."

The colonel picked up the phone.

"Ring Captain Walters for me," he said. Then: "What's your name, soldier?"

"It's Green, suh. Private Johnny Green."

"Captain Walters? This is Colonel Milton. Do you have anything in your files concerning Private Johnny Green? Oh yes, go ahead. Take all the time you need."

The colonel lit a long black cigar. Johnny waited. The clock on the wall spun its electric arms.

"What's that? Yes. Yes, yes, I see. Thank you, Captain."

He put down the phone and picked up a fountain pen. He wrote swiftly. Finally he straightened up and gave Johnny the slip of paper.

Johnny read it. It said: "Private Johnny Green is given express permission to go into town every evening of the week beginning August seventh and ending August fourteenth. He is further permitted to remain in town overnight every night during said week, so long as he returns to camp for reveille the following morning. By order of the commanding officer, Colonel H. H. Milton."

There was a hard knot at the base of Johnny's throat. He couldn't breathe. But he snapped to attention and saluted smartly.

"Thank yuh, suh," he said at last. Then: "Gawd bless you, suh!"

"Forget it, soldier. I was a young married man once myself. My compliments to Captain Walters."

Johnny saluted again and about-faced, then he marched out of the office and down the stairs. On the way back he saluted everybody—privates, N.C.O.s, and civilian visitors, his white teeth gleaming in a huge smile.

"That's sure one happy darky," one of the white soldiers said.

Johnny stood in the station and watched the train running in. The yellow lights from the windows flickered on and off across his face as the alternating squares of light and darkness flashed past. Then it was slowing and Johnny was running beside it, trying to keep abreast of the Jim Crow coach. He could see her standing up, holding each other, Johnny's arms crushing all the breath out of her, holding her so hard against him that his brass buttons hurt through her thin dress. She opened her mouth to speak but he kissed her, bending her head backward on her neck until her little hat fell off. It lay there on the ground, unnoticed.

"Sugah," she said, "sugah. It was awful."

"I know," he said. "I know."

Then he took her bags and they started walking out of the station toward the Negro section of town.

"I missed yuh so much," Johnny said, "I thought I lose m' mind."

"Me too," she said. Then: "I brought th' marriage license with me like yuh tole me. I doan' wan th' preacher's wife t' think we bad."

"Enybody kin look at yuh an' see yuh uh angel!"

They went very quietly through all the dark streets and the white soldiers turned to look at Johnny and his girl.

Lak a queen, Johnny thought, lak a queen. He looked at the girl beside him, seeing the the velvety nightshade skin, the glossy black lacquered curls, the sweet, wide hips and the long, clean legs striding beside him in the darkness. I am black, but comely, O ye daughters of Jerusalem!

They turned into the Bottom where the street lights were dim blobs on the pine poles and the dust rose up in little swirls around their feet. Johnny had his head half turned so that he didn't see the two M.P.s until he had almost bumped into them. He dropped one bag and caught Lily by the arm. Then he drew her aside quickly and the two men went by them without speaking.

They kept on walking, but every two steps Johnny would jerk his head around and look nervously back over his shoulder. The last time he looked the two M.P.s had stopped and were looking back at them. Johnny turned out the elbow of the arm next to Lily so that it hooked into hers a little and began to walk faster, pushing her along with him.

"What's yo' hurry, sugah?" she said. "I be heah a whole week!"

But Johnny was looking over his shoulder at the two M.P.s. They were coming toward them now, walking with long, slow strides, their reddish-white faces set. Johnny started to push Lily along faster, but she shook off his arm and stopped still.

"I do declare, Johnny Green! You th' beatines' man! Whut you walk me so fas' fur?"

Johnny opened his mouth to answer her, but the military police were just behind them now, and the sergeant reached out and laid his hand on her arm.

"C'mon, gal," he said, "lemme see it."

"Let you see whut? Whut he mean, Johnny?"

"Your card," the sergeant growled. "Lemme see your card."

"My card?" Lily said blankly. "Whut kinda card, mister?"

Johnny put the bags down. He was fighting for breath.

"Look heah, Sarge," he said; "this girl my wife!"

"Oh yeah? I said lemme see your card, sister!"

"I ain't got no card, mister. I dunno whut you talkin' about."

"Look, Sarge," the other M.P. said, "th' soldier's got bags. Maybe she's just come t' town."

"These your bags, gal?"

"Yessir."

"Aw right. You got twenty-four hours to git yourself a health card. If you don't have it by then we hafta run you in. Git goin' now."

"Listen," Johnny shouted; "this girl my wife! She ain't no ho'! I tell you she ain't—"

"What you say, nigger—" the M.P. sergeant growled. "Whatcha say?" He started toward Johnny.

Lily swung on Johnny's arm.

"C'mon, Johnny," she said; "they got guns. C'mon, Johnny, please! Please, Johnny!"

Slowly she drew him away.

"Aw, leave 'em be, Sarge," the M.P. corporal said; "maybe she is his wife."

The sergeant spat. The brown tobacco juice splashed in the dirt not an inch from Lily's foot. Then the two of them turned and started away.

Johnny stopped.

"Lemme go, Lily," he said, "lemme go!" He tore her arm loose from his and started back up the street. Lily leaped, her two arms fastening themselves around his neck. He fought silently but she clung to him, doubling her knees so that all her weight was hanging from his neck.

"No, Johnny! Oh Jesus no! You be kilt! Oh, Johnny, listen t' me, sugah! You's all I got!"

He put both hands up to break her grip but she swung her weight sidewise and the two of them went down in the dirt. The M.P.s turned the corner out of sight.

Johnny sat there in the dust staring at her. The dirt had ruined her dress. He sat there a long time looking at her until the hot tears rose up back of his eyelids faster than he could blink them away, so he put his face down in her lap and cried.

"I ain't no man!" he said. "I ain't no man!"

"Hush, sugah," she said. "You's a man aw right. You's my man!"

Gently she drew him to his feet. He picked up the bags and the two of them went down the dark street toward the preacher's house.

## For Better Reading: Those People, Back Then

To keep from limiting yourself as a reader, it's important to avoid putting the label "those people, back then" on others from different places and times.

Americans are known as being quick to embrace new fashions and new products. Yet American's fascination with change isn't new. In fact, it's a sign of—not a change in—a typically American way of thinking that being new and different is the same as being better. To be a good reader, it's essential to look past the outward changes caused by fashion and time, place, and individual backgrounds. It then becomes clear that "those people, back then" are very much like those, here and now.

As a novelist, Frank Yerby gained fame as the best-selling author of Southern historical romances, such as *The Foxes of Harrow* and *Pride's Castle*. With handsome, dashing heroes and lovely belles, his books sold by millions.

"Health Card" is Frank Yerby's first published story. Set at an Army base in the South during World War II, it touches closer to his own experience and background than the romantic fiction which brought him fame. It is the ability of both writers and readers to explore and share feelings common to everyone that makes "those people, back then" a phrase to avoid.

## Cause and Effect

1. Lily was coming to see Johnny because (a) she hoped to marry him (b) he had received orders to go overseas (c) he hadn't received a furlough to visit her (d) she was broke and out of work.
2. Johnny asked for a room at the pastor's house because (a) the town's hotels were not respectable (b) he could not afford hotel room rates (c) his hometown pastor suggested he call there (d) all the local hotels were full.
3. By offering to pay in advance and telling the pastor's wife that he would be coming with Lily, Johnny showed that he (a) didn't believe the woman's promise (b) was honest and truthful (c) was afraid her husband might object (d) was not thinking ahead.

## Questioning the Story

1. As Johnny walked to and from the pastor's house, what contrasts are evident between different streets in "Black Bottom," the black section of town? How were they all alike?

2. By writing that their "purple lipstick" was "smeared," their hair "stiffened with smelly grease," and the calves of their legs "knotty" and "bunching," what attitude does the author create toward the bar girls? When Johnny "thought about Lily," why would he consider himself lucky? Find several examples in support.

3. How did the girl called Mandy first anger the white M.P.? What drove him to slap her? What began the general free-for-all?

4. At the time of the fight, what justifies Johnny's decision "it was time for him to get out of there"? Give at least two reasons.

5. When the black soldiers "straggled in," what does Johnny see could have happen to him? How did the colonel punish all black soldiers for the acts of some?

6. Why did Little Willie consider Johnny a crazy fool for wanting to see the colonel? How did Johnny prepare himself for going? Why might these steps be important to him?

7. Johnny replied, "I ain't at liberty t'say" who sent him to the colonel. How does this show quick thinking and also have elements of truth?

8. How might Johnny have helped himself by disobeying regulations about saluting a sergeant?

9. What risks did Johnny take by going to see the colonel? Why might admitting "I come on m'own hook" impress his superior officer? What special order did the colonel issue for Johnny?

10. How did the two M.P.s differ in their attitudes toward Johnny and Lily? What prevented Johnny from fighting the two singlehanded? Why was he certain to lose?

## Looking Deeper

### I. "I Ain't No Man!"

There are two types of courage, physical and moral. Give an example of each from this story, and explain their differences.

Why might Johnny think himself guilty of physical cowardice? At such a time, why was Johnny caught in circumstances beyond his control?

Being "a man" involves more than physical courage. What admirable qualities did Johnny exhibit throughout this story? Do you feel he possessed physical, as well as moral courage? Explain why or why not.

### II. From One Side Only . . .

In a story such as "Health Card," it is difficult to avoid stereotyping. Find examples showing how Yerby portrays both black and white characters as possessing both positive and negative qualities.

Imagine yourself in Johnny or Lily's place, under identical conditions. Do you believe you would have acted as they did? Explain why or why not.

# Hunger Is Good Discipline

## *from A Movable Feast*

### *by Ernest Hemingway*

| | |
|---|---|
| **Born:** | *Oak Park, Illinois, 1899* |
| **Early job:** | *Writer for Kansas City* Star |
| **World War I:** | *Ambulance driver in Italy* |
| **Writing career:** | *Spent 1920-29 in Paris, refining skills as novelist* |
| **Adult life:** | *Lived in Florida and Cuba, covered European front in WW II, and died in Idaho in 1961* |
| **Famous novels:** | A Farewell to Arms, The Sun Also Rises, The Old Man and the Sea |

**Y**OU GOT VERY HUNGRY WHEN you did not eat enough in Paris because all the bakery shops had such good things in the windows and people ate outside at tables on the sidewalk so that you saw and smelled the food. When you had given up journalism and were writing nothing that anyone in America would buy, explaining at home that you were lunching out with someone, the best place to go was the Luxembourg gardens where you saw and smelled nothing to eat all the way from the Place de l'Observatoire to the rue de Vaugirard. There you could always go into the Luxembourg museum and all the paintings were sharpened and clearer and more beautiful if you were belly-empty, hollow-hungry. I learned to understand Cézanne much better and to see truly how he made landscapes when I was hungry. I used to wonder if he were hungry too when he painted; but I thought possibly it was only that he had forgotten to eat. It was one of those unsound but illuminating thoughts you have when you have been sleepless or hungry. Later I thought Cézanne was probably hungry in a different way.

After you came out of the Luxembourg you could walk down the narrow rue Férou to the Place St.-Sulpice and there were still no restaurants, only the quiet square with its benches and trees. There was a fountain with lions, and pigeons walked on the pavement and perched on the statues of the bishops. There was the church and there were shops selling religious objects and vestments on the north side of the square.

From this square you could not go further toward the river without passing shops selling fruits, vegetables, wines, or bakery and pastry shops. But by choosing your way carefully you could work to your right around the grey and white stone church and reach the rue de l'Odéon and turn up to your right toward Sylvia Beach's bookshop and on your way you did not pass too many places where things to eat were sold. The rue de l'Odéon was bare of eating places until you reached the square where there were three restaurants.

By the time you reached 12 rue de l'Odéon your hunger was contained but all of your perceptions were heightened again. The photographs looked different and you saw books that you had never seen before.

"You're too thin, Hemingway," Sylvia would say. "Are you eating enough?"

"Sure."

"What did you eat for lunch?"

My stomach would turn over and I would say, "I'm going home for lunch now."

"At three o'clock?"

"I didn't know it was that late."

"Adrienne said the other night she wanted to have you and Hadley for dinner. We'd ask Fargue. You like Fargue, don't you? Or Larbaud. You like him. I know you like him. Or anyone you really like. Will you speak to Hadley?"

"I know she'd love to come."

"I'll send her a *pneu*.* Don't you work so hard now that you don't eat properly."

"I won't."

"Get home now before it's too late for lunch."

"They'll save it."

"Don't eat cold food either. Eat a good hot lunch."

"Did I have any mail?"

"I don't think so. But let me look."

She looked and found a note and looked up happily and then opened a closed door in her desk.

"This came while I was out," she said. It was a letter and it felt as though it had money in it. "Wedderkop," Sylvia said.

"It must be from *Der Querschnitt.* Did you see Wedderkop?"

"No. But he was here with George. He'll see you. Don't worry. Perhaps he wanted to pay you first."

"It's six hundred francs. He says there will be more."

"I'm awfully glad you reminded me to look. Dear Mr. Awfully Nice."

"It's damned funny that Germany is the only place I can sell anything. To him and the *Frankfurter Zeitung.*"

"Isn't it? But don't you worry ever. You can sell stories to Ford," she teased me.

"Thirty francs a page. Say one story every three months in *the transatlantic.*

* *pneu*    letter sent by pneumatic message-sending system in Paris.

Story five pages long make one hundred and fifty francs a quarter. Six hundred francs a year."

"But, Hemingway, don't worry about what they bring now. The point is that you can write them."

"I know. I can write them. But nobody will buy them. There is no money coming in since I quit journalism."

"They will sell. Look. You have the money for one right there."

"I'm sorry, Sylvia. Forgive me for speaking about it."

"Forgive you for what? Always talk about it or about anything. Don't you know all writers ever talk about is their troubles? But promise me you won't worry and that you'll eat enough."

"I promise."

"Then get home now and have lunch."

Outside on the rue de l'Odéon I was disgusted with myself for having complained about things. I was doing what I did of my own free will and I was doing it stupidly. I should have bought a large piece of bread and eaten it instead of skipping a meal. I could taste the brown lovely crust. But it is dry in your mouth without something to drink. You God damn complainer. You dirty phony saint and martyr, I said to myself. You quit journalism of your own accord. You have credit and Sylvia would have loaned you money. She has plenty of times. Sure. And then the next thing you would be compromising on something else. Hunger is healthy and the pictures do look better when you are hungry. Eating is wonderful too and do you know where you are going to eat right now?

Lipp's is where you are going to eat and drink too.

It was a quick walk to Lipp's and every place I passed that my stomach noticed as quickly as my eyes or my nose made the walk an added pleasure. There were few people in the *brasserie* and when I sat down on the bench against the wall with the mirror in back and a table in front and the waiter asked if I wanted beer I asked for a *distingué*, the big glass mug that held a liter, and for potato salad.

The beer was very cold and wonderful to drink. The *pommes à l'huile* were firm and marinated and the olive oil delicious. I ground black pepper over the potatoes and moistened the bread in the olive oil. After the first heavy draft of beer I drank and ate very slowly. When the *pommes à l'huile* were gone I ordered another serving and a *cervelas*. This was a sausage like a heavy, wide frankfurter split in two and covered with a special mustard sauce.

I mopped up all the oil and all of the sauce with bread and drank the beer slowly until it began to lose its coldness and then I finished it and ordered a *demi* and watched it drawn. It seemed colder than the *distingué* and I drank half of it.

I had not been worrying, I thought. I knew the stories were good and someone would publish them finally at home. When I stopped doing newspaper work I was sure the stories were going to be published. But every one I sent out came back. What had made me so confident was Edward O'Brien's taking the "My Old Man" story for the *Best Short Stories* book and then dedicating the book for that year to me. Then I laughed and drank some more beer. The story had never been published in a magazine and he had broken all his rules to take it for the book. I laughed again and the waiter glanced at me. It was funny because, after all that, he had spelled the name wrong. It was one of two stories I had left when everything I had written was stolen in Hadley's suitcase that time at the Gare de Lyon when she was bringing the manuscripts down to me to Lausanne as a surprise, so I could work on them on our holidays in the mountains. She had put in the originals, the typescripts and the carbons, all in manila folders. The only reason I had the one story was that Lincoln Steffens had sent it out to some editor who sent it back. It was in the mail while everything else was stolen. The other story that I had was the one called "Up in Michigan" written before Miss Stein had come to our flat. I had never had it copied because she said it was *inaccrochable.* It had been in a drawer somewhere.

So after we had left Lausanne and gone down to Italy I showed the racing story to O'Brien, a gentle, shy man, pale, with pale blue eyes, and straight lanky hair he cut himself, who lived then as a boarder in a monastery up above Rapallo. It was a bad time and I did not think I could write any more then, and I showed the story to him as a curiosity, as you might show, stupidly, the binnacle of a ship you had lost in some incredible way, or as you might pick up your booted foot and make some joke about it if it had been amputated after a crash. Then, when he read the story, I saw he was hurt far more than I was. I had never seen anyone hurt by a thing other than death or unbearable suffering except Hadley when she told me about the things being gone. She had cried and cried and could not tell me. I told her that no matter what the dreadful thing was that had happened nothing could be that bad, and whatever it was, it was all right and not to worry. We would work it out. Then, finally, she told me. I was sure she could not have brought the carbons too and I hired someone to cover for me on my newspaper job. I was making good money then at journalism, and took the train for Paris. It was true all right and I remember what I did in the night after I let myself into the flat and found it was true. That was over now and Chink had taught me never to discuss casualties; so I told O'Brien not to feel so bad. It was probably good for me to lose early work and I told him all that stuff you feed the troops. I was going to start writing stories again I said and, as I said it, only trying to lie so that he would not feel so bad, I knew that it was true.

Then I started to think in Lipp's about when I had first been able to write a story after losing everything. It was up in Cortina d'Ampezzo when I had come back to join Hadley there after the spring skiing which I had to interrupt to go on assignment to the Rhineland and the Ruhr. It was a very simple story called "Out of Season" and I had omitted the real end of it which was that the old man hanged himself. This was omitted on my new theory that you could omit anything if you knew that you omitted and the omitted part would strengthen the story and make people feel something more than they understood.

Well, I thought, now I have them so they do not understand them. There cannot be much doubt about that. There is most certainly no demand for them. But they will understand the same way that they always do in painting. It only takes time and it only needs confidence.

It is necessary to handle yourself better when you have to cut down on food so you will not get too much hunger-thinking. Hunger is good discipline and you learn from it. And as long as they do not understand it you are ahead of them. Oh sure, I thought, I'm so far ahead of them now that I can't afford to eat regularly. It would not be bad if they caught up a little.

I knew I must write a novel. But it seemed an impossible thing to do when I had been trying with great difficulty to write paragraphs that would be the distillation of what made a novel. It was necessary to write longer stories now as you would train for a longer race. When I had written a novel before, the one that had been lost in the bag stolen at the Gare de Lyon, I still had the lyric facility of boyhood that was as perishable and as deceptive as youth was. I knew it was probably a good thing that it was lost, but I knew too that I must write a novel. I would put it off though until I could not help doing it. I was damned if I would write one because it was what I should do if we were to eat regularly. When I had to write it, then it would be the only thing to do and there would be no choice. Let the pressure build. In the meantime I would write a long story about whatever I knew best.

By this time I had paid the check and gone out and turned to the right and crossed the rue de Rennes so that I would not go to the Deux-Magots for coffee and was walking up the rue Bonaparte on the shortest way home.

What did I know best that I had not written about and lost? What did I know about truly and care for the most? There was no choice at all. There was only the choice of streets to take you back fastest to where you worked. I went up Bonaparte to Guynemer, then to the rue d'Assas, up the rue Notre-Dame-des-Champs to the Closerie des Lilas.

I sat in a corner with the afternoon light coming in over my shoulder and wrote in the notebook. The waiter brought me a *café crème* and I drank half of it when it cooled and left it on the table while I wrote. When I stopped writing I did not want to leave the river where I could see the trout in the pool, its surface pushing and swelling smooth against the resistance of the log-driven piles of the bridge. The story was about coming back from the war but there was no mention of the war in it.

But in the morning the river would be there and I must make it and the country and all that would happen. There were days ahead to be doing that each day. No other thing mattered. In my pocket was the money from Germany so there was no problem. When that was gone some other money would come in.

All I must do now was stay sound and good in my head until morning when I would start to work again.

# For Better Reading: On Writing

Frank Yerby said, "I write because I have to."

Like most highly respected writers, Ernest Hemingway thought and cared deeply about his work.

It's often called style—the individual handling of words and choice of sentence patterns that can make a writer's work unique. Style in writing means far more than a natural flair.

To perfect his style, Hemingway worked to make every word count and pared away all that he felt was nonessential. His style can be called lean, direct, and compact. Some find it cryptic, too abruptly stated and therefore difficult to grasp.

For example, Hemingway favored the immediacy of dialogue but did not identify speakers by name unless absolutely necessary. Because he avoids such phrases as "Sylvia Beach said" and "I answered," the Hemingway style invites you to participate in the conversation but requires close attention.

Just as he demanded much of himself, Hemingway didn't hesitate to ask for the thoughtfulness and attention that's the shared responsibility of both writers and readers.

## Inference

1. Because Hemingway "did not eat enough in Paris," he could (a) better appreciate starving artists like Cézanne (b) get greater enjoyment from the sights, smells, and sounds of Paris (c) repay old gambling debts and loans from friends (d) concentrate on writing for himself, not work as a journalist.
2. When hungry and short on money, Hemingway felt Paris bakeries, sidewalk cafes, and restaurants were places (a) to avoid passing (b) for seeking old friends to ask for loans (c) as inspiring as art galleries (d) where wealthy and poor were equally welcome.
3. After thinking Cézanne possibly forgot to eat while painting, Hemingway decided (a) the idea sounded good but wasn't true (b) he felt the same way while writing (c) the sacrifice was worth the results (d) to keep this discovery secret.

## Questioning the Selection

1. Find at least two pieces of evidence to prove Hemingway said he was going home to lunch to avoid answering Silvia Beach's question. Why wouldn't he want to admit the truth?
2. In quoting his conversation with Sylvia Beach, Hemingway rarely uses phrases such as "she said" or "she teased me." Copy ten or more lines

of this dialogue, and supply appropriate identification, using a variety of verbs such as *asked* and *replied.* Explain why you feel the change improves or weakens the effect.

3. Although Hemingway does not identify Wedderkop or *Der Querschnitt,* he comments, "It's six hundred francs. He says there will be more." Judged by his remark, who or what must each of these German words be?

4. Why does Hemingway object to Sylvia's remark about his selling stories to someone called Ford? What proves she expected this reaction?

5. Why does Hemingway call himself a "phony saint" with respect to money? What makes him afraid of "compromising" by accepting Sylvia's loan? Why can he now go to Lipp's restaurant?

6. When he quit journalism, why was Hemingway confident of his stories being published? Why did this confidence seem foolish later?

7. A famous episode in Hemingway's life concerns the loss of all but two unpublished manuscripts then written. Explain why his wife, Hadley, was unintentionally responsible. How had she intended to be helpful?

8. How did Hadley react to telling her husband of the stories' theft? What action did Hemingway take as a result of his disbelief?

9. After he read one of the remaining stories, was O'Brien's response caused mainly by the story itself or his awareness of Hemingway's loss? Explain the reasons for your feelings.

10. To make O'Brien not "feel so bad," Hemingway repeated "all the stuff that you feed the troops." During wartime, what "stuff" are troops "fed" to raise their spirits? Explain in your own words what Hemingway might have told O'Brien. What did Hemingway realize after saying this?

11. "Now I have them so they do not understand them," thinks Hemingway about his stories and readers. Replace *they* and *them* with *stories* and *readers* in this sentence and the remainder of the paragraph. Why is such confusion of pronouns a natural way of expressing thoughts?

12. What does Hemingway mean by "being ahead" of his readers? What are the pluses and minuses of this? What does Hemingway decide?

13. How did Hemingway plan to "train" for writing a novel?

14. While in a cafe writing about a river with "trout in the pool," what does Hemingway mean by saying, "I did not want to leave the river"? How could he "see" the trout? In what sense did he "make" the river "and the country and all that would happen"?

# Looking Deeper

## I. The Hidden Depths of Feeling

Hemingway compared his attitude towards his lost manuscripts to joking about having your own foot amputated after a crash. Why might someone make such jokes? What does this reveal about Hemingway's true feelings?

Most authors feel it's impossible to rewrite a story if the only copy were destroyed or lost. How do you account for this feeling?

Hemingway states, "I remember what I did in the night," but he does not give details about what happened in Paris after he "found it was true" his manuscripts were lost. Why doesn't he explain? How does this seem typically American?

## II. The Writer at Work

Hemingway said that he failed to copy "Up in Michigan," because an influential American writer, Gertrude Stein, called it *inaccrochable*. Although the word is French, approximately what must it mean? What does Hemingway's reaction reveal about his feelings towards himself and his work as a young man?

Hemingway decided, "You could omit anything if you knew that you omitted and the omitted part would strengthen the story and make people feel something more than they understood." How can you "feel something more" than you understand when you read?

Hemingway didn't want to write a novel "because it was what I should do if we were to eat regularly." What does this reveal about his purpose for writing?

Hemingway also felt he must be far from a place to write well about it. How does the story being written about the river illustrate this belief? Why might distance improve someone's ability to write about a place?

# If There Be Sorrow

*by Mari Evans*

***Born:***   *Ohio*
***Career:***  *Industrial magazine editor, civil service
employee, songwriter, poet, writer in
residence at Indiana and Purdue
Universities*

If there be sorrow
let it be
for things undone . . .
undreamed
   unrealized
    unattained
to these add one:
Love withheld . . .
  . . . restrained

## For Better Reading: In Training

Ernest Hemingway believed he must train to progress from writing short stories to novels just as an athlete must train for running longer races.

Yet some writers feel a good short paragraph or poem takes more concentrated effort than a longer piece. That's because the shorter it is, the more each word must contribute to its total sense.

Of course, Hemingway knew the worth of a word, and poets "in training" also know that a single word can carry a wealth of meaning.

A good poet chooses each word for a precise reason. And, because of the close bond between writer and reader, similar attention to the value of words helps you train to become a better reader, too.

## Questioning the Poem

1. To whom are the words of this poem directed?
2. In line one Evans uses the words, "If there be sorrow." How would the meaning differ if she had written, "If there is sorrow"?

3. There can, of course, be sorrow for things "done." Why would Evans imply that this kind of sorrow is useless?
4. "Things undone" could refer to someone's duties. Why might this be a valid reason for sorrow?
5. How are things "undreamed" different from "things undone"? Why should someone be regretful about having no dreams?
6. Why might someone feel sorrow about something he or she has not realized or attained? How are both related to dreams?
7. In your own words, explain what Evans considers the kind of regret that must be added to the rest.

## Looking Deeper

### I. A Poem of Possibilities

Hemingway wrote of people's ability to "feel something more than they understood." That's often how poetry affects someone, and deepest feelings are usually the hardest to express.

With that in mind, try to explain how this poem concerns being aware of possibilities as well as being about sorrow.

Evans writes of feeling sorrow for withholding love or restraining it. In addition to romantic love, what are other times one might "withhold" or "restrain" love?

### II. Relating to the Spirit

This poem was included in an anthology, *New Negro Poets: USA*. Do you feel it applies especially to someone who is black and a woman, or do you feel its ideas are meaningful for anyone? Explain the reasons for your viewpoint.

# Europe and America

*by David Ignatow*

**Born:** Brooklyn, New York, 1914
**Early jobs:** Worked in family butcher shop, bindery
**Career:** Journalist, editor, poet, lecturer at Kentucky and Kansas universities

My father brought the emigrant bundle
of desperation and worn threads,
that in anxiety as he stumbles
tumble out distractedly;
while I am bedded upon soft green money     5
that grows like grass.
Thus, between my father
who lives on a bed of anguish for his daily bread,
and I who tear money at leisure by the roots,
where I lie in sun or shade,     10
a vast continent of breezes, storms to him,
shadows, darkness to him, small lakes, rough channels
to him, and hills, mountains to him, lie between us.

My father comes of a small hell
where bread and man have been kneaded and baked
      together.     15
You have heard the scream as the knife fell;
while I have slept
as guns pounded offshore.

# Questioning the Poem

1. To *emigrate* means to leave one country to settle in another. What does the title and the father's "emigrant bundle" explain about the father's birth and the speaker's?
2. How might the "emigrant bundle" be both an actual object and a pyschological burden?
3. From lines 3–14, the speaker uses present tense verbs such as "stumbles" and "am bedded" referring to his father and himself. In light of this, when the father "stumbles," does this happen in Europe or America? How do lines 1 and 2 explain the father's reacting "in anxiety" to a minor mishap like stumbling? Why do his feelings seem to "tumble out distractedly"?
4. In what ways might the speaker seem "bedded upon soft green money?" What is the only reason the poem suggests for this?
5. The speaker contrasts his father's "bed of anguish" to his own bed of "soft green money." Furthermore, what are just breezes to the son seem like storms to the father. List three similar contrasts given in lines 12–13.
6. According to the speaker, these differences are a "vast continent" that lies "between us." What do these differences represent, and why do they cause such a vast separation between father and son?
7. Although the poem doesn't define the "hell" the father left, describe two or three elements you imagine this place having.
8. Lines 16–18 provide the final contrast. Why is hearing "the scream" worse than hearing guns that "pounded offshore"? Why is the speaker able to sleep?

# Looking Deeper

## I. ". . . Comes of a Small Hell"

Although the poem isn't rooted to an exact historical date, why have Americans generally considered themselves able to "sleep more soundly" than peoples of many European countries? Could the poem also be called "Asia and America" or "Africa and America"? Why or why not?

How does the word "You" in line 16 change the focus of the poem? Explain what feelings the speaker finds difficult to express to his father.

## II. A Sense of the Present

Sum up this poem's idea about what it means to live in America. Do you feel most Americans fail to appreciate the benefits they share? Why or why not?

The poem is mainly written in the present tense, with mention of Europe in the past. Do you think "living in the present" is typically American? Do you believe Americans pay too little attention to both their family's and country's pasts? Explain why or why not.

# Always There Are the Children

## by Nikki Giovanni

**Born:** _Tennessee_
**Educated:** _Fisk University, University of Pennsylvania, Columbia University, N.Y._
**Career:** _Poet, writer, lecturer, professor, columnist, founder of publishing firm_

and always    there are the children

there will be children in the heat of day
there will be children in the cold of winter

children    like a quilted blanket
are welcomed in our old age         5

children    like a block of ice to a desert sheik
are a sign of status in our youth

we feed the children with our culture
that they might understand our travail

we nourish the children on our gods       10
that they may understand respect

we urge the children on the tracks
that our race will not fall short

but children are not ours
nor we theirs    they are future    we are past    15

how do we welcome the future
not with the colonialism of the past
  for that is our problem

not with the racism of the past
    for that is their problem                 20
not with the fears of our own status
    for history is lived not dictated

we welcome the young of all groups
as our own with the solid nourishment
of food and warmth                    25

we prepare the way with the solid
nourishment of self-actualization

we implore all the young to prepare for the young
because always there will be children

*Rome 12 November 1974*

# For Better Reading: How Free?

Nikki Giovanni's poem, "Always There Are the Children" is an example of *free verse*: poetry that has no regular pattern of rhythm or rhyme.

But, like all good writing, free verse doesn't just tumble out haphazardly. It is the result of thought, care, and attention to every detail.

How "free" is free verse? Although its words are plainly stated without capitalization or punctuation, this poem asks you not only to be aware of words but also of spaces. There are spaces between stanzas, spaces within lines, spaces forming indentions: all are part of the poem's plan. And, they provide helpful guides about where to pause and when to note important relationships between words.

## Questioning the Poem

1. With regard to words and spacing, what are three differences between the first line and title? Read the title and first line together, and explain a logical purpose for the added words and space.
2. How do lines 2–3 support the word "always"?
3. What words in line 3 do "quilted blanket" and "old age" call to mind? How do children offer older people this kind of comfort?
4. What word in line 2 does "block of ice" call forth? Why might ice be a "sign of status" to a desert sheik? Why might children be a status sign to younger people?
5. Lines 8, 10, and 12 begin with the word "we." Whom do you believe

"we" includes? "Feed" and "nourish" are usually associated with food. How do they also fit the idea of "culture" and "gods"?

6. The poem speaks of the need for understanding "our travail." Since *travail* can mean both burdensome work and suffering, how does this echo the Ignatow poem "Europe and America"? Why is it also important to understand "respect"?

7. Line 13, "that our race will not fall short," contains multiple meanings. It can mean the human race, the black race, or the race to better the world. Explain why children should be "urged on" concerning each.

8. What contrast is introduced in lines 14 and 15?

9. Line 17 introduces three ideas, each beginning with *not*. Since independence is the goal of present and former colonies the world over, why should *colonialism* (a nation's control of a dependent territory) be considered "our" problem? Even though "of the past," why should *racism* (the idea that one's own race is superior) still be "their" problem?

10. Lines 23, 26, and 28 open with "we." Does line 23, "we welcome the young," refer to young of the past, present, or future? Use the poem to support your decision. In the final two lines, what does the speaker beg these young to do and remember?

## Looking Deeper
### I. Space for Reading

The following two examples say "almost" the same thing, yet Nikki Giovanni chose the second for her poem.

      a. children are like a quilted blanket that is welcomed in our old age

      b. children like a quilted blanket are welcomed in our old age

The first focuses on the question, "Why are children like a quilted blanket?" What answer would you give? What question is raised by Giovanni's version, and how would you answer it?

In lines 17–22, how does the placement of words emphasize important repetition and parallel phrasing? How does the final line, taken with the title first line, both enclose the poem and carry it one step further?

### II. A Sense of the Future

There can be two senses to the statement: Children belong to their parents. What are they? In what sense is line 14 true, "children are not ours"? In what sense don't parents "belong" to children?

What happens today becomes history in the future. Concerning lines 21–22, how do older generations sometimes try to "dictate history" to children? History sometimes judges past generations as having been wrong; for example, concerning slavery and the denial of voting rights to women. Considering this, how might "fears of status" make adults attempt to dictate what children should believe and to avoid having their beliefs questioned?

Explain why history can only be "lived not dictated."

The poem speaks of offering the young three types of nourishment: food, warmth, and self-actualization. How does the last, meaning to achieve or realize one's potential, differ from the others? Why would the poet call this "solid," too? Why is this kind of "nourishment" a main ingredient of the American Spirit?

# A Pilot's Apprentice
# from *Life on the Mississippi*
## by Mark Twain

| | |
|---|---|
| **Born:** | *Missouri* |
| **Given name:** | *Samuel Clemens* |
| **Early life:** | *Apprentice pilot on Mississippi River, miner in Nevada, printer's apprentice and typesetter, secretary, government worker* |
| **During Civil War:** | *Served as Second Lieutenant, Confederate Army* |
| **Final years:** | *Lived in Redding, Connecticut* |
| **Famous as:** | *Creator of Tom Sawyer and Huck Finn, author of books about world-wide travels* |

### Chapter XVIII. I Take a Few Extra Lessons

DURING THE TWO OR TWO and a half years of my apprenticeship I served under many pilots, and had experience of many kinds of steamboatmen and many varieties of steamboats; for it was not always convenient for Mr. Bixby to have me with him, and in such cases he sent me with somebody else. I am to this day profiting somewhat by that experience; for in that brief, sharp schooling, I got personally and familiarly acquainted with about all the different types of human nature that are to be found in fiction, biography, or history. The fact is daily borne in upon me that the average shore-employment requires as much as forty years to equip a man with this sort of an education. When I say I am still profiting by this thing, I do not mean that it has constituted me a judge of men—no, it has not done that, for judges of men are born, not made. My profit is various in kind and degree, but the feature of it which I value most is the zest which that early experience has given to my later reading. When I find a well-drawn character in fiction or biography I generally take a warm personal interest in him, for the reason that I have known him before—met him on the river.

The figure that comes before me oftenest, out of the shadows of that vanished time, is that of Brown, of the steamer *Pennsylvania*—the man referred to in a former chapter, whose memory was so good and tiresome. He was a middle-aged, long, slim, bony, smooth-shaven, horse-faced, ignorant, stingy, malicious, snarling, fault-finding, mote-magnifying tyrant. I early got the habit of coming on watch with dread at my heart. No matter how good a time I might have been having with the off-watch below, and no matter how high my spirits might be when I started aloft, my soul became lead in my body the moment I approached the pilot-house.

I still remember the first time I ever entered the presence of that man. The boat had backed out from St. Louis and was "straightening down." I ascended to the pilot-house in high feather, and very proud to be semi-officially a member of the executive family of so fast and famous a boat. Brown was at the wheel. I paused in the middle of the room, all fixed to make my bow, but Brown did not look around. I thought he took a furtive glance at me out of the corner of his eye, but as not even this notice was repeated, I judged I had been mistaken. By this time he was picking his way among some dangerous "breaks" abreast the woodyards; therefore it would not be proper to interrupt him; so I stepped softly to the high bench and took a seat.

There was silence for ten minutes; then my new boss turned and inspected me deliberately and painstakingly from head to heel for about—as it seemed to me—a quarter of an hour. After which he removed his countenance and I saw it no more for some seconds; then it came around once more, and this question greeted me:

"Are you Horace Bixby's cub?"

"Yes, sir."

After this there was a pause and another inspection. Then:

"What's your name?"

I told him. He repeated it after me. It was probably the only thing he ever forgot; for although I was with him many months he never addressed himself to me in any other way than "Here!" and then his command followed.

"Where was you born?"

"In Florida, Missouri."

A pause. Then:

"Dern sight better stayed there!"

By means of a dozen or so of pretty direct questions, he pumped my family history out of me.

The leads were going now in the first crossing. This interrupted the inquest. When the leads had been laid in he resumed:

"How long you been on the river?"

I told him. After a pause:

"Where'd you get them shoes?"

I gave him the information.

"Hold up your foot!"

I did so. He stepped back, examined the shoe minutely and contemptuously, scratching his head thoughtfully, tilting his high sugar-loaf hat well forward to facilitate the operation, then shouted, "Well, I'll be dod derned!" and returned to his wheel.

What occasion there was to be dod derned about it is a thing which is still as much of a mystery to me now as it was then. It must have been all of fifteen minutes—fifteen minutes of dull, homesick silence—before that long horse-face swung round upon me again—and then what a change! It was as red as fire, and every muscle in it was working. Now came this shriek:

"Here! You going to set there all day?"

I lit in the middle of the floor, shot there by the electric suddenness of the surprise. As soon as I could get my voice I said apologetically: "I have had no orders, sir."

"You've had no *orders!* My, what a fine bird we are! We must have *orders!* Our father was a *gentleman*—owned slaves—and *we've* been to *school.* Yes, we are a gentleman, *too,* and got to have *orders!* ORDERS, is it? ORDERS is what you want! Dod dern my skin, *I'll* learn you to swell yourself up and blow around *here* about your dod-derned *orders!* G'way from the wheel!" (I had approached it without knowing it.)

I moved back a step or two and stood as in a dream, all my senses stupified by this frantic assault.

"What you standing there for? Take that ice-pitcher down to the texas-tender! Come, move along, and don't you be all day about it!"

The moment I got back to the pilot-house Brown said:

"Here! What was you doing down there all this time?"

"I couldn't find the texas-tender; I had to go all the way to the pantry."

"Derned likely story! Fill up the stove."

I proceeded to do so. He watched me like a cat. Presently he shouted:

"Put down that shovel! Derndest numbskull I ever saw—ain't even got sense enough to load up a stove."

All through the watch this sort of thing went on. Yes, and the subsequent watches were much like it during a stretch of months. As I have said, I soon got the habit of coming on duty with dread. The moment I was in the presence, even in the darkest night, I could feel those yellow eyes upon me, and knew their owner was watching for a pretext to spit out some venom on me. Preliminarily he would say:

"Here! Take the wheel."

Two minutes later:

"*Where* in the nation you going to? Pull her down! pull her down!"

After another moment:

"Say! You going to hold her all day? Let her go—meet her! meet her!"

Then he would jump from the bench, snatch the wheel from me, and meet her himself, pouring out wrath upon me all the time.

George Ritchie was the other pilot's cub. He was having good times now; for his boss, George Ealer, was as kindhearted as Brown wasn't. Ritchie had steered for Brown the season before; consequently, he knew exactly how to entertain himself and plague me, all by the one operation. Whenever I took the wheel for a moment on Ealer's watch, Ritchie would sit back on the bench and play Brown, with continual reprimands of "Snatch her! snatch her! Derndest mud-cat I ever saw!" "Here! Where are you going *now?* Going to run over that snag?" "Pull her *down!* Don't you hear me? Pull her *down!*" "There she goes! *Just* as I expected! I *told* you not to cramp that reef. G'way from the wheel!"

So I always had a rough time of it, no matter whose watch it was; and sometimes it seemed to me that Ritchie's good-natured badgering was pretty nearly as aggravating as Brown's dead-earnest nagging.

I often wanted to kill Brown, but this would not answer. A cub had to take everything his boss gave, in the way of vigorous comment and criticism; and we all believed that there was a United States law making it a penitentiary offense to strike or threaten a pilot who was on duty. However, I could *imagine* myself killing Brown; there was no law against that; and that was the thing I used always to do the moment I was abed. Instead of going over my river in my mind, as was my duty, I threw business aside for pleasure, and killed Brown. I killed Brown every night for months; not in old, stale, commonplace ways, but in new and picturesque ones—ways that were sometimes surprising for freshness of design and ghastliness of situation and environment.

Brown was *always* watching for a pretext to find fault; and if he could find no plausible pretext, he would invent one. He would scold you for shaving a shore, and for not shaving it; for hugging a bar, and for not hugging it; for "pulling down" when not invited, and for *not* pulling down when not invited; for firing up without orders, and for waiting *for* orders. In a word, it was his invariable rule to find fault with *everything* you did; and another invariable rule of his was to throw all his remarks (to you) into the form of an insult.

One day we were approaching New Madrid, bound down and heavily laden. Brown was at one side of the wheel, steering; I was at the other, standing by to "pull down" or "shove up." He cast a furtive glance at me every now and then. I had long ago learned what that meant; viz, he was trying to invent a trap for me. I wondered what shape it was going to take. By and by he stepped back from the wheel and said in his usual snarly way:

"Here! See if you've got gumption enough to round her to."

This was simply *bound* to be a success; nothing could prevent it; for he had never allowed me to round the boat to before; consequently, no matter how I might do the thing, he could find free fault with it. He stood back there with his greedy eye on me, and the result was what might have been foreseen: I lost my head in a quarter of a minute, and didn't know what I was about; I started too early to bring the boat around, but detected a green gleam of joy in Brown's eye, and corrected my mistake. I started around once more while too high up, but corrected myself again in time. I made other false moves, and still managed to save myself; but at last I grew so confused and anxious that I tumbled into the very worst blunder of all—I got too far *down* before beginning to fetch the boat around. Brown's chance was come.

His face turned red with passion; he made one bound, hurled me across the house with a sweep of his arm, spun the wheel down, and began to pour out a stream of vituperation upon me which lasted till he was out of breath. In the course of this speech he called me all the different kinds of hard names he could think of, and once or twice I thought he was even going to swear—but he had never done that, and he didn't this time. "Dod dern" was the nearest he ventured to the luxury of swearing, for he had been brought up with a wholesome respect for future fire and brimstone.

That was an uncomfortable hour; for there was a big audience on the hurricane-deck. When I went to bed that night, I killed Brown in seventeen different ways—all of them new.

## For Better Reading: Reading a River

Many believe that Mark Twain's *Adventures of Huckleberry Finn* is the best novel of America yet written.

At its heart is a trip by raft down the Mississippi river, taken by the boy narrator Huck Finn and his adult companion and friend Jim, an escaping slave.

Both Jim and Huck have ready senses of humor and naturally good impulses. Yet, since both were born and raised in a society deformed by slavery, they are both products and victims of a prejudiced, narrow-minded upbringing. They can truly be themselves only on the river, where black and white are less important than the real relationship between two friends and fellow humans.

Able to worm his way out of trouble and speak his mind openly, Huck showed the spirit that Americans—both young and old—liked and admired.

Twain himself knew the river. While an apprentice steamboat pilot, he learned to "read" its currents and dangers, as well as "read" the characters of the boatmen who plied it.

In this selection from *Life on the Mississippi*, Twain recalls his apprentice days. Written after Twain had won fame as a writer, the book recounts Twain's return to journey down the river where he trained as a youth and which lies at the heart of his most honored novel.

## Important Details

1. Twain felt serving as an apprentice under many pilots (a) made him a good judge of men (b) improved his personality (c) added zest to his later reading (d) brought American history to life.
2. His way of becoming "personally acquainted with all the different types of human nature," Twain said, was (a) through a forty-year career of writing and traveling (b) during two to two and a half years of appren-

ticeship (c) by reading fiction, biography, and history (d) from listening to the stories and advice of steamboat pilots.

3. While serving on a steamboat with Brown as pilot, Twain developed the habit of (a) playing ingenious practical jokes (b) not listening to Brown's tiresome stories (c) finding fault with other crew members (d) dreading to report to duty.

## Questioning the Chapter

1. Where and why had Twain first "entered the presence" of the steamboat pilot, Brown?
2. Considering that the official executive family of a steamboat includes captain and pilot, why was Twain a "semi-official" member? At the outset, what were Twain's feelings about serving on the *Pennsylvania*? Why did he feel this way?
3. Upon reporting to the pilot house, how did Twain show proper respect and an awareness of a pilot's responsibilities? How was he giving Brown the benefit of the doubt?
4. How did Twain feel and act when Brown inspected him "deliberately and painstakingly from head to heel"?
5. In his opening description, Twain calls Brown "malicious" (liking to cause harm), "snarling," "fault-finding," and "mote-magnifying" (making much of something minor). Find one or more different examples of each of the four qualities, up to Brown's shriek, "Derndest numbskull I ever saw—"
6. Why did Brown "accuse" Twain of being a gentleman? Considering words such as "dod derned" and his red-faced fury, explain what reasons Brown had for disliking Twain's attitude.
7. On a steamboat, the officers' quarters were called the "texas" because each cabin bore a state's name, with Texas the largest. Why was Brown unfair to accuse Twain of lying about his search for it? How was Brown also at fault when Twain tried to steer?
8. How did George Ritchie, another apprentice pilot, "entertain himself and plague" Twain? Why might Ritchie's motives be called "good-natured"?
9. Why did Twain feel he had to "take everything" Brown gave? How did he "get even" in his imagination? Do you think, at the time, he was sincerely contemplating this? Why or why not?
10. What made Brown impossible to please? From what viewpoints was Twain's attempt to "round the boat to," or turn its course around, both a success and a failure?

### Chapter XIX. Brown and I Exchange Compliments

Two trips later I got into serious trouble. Brown was steering; I was "pulling down." My younger brother appeared on the hurricane-deck, and shouted to Brown to stop at some landing or other, a mile or so below. Brown gave no intimation that he had heard anything. But that was his way: he never condescended to take notice of an under-clerk. The wind was blowing; Brown was deaf (although he always pretended he wasn't), and I very much doubted if he had heard the order. If I had had two heads, I would have spoken; but as I had only one, it seemed judicious to take care of it; so I kept still.

Presently, sure enough, we went sailing by that plantation. Captain Kline-felter appeared on the deck, and said:

"Let her come around, sir, let her come around. Didn't Henry tell you to land here?"

"*No*, sir!"

"I sent him up to do it."

"He *did* come up; and that's all the good it done, the dod-derned fool. He never said anything."

"Didn't *you* hear him?" asked the captain of me.

Of course I didn't want to be mixed up in this business, but there was no way to avoid it; so I said:

"Yes, sir."

I knew what Brown's next remark would be, before he uttered it. It was:

"Shut your mouth! You never heard anything of the kind."

I closed my mouth, according to instructions. An hour later Henry entered the pilot-house, unaware of what had been going on. He was a thoroughly inoffensive boy, and I was sorry to see him come, for I knew Brown would have no pity on him. Brown began, straightway:

"Here! Why didn't you tell me we'd got to land at that plantation?"

"I did tell you, Mr. Brown."

"It's a lie!"

I said:

"You lie, yourself. He did tell you."

Brown glared at me in unaffected surprise; and for as much as a moment he was entirely speechless; then he shouted to me:

"I'll attend to your case in a half a minute!" then to Henry, "And you leave the pilot-house; out with you!"

It was pilot law, and must be obeyed. The boy started out, and even had his foot on the upper step outside the door, when Brown, with a sudden access of fury, picked up a ten-pound lump of coal and sprang after him; but I was between, with a heavy stool, and I hit Brown a good honest blow which stretched him out.

I had committed the crime of crimes—I had lifted my hand against a pilot on duty! I supposed I was booked for the penitentiary sure, and couldn't be booked any surer if I went on and squared my long account with this person while I had the chance; consequently I stuck to him and pounded him with my fists a considerable time. I do not know how long, the pleasure of it probably made it seem longer than it really was; but in the end he struggled free and jumped up and sprang to the wheel: a very natural solicitude, for, all this time, here was this steamboat tearing down the river at the rate of fifteen miles an hour and nobody at the helm! However, Eagle Bend was two miles wide at this bank-full stage, and correspondingly long and deep: and the boat was steering herself straight down the middle and taking no chances. Still, that was only luck—a body *might* have found her charging into the woods.

Perceiving at a glance that the *Pennsylvania* was in no danger, Brown gathered up the big spy-glass, war-club fashion, and ordered me out of the pilot-house with more than Comanche bluster. But I was not afraid of him now; so, instead of going, I tarried, and criticized his grammar. I reformed his ferocious speeches for him, and put them into good English, calling his attention to the advantage of pure English over the bastard dialect of the Pennsylvania collieries whence he was extracted. He could have done his part to admiration in a cross-fire of mere vituperation, of course; but he was not equipped for this species of controversy; so he presently laid aside his glass and took the wheel, muttering and shaking his head; and I retired to the bench. The racket had brought everybody to the hurricane-deck, and I trembled when I saw the old captain looking up from amid the crowd. I said to myself, "Now I *am* done for!" for although, as a rule, he was so fatherly and indulgent toward the boat's family, and so patient of minor shortcomings, he could be stern enough when the fault was worth it.

I tried to imagine what he *would* do to a cub pilot who had been guilty of such a crime as mine, committed on a boat guard-deep with costly freight and alive with passengers. Our watch was nearly ended. I thought I would go and hide somewhere till I got a chance to slide ashore. So I slipped out of the pilot-house, and down the steps, and around to the texas-door, and was in the act of gliding within, when the captain confronted me! I dropped my head, and he stood over me in silence a moment or two, then said impressively:

"Follow me."

I dropped into his wake; he led the way to his parlor in the forward end of the texas. We were alone, now. He closed the after door; then moved slowly to the forward one and closed that. He sat down; I stood before him. He looked at me some little time, then said:

"So you have been fighting Mr. Brown?"

I answered meekly:

"Yes, sir."

"Do you know that that is a very serious matter?"

"Yes, sir."

"Are you aware that this boat was plowing down the river fully five minutes with no one at the wheel?"

"Yes, sir."

"Did you strike him first?"

"Yes, sir."

"What with?"

"A stool, sir."

"Hard?"

"Middling, sir."

"Did it knock him down?"

"He—he fell, sir."

"Did you follow it up? Did you do anything further?"

"Yes, sir."

"What did you do?"

"Pounded him, sir."

"Pounded him?"

"Yes, sir."

"Did you pound him much? that is, severely?"

"One might call it that, sir, maybe."

"I'm deuced glad of it! Hark ye, never mention that I said that. You have been guilty of a great crime; and·don't you ever be guilty of it again, on this boat. *But*—lay for him ashore! Give him a good sound thrashing, do you hear? I'll pay the expenses. Now go—and mind you, not a word of this to anybody. Clear out with you! You've been guilty of a great crime, you whelp!"

I slid out, happy with the sense of a close shave and a mighty deliverance; and I heard him laughing to himself and slapping his fat thighs after I had closed his door.

When Brown came off watch he went straight to the captain, who was talking with some passengers on the boiler-deck, and demanded that I be put ashore in New Orleans—and added:

"I'll never turn a wheel on this boat again while that cub stays."

The captain said:

"But he needn't come round when you are on watch, Mr. Brown."

"I won't even stay on the same boat with him. *One* of us has got to go ashore."

"Very well," said the captain, "let it be yourself," and resumed his talk with the passengers.

During the brief remainder of the trip I knew how an emancipated slave feels, for I was an emancipated slave myself. While we lay at landings I listened to George Ealer's flute, or to his readings from his two Bibles, that is to say, Goldsmith and Shakespeare, or I played chess with him—and would have beaten him sometimes, only he always took back his last move and ran the game out differently.

## Questioning the Chapter

1. Twain said he would have repeated the order that his brother Henry was relaying from the captain, "If I had had two heads." Explain the serious and humorous side to this comment.
2. What are two reasons for Twain's feeling unable to avoid being "mixed up in this business" when the captain asked, "Didn't *you* hear him?" What prepares for Brown's being genuinely "surprised" and "speech-less" when Twain said, "You lie, yourself"?
3. Why might Twain's attack on Brown seem justified and even coura-geous? How do Twain's actions prove that his imagined dreams of re-venge were never seriously intended?
4. Why was the boat in genuine danger? Who or what was actually respon-sible? Why did Twain feel he committed a serious crime?
5. How was Twain surprised by the captain's reaction to the fight? Why would the captain think Brown got what he deserved?
6. How did the captain respond to Brown's threat not to stay on the same boat with Twain?

## Looking Deeper

### I. The Letter of the Law . . .

Explain how it is possible to obey "the letter of the law," but not its spirit. Why was this true of Brown's behavior? Why couldn't the captain take action against Brown earlier?

Why might Twain feel like a slave with respect to Brown? Before the final confrontation, why didn't Twain speak out openly to Brown or against him to the captain?

What proves that Brown was not a typical pilot? Do you believe the rules of discipline for apprentices were usually a good form of training? Explain why or why not.

### II. "Having Naturally Good Impulses"

How did Twain exhibit "naturally good impulses" while serving under Brown? Give at least three examples.

How did his sense of humor and good imagination help Twain handle serving under Brown? Did the "Few Extra Lessons" in the first chapter title concern steamship piloting or human nature? Explain the reasoning behind your answer. What is ironical about the second title, "Brown and

I Exchange Compliments?" What qualities of the American spirit do you find and admire in Twain? Why?

<hr>

## REFLECTIONS

Spirit. It can't be measured or seen but perhaps it can be felt.

Did the same spirit cause American soldiers to risk their lives for Russian prisoners of war and Mark Twain to risk his future to stand up for his brother?

How important is a sense of humor to the American spirit as it's evidenced in this chapter? Where does American humor spring from, and are Americans in danger of losing it?

What part does ingenuity play in the American spirit? Fairness? Willingness to live and let live? The determination to try to make things better?

Select two of the following qualities, or others of your choosing, and explain the part each plays in the American spirit. Include examples of each from this chapter or your own experience.

> Generosity
> Humor
> Ingenuity
> Fairness
> Willingness to live and let live
> Determination to make things better

## To Write About or Discuss

1. Are Americans so self-critical they sometimes overlook what's good about themselves and their country? Explain your views.
2. What selection or selections best express the American spirit for you? Discuss how and why.
3. Sometimes, in life as in sports, an excess of spirit makes people go too far. Support or attack this statement, based on your own observations.
4. What kind of spirit would you like to encourage Americans to emphasize more, and why?
5. A Difficult Decision I Had to Make. Hemingway as a young writer, Mark Twain as an apprentice pilot, Johnny as a young soldier—all faced tests of their spirit. Describe a decision you faced or face.

# UNIT 7

# A Sense of Place

YOU CAN'T SEE THE AMERICAN DREAM, the American spirit, or American values. You can only see the kind of nation and society that these inner qualities have created.

Yet, first, there was the land. It's not the world's largest country in size, but the United States of America contains many extremes: from the lands ripe for farming and ranching that lured pioneers westward, to the barren deserts and imposing mountains that stood in their way ... from northern regions of white winters to southern regions of year-round mildness.

And, though common bonds link Americans wherever you meet them, there is no one place to label the "real" America, no single spot on the map that represents the American nation as a whole. Seacoast towns, ranches and farm land, crowded inner cities, solitary hillside cabins, and quiet suburbs—one is as much America as the other.

Where do you go to find America? Some believe the only true America is right where they live. Others long to escape the push and stress of the city for the "good life" in the country. And, others yearn to escape rural dullness for big city opportunity and excitement. And, wherever they go, America will be there.

Where Americans live creates different sets of problems and calls forth differing responses. Yet, in a land of extremes in climate, geographical characteristics, and conditions, it's essential to recognize the qualities that make them Americans, all.

# Getting Scared

### *by William Stafford*

| | |
|---|---|
| **Born:** | Hutchinson, Kansas, 1914 |
| **Home:** | Lake Oswego, Oregon |
| **Early jobs:** | Worked on farms, in oil refineries, with peace churches |
| **Career:** | Poet, U.S. Information Agency lecturer in Egypt, Middle East, and Asia |
| **Honored as:** | Poet laureate of Oregon |

Tending our fire in the oil drum, we felt
that second earthquake begin. Near dawn it was,
when everything stills. To be safe, we had
slept in a field. We felt a long slow wave
in the earth. It wasn't the stars that moved,
    but ourselves,     5
in time to a dance the dead could feel. Our fire
stirred where it cooled. Sparks whirled up.
Crawling along by a breath at a time, we tried to
get low; we tried to sight across level earth
near dawn and let the time tell us about how     10
to be alive in the grass, the miles, the strangeness,
with only the sun looking back from the other end
    of light.
We moved out as far as we could. "Forever,"
    we thought,
"if we breathe too hard it will all be gone."
We spread our arms out wide on the ground     15
and held still. We set out for the cave we knew
above a stream, where early sunlight reaches
far back, willows all around, and clams in the river
for the taking. And we prayed for that steady event
we had loved so long without knowing it, our greatest   20
possession—the world when it didn't move.

# For Better Reading: The Influence of Setting

A writer's background may or may not be important to you as a reader.

Readers sometimes choose a book or article because it's written by a celebrity in sports, politics, or entertainment. Or perhaps the writer is known as an expert in a field or has published other works they've read and enjoyed.

Some readers like to trace the influences of family background and personal history in a writer's work. Others prefer to let the writing speak for itself.

A writer's background is important only if it matters to you as a reader. And, if you're unsure about the setting of a poem or story, knowing details of the writer's life can provide helpful clues.

When place and time aren't clearly stated, it's not "cheating" to scan biographical data or even check a reference.

In most cases, writers give details about setting early in a selection. When they don't, you're usually safe to assume the period and locale are the writer's own.

## Questioning the Poem

1. What in line 2 explains the speaker's decision to sleep in the field? Why was this safer than being in a house?
2. Since *we* means "you and I," its use seems to include the reader. Considering the title and subject, explain what effect the poet achieves by using *we* without naming those it included.
3. List at least three geographical features of the setting, mentioned anywhere in the poem.
4. What part of the United States fits best as the poem's setting? Explain the reasons for your choice.
5. Why was the earth's motion "a dance the dead could feel"? What are two details that show the length and intensity of the quake?
6. From lines 8–19, describe at least two physical precautions or acts meant to increase chances for safety.
7. Find at least two reactions that show the fear felt by the speaker and his companions.

## Looking Deeper

### I. "Being Scared"

What is the difference between being "scared" and "terrified"? Why is "scared" a better choice for this poem?

## II. "Our Greatest Possession . . ."

In what sense is it true that "the world when it didn't move" is "our greatest possession"? Do you believe this idea contains elements of exaggeration? Why or why not? What other similar properties of the natural world do people sometimes take for granted?

## III. A Carefully Chosen Pronoun

Do you believe those called "we" in the poem feel and respond as most Americans would, if faced by a natural disaster? Explain why or why not. What are three or more types of natural disasters that threaten different parts of America? How do they all represent similar kinds of danger?

# July

## by Elizabeth Knies

**Home state:** *New Hampshire*
**Member:** *Alice James Poetry Cooperative in Cambridge, Massachusetts*

July blows through the trees,
right through the center of town,
leaving a wide swath
redolent of roses and berries.

In kitchen larders                                    5
glass jars begin to line the shelves,
and petals wait in dishes
to be spiced and sealed.

There is no stopping the headlong rush
of bicycles, sailboats, races;                        10
bodies are strewn on beaches
like pieces of shipwreck.

Kites bob overhead
on long strings that want to fly
into the endless blue.                                15
High spirits bubble up in wide-mouthed crystal.

Light-headed life is dashing everywhere,
this way and that, laughing, laughing—
impassioned, deaf to any warning.

# For Better Reading: Playing on Your Memory

July . . .

More than the seventh month of the year, what does July mean to you?

In this poem, Elizabeth Kneis invites you to participate in a mental exercise called word association. All you do is reply with the first word or words that pop into your mind in response to one that's given.

For *snow*, you might say *cold* or *white*, *skiing* or *Christmas*, almost without thinking. The word *farm* might trigger you to respond *cows* or *barns*, *green fields* or *wheat*.

Word associations are exercises that poets and writers often ask you to make. Instead of seeking precise definitions, they tap your feelings and memories. There are no right or wrong answers, but writers usually count on their readers to feel much the same as themselves.

July. It may be *hot weather*, but it's surely *summer*, too—a season that's hard to think all bad. As you read, look for the words the writer associates with July—and compare how closely her feelings match your own.

## Questioning the Poem

1. Name two positive things the poet associates with July in stanza one. Explain how each is "redolent" or suggestive of something good.
2. In what ways is summer at its height in July? What words in stanza one make July seem full of energy and power?
3. How are the glass jars in the kitchen larder or storeroom connected with the berries in line 4? What future use will be made of the spiced, dried, and scented petals?
4. Stanza three tells of a "headlong rush" of bicycles, sailboats, races. How does this make New England seem a more likely setting than Florida or California? Name another detail supporting this setting.
5. Why would some people want to lie "strewn on beaches"? What negative comparison does this stanza contain?
6. What are three words in stanza four that indicate lively activity? What proves this stanza refers to people and their feelings about July, as well as kites and summer's fruits in "wide-mouthed crystal"?

## Looking Deeper

### I. Light-hearted or Light-headed

Give at least three examples from the poem that make July seem like a "light-hearted" time. In stanza four, the kites want to fly into "the endless blue." How could you apply this to people and their feelings in July?

According to stanza five, "light-headed life" is "dashing everywhere," always laughing, and "deaf to any warning." Considering the month is July, what warning must people not hear? Why would the poet choose to call them "light-headed," not "light-hearted"?

## II. Extending the Metaphor

The sunbathers are compared to "pieces of shipwreck." How can ship-wrecks also result from being "deaf to any warning"?

Explain how "light-headed life" and being "deaf to any warning" apply to other situations that people face in their lives, and give appropriate examples.

# from *The House on Mango Street*
## *(Three Vignettes)*

### *by Sandra Cisneros*

| | |
|---|---|
| ***Born:*** | *Chicago, Illinois, 1954* |
| ***Family background:*** | *Mexican-born father, Mexican-American mother* |
| ***Career:*** | *Poet, fiction writer, teacher of high school dropouts, college recruiter, arts administrator* |
| ***Home:*** | *San Antonio, Texas* |

## The Three Sisters

THEY CAME WITH THE WIND that blows in August, thin as a spider web and barely noticed. Three who did not seem to be related to anything but the moon. One with laughter like tin and one with eyes of a cat and one with hands like porcelain. The aunts, the three sisters, *las comadres*, they said.

The baby died. Lucy and Rachel's sister. One night a dog cried, and the next day a yellow bird flew in through an open window. Before the week was over, the baby's fever was worse. Then Jesus came and took the baby with him far away. That's what their mother said.

Then the visitors came . . . in and out of the little house. It was hard to keep the floors clean. Anybody who had ever wondered what color the walls were came and came to look at that little thumb of a human in a box like candy.

I had never seen the dead before, not for real, not in somebody's living room for people to kiss and bless themselves and light a candle for. Not in a house. It seemed strange.

They must've known, the sisters. They had the power and could sense what was what. They said, Come here, and gave me a stick of gum. They smelled like Kleenex or the inside of a satin handbag, and then I didn't feel afraid.

What's your name, the cat-eyed one asked.

Esperanza, I said.

Esperanza, the old blue-veined one repeated in a high thin voice. Esperanza ... a good good name.

My knees hurt, the one with the funny laugh complained.

Tomorrow it will rain.

Yes, tomorrow, they said.

How do you know? I asked.

We know.

Look at her hands, cat-eyed said.

And they turned them over and over as if they were looking for something.

She's special.

Yes, she'll go very far.

Yes, yes, hmmm.

Make a wish.

A wish?

Yes, make a wish. What do you want?

Anything? I said.

Well, why not?

I closed my eyes.

Did you wish already?

Yes, I said.

Well, that's all there is to it. It'll come true.

How do you know? I asked.

We know, we know.

Esperanza. The one with marble hands called me aside. Esperanza. She held my face with her blue-veined hands and looked and looked at me. A long silence. When you leave you must remember always to come back, she said.

What?

When you leave you must remember to come back for the others. A circle, understand? You will always be Esperanza. You will always be Mango Street. You can't erase what you know. You can't forget who you are.

Then I didn't know what to say. It was as if she could read my mind, as if she knew what I had wished for, and I felt ashamed for having made such a selfish wish.

You must remember to come back. For the ones who cannot leave as easily as you. You will remember? She asked as if she was telling me. Yes, yes, I said a little confused.

Good, she said rubbing my hands. Good. That's all. You can go.

I got up to join Lucy and Rachel who were already outside waiting by the door, wondering what I was doing talking to three old ladies who smelled like cinnamon. I didn't understand everything they had told me. I turned around. They smiled and waved in their smoky way.

Then I didn't see them. Not once, or twice, or ever again.

## Alicia & I Talking on Edna's Steps

I LIKE ALICIA BECAUSE ONCE SHE gave me a little leather purse with the word GUADALAJARA stitched on it, which is home for Alicia, and one day she will go back there. But today she is listening to my sadness because I don't have a house.

You live right here, 4006 Mango, Alicia says and points to the house I am ashamed of.

No, this isn't my house I say and shake my head as if shaking could undo the year I've lived here. I don't belong. I don't ever want to come from here. You have a home, Alicia, and one day you'll go there, to a town you remember, but me I never had a house, not even a photograph . . . only one I dream of.

No, Alicia says. Like it or not you are Mango Street, and one day you'll come back too.

Not me. Not until somebody makes it better.

Who's going to do it? The mayor?

And the thought of the mayor coming to Mango Street makes me laugh out loud.

Who's going to do it? Not the mayor.

## A House of My Own

NOT A FLAT. NOT AN apartment in back. Not a man's house. Not a daddy's. A house all my own. With my porch and my pillow, my pretty purple petunias. My books and my stories. My two shoes waiting beside the bed. Nobody to shake a stick at. Nobody's garbage to pick up after.

Only a house quiet as snow, a space for myself to go, clean as paper before the poem.

## Mango Says Goodbye Sometimes

I LIKE TO TELL STORIES. I tell them inside my head. I tell them after the mailman says, Here's your mail. Here's your mail he said.

I make a story for my life, for each step my brown shoe takes. I say, "And so she trudged up the wooden stairs, her sad brown shoes taking her to the house she never liked."

I like to tell stories. I am going to tell you a story about a girl who didn't want to belong.

We didn't always live on Mango Street. Before that we lived on Loomis on the third floor, and before that we lived on Keeler. Before Keeler it was Paulina, but what I remember most is Mango Street, sad red house, the house I belong but do not belong to.

I put it down on paper and then the ghost does not ache so much. I write it down and Mango says goodbye sometimes. She does not hold me with both arms. She sets me free.

One day I will pack my bags of books and paper. One day I will say goodbye to Mango. I am too strong for her to keep me here forever. One day I will go away.

Friends and neighbors will say, What happened to that Esperanza? Where did she go with all those books and paper? Why did she march so far away?

They will not know I have gone away to come back. For the ones I left behind. For the ones who cannot out.

# For Better Reading: A Series of Vignettes

In art, a *vignette* is a drawing or photograph that shades gradually toward the edges so there's no visible separation between the artwork and its border.

In writing, a *vignette* is similar to a quickly drawn sketch. And, like photographic vignettes, these brief sketches from *The House on Mango Street* lack well-defined beginnings and endings. They have no fully described characters nor highly detailed plots.

Instead, you share the feelings and thoughts of the first person narrator, a girl called Esperanza. In Spanish, her name means "promise" or the expectation of wishes coming true.

In reading these vignettes, you'll find it helpful to approach them as if they were poetry. By associating your feelings with Esperanza's, you'll discover what life on Mango Street is like.

## Inference

1. At their arrival on Mango Street, the three sisters (a) gave an open house for their neighbors (b) came by the light of a full moon (c) faced superstitious distrust (d) were hardly noticed by their neighbors.
2. Since the three sisters called themselves *comadres* or co-mothers, the reader should conclude (a) Lucy and Rachel were adopted (b) Lucy and Rachel's parents were divorced (c) the aunts shared in the girls' upbringing (d) the aunts were younger than they looked.
3. Esperanza described the three sisters as differing only in (a) the degree to which they "had the power" (b) whether they smelled like cinnamon, Kleenex, or the "inside of a satin handbag" (c) what they foresaw in Esperanza's future (d) details such as having "blue-veined hands" or being "cat-eyed."

## Questioning the Selection

### The Three Sisters
1. By stating "Before the week was over, the baby's fever was worse," what superstitious connections does Esperanza make concerning the baby's death?
2. Besides calling to show respect, what other reason did visitors have for coming to the sisters' house?
3. What proves the sisters did not know Esperanza before this visit? What made it appear they "had the power" and "could sense what was what," even before telling her to make a wish?

4. After being told "you must remember to come back," Esperanza felt ashamed. What must she have wished?

## Looking Deeper

### I. "In Their Smoky Way"

As Esperanza leaves the sisters, why do her feelings seem blurry and uncertain, like a photographic vignette? The sister with marble hands said, "You can't erase what you know. You can't forget who you are." In what ways is this statement true or untrue for everyone? Does the fact that Esperanza never saw the sisters again tend to support or disprove this statement? Explain the reasons behind your belief.

## Questioning the Selection

### *Alicia & I Talking on Edna's Steps*
5. Why does Esperanza feel that her friend Alicia, who came from Guadalajara, Mexico, is luckier than she? How does Esperanza feel about her house and life on Mango Street?
6. While talking to Alicia, how long did Esperanza say she had lived on Mango Street?
7. Why would Esperanza "laugh out loud" at the thought of the mayor coming to Mango Street?
8. Esperanza says she wouldn't come back to Mango Street until "somebody makes it better." Considering the references to the mayor, evaluate the possibilities of this happening.

## Looking Deeper

### II. "Like It or Not . . ."

Alicia says, "Like it or not you are Mango Street ..." What similar idea did the sister "with marble hands" express to Esperanza in the previous vignette?

## Questioning the Selection

### *A House of My Own*
9. By naming what kind of house she wants, Esperanza also reveals what she dislikes about the house on Mango Street. What do the four items beginning with "Not" reveal about the place she lives?

10. After stating, "A house all my own," Esperanza says she wants "my pretty purple petunias," and "my books and my stories." What does each tell of her interests?

11. What three problems in her present situation are revealed in the final sentence? List an example from the previous paragraph that underscores each of the three problems.

***Mango Says Goodbye Sometimes***

12. How do the first two paragraphs prove that Esperanza's story of "a girl who didn't want to belong" is really about herself?

13. How many places does Esperanza mention having lived before? How might this and the amount of time she's lived on Mango Street affect her feeling "I do not belong"?

14. Esperanza says Mango Street sometimes "sets me free." How does she herself make this happen?

15. Twice, Esperanza mentions only two things that she will pack and take with her when she goes away. What are these, and how will they make her "too strong" for Mango Street "to keep me here forever"?

# Looking Deeper

## III. Filling in the Picture

From these vignettes, give a fuller description of Esperanza's neighborhood as you envision it. Include the part of the country where it's located, the size of the town or city, the type of housing, the kinds of people who live there, and any other appropriate details you wish to add.

Esperanza wants to come back some day for "the ones I left behind . . . the ones who cannot out." Who are they, and what does her desire show about Esperanza herself—"who she is" and "what she knows"?

# First Impressions

## from *The Third Life of Per Smevik*

### *by Ole Rolvaag*

| | |
|---|---|
| ***Born:*** | *1876 in Norway* |
| ***Early life:*** | *Fisherman in homeland* |
| ***In America:*** | *Came to farm in South Dakota at age 20, worked as door-to-door salesman and did odd jobs to attend college* |
| ***Adult life:*** | *Author, teacher at St. Olaf College in Minnesota* |

*Clarkfield, South Dakota*
*August 26, 1896*

Dear Father,

Here I am at last! And now I must try to write. The worst of it is, I don't know where to begin and where to end. It's not quite a month since I left home, but it seems like an eternity—and a long one at that! It is as if I have already lived two lives here on earth: the first was in Smeviken, and that lasted almost twenty-one years. The second one I lived through on the trip from Smeviken in Helgeland to Clarkfield, South Dakota. Now I am about to begin a third. Strangely enough, although the second life lasted only a little more than three weeks, it seemed much longer than the first. God alone knows how long the third will last or how long it will seem, and only He knows if I will ever experience a fourth life!

These were my thoughts this morning when Uncle Hans woke me with, "Now you must get up and have some 'brakkfest'." "Brakkfest" is English, of course, but what it means, I haven't the slightest idea. I thought it must be something to eat but I can't imagine what kind of food it is. All we had was bread, butter, eggs, fried pork and coffee—and something strange in a glass, which we spread on our bread. It was sweet and awfully good. Perhaps that's what is called "brakkfest." I didn't like to ask about it, you see, because it seemed so dumb not to understand such a simple word. In Norwegian, I suppose we would have called it "American syrup." Oh well, I'll find out sometime.

Uncle Hans looks about the same as he did when he left us twelve years ago. He has kept house for the same man for eleven years now, and believe me, he is good at it; the house is so clean and tidy that the rooms fairly shine. And such good meals he makes! But then he has plenty to work with; there is certainly no shortage of supplies here. Uncle Hans says that he has arranged with his boss to let me stay here for the first few weeks so I can get my bearings before I look for a job. He certainly must realize that I can't afford to spend two weeks doing nothing—that I have come to America to make money! However I thought it best not to say anything just yet.

America is surely a strange country. Would you believe that the *men* do all the chores? They don't get out of it even on Sunday. I wonder if I will have to milk. Well, if they demand that of me, then—! That isn't so unlikely either; the boss teased me this evening by saying that he wouldn't expect me to milk all seventeen cows—not tonight, at least. But he hinted that if I'm going to stay in America I will certainly have to learn how. Well, "That's some butter," as the old lady in the fairy tale said when she got lard on her bread. I simply will not do it. Imagine! A grown man sitting down to pull at cow teats, a man as dairy maid, as *chore boy!*

I know, of course, that on some of the big farms in Norway hired men worked in the barns, but they were the laughing stock of all the young people and we called them names that certainly aren't found in any Bible. No, before I do that kind of work I'll give myself up to the Indians. (Haven't seen any Indians yet, even though I have traveled across most of America. This seems quite odd. From all the Indian stories we read at home I should have thought that every grove would be swarming with them.)

But now I absolutely can't write any more. I'm still tired from the trip and my eyes won't stay open any longer. I'll write to Andreas and tell about my trip. That will be a terribly long letter, so I thought I'd write a little each evening until the story is told. Hope this finds you all well, and that you have already written.

Your devoted son,<br>
Peder Andersen

My address is:   P. Andersen
<br>                       Clarkfield P.O.
<br>                       Beaker County, South Dakota
<br>                       U.S.A.

Clarkfield, South Dakota<br>
September 2, 1896

Dear Brother,

If I'd had any idea how much I would see and experience on my trip over I would never have promised to write about everything, for that would fill a book. In fact I doubt that I could get it all into one volume. It certainly seems as if no one has time to write books in America, not the men anyway. I haven't seen many women yet, so I don't know if they can write books.

It is absolutely impossible for me to describe how I felt as I stood alone on the pier and watched the boys sail home in that boat I was so fond of—well, fond of the boys too, of course. I assure you that at that moment I had no more desire to go to America than I had to throw myself right into the sea. As a matter of fact, I've never had any great longing for America.

But, there I stood on the pier and stared after the boys and the boat until they had completely disappeared behind Skarvholmen on the other side of the fjord. When the last corner of the square sail was gone, I felt as if a door closed within me and a room was locked forever. But people were coming and going on the dock and I couldn't stand there gaping like a fool, so I sauntered up to the store and went in as if there were nothing at all the matter with me. Can you guess what I did then? I went right up to the counter and bought a neat little pipe and half a pound of shredded Langaard's tobacco. You remember I quit smoking last winter at Lofoten and haven't had so much as a taste since, but I got so desperately lonesome as I stood around waiting for the coastal steamer that I had to do something. So I sat and smoked. Perhaps I shouldn't have done it for now you shall hear what happened.

This tobacco lasted me most of the trip, until the second day on the train from New York to South Dakota. By that time there was nothing left but the crust in my pipe. It was lonely enough to walk about there on the pier waiting for the boat, but it was ten times worse to sit in that crowded train hour after hour, watching the endless bustle of people getting on and off, and listening to the incessant drone of voices without understanding a single word. Well yes, I did hear the word "money" many times and I knew at least that much English. I had noticed that every once in a while a young fellow in a uniform, a regular dandy, came through the car with a basket full of all kinds of good things which he sold to the passengers. In the basket he had the nicest looking apples and oranges, and many other fruits and good things that I did not recognize. I surely would have liked some of those too, but even more I wanted a good pipeful of tobacco. So once when he came past me, I resolutely grabbed hold of his leg. Then he had to stop, you see. I held out my pipe and made signs that I wanted something in it. Yes indeed. He understood Norwegian remarkably well. He sat down beside me and from his basket brought out a beautiful packet all wrapped up in silver paper. They must have plenty of money here in this country. Now the question was how much did this packet cost? I asked in Norwegian, but he only shook his head and laughed. So I held up one hand and stretched out all five fingers, but do you suppose that was enough? Oh no! He immediately held up both hands and I understood that he wanted ten for it, but ten of what I had no idea. I brought out the only American coin I had left, and on it was written "one dime." This and a Norwegian five-øre piece was all the money I had. As soon as I showed him the coin, he grinned in approval, so I gave it to him and took the packet.

True enough, I'd had no food for a day and a half except a bit of dry bread, and now that was all gone; and I didn't know how much longer it would be before I arrived. But I also knew from previous experience that tobacco silences hunger pangs rather well. Besides I had gone without food for as long as three whole days and survived, so I supposed I could survive this time too. If worst came to worst, I still had the five-øre piece. It has the Norwegian crown on it and surely must be worth something even in this foreign land. I took the tobacco and the fellow even gave me a box of matches besides. Well, the package turned out to be better in appearance than in reality. The tobacco was dry as dust so it burned too fast and made my tongue sore. Not all products are first class in America.

But now I can't write any more tonight. I think I have already written a lot. This week I've just rested and tried to learn a little of this and that on the farm. Tomorrow we begin haying, and then I'll have a real job, and be paid full wages. Goodnight for now.

### September 3

Believe me, today I have been put to the test! I was up with the hired man at daybreak, helped him as well as I could with the barn chores, and most of the day tried to do my share. Was it hard work! And so hot—especially late in the afternoon. I could feel the sweat running all the way down into my shoes. As luck would have it, towards five o'clock my nose began to bleed and even though I stuffed grass into both nostrils I could not get it to stop. There was nothing else for me to do but quit working. I can't tell you how disgusted I was that I couldn't last the whole day. I wanted to show these fellows that I was just as good a worker as any of them, which they certainly won't believe now. I am positive they talked about me as I went home, that I could understand from a few words I heard, even if I don't know any English. But just wait! The day will come when I'll do my share as well as any one of them, and perhaps even a little better. This evening, however, I ache in every joint and my hand shakes so I can scarcely hold the pen. You can see that in America life is not all leisure. I'll write about the work and everything else later.

Before I crawl into bed I'll tell you about how I found Uncle Hans. It was like this: You remember how Uncle always wrote "Peary P.O." in his address? I thought this must be the name of the farm he worked on. Now I know better. In America, you see, farms don't have any names. How do they keep things straight then? I wish I knew! I'll explain that later when I've had a chance to find out. "Peary P.O." is the name of the post office where he gets his mail, and is seven English miles from the farm where he works. Uncle Hans wrote in his last letter that I should get off the train in Clarkfield, and he would meet me at the station.

### September 4

Saturday evening the twenty-fifth of August, three days after I got on the train in New York, I was put off in Clarkfield. Actually, I should have said thrown off, for the immigrant is handled like a piece of freight; he is pushed and shoved and pointed along, sometimes he is even kicked and pinched forward—that I saw in New York. If I had gotten that kind of treatment you can bet I would have pinched back! But what can you do when you are in a strange country and you don't understand a syllable of what is said, and where everything moves like lightning? You just have to bite your tongue and take it, and be thankful to get where you are going.

As soon as I came out on the platform I began to look around for Uncle Hans, or for someone who resembled the picture of him I had in my mind's eye. Every now and then I stepped forward thinking I saw a familiar face. There must have been two or three hundred people at the station, so that made it easier to make a mistake. Little by little the crowd thinned out, but still no Uncle Hans. Each time I mustered up enough courage to greet someone with a face that could have been his, I got only a surprised smile and a shake of the head. Stones for bread is a poor diet, but smiles and strange faces instead of uncles is certainly not much better—especially towards evening in a strange place when one is dead tired and has only an old Norwegian five-øre piece in his pocket. One by one, the people disappeared until at last I stood there alone.

Then and there I could have used some good advice. Finally an official came out and spoke to me; he used both words and gestures, but still I couldn't make out a single syllable of what he said. English is certainly difficult to understand. After he had gone back inside I sat right down on the station platform and began to study the situation. Perhaps Uncle Hans would come later? It could be that the train had been early, for it had gone at breakneck speed at times. Well, there I sat and pondered. It came to me as a comforting thought that Uncle Hans must be somewhere nearby.

While I sat there thinking about my problem, I saw six men come walking along the tracks toward the station. They carried spades and pickaxes over their shoulders, and tin pails in their hands. I could tell by their clothes they were working men. Suddenly the thought struck me that one of these must be Uncle Hans. As they came nearer I took special notice of a tall fair man with a blond mustache. My heart pounded with joy. It's true, the man looked somewhat older than I expected Uncle Hans to look, but then I knew that people aged faster over here in this country. When they got close I stood up and greeted them politely, but they just nodded and went on into the station. Then my heart sank! The sun was already setting and by now I was so hungry my stomach growled and I was terribly thirsty as well. This began to look very strange.

Suddenly the blond man came out again and walked over to me. Without further ceremony he asked in Swedish, "Are you Scandinavian?" I would never have believed I could be so happy to see a Swede. And I can assure you that never have words sounded sweeter than those Swedish words sounded to me then. I could have hugged that good-hearted fellow right on the spot. I began to explain that I was on my way to Peary P.O., and that I had an Uncle named Hans Hansen, or Hans Hansen Smevik. Did he know him?—No, he had never heard of him.—Well, that didn't matter; if I could only get directions to Peary, I could certainly find my way form there.—But it's more than seven miles.—Oh, that was nothing! Seven, eight English miles were only a little more than one Norwegian mile, and to walk one Norwegian mile was nothing, even if I was tired. At least that's what I thought then. He didn't know the way but could easily find out, and back into the station he went to get directions. Soon he returned and explained carefully: I was to walk two miles straight that way and then I would come to a crossroad; from there I must go north exactly four miles; there I would find another crossroad; then I should go west. It was only one and a half miles to Peary from that corner. Clearly and distinctly he repeated the entire explanation; slowly and carefully I said each word after him to fasten them even better in my memory. Thereupon I thanked him heartily for the information.

Just as I was about to start off, he asked in Swedish, "Are you very hungry?" I felt my face turn red. I had never begged for food, but—this was not exactly begging. In my best Swedish, I stammered bashfully, "Yes, I'm rather hungry." At this the Swede laughed heartily, went into the station, and came out again with his tin pail. From it he took some bread and butter and a bottle half-full of cold coffee. "If you're that hungry, I think this will go down!" With these words he handed me both the sandwich and the coffee. And down it went. I drank the coffee in one gulp and the sandwich quickly followed. Again I said good-bye, this time even more heartily. "God bless his good Swedish heart," I said to myself many times as I walked along the country road. And now I shall ask one thing of you, Andreas, and you must ask Mother and Father too: Whenever a Swede comes drifting in to Smeviken, as so often happens, be kind to him, no matter how ragged and dirty he is. Don't forget!

As I trudged along the road, my courage rose several degrees. Life was not so bad after all. It's wonderful how a friendly Swede with a sandwich and a little cold coffee can brighten the outlook of a tired and hungry young man. I was in such good humor that I began to whistle as I hurried along. It was so stifling hot that first I shed my coat, then the vest. My shirt was unpardonably dirty, but that was no wonder for I hadn't had it off since I put it on in Smeviken. Fortunately dusk was coming on, so if I happened to meet someone it wouldn't be noticed anyway.

Well, I said it was fortunate dusk was coming on—but actually it was unfortunate because it got dark so terribly fast which I should have known had I given it any thought. But it's not always so easy to keep everything in mind. It was almost completely dark by the time I reached the first crossroad. Sure enough, there were four roads, and here I was to go north. But now I was in a fix. Believe it or not, I couldn't decide which way was north! Of course you will think this was stupid of me, but I assure you that the same thing would have happened to you. Suddenly the thought struck me that surely the sun must set in the west here just as it does everywhere else, and I scanned the horizon to see where the sun had gone down. It had already set but on the horizon to the northeast (or what I thought was northeast) there was still a faint streak of red. The only conclusion I could draw from this was that in America the sun sets in the north or northeast. It makes me laugh now, when I think back on my stupidity. Anyway I took the road that I thought went north, but which actually led west.

By now I had walked two miles, so there should be less than six left. But what a landscape! I know you won't believe this, but it was flat as the flattest floor in our house at home. I could see no houses anywhere, only endless fields and meadows. Some of the fields were freshly plowed; others seemed to have just been cut, for there were shocks of grain in long rows as far as the eye could see. My feet were beginning to hurt so I took off my shoes and socks. Then I really put on speed! I walked and walked, and occasionally I ran. I wanted to reach Uncle Hans's place before everyone went to bed. Once after having raced along for quite a distance I stopped to catch my breath and rest awhile. This was beginning to wear me out.

It had been completely dark for some time. The stars twinkled and shone brightly, and that seemed to give me courage—although I can't really say I was afraid either. But good heavens! There was the North Star directly to the east! This made me so discouraged and upset that I sat right down in the middle of the road. The only conclusion I could draw from this was that either the North Star was off course, or the sun was, or I was. And no matter how much I disliked the idea, I had to admit that I was the one. What I had taken for north or northeast was west, just as it ought to have been. Instead of going north at the first crossroads, I had gone west. The North Star can be depended upon, this I knew from that dreadful night when we sailed from Fleinvær to Værøy without a compass. My situation now was not much better. At this moment I would gladly have traded a stormy night on the Vestfjord for this summer night on the prairie. Now what should I do? Should I walk back to the last crossroads? That would take at least three quarters of an hour or more, as tired as I was. Or should I continue along this road until I found people, for there must be some people in the vicinity; there were, after all, cultivated fields all around. My legs ached and I was so exhausted that I chose the latter. This road would just have to lead wherever and to whomever it would. If necessary I could always sneak into a barn and sleep in the hay.

I walked more slowly now to save my strength so I could hold out longer. For the first time I noticed that the night was alive around me; I heard a steady monotonous humming and buzzing. It whirred and whirred and whirred all around me. Suddenly I stopped dead in my tracks. "Indians!" I thought. "Now you'll see, in a moment they'll take your scalp!" I might as well admit it; at that moment, I was scared. Instinctively I felt back on my hip for my sheath knife, but of course it was in my trunk. Soon I realized that it couldn't possibly be redskins, because the sound was too steady and monotonous, and it blended so well into the darkness around me. It seemed to come from every straw and stem and from every particle of dust in the air. (Uncle Hans told me later it was insects I heard.)

I calmed down after I gave up all thoughts of scalping and even began to whistle a little. Imagine my joy when suddenly I saw a light by the side of the road not far ahead of me. Maybe there were Norwegians living there? Then there would be both food and a bed for me and I could find out the way to Uncle Hans and amble over in the morning. How wonderful it would be to crawl into bed. In high spirits I sat down on the edge of the road and pulled on my shoes and socks; it would never do to come in barefooted.

Soon I reached the house. With my heart in my throat, I knocked on the door.

"Come in," called a man's deep voice from within. Hmm, this sounded just like Norwegian. Boldly I opened the door and stepped in. Coming in from the dark I was blinded by the bright light, so it took a moment before I could get my bearings and say hello properly. The family sat around the table eating supper. In response to my greeting, I got nothing but blank looks. Some of them sat there staring at me with their mouths full of half-chewed food. I thought perhaps they had not understood me so I repeated my greeting, slowly and distinctly. I even added "Bless the food" so they might know that I was properly brought up, and not just a common tramp. The man just shook his head and said something that I couldn't understand.

Of course I got flustered, especially when I looked around the room and saw how elegant everything was. But they all looked so kind that I took courage and began to explain and gesture. First I mentioned Peary, and then pointed this way and that. Yes, the man understood me. And he began to talk and to point, point and talk, but I understood nothing except the pointing—and not much of that either, for first he pointed here and then there, until he had pointed to all the corners of the earth. I thought, however, that he meant I could either go back to the crossroad where I had gone wrong, and go north from there, or else I could continue on to the next crossroad, and go north and then east.

It was easy enough for him to sit before a table full of food and point to the four corners of the earth, not quite so easy for me to get there. Oh, how tempted I was to ask for food. And that I could have gotten him to understand, too, but I have never begged and I never will either. I'd croak first. With a longing look at the food that would have brought tears to the eye of any kind hearted Nordlander, I said "Thank you" and "Good night." With that I left. (Uncle told me today this was an Irish family.)

It seemed even darker when I came out again. What in the world should I do now? I wanted more than anything else to lie right down there by the side of the road and sleep for now I was dead tired. I might have done it too, if it hadn't been for my stomach; it literally gnawed down there under my ribs, I was so hungry. The Swede's coffee and sandwich had long since disappeared.

After thinking it over awhile I decided it was best to continue on in the same direction. Again I took off my coat and vest and set out. I walked and walked. My feet were tender and sore, but I trudged on just the same. At last I was so tired I just had to sit down. Although the grass at the side of the road was stiff and tall, it was a great relief to stretch out and rest there. And do you know what I saw as I lay there? No, Andreas, I doubt that you do, for I saw Smeviken! It seemed as though I lay on the hillside in front of our house. I saw the bay lying mirror-like before me; now and then there was a rippling in the water. And as clear as day I could see our boat (yours, I suppose I should say now) moored there, and could even hear the lapping of the waves as they reached the boat and slapped gently against the sides. I would have given any one of my limbs at that moment if I could have traded the vision for reality.

Finally I became so melancholy that I sat up, reached for my pipe, and began to smoke. No, it wasn't the smartest thing to do, you're right about that, but then we don't always live according to reason.

Suddenly I awoke from my reverie when the grass rustled beside me. In spite of my weariness I shot up and listened breathlessly. No sound came. That was strange, I thought, so I struck a match and looked down at the ground. This time, I tell you, your brother was scared—for there lay a snake coiled up right beside me. It raised its head, flicked its tongue in and out, and hissed horribly. I didn't stick around there very long, you may be sure! I ran—no, flew down the road. Every now and then I thought I heard a rustling in the grass, first on one side of the road and then the other. I ran and ran for at least a quarter of an hour until I couldn't take it any longer, and had to slow down to a walk. Little by little that dreadful fear left me but as the fear left, the tiredness returned. I dragged one foot after the other. Oh how sore they were! Each step was torture. Now after seeing the snake, I didn't dare take my shoes off again. In the midst of my weariness the thought came to me that perhaps this was to be my last night on earth. I went so far as to begin to make my peace with God. I can't say that I felt any special fear of death. It just seemed so ironic that I should die of exhaustion and hunger, right here in the promised land—and then likely be eaten up by serpents, too. And it was too bad to die now, just as I was about to begin a new life.

These sad thoughts were suddenly interrupted when a short distance ahead of me I saw the silhouette of a house against the dark night sky. In front of the house a man was working with a team of horses and a wagon; it looked as if he were just hitching up. I went up to him, and as boldly as I could, said "Good evening." I assure you that when he answered in broad Trondheim dialect, I was so happy that I was close to tears. It sounds silly, I know, but I doubt that even you would have felt any different. Could he tell me the way to Peary? Oh yes, I had a straight road from the corner here to Peary. (For "road" he used a word I had never heard, but I understood what he meant.) And now I noticed that I stood right at a crossroads.—How far was it?—About six miles.—Six miles! Did he know a man hereabouts by the name of Hans Hansen?—Yes, of course. He knew him very well. I could have hugged that man, I was so happy.—Did he live far from here?—About five miles.—That far?—Yes, was I looking for him?—Yes. Then I told him who I was, that I had just come from Norway, that Hans Hansen was my uncle.—Well then, I could just sit up beside him on the wagon, for he was driving right past the place on his way home. I didn't say much on that ride, though the Trondheimer asked and asked for news from Norway. I just sat there the whole time and wondered what good deed I could do for this man, or how I could best show my gratitude when I became rich.

We arrived there safe and sound. Uncle Hans was so happy that he nearly cried when I came. He hadn't expected me in Clarkfield until the next day, and had all the time worried that I would get lost. I came in and washed up, and was given good food also, but best of all was certainly the bed. And that's where I am headed now, for it is way past midnight. I have been writing this letter for four nights, and it is almost a book. I'll put three stamps on it to make sure it gets there. I have written so much because both you and Father warned me not to do as the others who went to America, and never bothered to write home.

You will have to read this letter to Mother and Father. Hearty greetings to you all, especially Mother!

Your loving brother,
*Peder Andersen Smevik*

P.S. Next time I will write to Father. I plan to change about and write one letter to you and the next to him. Don't forget to tell all about the summer herring, both the net fishing and the trawling. Uncle Hans sends greetings.

*P.A.S.*

*Clarkfield, South Dakota*
*September 11, 1896*

Dear Andreas,

How are you, Brother? Here comes a letter from America. Actually this one should have been addressed to Father, but I don't suppose it matters who gets the letter, just so someone does. You know I have to be careful when I write Father; though he is only a fisherman, he has had some education, and is very critical, but to you I can fire away as I please.

I hope this letter finds you in the best of health and victorious in your fight with the cod. How many of those fellows have you nabbed since I left you this summer? Yes, summer! For it is still summer here even though it is the middle of September, and so hot during the day that I am tempted to wear only my birthday suit.

America is certainly a peculiar country. Here everything is topsy-turvy. Take the summer for example. Even this late in the season it is hotter than in the middle of July at home in Smeviken. By eight o'clock in the evening it is already dark as night. The food and mealtimes are even more upside-down. Here they eat only three times a day, but the evening meal does come as early as six o'clock. The food is very good, mostly meat and potatoes, white bread and jam. Bread and butter is served at every meal, and so is coffee. They have such curious names for their meals. Even Uncle Hans, whose dialect is the same as mine, calls the evening meal "supper," the noon meal "dinner," and the morning meal "breakfast." Yes, now I know what Uncle Hans meant that first morning when he told me to get up and have some "brakkfest." And I thought it was some kind of food!

So it is with other things too, especially the names of dishes, tools and even buildings. It is almost impossible to know what they mean. Uncle Hans calls some of the dishes we use "plait" and "pitsher"; the stove is "stoven," monkey wrench is "maunkirenshen," the cowshed is "barn," and the summer kitchen is "kukshenti." Of course this is English, so you see I have learned quite a bit already. But don't you ever believe that this is all I have learned in these two weeks. I bet I could come up with at least a hundred words if I wanted to, but that would give you no pleasure. However I can't say I like their way of talking; they could just as well use Norwegian words when they speak Norwegian. But they don't do that; they stick in English words here and there. If Uncle Hans came home now and spoke Norwegian the way he does here, you would think it was English and I am sure you couldn't possibly understand all he said.

It is very embarrassing when Uncle Hans tells me to do something; I stand there like a fool—a real nincompoop who can't understand a thing. I know very well that I'm not dumb, but they don't know that here. This evening Uncle Hans told me to "Take this 'svill peil' and 'slabba pigsa'." That stumped me. I did understand "pigsa" meant the pigs, but "svill peil" and "slabba" were beyond me. Even such a smart fellow as you think you are could not have understood that command. Well, in good Norwegian we would say, "Take this swill pail and feed the pigs." That is what it means!

When I began this letter I intended to tell you a little about my trip over. I saw and heard so much it's hard to know where to begin and where to end. I must try to tell a little anyway.

The trip to Trondheim on the coastal steamer was fine. There was nothing left of my lunch when I got there and I was desperately hungry, as usual. My, what a big city I thought it was. You remember how you and Father warned me to be careful and not get lost in the big cities. It was good advice indeed. And if you ever intend to venture out into the world I beg you to heed the same advice. Never mind wrinkling your nose at that, even though you have been to Tromsø, Hammerfest, and Vardø. I assure you, and I mean no slight by it, those towns of yours up North are only dinky little burgs; not even a baby could get lost there. But come to Chicago! Or New York! There you would have to follow your own advice. I was pretty careful in Trondheim; each time I went out, I noted the streets and paid particular attention to the corners and signs. All went well as long as I was in Norway where I could read; it wasn't quite so easy here where I couldn't understand a word.

The trip by train from Trondheim to Oslo was interesting. I saw much that was beautiful. The fine, broad country around Lake Mjøsa impressed me as it lay there smiling in the sun. I thought Eidsvoll the most beautiful place I saw on this trip. But mountains? No, to see mountains there is no other place to go but to Nordland.

Oslo seemed awfully big, much bigger than Trondheim. I saw neither the King nor the Queen, nor do I care much; expect they were in Sweden at the time. I am a republican now and have lost all interest in kings.

At the emigrant hotel in Oslo I met two Swedes who were also going to America. One was from Gothenburg, the other from Värmland. We were assigned to the same room and soon became good friends. They had been in the city two whole days before I came, and one of them was born and raised in Gothenburg—a really big city, he said. We spent the two days we had in the city tramping around with the Gothenburger as pilot. The last day he got the notion that we should see the art gallery. I agreed heartily without having the slightest idea what that might be. We started off in the afternoon and found the place without much trouble, thanks to the Gothenburger's perseverance in asking.

You have never seen an art gallery, Brother, and it is just as well if you never do, for frankly I can't say it was particularly uplifting. One grayish stone figure after another stood along all the walls. These figures were life-size and without a stitch of clothing on their bodies. I was dreadfully embarrassed but pretended it was nothing. I walked around in the crowd (there must have been a whole church full) and looked at those figures as if I had done nothing else in all my life but walk around among naked people. If only that Värmlander had been just as bold, but he certainly wasn't. He began to snicker as soon as we came in, and to make all kinds of indecent remarks. It didn't get really bad until we came to a giant of a fellow. A large group of men and women dressed in velvets and furs were looking at this same figure. Such shamelessness was too much for the Värmlander's honest heart. At first he only chuckled good-naturedly, but the laughter soon got the best of him. He stood doubled up, his hands on his knees and laughed until the tears rolled. Before long everyone was staring at him. I was so ashamed I could have sunk through the floor, and sneaked away as fast as I could. I didn't see him again until I went to bed that night. He was still laughing. I can't quite see why people want to show anything like that; it certainly doesn't do any good.

Oh what weeping and wailing on the pier at Oslo when the ship was ready to sail. It was enough to make one hate the thought of America. We sailed out through the Oslo fjord in the most delightful weather and in the early evening reached Kristiansand where we lay until the next forenoon. Then we set out to sea. The next landing place was to be New York. I stood on deck all afternoon. The mountains sank lower and lower into the horizon as the day waned. When nothing more could be seen but a low, rugged cloud bank, I went below, crept into my bunk and bawled like a whipped child. That was my farewell to the Fatherland.

The days on the ocean were the most glorious I have ever spent. I never expect to experience such luxury again. There was plenty to eat and the food was fairly good. The sea rolled just enough for good sleep. We had only a couple of nasty days, scarcely worth mentioning, but my goodness how sick some of those landlubbers were! I can't quite see what made them sick, for with the kind of vessel we were on I considered this fine weather and smooth sailing. Anyhow, we who were well gained by the others being sick because we got all the food we could chuck into ourselves. Of course it was gluttony, but would it have been less sinful to have thrown all that good food overboard into the sea?

I shall never forget sailing into New York—not even if I get to be twice as old as the oldest man in the Bible—which I really don't wish for in this heat. Not even if I were as good a poet as Petter Dass could I describe the sight of the city as we sailed up the Hudson River at sunrise on that sparkling morning. Sure as I'm sitting here writing this letter, I didn't come to my senses until we landed at the pier. Do you remember when Lars Johansen came home from America last winter, how we all declared he lied when he told about New York? I'll tell you what was the matter with him: he didn't lie enough! By that I mean he did not exaggerate in the least. We landed in the morning and by evening I was on the train heading for Clarkfield. Isn't it strange that of all the people I saw on board ship not one of them was on the train with me?

With this I had better close. How I got along on the train and how I found

Uncle Hans's place, you already know. Now you have the story of my trip to America. But if you are not just as faithful in return and tell me about absolutely everything from home, you will have to deal with me when I get back. Just remember that.

Your devoted brother,
*Per Smevik*

## For Better Reading: The Truth in Fiction

A piece of advice often given to would-be writers is, "Write about what you know."

Doesn't that mean writing nonfiction instead of fiction? The answer: not necessarily.

Sandra Cisneros wrote, "I put it down on paper and then the ghost does not ache so much." But she wrote these words as if a little girl named Esperanza had said them.

For writers, fiction is often a way of stepping back and getting at the truth by drawing from their own experience. It means eliminating details and adding others—sometimes to create more conflict and action, sometimes to look more deeply into characters and situations than nonfiction would allow.

Ole Rolvaag chose to write his novel, *The Third Life of Per Smevik*, as a series of letters. Its technique lets him focus on the differences between a young immigrant's life in America and the world he left behind. There are obvious similarities between Peder Andersen and Rolvaag himself, and even though they aren't his personal letters home, you can recognize their accurate picture of a young man's first experiences in America.

### Important Details

1. Peder Andersen's "second life" was (a) his teenage period from 13-19 (b) his imaginary life of dreams about coming to America (c) his journey from Norway to South Dakota (d) the world of books and education.
2. Peder's Uncle Hans is a (a) well-to-do South Dakota rancher (b) housekeeper and cook (c) chore boy in the dairy barn (d) different person after 12 years in America.
3. Because he doesn't speak English, Peder thinks that *brakkfest* means (a) wagon brake (b) American syrup (c) morning chore (d) alarm clock.

### Questioning the Selection (August 26, September 2, 3, and 4, 1896)

1. What was Peder's main purpose in coming to America? What plans of Uncle Hans prevent his starting on it at once?

2. What differences between "men's" and "women's" work made Peder call America "surely a strange country"? What did he also think "quite odd" concerning Indians?

3. Before sailing to America, how did Peder feel after being left alone on the pier?

4. How and why did Peder "throw away" his only dime on the train to South Dakota? Why was he sure he could survive on his last remaining Norwegian coin?

5. Why was Peder disgusted with himself about his first day of American farm work?

6. In addition to being broke except for one old Norwegian coin, what are three other difficulties Peder faced when he arrived at Clarkfield?

7. How was Peder first disappointed and then helped by the "tall fair man with a blond mustache"? What two changes in Peder's attitude resulted from this meeting?

8. Why did Peder become lost on the way to Uncle Hans' place? How did he discover his error, and what decision did his exhaustion cause him to make?

9. What are two reasons Peder was confused by the directions given at the first house he came to? Although the family was eating supper, why did Peder leave, still "so hungry"?

10. After stretching out at the roadside, what did Peder "see" as he lay there? What feelings caused this vision? What real and what imaginary frights made Peder run till he "couldn't take it any longer"?

11. What was Peder's "lucky break" at the second house? Why hadn't his Uncle Hans met him at Clarkfield?

## Questioning the Selection (September 11, 1896)

1. Why does Peder feel freer in writing his brother than his father? What had his father warned Peder that lead him to write "I don't suppose it matters who gets the letter"?

2. What are two things that cause Peder to say, "Here everything is topsy-turvy"?

3. Peder was writing in Norwegian but "showed off" the following words from his new English vocabulary. Try to pronounce and spell the standard versions of those you recognize: *plait, pitsher, kukshenti, svill peil,* and *slabba pigsa.*

4. Why did Peder object to the way Norwegian-Americans spoke Norwegian? Do you think his complaint valid? Why or why not?

5. What accounts for the "weeping and wailing" when Peder's ship sailed from Oslo, Norway? How was Peder's reaction different, yet similar?

6. How did Peder benefit from the "landlubbers'" seasickness? Why didn't he feel guilty?

7. Why doesn't Peder attempt to describe the ship's arrival at New York

harbor? How does he compare Lars Johansen's "lies" to his own observations?

8. By asking his brother to "tell me about absolutely everything from home," what does Peder reveal about his present feelings?

## Looking Deeper

### I. An Immigrant's Arrival

In his entry of September 4, how does Peder describe the treatment of immigrants on their journeys onward from New York? What are two possible causes of such "handling"? Do you feel behavior toward immigrants is different or similar today? Explain the reasons for your opinion.

How do unrealistic expectations affect immigrants' first impressions? Include two or three examples from this selection, your own experience, or your reading.

### II. Becoming Americanized

Peder signs his letters in three different ways. What are they, and how would you account for the differences?

Peder objected because his fellow immigrants no longer spoke good Norwegian. Why are such language changes natural?

In light of the first three letters, explain at least three ways living in America will be like a "third life" for Peder.

# Nevada Old and New

## by Ernie Pyle

| | |
|---|---|
| **Born:** | Dana, Indiana, 1900 |
| **Killed:** | Ii Shima, Ryukyu Islands in 1945 by Japanese machine gun fire |
| **Buried:** | National Memorial Cemetery, Hawaii |
| **Known as:** | America's most famous World War II newspaper correspondent, who covered London bombings, North African and South Pacific campaigns |
| **Honors:** | Pulitzer prize-winning writer |

JOSIE PEARL LIVED THIRTY-FIVE miles from the town of Winnemucca, Nevada. Lived all alone in a little tar-paper cabin, surrounded by nothing but desert. From a mile away you could hardly see the cabin amidst the knee-high sagebrush. But when you got there it seemed almost like a community—it was such a contrast in a place filled with only white sun and empty distance.

There really wasn't any road to Josie Pearl's cabin—merely a trail across space. Your creeping car was the center of an appalling cloud of dust, and the sage scratched long streaks on the fenders.

Josie Pearl was a woman of the West. She was robust, medium-sized, happy-looking, and much younger than her years, which were sixty-some; there was no gray in her hair. Her dress was calico, with an apron over it; on her head was a farmer's straw hat, on her feet a mismated pair of men's shoes, and on her left hand and wrist—six thousand dollars' worth of diamonds! That was Josie—contradiction all over, and a sort of Tugboat Annie of the desert. Her whole life had been spent in the weirdest of all professions, hunting for gold in the ground. She was a prospector. She had been at it since she was nine, playing a man's part in a man's game.

She was what I like to think of as the Old West—one day worth one hundred thousand dollars, and the next day flat broke, cooking in a mining camp at thirty dollars a month. She had packed grub on her back through twenty-below Nevada blizzards, and had spent years as the only woman among men in mining camps, yet there was nothing rough about her—she didn't drink, smoke, or swear, and her personality was that of a Middle-western farm woman.

She had been broke as much as she'd been rich; but she could walk into any bank in that part of the country and borrow five thousand dollars on five minutes' notice. She had run mining-camp boardinghouses all over the West. She had made as much as thirty-five thousand dollars in the boardinghouse business and put every cent of it into some hole in the ground. She had been married twice, but both husbands were dead now. She never depended on men, anyhow.

She had lived as long as nine years at a stretch at one of her lonely mines. She had found her first mine when she was thirteen and sold it for five thousand dollars. She had recently sold her latest mine and was well off again, but she was staying on in the desert.

Her cabin was the wildest hodgepodge of riches and rubbish I'd ever seen. The walls were thick with pinned-up letters from friends, assay receipts on ore, receipts from Montgomery Ward. Letters and boxes and clothing and pans were just thrown—everywhere. And in the middle of it all sat an expensive wardrobe trunk, with a seven-hundred-dollar sealskin coat inside.

She slept with a 30-30 rifle beside her bed, and she knew how to use it. In the next room were a pump gun and a double-barreled shotgun. And a dog. But Josie Pearl was no desert hermit, and she was not an eccentric. Far from it. She had a Ford pickup truck and when she got lonesome she would go and see somebody. She had a big Buick in town, but didn't drive it much because it made her look rich. She would put on her good clothes and take frequent trips to Reno and San Francisco. She knew the cities well and was no rube when she got there.

She talked constantly, and liked people to like her. Her favorite word was "elegant." She would say, "I have elegant friends all over the West." And, "I may tear down this cabin and build an elegant house here." Nobody could deny that Josie Pearl was elegant toward the human race. She had educated three girls and grubstaked scores of boys and found them jobs. She had nursed half the sick people in northern Nevada. She was known all over the western mining country.

She said gold brought you nothing but trouble and yet you couldn't stop looking for it. The minute you had gold, somebody started cheating you, or suing you, or cutting your throat. She couldn't even count the lawsuits she'd been in. She had lost fifteen thousand dollars, and sixty thousand, and eight thousand, and ten thousand, and I don't know how much more. "But what's eight thousand dollars?" she said. "Why, eight thousand doesn't amount to a hill of beans. What's eight thousand?" Scornfully.

People had been doing her dirt for forty years. But here's a strange thing: every person who had ever done Josie Pearl dirt had died within a couple of years. She wasn't dramatic or spooky about it when she told you, but she thought she had put the hex on them. She had been trimmed out of fortune after fortune by crooked lawyers, greedy partners, and drunken helpers. Yet she still trusted everybody. Anybody was her friend, till proved otherwise. On one hour's acquaintance she said to me, "You get your girl friend and come out and stay with me two days and I'll take you to a place where you can pick nuggets up in your hand. I'll make you rich."

Which I consider exceedingly elegant of Josie Pearl. But if I got rich I'd have lawsuits, and even one lawsuit would put me in my grave, so I started back to town—goldless and untroubled. But on the way, a stinging little flame of yellow-metal fever started burning in my head. Me? Rich? Maybe just one little old lawsuit wouldn't kill anybody.

*　*　*

Virginia City, Nevada, sits right on top of the famous Comstock Lode, the richest vein of ore ever found in America. By the late 1930s, the Comstock had produced more than seven hundred million dollars in silver and gold. It was so rich it was ridiculous. It had ore running as high as five thousand dollars a ton—while all over the West they were mining five-dollar ore at a profit.

The Comstock was discovered in 1859, when Nevada was merely a territory and there were no more than a few dozen people in it. Within a couple of eyewinks Virginia City had a population of thirty thousand. It went wild; it splattered money in its Civil War type of splendor; the great actors of the world came to perform; there was a man for breakfast every morning, as the saying goes, and in the first seventy-two murders there were but two convictions; it was in Virginia City that a Samuel Clemens started reporting on a newspaper, and assumed the pen name of Mark Twain.

For nearly twenty years Virginia City was the hottest thing between Chicago and San Francisco. And then exhaustion came to the Comstock Lode; it had given its all and could give no more, they thought. The tycoons moved out in '78.

Virginia City didn't show until we came around the last bend on the twenty-mile drive from Reno and looked straight upon it. There it clung, six thousand feet high, plastered to the side of a steep hill—a little old town surrounded and impregnated with countless old shaft houses and long gray piles of dirt and rocks from the tunnel depths. An old town set amid rolling hills and deserts.

I wanted to be impressed and excited when I came round the bend and saw this sight of my grandfather's day. But I couldn't even have that privilege. The skeleton was there, but progress had slipped inside the bones and made a mundane stirring. There was life in Virginia City again—not the old riotous life of bonanza times, but twentieth-century life, flowing just as it flowed in countless hundreds of other American towns.

Virginia City could not truthfully be called a ghost town. True, it had withered and dwindled. Where it used to sprawl for blocks up the mountainside and spill over the divide for more blocks and blocks into Gold Hill, now the slope was bare and the houses stretched a mere two blocks from "C" street. But the houses were full. You couldn't rent a house in Virginia City. The mines were working again, since Roosevelt had raised the price of gold.

Why, I wonder, can't an old place really die? Why can't it lie down amid its old drama and pose there, ghostlike, for the trembling contemplation of us latecomers?

There was an old whitish house on a sort of ledge in the hillside on the upper edge of Virginia City. There was a white fence around it, and a gate with an old-fashioned latch. An oldish man, small, a little stooped, and wearing overalls, came out and shook hands. This was Jimmy Stoddard, the Comstock's only living bridge between the distant past and the present. He had been on the Comstock for seventy-five years.

"I guess you go back further than anybody else in Virginia City, don't you?" I asked. People had told me that.

"I think you called the turn on that one, son," he said. "I think you called that one right. I guess I'm the oldest, all right."

Jimmy Stoddard arrived in Virginia City with his parents from New York in 1864. He went to work in the bowels of the Comstock when he was thirteen, and there he worked until he was seventy-one—fifty-eight years in the mines, right beneath Virginia City. Jimmy Stoddard was eighty-four, but he was still going out into the hills and prospecting around.

He was a truthful man, and admitted he didn't remember awfully much about the early days. He didn't recall that he ever saw Mark Twain; he did remember seeing many a man hanging from the beams of the shaft houses in the old days; he said he ran the cage that brought General U.S. Grant up from the mines on his visit there in '78; he said that in the boom days miners on their way to work would slip an order for stock under the bank door, and when they came out of the earth that evening they'd be five hundred dollars richer, just by speculation; and then they'd go to San Francisco and spend it all. He was one of them. His memory was clear but not spectacular. Seventy-five years is a long time to recall details and keep things straight in your head.

Not all the old-timers remembered as unspectacularly as Jimmy Stoddard. The most remarkable remembering was done by those who would tell you all about Mark Twain. It was truly amazing how sharp their recollections were. One old fellow told me that although Twain came to be known as a humorist nobody around Virginia City ever saw him smile. This old man remembered him well, even referred to him as "Sam."

He said Twain used to stand all the time in the doorway of the *Enterprise* building and spit tobacco juice onto the steps of the adjoining doctor's office, which happened to belong to this old man's uncle. So this old man—just a boy then, of course—called his uncle's attention to it, and the uncle put up a sign not to spit there. After that Twain stood in the doorway and instead of spitting on the steps he spit on the new sign.

I thought that was a grand little story, and I had a sort of thrill from talking with a man who had actually known Mark Twain in those far days when they called him "Sam." Before parting, I asked the old man his age, and he told me. When I got home I figured back on the dates, and discovered that this old man wasn't even born till a year after Mark Twain left Virginia City forever. That's the kind of memory I admire.

## For Better Reading: A Personal Filter

Whether labeled nonfiction or fiction, a piece of writing is always filtered through someone else's mind and colored by that person's way of looking at life.

For this reason, a good reader doesn't judge the truth or factualness in books, articles, or stories by their labels. You must make that decision for yourself.

In "Nevada Old and New," correspondent Ernie Pyle expresses very personal viewpoints. While some writers are quick to note and condemn all the greed and evil in people, Pyle takes people as they are and seems to like them.

As you question the selection, be aware of how much all writing, including nonfiction, is affected by its passage through a writer's personal filter that consciously or unconsciously influences its emphasis, details, and every word chosen.

## Fact or Opinion

Identify the following as fact, opinion, or a combination. Be prepared with proof to support your answer.
1. "But when you got there" (to Josie Pearl's place) "it seemed almost like a community."
2. "Her whole life had been spent in that weirdest of all professions, hunting for gold in the ground."
3. "She had been at it since she was nine, playing a man's part in a man's game."

## Questioning the Selection

1. What details of Josie Pearl's costume made her seem like a "contradiction all over"?
2. Give two examples that support Josie Pearl's being a "Tugboat Annie of the desert," a woman able to hold her own in a "man's game." What evidence supports her having "nothing rough about her"?
3. In spite of her wild "hodgepodge of riches and rubbish," Pyle believed that Josie Pearl was "not an eccentric." Compare her with Mr. Kirk in John Steinbeck's "My First Eccentric," and explain why you agree or disagree with Pyle's opinion. What proof does Pyle offer that she is "no desert hermit"?
4. What was contradictory about Josie Pearl's attitude toward gold? What might make her scornful of money?
5. Josie Pearl "still trusted everybody.... till proved otherwise." Does

Pyle lead you to admire this attitude or feel it foolish? Have evidence from the selection as support.

6. On the way back to town, how did Pyle change his mind about gold? What makes this decision humorous?
7. In describing Virginia City, what factual statistics does Pyle give of its wealth? Of its lawlessness? How does the saying "there was a man for breakfast every morning" relate to crime reports in a daily newspaper?
8. Describe two changes taking place in Virginia City about twenty years after discovery of the Comstock Lode. Why was Ernie Pyle disappointed to see Virginia City in the 20th century?
9. Why did Pyle call Jimmy Stoddard "Comstock's only living bridge"?
10. What conclusion does Pyle draw about Stoddard's admission that he "didn't remember awfully much about the early days" and "didn't recall" seeing Mark Twain? How is Stoddard contrasted with the oldtimer who referred to Twain as "Sam"?

# Looking Deeper

## I. The "Itch" for Gold

How were Josie Pearl and Jimmy Stoddard alike in their attitude toward gold? How different? Explain at least two reasons why Pyle seemed to admire these old timers.

What is humorous and ironic about Pyle stating "That's the kind of memory I admire" about the oldtimer who "had actually known Mark Twain"? How did Pyle prove himself a good reporter in reference to this old man? Why was the oldtimer's story actually harmless, both in intent and from Pyle's point of view?

## II. A Gathering of Ghosts

Pyle would rather have found an abandoned Virginia City, left to "lie down amid its old drama" as a ghost town. What warning and reminder would it offer future generations if left to "pose there, ghostlike, for the trembling contemplation of us latecomers"? Find at least two additional quotations illustrating Pyle's highly personal approach to this nonfiction account.

# The Guided Tour of 7th Avenue

## by Leonard S. Bernstein

**Profession:** President of children's clothing manufacturing company of New York and Pennsylvania

I HAVE AGREED TO TAKE YOU to the garment center, and we begin at 7th Avenue and 38th Street where the cutters are milling around at lunchtime. I approach one of the cutters who has been here a few hundred years and say, "How's business, Benny?"

"Terrible," he answers. "Never in my entire life have I seen it as bad as this." That means business is O.K.

You ask me how terrible can mean O.K. and I consider sending you to Berlitz for a course in a foreign language.

Clack-clacking down the street come the dress racks and the dollies pushed by the blacks and Hispanics. And you ask, "How come only blacks and Hispanics—thirty years ago there were only blacks and Hispanics!—where are the whites?" And I answer that thirty years is not much time in the garment center.

And then you notice that the street signs read FASHION AVENUE, and you ask, "Why is it still called 7th Avenue when that is no longer its name?" And I answer that yes, the name was changed but change does not take hold easily here.

You don't believe me. You ask *why* is there no change? You mention Park Avenue and Madison Avenue—the breathtaking skyscrapers, the dazzling shop windows. "And here, pushcarts?" you ask.

I consider how to explain. It is difficult to explain 7th Avenue to an outsider. How to explain civilization standing still?

What the hell, I try. "You want to know why there is no change? Because it takes imaginative people to effect change, and all of them have left for the South. Do you know how long it takes to get twelve cartons of fabric up to the fifteenth floor of a garment center loft? In that amount of time a manufacturer in Georgia can sew enough dresses to clothe a medium-sized city."

You are astounded. You've heard of Bill Blass and Halston. You thought they were here. Where are they? Yes they are here, as the Taj Mahal is in India, but India is not the Taj Mahal.

You are incredulous. I don't know what to do with you. I decide to show you one of our modern industrial achievements, and we enter 257 West 36th Street where Meyer Kaufman runs forty machines making children's underwear.

I tell you that Meyer runs a pretty smart operation and you tell me that everybody smart is in Georgia. I tell you it's good that you are listening, but there remain two reasons why anyone could be left: because they make highly intricate handsewn operations and must hire the old-time workers who still remember how to stitch a buttonhole or turn a collar, or because they themselves are too old to move to Atlanta. Meyer is sixty-three.

How does Meyer compete, you want to know. I am pleased that you are asking intelligent questions, or at least questions that I am able to answer.

"On price and value Meyer cannot compete against the conveyer belts and automation of the South, but there remains customer service. There are a lot of retail stores in New York like Korvettes and Alexander's, and sometimes these stores can't wait for a shipment of underwear from Alabama. Meyer can get fifty dozen over to them on a handtruck within a few hours."

I tell Meyer I am showing my friend the garment center and he smiles. "So what are you doing *here*? This is ancient history."

Meyer is a small man with a narrow, pointed face and thin wisps of brown-grey hair wandering over his forehead. He is nervous, and makes quick, mouse-like movements, as though he fences jewelry and the cops are closing in. He welcomes us but says he only has a half hour. The union agent is coming up at 3:30—they have a labor dispute to settle. Meyer laughs. "A half million garment workers in Alabama and Georgia. No unions and no labor disputes. Only conveyer belts and laser beams."

We walk out into the shop. There are two long rows of sewing machines with operators facing each other, mostly Hispanic in bright flowered dresses, their hands and fingers fluttering over the garments.

"Piece work," Meyer says for the benefit of our guest. "They get paid for how much they produce."

Alongside the rows of sewing machines, is a long wooden cutting table with about nine inches of fabric piled up. The cutter says hello and we shake hands. The index finger is missing—not uncommon. Left-handed cutter, I think. The cutters don't lose fingers from the hand that guides the machine. It's the other hand; the one that holds the fabric in place in front of the spinning blade. The hand that guides the machine grips a wooden handle *behind* the machine, always out of danger. The other hand is brought around in front of the blade and presses down the nine inches of fabric. The blade spins forward into the V-shaped opening formed by the thumb and index finger. In an accident it is usually the index finger. There's an old joke that if you went to visit Local 12—the cutter's local—and didn't know where you were, you could find out quickly just by shaking hands.

There's a scissors on the table and I grip it just to confirm my notion. It's a left-handed scissors and I think back twenty years to when I first arrived in the garment center and didn't believe there were left-handed scissors.

Meyer says to the cutter, "Kroloff is coming up at 3:30. I'll send Mary in to let you know when he arrives. Then I'll walk out here with him, both of us together."

The cutter returns to work and Meyer starts to explain—stops—starts again. Is clearly pained. "We have to set things up when Kroloff arrives. Sam can't see ten feet in front of him. Take a look at his glasses. Madame Curie didn't have lenses like that when she discovered radium. Sam can see up close; he can see the pencil marks that guide the cutting knife, but he can't see far. If Kroloff finds out, Sam is retired on the spot. So we have a warning system. We identify Kroloff before he gets close enough to notice the problem. That way Sam gives him a big hello and Kroloff doesn't realize that Sam can't see who he is saying hello to. Today I'll walk in with Kroloff. Sam will vaguely make out two figures and right away he'll shout hello Kroloff. When we get closer he'll know because Kroloff is six inches taller than me and Sam can make that out, so he'll reach out to shake hands with the right person."

"But the cutting blade ... surely. And he's lost one finger already."

Meyer sighs, as though why am I bothering him with something he already knows. "Sam lost his finger thirty years ago when he could see perfectly. Thank God it didn't happen here. You know, they don't lose fingers because they can't see. They lose them because they think they're hot-shots and don't need to drop the guard in front of the blade."

We're back in Meyer's office. The phone rings. We turn to leave. Meyer raises his hand to say wait. Kroloff is delayed. "Sit down," Meyer says, "we can talk a while."

Meyer is tired. His eyes are bloodshot from the dust of threads and cotton shavings. He slumps in his high-backed chair, behind him a window, framed with the thin silver tape of an alarm system.

"Just as well. It's about Sam. I can't pay him the standard cutter's hourly wage any longer. Kroloff says I have to. The union contract ... something like that. What do I care? The thing is, Sam is good but of course he can't see. I have to give him a helper for anything over ten feet. The helper always has to be around, and of course he gets paid. If you add the helper to Sam their combined wages make Sam the best paid cutter in New York."

"Why can't you explain this to Kroloff?"

"Because if Kroloff suspects anything about Sam's eyesight he'll stop him from working. Maybe he's right—how do I know? The union has too much at stake. If it would ever be discovered that the union had a cutter on the job with 200/200 vision it would make the newspapers. And can you imagine what they would say about the finger? Kroloff would get indicted. I would get indicted. There would be a whole investigation. You know how those things are. The newspapers get it, it will sound like the garment center uses only blind cutters."

"What does Sam say?" I ask.

"Sam says pay him less and don't let Kroloff near him. What else is Sam going to say? This is the only company on the face of the earth where he could work."

"It's you and Sam against Kroloff," I mutter, thinking this defies any labor problem I've ever heard of. "What about letting Sam go and hiring a competent cutter? Sam's old ... he can't see...."

Meyer nods, conceding the sense of that. "Sam's old—he can't see. I'm old—I can't see so good either. A new cutter? What will I say to him after all these years?"

At that moment a young lady—slightly agitated—rushes into Meyer's office. "Kroloff is in the shop, talking to Sam," she says.

"How did he get in?" asks Meyer, but he doesn't wait for an answer.

We sit there quietly, not knowing whether to stay or to leave. In five minutes Meyer is back in the office. "Kroloff is walking around the shop, talking to the operators. He'll stop in my office in a little while and I'll introduce you."

"Shouldn't we leave now?" I ask.

"You wanted to show your friend the garment center—this is the garment center. Wouldn't you like to meet a business agent?"

Within fifteen minutes Kroloff walks into the office, a large bear of a man, enormous hands—meat-packing hands. Could have been a wrestler, maybe.

Nice smile though—hellos all around.

"So how do things look, Kroloff? You think I'm ready for IBM?"

"Not bad Meyer; you run a good shop."

"So maybe one year I'll make a profit?"

"A few things, Meyer," and Kroloff turns toward us.

"Friends," Meyer says. "Say whatever you want."

"Josie claims that you have her sewing bottom ruffles and she can't make out. She says you took her off hemstitched sleeves and put her on ruffles, and she wants to know when she can go back on sleeves."

"She can go back when the stores want hemstitched sleeves. Right now they want ruffles. Am I responsible for the style changes in America?"

"What can I tell her, Meyer?"

"Tell her as soon as we have hemstitched sleeves again she will be the first one to get them. I don't know what else to tell her."

Kroloff jots something down.

"You remember, Kroloff, in the old days we argued over the minimum wage. We argued over piece work prices and Saturday work and time-and-a-half for overtime. We argued over *something*. Now we argue over hemstitched sleeves which went out of style five years ago. You remember you used to holler about the price of groceries and how could workers survive on what we were paying? We argued that the Southern factories were paying half as much as we were, and how could we compete with that.

"Two o'clock in the morning—we fought till two o'clock in the morning! Name calling. Everything. No time-outs. You once marched out of this office and said the shop was on strike. We said go ahead, we're closing down the business anyway."

"That was a long time ago," Kroloff says.

"Now we fight over whether Josie works on bottom ruffles. In the South nobody works on bottom ruffles—they do it with an automatic machine. The automatic machine doesn't know the difference between bottom ruffles and hemstitched sleeves. In the South they have machines that cut automatically. A laser beam follows the pencil marks. Here we fight over whether Sam should have an assistant."

Kroloff smiles and nods. He stands, and I think, "The Man with the Hoe." *Bowed by the weight of centuries.*

"What about Sam," he asks. "You think maybe he'll retire?"

"I think maybe I'll retire," says Meyer.

Kroloff says goodbye, turns toward the door. "You know, Meyer," he says, "we are taking a terrible chance."

It is four o'clock in the afternoon and we are standing at 7th Avenue and 36th Street. The operators are emptying out of the buildings, chattering and laughing, speaking rapidly with their hands. The cutters follow, moving more slowly—a caravan of grey cardigan sweaters—each one complaining that nowhere in the world is there a job as bad as his.

I ask if you know what that means, and you answer that means his job is O.K.

We look for Bill Blass—he's not here. He must be uptown having cocktails at The Four Seasons. We look for Yves St. Laurent. He must be in Paris, negotiating to embroider his initials on a new line of scarves. We look for the fashion models, but this is 7th Avenue and 36th Street—there are no fashion models here.

I turn to see if you are disappointed, and think maybe I should have done this differently.

"This is the garment center," I tell you, not knowing what else to say.

We walk another block or two. The sun is setting, casting shadows over the buildings and making them frown, the same way they have for as many years as anyone can remember.

## For Better Reading: The Confusing You

Ask "Who are you?" and the answer would come easily, if ungrammatically, "I am me."

Yet it's often not clear who "you" might be when you're reading. *You* is sometimes used informally to mean *anyone* or *somebody*. And, when used by an inexperienced writer, it may actually mean "I."

In the following sentence, who is "you"?

*When you're embarrassed by something, you always seem to do something else stupid, which makes you feel worse.*

It's hard to decide whether "you" is the reader, all people, or the person writing, who really means "I."

Because of such confusion, many writers of nonfiction and fiction avoid the word *you* as much as possible, unless quoting someone's conversation.

In poetry, *you* may be the reader—or perhaps someone or something else, like a loved one, the ocean, or even a rose.

In this story, Leonard S. Bernstein makes unusual use of *you*, by asking you, the reader, to play a role in "The Guided Tour of 7th Avenue." It's another example of the blurred line between fiction and nonfiction, as you're invited to "step inside," tour a New York garment factory, and become a character in the story.

## Inferences

1. The "you" in the story is assumed to be (a) an outsider to the garment business (b) seeking a job in the fashion field (c) collecting material for an article (d) inspecting working conditions on 7th Avenue.
2. The first person narrator (a) guides groups of tourists (b) writes a New York newspaper column (c) doesn't hesitate to say what he thinks (d) believes in avoiding change.
3. By writing "I have agreed" and "we begin," the author tries to create an impression that the tour (a) is happening as you read (b) will be difficult to undertake (c) is the first of its kind (d) was meant to settle an argument.

## Questioning the Story

1. In the first paragraph, how does the author create a humorous effect through the speaker's use of exaggeration?
2. By saying "I consider sending you to Berlitz for a course in a foreign language," the speaker implies "you" don't know his and Benny's New York version of English.

   How and when does "terrible" mean O.K.? Why would someone, who thinks like Benny, avoid saying business was great or even good?
3. What are two indications "change does not take hold easily" in New York's garment district? What does the speaker blame for this lack of change?
4. The speaker assumes "you" believe New York is the center of the fashion and garment industry. Considering this, what information must have "astounded" you? What comparison illustrates that New York is a symbol of the fashion industry, but not its entirety?
5. What are two reasons for a garment manufacturer to stay in New York? Name one advantage concerning workers and one, equipment gained by manufacturers in Alabama and Georgia.
6. What common accident do fabric cutters suffer? According to Meyer, what attitude was usually its cause?
7. Why did Sam need to be warned when Kroloff, the union agent, came? What plan did Meyer and Sam have for tricking him?
8. Why might Sam be considered "the best paid cutter in New York"? Why can't Kroloff know the whole story?

9. Sewing machine operators are paid by piece work. How does this explain Josie's objection to sewing bottom ruffles instead of hemstitched sleeves?
10. Why does Kroloff feel he and Meyer "are taking a terrible chance"? What motives would make Kroloff willing to take this chance? Why doesn't he wish to speak more openly?
11. Name at least two ways the story's last paragraphs echo its beginning.

# Looking Deeper

## I. A World of Glamour

Famous designers like Bill Blass, Halston, and Yves St. Laurent. Glamorous models. Fashionable restaurants like The Four Seasons. After "The Guided Tour of 7th Avenue," why does the speaker feel "you" may be disappointed?

After the speaker says "This is the garment center," the author concludes it has been the same "for as many years as anyone can remember." List two or three ways you are expected to find this true, outside of physical details of buildings and streets.

## II. Reaching an Understanding

What important information would be hard to include if the story were written without "you" taking part? Why might both Meyer and Kroloff seem like negative characters to someone not knowing the "inside" story?

Why can the two men be considered "old enemies"? How did Kroloff's threat to strike and Meyer's to close down both have the same purpose? What are two good qualities both men possessed? How had the focus of their differences changed through the years? What do you think the author wants you to see as the main characteristics of those working on 7th Avenue, as exemplified by Meyer, Kroloff, and Sam?

# A Desert Romance

## by Frederic Remington

| | |
|---|---|
| **Born:** | Rural north country of New York State, 1861 |
| **As a young man:** | Traveled and lived in Arizona, Montana, and Wyoming |
| **Early occupations:** | Ranch owner in Kansas, unsuccessful businessman in Missouri |
| **Famous as:** | Illustrator, sculptor, and writer, who traveled Indian territories for subjects to write, paint |

OCHOA WATER-HOLE IS IN NO way remarkable, and not regarded as such by people in Arizona, but if the waters could speak and tell about what happened at their sides in the long ago, men would listen. Three generations of white men and Mexicans have fought Apaches since then, and one generation of Apaches has walked in the middle of the big road. There have been stories enough in the meantime. Men have struggled in crowds over similar water-holes throughout the Southwest, and Ochoa has been forgotten.

With the coming of the great war, the regular soldiers were withdrawn to participate in it. The Apaches redoubled their hostilities. This was in Cochise's day, and he managed well for them.

Volunteers entered the United States service to take the places of the departed soldiers, to hold the country, and to protect the wagon-trains then going to California. A regiment of New Mexican volunteer infantry, Colonel Simms commanding, was stationed at Fort Bowie, and was mostly engaged in escorting the caravans. There was a military order that such trains should leave the posts only on the 1st of every month, when the regular soldier escort was available; but in enterprising self-reliance the pioneers often violated this.

One lazy summer day a Texan came plodding through the dust to the sentries at Bowie. He was in a state of great exhaustion, and when taken to Colonel Simms he reported that he had escaped from a Texas emigrant caravan, which was rounded up by Apaches at Ochoa water-hole, about forty-five miles east and south of this point, and that they were making a fight against great odds. If help was not quickly forthcoming, it was death for all.

Immediately the colonel took what of his command could be spared, together with a small cavallard of little hospital mules, and began the relief march.

These Americo-Mexican soldiers were mountain men and strong travelers. All during the remainder of the day they shuffled along in the dust—brown, blue-bearded men, shod in buckskin moccasins, of their own construction, and they made the colonel's pony trot. There are many hills and many plains in forty-five miles, and infantry is not a desert whirlwind. Night settled over the command, but still they shuffled on. Near midnight they could hear the slumping of occasional guns. The colonel well knew the Apache fear of the demons of the night, who hide under the water and earth by day, but who stalk at dark, and are more to be feared than white men, by long odds. He knew that they did not go about except under stress, and he had good hope of getting into the beleaguered wagons without much difficulty. He knew his problem would come afterward.

Guided by the guns, which the white men fired more to show their wakefulness than in hopes of scoring, the two companies trod softly in their buckskin foot-gear; but the mules struck flinty hard against the wayside rocks, and then one split the night in friendly answer to the smell of a brother mule somewhere out in the dark. But no opposition was encountered until occasional bullets came whistling over there from the wagons. "Hold on, pardners!" shouted the colonel. "This is United States infantry; let us in."

This noise located the command, and bullets and arrows began to seek them out in the darkness from all sides, but with a rush they passed into the packed wagons and dropped behind the intrenchments. The poor people of the train were greatly cheered by the advent. By morning the colonel had looked about him, and he saw a job of unusual proportions before him. They were poor emigrants from Texas, their wagons piled with common household goods, and with an unusual proportion of women and children—dry, care-worn women in calico shifts, which the clinging wind blew close about their wasted and unlovely frames. In the center stood a few skeletons of horses, destined to be eaten, and which had had no grass since the train had been rounded up. What hairy, unkempt men there were lay behind their bales, long rifles in hand, bullets and powder-horns by their elbows—tough customers, who would "sell out" dearly.

Presently a very old man came to the colonel, saying he was the head person of the train, and he proposed that the officer come to his wagon, where they could talk over the situation seriously.

The colonel was at the time a young man. In his youth he had been afflicted with deskwork in the great city of New York. He could not see anything ahead but a life of absolute regularity, which he did not view complacently. He was book-taught along the lines of construction and engineering, which in those days meant anything from a smoke-house to a covered bridge. Viewed through the mist of years he must, in his day, have been a fair prospect for feminine eyes. The West was fast eating up the strong young men of the East, and Simms found his way with the rest to the uttermost point of the unknown lands, and became a vagrant in Taos. Still, a man who knew as much as he did, and who could get as far West as Taos, did not have to starve to death. There were merchants there who knew the fords of the Cimarron and the dry crossings of the Mexican custom-house, but who kept their accounts by cutting notches on a stick. So Simms got more writing to do, a thing he had tried to escape by the long voyage and muling of previous days. Being young, his gaze lingered on the long-haired, buckskin men of Taos, and he made endeavor to exchange the quill for the rifle and the trap, and shortly became a protégé of Kit Carson. He succeeded so well that in the long years since he has been no nearer a pen than a sheep-corral would be.

He succumbed to his Mexican surroundings, and was popular with all. When the great war came he remembered New York and declared for the Union. Thus by hooks which I do not understand he became a colonel in the situation where I have found him.

As he approached the old man's part of the train he observed that he was richer and much better equipped than his fellows. He had a tremendous Conestoga and a springwagon of fine workmanship. His family consisted of a son with a wife and children, and a daughter who looked at the colonel until his mind was completely diverted from the seriousness of their present position. The raw, wind-blown, calico women had not seemed feminine to the officer, but this young person began to make his eyes pop, and his blood go charging about in his veins.

She admitted to the officer in a soft Southern voice that she was very glad he had gotten in, and the colonel said he was very glad indeed that he was there, which statement had only become a fact in the last few seconds. Still, a bullet-and-arrow-swept wagon-park was quite as compelling as the eyes of Old Man Hall's daughter, for that was her father's name. The colonel had a new interest in rescue. The people of the train were quite demoralized, and had no reasonable method to suggest as a way out, so the colonel finally said: "Mr. Hall, we must now burn all this property to prevent its falling into the hands of the enemy. I will take my hospital mules and hook them up to a couple of your lightest wagons, on which will be loaded nothing but provisions, old women, small children, and what wounded we have, and then we will fight our way back to the post."

Mr. Hall pleaded against this destruction, but the officer said that the numbers of the investing enemy made it imperative that they go out as lightly as possible, as he had no more mules and could spare no more men to guard the women. It seemed hard to burn all that these people had in the world, but he knew of no other way to save their lives.

He then had two wagons drawn out, and after a tussle got his unbroken pack-mules hooked up. Then the other stuff was piled into the remaining wagons and set on fire. The soldiers waited until the flames were beyond human control, when they sprang forward in skirmish formation, followed out of bow-shot by the wagons and women. A rear-guard covered the retreat.

As the movement began, Colonel Simms led his pony up to the daughter of Mr. Hall, and assisted her to mount. Simms was a young man, and it seemed to him more important that a beautiful young woman should be saved than some sisters who carried the curbs and collar-marks of an almost spent existence. This may not be true judgment, but Simms had little time to ponder the matter.

Now the demons of the Arizona deserts began to show themselves among the brush and rocks, and they came in boldly, firing from points of vantage at the moving troops. A few went down, but the discipline told, and the soldiers could not be checked. Scurrying in front ran the Indians, on foot and on horseback. They had few guns, and their arrows were not equal to the muzzle-loading muskets of the troops or the long rifles of the Texans. A few of the savages were hit, and this caused them to draw off. The wounded soldiers were loaded into the wagons, which were now quite full.

What with having to stop to ram the charges home in their guns, and with the slow progress of the women on foot, the retreat dragged its toilsome way. There were bad places in the back trail—places which Simms knew the Apaches would take advantage of; but there was nothing for it but to push boldly on.

After a couple of hours the command drew near a line of bluffs up which the trail led. There was no way around. Simms halted his wagons at the foot of the coulée leading up, and sent his men in extended order on each flank to carry the line of the crest, intending to take the wagons and women up afterward. This they did after encountering some opposition, and when just in the act of reaching the level of the mesa, a score of mounted warriors dashed at the line and rode over it, down the coulée in a whirl of dust, and toward the women, who had no protection which could reach them in time to save. The men on the hill, regardless of the enemy in front, turned their muskets on the flying bunch, as did the rear-guard; but it was over with a shot, and the soldiers saw the warriors ride over the the women and wagons, twanging their bows and thrusting with their lances. The mules turned, tangled in their harness, and lay kicking in a confused heap. The women ran scurrying about like quail. The cloud of dust and racing-ponies passed on, receiving the fire of the rear-guard again, and were out of range. With them went the colonel's horse and Old Man Hall's daughter, stampeded—killed by the colonel's kindness. No arm could save.

When the dust settled, several women and children lay on the sand, shot with arrows or cut by lances. The mules were rearranged, the harness was patched, and the retreat was resumed.

Old Man Hall was hysterical with tears, Simms was dumb beyond speech, as they marched along beside the clanking wagons, with their moaning loads. On all sides strode the gallant New Mexicans and Texans, shooting and loading. The Apaches, encouraged by success, plied them with arrows and shots from every *arroyo* which afforded safe retreat. The colonel ran from one part of the line to another, directing and encouraging his men. By afternoon every one was much exhausted, Colonel Simms particularly so from his constant activity and distress of mind.

Old Man Hall had calmed down and had become taciturn, except for the working of his hollow jaws as he talked to himself. Going to the rear wagon, he took out a cotton bag, which he swung across his shoulders, and trudged along with it. "Some valuables he cherishes," thought Simms; "but to add such weight in this trying march seems strange. Demented by the loss of his daughter, probably."

Slower and slower moved the old man with his sack, falling back until he mingled with the rear-guard, and then even dropping behind that.

"Come, come, camarado, stir yourself! The Indios are just behind!" they called.

"I don't care," he replied.

"Throw away the sack. Why do you carry that? Is your sack more precious than your blood?"

"Yes, it is now," he said almost cheerfully.

"What does it contain, senōr? Paper money, no doubt."

"No; it is full of pinole and pemochie and strychnine—for the wolves behind us"; and Old Man Hall trod slower and slower, and was two hundred yards in the rear before Simms noticed him.

"Halt! We will go back and get the old man, and have him put in the wagons," he said.

The soldiers turned to go back, when up from the brush sprang the Apaches, and Hall was soon dead.

"Come on; it is of no use now," signaled Simms.

"The old man is loco," said a soldier. "He had a sack of poisoned meal over his shoulder. He is after revenge."

"Poisoned meal!"

"Yes, señor; that is as he said," replied the soldier.

But under the stress Simms's little column toiled along until dusk, when they were forced to stop and intrench in a dry camp. There was no water in those parts, and the Indians had no doubt drawn off for the night—gone to the Ochoa spring, it was thought, and would be back in the morning. By early dawn the retreat started on its weary way, but no Indians appeared to oppose them. All day long they struggled on, and that night camped in the post. They had been delivered from their peril: at little cost, when the situation was considered, so men said—all except Hall's son and the young commanding officer. The caravan had violated the order of the authorities in traveling without escort, and had been punished. Old Man Hall, who had been responsible, was dead, so the matter rested.

## II.

The people who had so fortunately come within the protecting lines of Bowie were quite exhausted after their almost ceaseless exertions of the last few days, and had disposed themselves as best they could to make up their lost sleep. Some of the soldiers squeezed the *tequela* pigskin pretty hard, but they had earned it.

Colonel Simms tossed uneasily on his rude bunk for some time before he gained oblivion. Something in the whole thing had been incomplete. He had had soldiers killed and soldiers wounded—that was a part of the game. Some emigrants had suffered—that could not be helped. It was the good-looking girl, gone swirling off into the unknown desert, in the dust of the Apache charge, which was the rift in the young colonel's lute, and he had begun to admit it to himself. What could be done? What was his duty in the matter? His inclination was to conduct an expedition in quest of her. He knew his Apache so well that hope died out of his mind. Even if she could get away on the colonel's swift pony, an Apache on foot could trail and run down a horse. But the tired body and mind gave over, and he knew nothing until the morning light opened his eyes. Sitting opposite him on a chair was the brother of Hall's daughter, with his chin on his hands, and his long rifle across his knees.

"Good morning, Mr. Hall," he said.

"Mornin', colonel," replied Hall. "Ah 'm goin' back after my sista, colonel. Ah 'm goin' back, leastwise, to whar she was."

"So am I," spoke up Simms, like a flash, as he swung himself to his feet, "and right now." With men like Simms to think was to act.

He was refreshed by his rest, and was soon bustling about the post. The day before two companies of his regiment had come into the post on escort duty. They were pony-mounted, despite their being infantry, and were fresh. These he soon rationed, and within an hour's time had them trailing through the dust on the back track. Hall's sad-faced son rode by his side, saying little, for both felt they could not cheer each other with words.

Late in the afternoon, when coming across the mesa which ended at the bluff where the misfortune had overtaken the girl, they made out mounted figures at the very point where they had brought up the wagons.

"If they are Apaches, we will give them a fight now; they won't have to chase us to get it, either," said the colonel, as he broke his command into a slow lope.

Steadily the two parties drew together. More of the enemy showed above the bluffs. They formed in line, which was a rather singular thing for Apaches to do, and presently a horseman drew out, bearing a white flag on a lance.

"Colonel, those are lanceros of Mexico," spoke up the orderly sergeant behind the officer.

"Yes, yes; I can see now," observed Simms. "Trot! March! Come on, bugler." Saying which, the colonel, attended by his man, rode forth rapidly, a white handkerchief flapping in his right hand.

So they proved to be, the irregular soldiers of distracted Mexico—wild riders, gorgeous in terra-cotta buckskin and red serapes, bent on visiting punishment on Apache Indians who ravaged the valleys of Chihuahua and Sonora, and having, therefore, much in common with the soldiers on this side of the line.

In those days the desert scamperers did not know just where the international boundary was. It existed on paper, no doubt, but the bleak sand stretches gave no sign. Every man or body of men owned the land as far on each side of them as their rifles would carry, and no farther. Both Mexico and the United States were in mighty struggles for their lives. Neither busied themselves about a few miles of cactus, or the rally and push of their brown-skinned irregulars.

Shortly the comandante of the lancers came up. He was a gay fellow with a brown face, set with liquid black eyes, and togged out in the rainbows of his national costume. Putting out his hand to Simms, he spoke: "Buenos dias, señor. Is it you who have killed all the Apaches?"

"Si, capitan," replied Simms. "I had the honor to command, but I do not think we killed so many."

"Madre de Dios! you call that not many! Ha, you are a terrible soldier!" And the lancer slapped him on the back. "I saw the battle-ground; I rode among the bodies as far as I could make my horse go. I saw all the burned wagons, and the Indios lying around the water-hole, as thick as flies in a kitchen. It smelled so that I did not stop to count them; they were as many as a flock of sheep. I congratulate you. Did you lose many *soldados?*"

"No, capitan. I did not lose many men, but I lost a woman—just down below the bluffs. Did you see her body there?"

In truth, the poisoned sack of meal had come only slowly into Simms's mind when he thought of the dead Indians about the water-hole, and he did not care to enlighten a foreign officer in a matter so difficult of explanation.

"No," answered the Mexican; "they were all naked Apaches—I made note of that. We looked for others, but there were none. You are a terrible soldier. I congratulate you; you will have promotion, and go to the great war in the East."

"Oh, it is nothing, I assure you," grunted Simms, as he trotted off to get away from his gruesome glories. "come, señor; we will look at the girl's trail below the bluffs."

"Was she mounted well?" inquired the lancer, full of a horseman's instinct.

"Yes; she had a fast horse, but he had been ridden far. He was my own."

"She was of your family?"

"No, no; she was coming through with the wagon-train from Texas."

"She was a beautiful señorita?" ventured the lancer, with a sharp smile.

"Prettiest filly from Taos to New Orleans," spoke our gallant, in his enthusiasm, and then they dismounted at the wagon place, which was all beaten up with the hoof-marks of the lancers.

The best trailers among the mountain men of the command were soon on the track of the horsed Indians who had driven off the girl, and this they ran until quite dark. The enemy had gone in full flight.

Simms made his camp, and the Mexican lancer pushed on ahead, saying he would join him again in the morning.

By early light Simms had his troops in motion; but the trail was stamped up by the lancer command, and he could follow only this. He was in a broken country now, and rode far before he began to speculate on seeing nothing of his friend of yesterday. Some three hours later he did find evidence that the lancers had made a halt, but without unsaddling. Simms had run the trail carefully, and had his flankers out on the sides, to see that no one cut out from the grand track. Soon he was summoned by a flanker who waved his hat, and toward him rode the officer. Nearing, he recognized the man, who was a half-breed American, well known as a trailer of great repute.

"Colonel, here are the prints of the Apache ponies; I know by their bare feet and the rawhide shoes. Your pony is not among them; he was shod with iron. These ponies were very tired; they step short and stumble among the bushes," said the man, as he and the colonel rode along, bending over in their saddles. "See that spot on the ground. They had run the stomachs out of their horses. They stopped here and talked. They dismounted." Both the colonel and the trailer did the same. "There is no print of her shoe here," the trailer continued slowly. "See where they walked away from their horses and stood here in a bunch. They were talking. Here comes a pony-track back to them from the direction of the chase. This pony was very tired. His rider dismounted here and walked to the group. The moccasins all point toward the way they were running. They were talking. Colonel, the girl got away. I may be mistaken, but that is what the trail says. All the Indians are here. I have counted twenty ponies."

There is nothing to do in such places but believe the trail. It often lies, but in the desert it is the only thing which speaks. Taking his command again, the colonel pushed on as rapidly as he dared, while feeling that his flanking trailers could do their work. They found no more sign of the Indians, who had evidently given up the chase, thinking, probably, the wagons more important than the fast horse-girl.

All day long they progressed, the colonel wondering why he did not come up with the lancer command. Why was the Mexican in such a hurry? He did not relish the idea of this man's rescuing the girl, if that was to be fate. Long he speculated, but time brought only more doubt and suspicion. At places the Mexican had halted, and the ground was tramped up in a most meaningless way. Again the trailer came to him.

"Colonel," he said, "these people were blinding a trail. It's again' nature for humans to walk around like goats in a corral. I think they have found where the girl stopped, but I can't run my eye on her heel."

The colonel thought hard, and being young, he reached a rapid conclusion. He would follow the Mexican to the end of his road. Detailing a small body of picked trailers to follow slowly on the sides of the main trail, he mounted, and pushed on at a lope. Darkness found the Mexicans still going. While his command stopped to feed and rest, the colonel speculated. He knew the Mexicans had a long start; it was unlikely that they would stop. He thought, "I will sleep my command until midnight, and follow the trail by torch-light. I will gain the advantage they did over me last night."

After much searching on the mountainside in the gloom, some of his men found a pitch-tree, which they felled and slivered. At the appointed time the command resumed its weary way. Three hundred yards ahead, a small party followed the trail by their firelight. This would prevent, in a measure, an ambuscade. A blanket was carried ahead of the flaming stick—a poor protection from the eyes of the night, but a possible one. So, until the sky grayed in the east, the soldiers stumbled bitterly ahead on their relentless errand. It was a small gain, perhaps, but it made for success. When the torches were thrown away, they grazed for an hour, knowing that horses do not usually do that in the dark, and by day they had watered and were off. The trail led straight for Mexico.

Whatever enthusiasm the poor soldiers and horses might have, we know not, but there was a fuel added to Simms's desire, quite as great as either the pretty face of Adele Hall or his chivalric purpose kindled—it was jealousy of the lancer officer. When hate and love combine against a young man's brain, there is nothing left but the under jaw and the back of his head to guide him. The spurs chugged hard on the lathering sides, as the pursuers bore up on the flying wake of the treacherous man from Mexico.

At an eating halt which the lancers made, the trailers sought carefully until, standing up together, they yelled for the colonel. He came up, and pointing at the ground, one of the men said: "Señor, there is the heel of the white girl."

Bending over, Simms gazed down on the telltale footprint, saying, "Yes, yes; it is her shoe—I even remember that. Is it not so, Hall?" The girl's brother, upon examination, pronounced it to be his sister's shoe. Simms said: "We will follow that lancer to hell. Come on."

There were, in those days, few signs of human habitation in those parts. The hand of the Apache lay heavy on the land. The girl-stealer was making in the direction of Magdalena, the first important Mexican town en route. This was a promise of trouble for Simms. Magdalena was populous and garrisoned. International complications loomed across Simms's vision, but they grew white in the shadow of the girl, and, come what would, he spurred along, the brother always eagerly at his side.

By mid-afternoon they came across a dead horse, and soon another. The flatsoled tegua-tracks of the dismounted riders ran along in the trail of the lancer troop. The country was broken, yet at times they could see long distances ahead. Shortly the trailers found the tegua-prints turned away from the line of march, and men followed, and found their owners hidden in the mesquit-bush. These, being captured, were brought to Colonel Simms, who dismounted and interrogated them, as he gently tapped their lips with the muzzle of his six-shooter to break their silence. He developed that the enemy was not far ahead; that the girl was with them, always riding beside Don Gomez, who was making for Magdalena. Further, the prisoners said they had found the white woman asleep beside her worn-out pony, which they had taken aside and killed.

This was enough. The chase must be pushed to a blistering finish. As they drew ahead they passed exhausted horses standing head down by the wayside, their riders being in hiding, doubtless. On a rise they saw the troop of lancers jogging along in their own dust, not three hundred yards ahead, while in the valley, a few miles beyond, was an adobe ranch, for which they were making. With a yell from the United States soldiers, they broke into the best run to be got out of their jaded ponies. The enemy, too, spurred up, but they were even more fatigued, and it was not many minutes before the guns began to go. A few of the enemy's horses and men fell out, wounded, and were ridden over, while the rest fled in wild panic. They had doubtless thought themselves safe from pursuit, and they would have been, had their booty been anything less than Adele Hall. Many lancers turned and surrendered when the tired horses could go no more. The commands tailed out in a long line, the better horses of the Americans mixing gradually with the weaker ones of the lancers. Still well ahead rode Don Gomez and his reluctant companion. These drew up to the blue walls of the long adobe ranch (for it was now sunset), and were given admittance, some dozen men in all, when the heavy doors were swung together and barred, just as the American advance drew rein at their portals.

Finally having all collected—both Americans and prisoners—and having carefully posted his men around the ranch, Simms yelled in Spanish: "Come to the wall, Capitan Gomez. I am Colonel Simms. I would speak a word with you."

Again he spoke to the walls, now blackening against the failing light. From behind the adobe battlements came excited voices; the inhabitants were trying to digest the meaning of this violence, but no one answered Simms.

Turning, he gave an order. Instantly a volley of musketry started from near him, and roared about the quiet ranch.

Once more Simms raised his angry voice: "Will you come on the roof and talk to me now, Don Gomez?"

At length a voice came back, saying, "There are no windows; if I come on the roof, I will be shot."

"No, you will not be shot, but you must come on the roof."

"You promise me that?"

"Yes, I promise you that no soldier of mine will shoot at you," and in loud military language Simms so gave the order.

Slowly a dark figure rose against the greenish light of the west.

"Don Gomez, I ask you truly, has one hair of that girl's head been harmed? If you lie to me, I swear on the cross to burn you alive."

"I swear, my colonel; she is the same as when you last saw her. I did not know you were coming. I was trying to save her. I was taking her to my commander at Magdalena."

"You lie!" was the quick response from Simms, followed by a whip-like snap peculiar to the long frontier rifles. The dark form of Don Gomez turned half round, and dropped heavily out of sight on the flat roof of the adobe.

"Who fired that shot?" roared Simms.

"Ah did, sah," said Hall, stepping up to the colonel and handing him his rifle. "Ah am not one of yer soldiers, sah—I am Adele Hall's brother, and Mr. Gomez is dead. You can do what you please about it, sah."

While this conversation was making its quick way, a woman sprang up through the hole in the roof, and ran to the edge, crying: "Help, Colonel Simms! Oh, help me!"

"Cover the roof with your guns, men," ordered Simms, and both he and the brother sprang forward, followed by a general closing in of the men on the building.

As they gained the side wall, Simms spoke. "Don't be scared, Miss Hall; jump. I will catch you," and he extended his arms. The girl stepped over the foot-high battlement, grasped one of the projecting roof-timbers, and dropped safely into Colonel Simms's arms. She was sobbing, and Simms carried her away from the place. She was holding tightly to the neck of her rescuer, with her face buried in a week's growth of beard.

# For Better Reading: A Touch of Romance

The word *romance* means much more than "love stuff," although elements of its definition concern love, too.

Originally, romances were tales of daring knights, heroic exploits, and chivalric deeds—often performed in honor of fair ladies. It follows that a *romantic* person is someone who seeks his ideal, whether it's a place or a person, an opportunity for adventure or the fulfillment of a dream. Some use *romantic* in the sense of unrealistic and impractical. And the word can clearly apply to love.

Author and artist Frederic Remington became rich "at a trade thought to be for dreamers." His drawings and stories fired people's imaginations, and, in a sense, the West became "what Remington made it."

A genuine romantic, Remington's first writing assignment was the black cavalry, the Buffalo soldiers. Although a white officer tried to exhaust and discourage the "tenderfoot," Remington delighted in the experience. He also upheld the Indians' viewpoint in a novel described "best of its kind."

"A Desert Romance" should remind you of the indistinct line between fiction and nonfiction. Writing from experience, Remington pictures the West that he in some ways "made" and the good reader, as always, is aware of the writer's personal filter.

## Details

1. Ochoa was a waterhole (a) in a small Arizona town (b) out in the desert (c) which Indians named "Talking Waters" (d) controlled by sheepherders.
2. The "great war" must have been the (a) Revolutionary War (b) French-Indian War (c) War Between the States (d) Mexican-American War.
3. The Texas emigrants were going from (a) Texas to New Mexico (b) Louisiana to Texas (c) Arizona to Texas (d) Texas to California.

## Questioning the Selection

### Part I.
1. How had the Texas emigrant wagon train violated military orders? Why was it necessary to begin a relief march at once?
2. Why wasn't Colonel Simms' regiment made up of "regular soldiers"? How does Remington evaluate these Americo-Mexican volunteers?
3. Why did Simms have "good hope" of getting to the wagons with little difficulty? Once within the circled wagons, what did Simms see the next morning that made his job especially difficult? Give at least two factors.

4. What in Simms' background reveals a romantic side to his nature? When Simms meets the Hall family, what new element of romance is introduced?
5. What is Simms' suggestion concerning the emigrants' property and wagons? Why might Hall be especially opposed? How did Simms himself feel about this plan?
6. Himself an artist, Remington could vividly picture the desert landscape with its *bluffs* (or cliffs) with flat *mesas* at their tops and its *coulées* and *arroyos* (steep-sided ravines). How did the landscape itself work against the soldiers' and emigrants' getting to Fort Bowie?
7. Although not witnessed, why did it seem Hall's daughter had been "killed by the colonel's kindness"?
8. Upon leaving Simms' troops, what did Old Man Hall carry with him? What did a soldier say Hall intended to seek?
9. Why did everyone but Colonel Simms and Hall's son feel the relief march succeeded "at little cost"? Why did these two react differently?
10. Why might Old Man Hall seem to deserve his fate?

**Part II.**
1. Why did Simms believe Hall's daughter could not escape the Apaches, even riding his swift pony?
2. What doubts did Simms have about his duty? What was his "on the spot" decision the following morning?
3. At the spot where the Apache had struck, what was the first indication that the mounted figures on the bluff were not Indians? Why did these "irregular soldiers" and the American ones have "much in common"?
4. What irony does the Mexican commander intend by calling Simms "a terrible soldier"? What really killed the Apaches at the waterhole?
5. What evidence made the half-breed American trailer believe Hall's daughter got away? Why must Simms "believe the trail," though it often lied?
6. What caused Simms to suspect the Mexican lancer officer also sought Adele Hall? Find at least two reasons.
7. What did Simms' trailers discover at a spot where the Mexicans stopped to eat?
8. Why did a "promise of trouble" await Simms in the town of Magdalena? Why were the American soldiers able to overtake the Mexicans?
9. After posting men around the adobe ranch, what did Simms promise Don Gomez, the Mexican captain? Why did he accuse Gomez of lying?
10. Why couldn't Simms' promise protect Don Gomez? How did Adele Hall reach safety?

# Looking Deeper

## I. "A Desert Romance"

What features of the Arizona landscape are necessary to the plot? Give at least three examples, and explain their importance.

*Chivalry* is the knightly code, which includes such qualities as courage, generosity, truthfulness, and loyalty. Point out examples of Simms' having at least three such characteristics of a romantic hero.

How are "daring" and "search for an ideal" both part of this romance?

## II. "Demons of the Deserts"

Remington calls the Apaches "demons of the deserts." Do you believe Remington used this term to reflect the attitudes of soldiers and emigrants, to express his own opinion, or to add to the romantic effect? Decide upon one or more of these reasons, and explain the reasons behind your choice.

# Wildwest

## by Archibald MacLeish

| | |
|---|---|
| **Born:** | Glencoe, Illinois, 1892 |
| **World War I:** | U.S. Army field artillery, captain |
| **Education:** | Law Degree from Harvard |
| **Career:** | Poet, dramatist, educator, Librarian of Congress, Undersecretary of State, Pulitzer prize winner |

There were none of my blood in this battle:
There were Minneconjous: Sans Arcs: Brules:
Many nations of Sioux: they were few men galloping:

This would have been in the long days in June:
They were galloping well-deployed under the
    plum-trees:                5
They were driving riderless horses: themselves they
    were few:

Crazy Horse had done it with few numbers:
Crazy Horse was small for a Lakota:
He was riding always alone thinking of something:

He was standing alone by the picket lines by
    the ropes:                10
He was young then, he was thirty when he died:
Unless there were children to talk he took no notice:

When the soldiers came for him there on the other side
On the Greasy Grass in the villages we were shouting
"Hoka Hey! Crazy Horse will be riding!"        15

They fought in the water: horses and men were
    drowning:
They rode on the butte: dust settled in sunlight:
Hoka Hey! they lay on the bloody ground.

No one could tell of the dead which man was
    Custer ...
That was the end of his luck: by that river:          20
The soldiers beat him at Slim Buttes once:

They beat him at Willow Creek when the snow lifted:
The last time they beat him was the Tongue:
He had only the meat he had made and of that little:

Do you ask why he should fight? It was his country:   25
My God should he not fight? It was his.
But after the Tongue there were no herds to
    be hunting:

He cut the knots of the tails and he led them in:
He cried out "I am Crazy Horse! Do not touch me!"
There were many soldiers between and the gun
    glinting ...                30

And a Mister Josiah Perham of Maine had much of the
land Mister Perham was building the Northern Pacific
railroad that is Mister Perham was saying at lunch that

forty say fifty millions of acres in gift and
government grant outright ought to be worth a    35
wide price on the Board at two-fifty and

later a Mister Cooke had relieved Mister Perham and
later a Mister Morgan relieved Mister Cooke:
Mister Morgan converted at prices current:

It was all prices to them: they never looked at it:   40
why should they look at the land: they were Empire
    Builders:
it was all in the bid and the asked and the ink on
    their books ...

When Crazy Horse was there by the Black Hills
His heart would be big with love he had for
    that country
And all the game he had seen and the mares he
    had ridden                45

And how it went out from you wide and clean in
    the sunlight

# For Better Reading: "None of My Blood"

Chief of the Oglala Sioux Indians, Crazy Horse repeatedly defeated United States troops in his attempts to keep the Black Hills of South Dakota from falling under white man's control.

With the Sioux chief Sitting Bull and his lieutenant Gall, Crazy Horse commanded the Indian defeat of General George Armstrong Custer at Little Big Horn in Montana.

Yet Crazy Horse and his band of 1,000 followers were finally driven to the point of starvation and forced to surrender. Even in defeat, he was considered "one of the bravest of the brave and ... most capable of captains" by one of his conquerers.

Crazy Horse was stabbed to death trying to escape from prison.

This poem is based on the memories of Black Elk, which were recorded by John G. Neihardt in the book, *Black Elk Speaks*. When the speaker in the poem says, "There were none of my blood," he means no member of his immediate family. And, in giving voice to Black Elk's feelings, poet Archibald MacLeish, whose ancestors were Scottish immigrants, attempts to show that blood is less important than the ability to see and understand.

## Questioning the Poem

1. Are the "many nations" of the Indian war party more likely to be different countries or different tribes? Explain your reasoning. Which side in the battle seems stronger and why?
2. Stanza two states the Indians were "well-deployed"—or spread out in an extended line—under trees. Why is this good military strategy? Why was "driving riderless horses" also a clever tactic?
3. List three personal characteristics of Crazy Horse given in lines 8–11. Which explains his success as a leader and why?
4. Lines 13–19 apparently describe the battle of Little Big Horn. From where did the narrator view the battle? How do you explain the meaning of "Hoka Hey!"?
5. Line 20 states "That was the end of his luck." Why might "his" seem ambiguous? How does line 21 make its reference clear?
6. What key reasons for the Indians' surrender are given in lines 24 and 27? How does the background information support this?
7. What does line 25 give as Crazy Horse's reason for fighting? Find one or two personal characteristics in stanzas three and four to account for his decision to surrender. Explain the reasons for your choices.
8. According to the narrator, what did the Empire Builders want from the land?

# Looking Deeper

## I. A Love of Land

The poem states that the Empire Builders "never looked at" the land. Why didn't these men care about seeing it? Although Crazy Horse didn't enter their calculations, explain the attitudes you imagine their having towards him.

According to the background, Crazy Horse was called "one of the bravest of the brave ... most capable of captains" by a U.S. Army officer who fought against him. Considering this, explain how and why the U.S. soldiers' attitudes towards Crazy Horse would likely differ from the Empire Builders'.

Why did Crazy Horse's heart deserve being called "big with love"? Give at least two reasons. In contrast, might the Empire Builders' hearts be considered "small"? Explain why or why not.

## II. How Wild The West?

Speaking of the "wild west" often brings to mind "shoot 'em up" gunfights and senseless Indian massacres. Why does the title "Wildwest" for this poem therefore seem ironic?

What is also ironic about Misters Perham, Cooke, and Morgan being called "Empire Builders"? Do you feel most of today's readers sympathize more readily with the viewpoints of Black Elk and Crazy Horse or Perham, Cooke, and Morgan? Explain the reasons behind your views.

# Holy Toledo

## by Joseph Geha

| | |
|---|---|
| **Born:** | *Zahleh, Lebanon* |
| **Home state:** | *Iowa* |
| **Early life:** | *Came to America in 1946, through Ellis Island to the American Midwest; spoke no English when he entered school* |
| **Career:** | *Writer; faculty member at Iowa State University* |

LOOKING FOR THE CHARM AGAINST the Evil Eye, Nadia stretched up on the footstool—a tomboy in her dungarees—and searched the shelves of the bathroom cabinet one by one. The charm was a tiny object, no larger than a rosary bead, and it was forever getting lost. But despite the clutter of this house (her grandmother threw nothing away) it was forever turning up again, too.

Sitti, her grandmother, had had the amulet ever since the old country when she herself was a child. A Lazerine monk claimed he'd found it lying amid the rubble of an ancient excavation and, hoping to gain some favor, he brought it directly to Sitti's uncle, the district magistrate. When the monk was gone—the favor granted or not, Sitti never said—her uncle simply looked down at the charm in his hand and shrugged. After all, what was this thing to him? Nothing more than a drop of porcelain painted to look like a miniature eyeball. And so the amulet was forgotten, mislaid until after his death when it turned up again among his things. No one claimed it, so Sitti decided to keep the charm for herself. Attaching it to a stiff golden thread, she'd had the amulet ever since, over the years misplacing it, yet always finding it again somewhere.

But not here. Here on the top shelf there were only razors, old women's salves, and jars of black ointments meant to be kept out of a child's reach. Nadia stepped down from the footstool and carried it back into the front room.

"Achhh...."

The long, familiar moan floated down the hallway from the kitchen; Sitti must be searching there now. And Mikhail was still in the front room where Nadia had left him, still doing nothing to help.

"Mikhi," she said, "it wasn't in the bathroom either."

"It doesn't matter," he said. Crossing his legs on the sofa, her brother spoke without turning to look at her.

"Then it has to be in the cellar. Me and Sitti, we looked everyplace else." Mikhail said nothing. "I bet I know where in the cellar, too." She waited for him to ask where. He didn't. "How much you want to bet," she went on anyway, "that it's in one of those boxes Uncle Eddie took down there last spring?"

Still her brother said nothing. He would not even look at her.

"Mikhi? You wouldn't just sit there if Uncle Eddie was here. He'll give you the belt again for not helping."

At that, Mikhi turned his gaze, slowly, the wide brown eyes of their father. "You telling?"

"No, not *me.*" She wanted very much for him to believe this, but even as she spoke she realized that her voice was too solemn, unnatural in its earnestness. "I meant *Sitti.*"

"Don't make me laugh." He was her little brother by two years, yet it seemed always as if he were the older one. Nadia was the one who giggled and could keep no secrets.

With another loud moan, Sitti left the kitchen and went into the dining room directly next to them. They remained motionless, silent in the ticking stillness of the front room lest she hear them and be reminded of their presence in her house: maybe if she forgot that someone was here to listen she would stop groaning that way—achh—every time she bent over, every time she pulled open a drawer or leaned back her head against the dizziness.

"Achhh. . . ."

(It hadn't been long after breakfast—maybe she was still drinking her coffee—when the pain and the groaning began. "What's wrong, Sitti?" Mikhi kept asking her over and over, but she wouldn't answer. Later, as the noon heat grew unbearable to her, she undressed, put on a nightgown, and braided her hair up off her neck.)

Sitti was a short woman, her broad hips spreading the nightgown as she bent low to pull and shove at the buffet drawers. Nadia almost smiled, watching her through the archway; the nightgown was white, and except for the three iron braids sticking out, her grandmother looked from behind like a little fat altar boy.

"Achhh. . . ."

Her groans were getting louder, and a hint of worry flickered across Mikhi's eyes. Then, just as quickly, he brightened, curling himself into a hollow of the sofa and tucking the souvenir cushions one under each arm so that their tasseled corners met beneath his chin like a silver beard. He grunted twice, as if to hold his sister's attention, then he made a face at her—an old man wagging a toothless mouth—and she had to turn away to keep from laughing out loud.

"Achh. . . ." It was Arabic, but Nadia knew it meant nothing, wasn't even a word so much as the sound of effort and pain.

The drawers were crammed full of all sorts of odds and ends, and Sitti would be busy there a long time. That was her way: looking for one thing, she had to stop and muse over every other thing she came across. She could throw nothing away.

The satin pillows looked smooth and cool against Mikhi's hands. The American pillows, Sitti called them. Uncle Eddie had brought them home for her from the navy. The blue one had on its decorated side the figures of anchors and stars, the red one a poem stitched in silver thread. When he came home to stay, Uncle Eddie read the poem aloud to Sitti, showing her how the first letter of each line spelled the word *Mother*. The women said that Sitti was lucky to have at least one son who cared so much for his mother. What they meant, of course, was that the children's father did not care so much because he left. Especially since Papa was the elder son and it was his duty to stay. More than that, the custom still held, even here in America: a widower with children is expected to either remarry or else return to his mother's house. Papa did neither. Instead, he remained in his own house after the funeral. For almost five years until, one hot July morning, he dressed Mikhi and Nadia in their Sunday clothes and brought them to Sitti's house, all their things packed in grocery bags. And after that he simply went away.

Nadia watched a moment more as her brother's fingers brushed lightly over the stitching, tracing stars and letters, then she stood up. "I'm going to look in Sitti's room again."

Mikhi looked up from the cushions. The charm wasn't in Sitti's room, they both knew that; the bedrooms had been searched twice already, and all she was doing now was simply trying to put off having to go down to the cellar alone. Mikhi's wry, sidelong glance mocked her.

She crossed in front of him, ignoring the face he once more made at her, lipping his teeth that way to get her laughing. She was only eleven, and a girl given to giggling, but she wasn't a fool. Mikhi was up to something, all day just sitting there and doing nothing to help. There was going to be trouble—once more Uncle Eddie would have his snakeskin belt out and flashing—and she would be a part of it. She'd have to be. Mikhi was younger than her, yet she had always followed his lead, even into trouble.

"Mikhi?" she paused in the doorway. "I don't want to go down there alone." Nadia kept her eyes downward on a curled edge of the rug. Sitti was dying, or said she was, and she needed the amulet to ease the pain of her dying. At least it might quiet her. "Will you come with me when I go?"

Again he didn't answer. Nadia stomped angrily into the hall—her dungarees, bought large so she'd grow into them, slap-slapping at her ankles—and pushed open the bedroom door.

Sitti's room was papered with dark flowers. The walls, like everything else in that house, were cluttered. Holy pictures hung in uneven diamond patterns above the bed, and there were photographs everywhere, dark-framed pictures of Sitti when she was young, of Jiddo—Nadia's grandfather—rimmed in black because he was dead, and of Papa and Uncle Eddie when they were little boys. None of them were smiling, not even little Papa, his big eyes staring blankly at her through the dusty glass.

The dresser top had been cleared at least twice that day, and there was nothing on it now but a small statue of the Virgin. Almost two years before, when Uncle Eddie was still in the navy and it looked like he might be sent to Korea, Sitti had taped a folded dollar bill to the statue's base. Like a prayer, almost.

(" ... Great to be back," Uncle Eddie had kept saying after his discharge. "Great to be back."

"What was it like?" visitors would ask.

"We never did go overseas, unless you count once to Panama. Mostly it was up and down the West Coast."

"And how was that?"

"Truth is, I was lost the whole time. Really. I never knew where I was. And when we put in it was even worse. I was always getting lost in the cities. You honestly don't know what homesick is until you've been out there."

Then Uncle Eddie would take his mother's hand in both of his. "Great to be back." He praised her cooking every single day of that first week home. "Great to be back," he said it even to himself, idly fingering one of the sofa doilies, then actually noticing it, as if discovering at his very fingertips yet one more familiar marker against the lostness from which he had returned. ... )

The bedroom was warm, musty with the smell of sleep. Nadia opened a window, then knelt and put her face to the faint breeze. Except for the furniture and the pictures, this could have been her old bedroom at home. The two houses were almost identical, both built of glazed brick with tall, narrow windows and rooms that were dark even in daytime since they shared walls with the row-houses on either side (and beneath those rooms the cellars, damp honeycombs of thick walls and uneven floors); both houses, too, were within that same general neighborhood of East Detroit, the Little Syria centered at Congress Street and Larned. Pressing her face to the window screen, she could see the dome of the Maronite Catholic Church and the onion shaped twin steeples of the Greek Orthodox. Farther up Congress there were shops that sold woven artifacts and brass from the old country. They had food, too, things that couldn't be found anywhere else in Detroit; pressed apricots, goat cheese, sesame paste and pine nuts and briny olives. ("The food, that's what I missed most," Uncle Eddie said. "The Americans, they don't know how to eat.") And there were the *ahwa* shops too, where old men sat all day amid tobacco smoke and the bitter smell of Turkish coffee.

On Saturday mornings Americans came into the neighborhood to shop. Women, mostly, the merchants called them "Mum" (and behind their backs "College Mum," not so much because of the university nearby as for the way these women spoke English—everything in the nose). Nadia often used to sit outside just to watch the college mums pass. While most women dressed up in hat and gloves to go shopping, clutching a narrow black purse, the college mums seemed younger than that. They always had on something bright, like a scarf or a bandanna. The handbags slung carelessly from their shoulders were huge, made of woven rope or straw, and patterned with beads. Usually they wore no makeup, and with their hair pinned up or back there was always something boyish about their faces. A few even dressed in trousers, like men. And they were always excited about something, always smiling as they pointed out this or that to a companion who'd never been there before, exclaiming too loudly about the inlay work on a cedar music box or the smell of a foreign spice, and always asking "Oh, and what do you call *this?*" as if they'd never seen a barrel of olives before. The shopkeepers would smile back at them and say *olives* in Arabic, and the college mums loved that, chattering on and on as they spent their money. By early afternoon they would begin leaving—silly women—and always Nadia wished that she were one of them, returning with them into that huge strangeness, America, luring her despite the threat it seemed to hold of loss and vicious homesickness.

*

"Achhh. . . ."

The drawers of Sitti's dresser were sticking with the heat, and Nadia had to tug hard to open them. In a corner of the bottom drawer, tucked beneath the stockings and yellowed underwear, were several envelopes banded together. These contained photographs never pasted into the album books, among them the two or three remaining pictures of Nadia's mother. Since she was an American, the old people hardly ever mentioned her when they talked of the dead. Nadia barely remembered her at all, and she always envied Mikhi who, though younger, could state with the quiet assurance of a witness that their mother's eyes, which were so dark in the photographs, had been bright blue.

Cached also amid the underthings were broken rosaries, pages from Arabic prayerbooks, shreds of holy palms plaited years ago into the shapes of crosses and crowns of thorns. Although the younger people gave such things a kind of grudging respect (the whole time he was at sea Uncle Eddie wore the charm against the Evil Eye—the very one that was missing now—and he said he wasn't the only one on his ship with a lucky piece), it was usually just the old people who were careful not to point at certain stars, who never ate from a yellow dish or left a slipper upside down with its sole stepping on God's face. Once, Nadia told her uncle about how Mikhi had imitated the ritual that old people had of kissing a piece of bread that had fallen to the floor. It was so funny, she had to tell somebody; Mikhi popping his eyes in exaggerated horror as the bread fell, the reverence with which he picked it up and kissed it, finally working his mouth sideways and sucking passionately, the way people kissed in movies.

Uncle Eddie didn't laugh. Instead, he simply lit a cigarette. Nadia began to worry as she watched the smoke puff twice with each rapid double-drag. It was a busy, nervous way of smoking that Uncle Eddie had learned in the navy. Her uncle had always been quick to laugh at almost anything. But as the months passed after his return from the service, Eddie seemed to grow more serious, more easily irritated. Some said that it had started while he was still in the navy, just after he'd heard that Papa was gone.

The cigarette was still lit when Mikhi came in from playing outside. Uncle Eddie drew one last double-drag and tapped it out in a saucer. Then he removed his belt and called Mikhi into the kitchen. Nadia hadn't meant to tattle. She tried to show Mikhi this by the look on her face, but Mikhi saw only the belt as he backed slowly away from the kitchen door.

The narrow snakeskin belt was one of the first things that Eddie had bought after the service. He was in San Diego and not yet out of uniform when he passed a shop window, and the gleam of its scales caught his eye.

"Achhh...."

The moans were growing louder, and from the front room Nadia heard a sound like something thrown against the wall, something soft. She pushed the last drawer shut and went out to see.

The front door stood wide open, the screen door ajar. And Mikhi was gone. The cushion he'd thrown, the red one, lay across the room, wedged between the baseboard and an end table.

Nervous, like Papa, he never could bear it the way she could. ("She's old, Mikhi," she used to tell him. "Old people get sick, then they die. That's all.") And so to find the amulet, she would have to go down alone into the cellar. He had left that to her.

She lingered a moment, listening while the groans became soft again, as regular as the tiny pendulum swings of the mantel clock. Nadia was afraid to go down there alone, and Mikhi knew it, and here he'd gone off anyway and left it to her.

She ran the fingers of one hand through her hair, an absent gesture; then, suddenly aware of the gesture, she dropped her hand to her side. Another moment of that and the tears would have started for sure.

*

Her father had a way of combing his fingers through his hair when he was worried, the nervous habit of a nervous man. His gray hair stood out in whorls because of it. And on that day almost three years ago (even into adulthood she and her brother would remark the very date their father brought them to Sitti's house and left them there: Sunday, July the eighth, 1951) it seemed that every few seconds his hand would go up to his hair as they waited on the front stoop for Sitti to answer her door. They waited a long time, and when she did answer, how grim she was, how stone-faced, as she let them in. The bags they carried were heavy, even though Nadia herself had repacked them. (Papa had packed them first, confused from the start, unsure of what to take and what to throw out, or leave behind.) He never came in after them but remained on the stoop as if still confused. There was a frightened sadness in the way he stood there, and his kiss was a good-bye.

Afterward, nobody spoke much of him except to repeat what was already known: that Mikhail Yakoub—married late in life (and to an American), a failure at any business he tried, finally a widower with children—was never a lucky man.

But then Mikhail Yakoub never respected luck as the others did, not even grudgingly. He preferred to be free of it. "Bad luck or good luck," Nadia remembered him saying, "to hell with them both." One time, he took her and Mikhi with him on an errand down Congress Street. While there, he stopped in at one of the *ahwa* shops to talk to a man. The coffee shops did not admit females, not even little girls; she had to wait at the door while her father and brother went inside. The windows, like the doorway, were wide open, and flies buzzed everywhere among the tables. Old men sat drinking from tiny cups, all of them smoking cigars or water pipes. A group at a near table were playing cards. Suddenly, one of these men looked up as a shadow flitted past the lamp shade dangling above him. Then they were all scrambling to their feet, crying out and cursing. A chair was overturned, and Nadia had to step aside to keep from getting trampled as the men jostled and elbowed one another out the door and onto the street. She heard her father before she saw him, His loud laugh booming above the confusion. Only after the three of them had woven their way through the small crowd did Mikhi, himself red-faced with laughter, pause long enough to explain it to her.

"What happened is, is a bird flew in the window."

"So?" she said.

"It's an omen," her father said.

"A bad one?"

"The worst. It means a death in the house. Holy Toledo," her father began laughing again, "I never saw a room clear out so fast."

Nadia chuckled a little, even though she didn't see anything funny, not at first. Holy Toledo was a city near Detroit, and Papa called out its name sometimes when things were funny. But after a moment, remembering how quickly the old men had moved, their baggy trousers flapping as they shuffled and pushed, she began to laugh in earnest.

"I almost hurt myself," Papa was saying, and the children hurried after him to hear, "when old Stamos the Greek tried to climb out a window. I had to grab him by the suspenders and hold him back."

And so her father never respected luck, himself luckless. After he went away, those people who mentioned Mikhail Yakoub at all spoke of him as if he were gone forever. But he wasn't dead—she and Mikhi had been able to wheedle that much out of them. He had simply disappeared from the neighborhood. And when the children pressed to know where he'd gone, some said "Boston," others "Chicago," but none of them was certain. Sitti answered them only by saying "America!" and fluttering fingers to temple in the Arabic gesture *tarit*, which meant *it has flown out*. Yet how could that which was sealed within the hard bone of the skull simply fly away? Nadia couldn't understand it, and so she clung to what was certain: he was gone, swallowed up somehow by the vast America beyond these streets, alive, forever luckless, and free. And in her imagination forever homesick, too, forever standing at a closed door somewhere, lost, running his fingers through his hair.

\*

Still blinking against the tears—not much of a tomboy after all—she was startled to find the cellar stairs already lit. "Mikhi?" she called.

The stairwell before her was cool despite the day's heat, its walls seeping spiderwebs of black moisture.

"Mikhi?"

"Down here, Nadia. Come on down here." Her brother's voice was clapped instantly from behind by a thin, sharp echo.

"Did you find it?" she asked, leaning into the doorway. It was quiet for a moment, then she heard his voice again, thinned so by the echo that she thought of the sound of her own voice, as if from far away.

"Okay, Nadia?"

"Okay, what?"

"Are you coming down?"

"Is it there? Did you look in the boxes?"

"Aww, Nadia!" The way he called her name, thin and sad from within that darkness, it was a plea. She hesitated, then descended quickly after it, the way medicine is swallowed quickly so as not to taste it.

"Where are you?" she called. The cellar gradually deepened into its maze of half-walls that baffled, then blocked altogether the faint stairwell light.

"In here."

She stepped cautiously along the uneven floor, following her brother's voice into a corner room. The only light was a smudged glow from the single high window. Mikhi sat beneath the window, legs dangling atop Sitti's old steamer trunk.

"Did you find it?"

"I didn't look." Mikhi's voice caught. "Aww, Nadia. It doesn't matter."

"But why didn't you just—" she stopped herself, realizing that Mikhi probably had come down here for her sake, because she was afraid and she'd asked him to come with her. And the strange thing was that she wasn't so scared anymore. At least not now. There she was in the deepest corner of the cellar; she almost laughed.

When she turned to Mikhi, his head was down, eyes on the trunk beneath him. Brass and black leather, one side of the trunk was crayoned with writing from forty years ago. Their father had once pointed out to them the different languages—Turkish, Arabic, French, and finally, in English, the yellow and blue admittance stamp of Ellis Island, New York.

"What is it, Mikhi? What's wrong?"

"She's not going to die," he said with sureness. Then, the sureness faltering: "Do you think she's going to die?"

"Yes."

"Honest?"

"She's old, Mikhi. Old people—"

"I don't care," he said quickly. "I'm going anyway."

"Where?"

For a moment there was silence—only the muffled sounds of Sitti's footsteps above them—before Mikhi sighed, "I don't know . . . out there. Away from here." Then he touched his hair with his fingertips.

"Don't do that," Nadia said, and he lowered his hand. "When are you going?"

"I don't know."

She nodded once, slowly, as if in solemn agreement, but it was relief that she felt. If he didn't know where and he didn't know when, then maybe he wouldn't really go. And then she wouldn't have to go either, because what would they do? Who would take care of them out there in America, a girl and her little brother?

"I mean it, Nadia."

But he didn't mean it, not really. Alone, Mikhi wouldn't know what to do. Not even what to take and what to leave behind. Especially that. He wouldn't know that any more than Papa had known it.

"Nadia, will you come with me?"

"Sure," she answered quickly, easily. After all, a boy can't just walk off the way a man does.

"It doesn't matter," Mikhi said, the disappointment in his voice showing her that she'd answered too quickly. "But at least you won't tell on me, will you?"

"I don't tattle. Not anymore."

Above them, Sitti was moving something heavy, dragging it across the floor. Her moans carried even to the cellar.

"You promise?"

He still didn't believe her. She began to promise, but just then the moans from upstairs were cut short by a brief cry of surprise as something, glass or china, shattered on the dining room floor. The two of them remained still for a moment of teetering imbalance that ended abruptly with a heavy, resounding thump. Mikhi leaped from the trunk and ran ahead of her up the stairs.

"Help to stand," Sitti said, hearing the sound of their feet. She had fallen to her knees, the side of her face leaning against an open drawer of the buffet. She must have been trying to shove the buffet away from the wall so she could search behind it.

"Sitti," Mikhi spoke quickly, "should I go find Uncle Eddie?"

"No," Sitti said, whispering, as if she had strength only for that. "Jus' help to stand." She held out one arm, and Mikhi took it.

"Ach!" she cried out at the force of his grip. Immediately, Mikhi released the hand.

"My heart," Sitti hugged herself, "my heart. Achhh. . . ."

"Is it a heart attack?" Mikhi's voice rose on the word *attack*, threatening to rise to a screech if she answered yes, but Sitti didn't answer. Instead, she braced her forearms against the buffet and slowly, but with less effort than Nadia had imagined it would take, raised herself to her feet.

"Did you find it, Sitti?" Nadia asked. She looked down at the shattered remains of what had been the china teapot. "Was it in the tea—"

Sitti closed her eyes as if to silence her. She stood that way for a few seconds, consulting some inner pain. Then the three braids that stuck out over the collar of her nightgown quivered a little, and she belched, a low weak sound.

"G'wan," she told them—they were staring at her—"G'wan, don't lookit me." She leaned against the buffet. "Achhh. . . ."

"What *is* it, Sitti?" Again Mikhi's voice rose, like a girl's.

"Nothing. G'wan."

"Can I get you something? What do you want us to *do?*"

"Nothing," she answered, but simply, even lightly, as if somehow pleased.

Mikhi looked to Nadia. His eyes were wide, near panic. Then he lowered his head and spoke. "You're not sick," he said.

There was utter silence, and Nadia was frightened by the sudden realization that she was about to laugh.

"You're not sick at all," Mikhi said once more, looking up now. He was actually smiling, although his eyes kept blinking as if somebody were shaking a fist in front of them. "You're all right. It's just gas. I know it is."

"You be shaddap!" Sitti growled. Then she cursed him in Arabic, "*Ibn menyouk!*"

Mikhi flinched, but stood firm. "You're not sick," he said again.

Sitti turned furiously to Nadia, as to a witness. Mikhi, too was looking at her now. Then, slowly, he shifted his gaze to Sitti, and her face collapsed in fear at the sight of him. She raised both hands to her eyes and began to cry out weakly, muttering like a child on the verge of tears.

\*

"And that was when he give to me the Evil Eye, *ya djinn, ya ibn menyouk!* The girl here, she see it all!"

Uncle Eddie listened patiently while Sitti went on and on, slipping in and out of Arabic and rushing the words so rapidly together that the children—made to sit quietly at the kitchen table—could barely follow it. She paced back and forth behind Mikhi's chair, and Nadia watched her uncle smoke his cigarette with those nervous double-drags. Now and then, distractedly, he reached to his neck and touched the golden thread. The charm against the Evil Eye was suspended from it, a single porcelain gleam at the hair of his throat. Nadia had noticed it as soon as he walked in the house. She was sure Mikhi must have seen it. And Sitti too, as she hurried to the door, grasping Eddie's sleeve with both hands before he was hardly inside. Uncle Eddie didn't even try to hide it. All he did was shrug—a son cowed by the suddenness of his mother's fury—and call her and Mikhi into the kitchen. Then Sitti started all over again from the beginning: Mikhi had been tormenting her all day. Worse yet, she was sick to dying, and the boy gave her the Evil Eye—wasn't that so, Nadia?

She squirmed in her chair, answering neither yes nor no. She was innocent, but for the first time uneasy in the tattletale pleasure of such innocence; after all, Mikhi was right. Here their grandmother stood, alive, hands working as she spoke, and her voice strong. She wasn't sick at all. Mikhi knew that. She wasn't going to die.

"Isn't that so, Nadia? Speak up, girl," Sitti paused only a second before again launching into an angry jabber of Arabic.

And the charm, all the good luck of it hanging there at Eddie's throat the whole time they were searching, seemed forgotten; its luck granted or not—both Sitti and Uncle Eddie were acting now as if it never mattered in the first place. And Mikhi had known that too.

Her brother was watching her. She could feel the heat of his stare, and she turned to him. *No matter what you answer*, his look told her, *I'm still going to catch it*. Then he turned away. *So save yourself*, his turning away said, and she was free.

"Well, Nadia?"

Uncle Eddie put out his cigarette. Then he reached down and rested one hand on the buckle of the snakeskin belt, waiting.

"Sitti isn't sick," she found herself saying, and so calmly that her own voice sounded strange to her. "And all Mikhi did, he just looked at her, that's all. It wasn't the Evil Eye."

"Ach!" Sitti was furious, betrayed.

And so, after Mikhi got the belt, Nadia would be next. She knew that. But already, calmly, she was beginning to think about what it would be like for them afterward. It would not be easy; even so, she felt a wordless yet certain anticipation: the two of them luckless, free in Boston and Chicago and Holy Toledo, the rest of their lives lost in the American homesickness. What should they take with them?

Next to her, Mikhi released a nervous sound, almost a laugh.

Then it was over, her brother's voice cut off in the suck of breath as Uncle Eddie reached out to grasp him by the arm. The belt flashed, and Mikhi shrieked with each sharp flick and slap, again and again and again.

Nadia would be next. Calmly, she closed her eyes and tried to imagine America, how it will be, and what they should take with them when they go.

## For Better Reading: Reading On

Immigrants have come to America from every part of the world. Although their addresses are officially San Francisco, New York, Detroit, or Chicago, many live in neighborhoods and communities with names of their own—names like Greektown and Chinatown, Harlem and El Barrio.

Do they live together by choice or by necessity? Is this the "real" America? To an outsider, such communities can seem like foreign countries, where different languages are spoken, different clothes worn, and different food displayed in the shops.

Yet by getting acquainted with the people—not trying to understand everything at once but not giving up—you'll discover here too is America.

You might feel a similar strangeness at the beginning of "Holy Toledo," in which even the title is misleading if you don't read on.

## Important Details

1. At the beginning of the story, Nadia and her younger brother Mikhail, or Mikhi for short, live with their grandmother and uncle in (a) Zahleh, Lebanon (b) Detroit, Michigan (c) Lazarine, Illinois (d) Toledo, Ohio.
2. After the death of the children's mother, their father (a) left America, promising to send for them later (b) brought them to his mother, then just went away (c) enlisted in the United States Navy (d) blamed the family's problems on the Evil Eye.

3. One reason Nadia wanted to find the amulet, or good luck charm, was (a) she had borrowed it without permission (b) it was worth a great deal of money (c) to avoid Uncle Eddie's punishment (d) she was angry at her brother Mikhail.

## Questioning the Story

1. After the death of Sitti's uncle, why did the amulet become hers? What does this indicate about its probable powers and value? What makes it likely the amulet is not permanently lost?
2. What effect does Nadia hope finding the amulet will have on Sitti, her grandmother? How does Mikhi react when her groans get louder?
3. Why was Sitti considered "lucky" to have a son like Eddie? How does this uncle mean trouble to the children?
4. Name at least two special feature of "Little Syria," where Nadia lived. In reality, who are the "college mums" who shop there Saturdays? Why would Nadia think America was a "huge strangeness"?
5. Uncle Eddie felt "lost the whole time" he was in the Navy. Why might he have felt more lost and homesick than most of his shipmates? What effect might hearing of Eddie's experiences have had upon Nadia?
6. What happened to the charm during Eddie's naval service? How did he react to Nadia's "funny story" about Mikhi's imitating the old people? How were her motives misjudged?
7. Name a trait of Nadia and Mikhi's father exhibited by each of his children. Explain their father's attitude toward luck and bad omens, and give an example.
8. What did Nadia suddenly recognize was Mikhi's reason for going to the cellar? When she found him sitting on the steamer trunk, what decision had Mikhi just made? What problems did Nadia foresee that Mikhi didn't? By answering "sure" too quickly, what did Nadia make him realize?
9. What caused Mikhi and Nadia to rush upstairs? After coming to his grandmother's aid, what did Mikhi realize about her illness? Why was the old woman frightened by his knowing this?
10. Where did the children actually "discover" the amulet? Of what did Mikhi's grandmother accuse him and why? How did both children show loyalty to one another in regard to this accusation?

# Looking Deeper

## I. "Yearning to Breathe Free . . ."

The old steamer trunk bore the admittance stamp from Ellis Island, where the nearby Statue of Liberty greets immigrants with promises of freedom. How do the amulet and evil eye represent one way in which Sitti and Uncle Eddie were not free?

How does their father's reaction toward the yellow bird show a different attitude? Why might he seem most likely to believe in the power of fate or luck?

## II. "The Huge Strangeness, America"

Nadia and Mikhi's mother was an "American." Does the story lead you to believe the marriage was happy? Why or why not? In general terms, where do you believe their father has gone and why?

At the end, Nadia imagines being "lost in the American homesickness." What does she envision happening? Do you think Nadia and Mikhi will really feel "lost" or will they "find themselves" there? Explain the reasons for your answer. How does the father use the expression "Holy Toledo," and how does the phrase help show the children's attitude toward this "huge strangeness, America"?

# Snatched Away

## by *Mary TallMountain*

**Indian Name:** *Kayukon Athabascan*

NEAR FOUR MILE SUMMER CAMP, the Indians were nudging their fishwheel into calmer water. The Yukon was in a fierce, frowning mood. It tossed spray hissing skyward, hurled it back down like heavy rain into the weltering currents. Where stubborn little creeks shouldered out insistently, the river surged to attack, writhing up in silt-brown rapids. Accustomed to its tempers, the men kept tending the wheel, which alternately plunged two carved spruce arms into the current to rotate with the tide. An oblong wire basket at the end of the arm scooped up fish; on the next rotation, as the arm tipped, the fish slithered into a box nailed to the raft deck of the fishwheel; the arm loomed up again like a windmill blade, fell back, and turned with the force of the tides. The ascent of dog salmon heralded the coming of autumn; fish flowed in a stream of silvery rose.

Quick dark silhouettes against the greens of alder and cottonwood, the Indians were part of sky, river, earth itself: they wove dories through tumbling water, poled schools of darting salmon, strode like lumberjacks. Born rivermen, Clem thought with respect. Still, the river was a tough customer. In the seven years he'd been here, ten men and boys had drowned between Nulato and Kaltag.

Andy was the latest, and him only 22.

The day in 1916 when Clem had unloaded his gear at Nulato Garrison, he had met 15-year-old Andy on the riverbank, where the Army had barged the new soldiers upriver. A crooked tooth leaning into his wide white grin, the lad had offered to help Clem with his violin and banjo cases. Even then, Andy was the best there was: hunter, fisherman, trapper, nobody could beat him. Only the river could have beaten Andy.

Clem's boat chugged into the immense, misted expanses.

He wondered how Andy had felt, knowing himself caught, fighting. Did he see sky and trees flashing past? How long had he struggled, tumbled over and over in the fast rips out here where nothing existed to snag a man and hold him solid so he could keep his head above the deadly tides. Andy had never been found, though two months had passed. A cry had been heard on shore, but when the men got out and rowed toward the sound, only the voice of the river met them. Andy's empty canoe had floated in a gentle riff behind the island of silt growing in midstream.

Their friendship had stretched through the years. Clem had eaten with Andy's large family, gone with the men on hunting trips when he had leave from duty. He had thought the natives liked him as well as any *Gisakk*, the word they had for white men.

Clem thought of the afternoon he had spent talking on the riverbank with Andy and Little Jim. He thought Little Jim was related too, some way. Cousins, maybe? He couldn't find out how these people were hooked up together. Something about the families, how their forebears were related, the kinship among the whole Athabascan people, was dim and old as time.

*Clem glanced over at Andy now and then. He had already discovered that these natives didn't like to be stared at; he tried to keep them from catching him. Andy didn't seem to notice. In the tall grass he lounged on his side, wearing a white man's wool shirt and store-bought overalls, chewing a grass stem, fur cap low over his eyes. He looked just like his father, Big Mike, the stubby Russian, the way Mike must have looked when he was 15 and a lot skinnier. Andy's eyes were fixed on the river. About 50 feet out, a small bundle came rolling down fast, something tied tight in a gunnysack.*

*"Hey what's that?" Clem asked.*

*"Yeah," Little Jim muttered.*

*"It's a baby," Andy said, following it with his gaze as it tossed and turned round and round downriver.*

*"What the hell?" Clem thought he'd heard wrong.*

*"Baby." Throwed away." Andy chewed fast, wagging the grass back and forth. "When baby come out, maybe he got bum leg, maybe no leg, or he come out wrong, head mashed. Women say he's no good, tie him up, dump him over riverbank." He appeared to draw in his breath, but Clem couldn't fathom any change in his expression. "They use to do it in old time," Andy said. "Things were worse then. They quit doing it, but sometimes women still throw them if they're too bad." Andy looked out over the river, barely rippling, shining, innocent. A flock of snowgeese, in formation passing south, announced their departure in ancient ceremonial voice.*

*Little Jim said, "Lots of babies die in old time. They get* Gisakk *disease. That mean white-man sickness. We got a doctor now, but when Grandfather was living it was real bad. The people name him Old Russian."*

*Clem asked, "How did Old Russian get here on the river?" Andy said, "Grandfather—well, he's really my grandfather's papa, you know, he come upriver with three Russians. We call them* Gisakk *too, like all white men. They talk-talk all the time, maybe we call them that name because they talk about Cossack, it go round, get to be called Gisakk." Both men chuckled as if at an old joke. Andy went on, "But then came other Russians, buy furs from our people in our old hunting mountains, we call Kaiyuh. Those ones build big Russian* kashim *to live in, and trader's post store, on the river south of where Nulato sits now." He pointed the grass stem south. "Down there. That town is all gone now. Koyukuk warrior start war, burn down* kashim, *everybody die inside." Silence followed while the men considered the ancient violence.*

*"After they die, sickness come," Little Jim said. "First, it's smallpox. Old people say* Gisakk *bring it, who knows where it come from. No way to write it down. That's long time ago. Those people only talk, not read. Now we have this new sickness, this consumption, TB."*

*"That pretty bad?" Clem asked.*

*Little Jim frowned. "Yeah, no way to cure that when it get ahold. If they could go Outside, there's hospitals for it, but who could go Outside? Cost too much* dinga.*" He rubbed his thumb against his finger in the universal sign for money.*

*Andy swept his arm wide. "Many other ways to die, though," he said, crossing his legs, settling deeper into the grass. "Sometimes a house catch fire, we fight it with river water, maybe people burn up anyway. Short life for some of us. That's why our people get married so young." He laughed.*

*Little Jim stared downriver. "Lots of people drown. The current play tricks, hide, next thing it's got you. Pretty near got me, couple times." He grinned. "We don't swim. Nobody swims."*

*"Jesus," Clem said.*

With a heave of brown water, the river slammed a log into the bow of the boat, jolting Clem out of his flashes of reverie. Whew! No damage done! Seven years ago, he would have been alert to the river's tricks at a safe enough distance to get out of the way, he thought, steering away from the middle. The river hadn't been too tough for him back then; he was already a rugged fellow fresh from cavalry duty on the Mexican border, lean as a malamute, hair a sunbleached shock against perennially brown skin. His intent sea-colored eyes incessantly changed with the lights, focusing as if to X-ray everything he saw. His air was alert and confident. Seven years on the Yukon had converted him into a critter tough as walrus hide. It was his first taste of the the wilderness: raising dogs, training them for sled work and distance travel; running search-rescue missions by dogteam in winter, by motorboat in summer. All around him stretched the stark and beautiful land. He tried to write his feelings in notes of music on scraps like the secret fragments of a poet, but they escaped him.

Away in a corner of his mind, an old piano tinkled, playing Mary Joe's favorites, "Yum Yum Waltz" and "Pitti Sing Polka." The notes echoed tinnily in his head. At Ruby, a red-hot boom town, he had been playing the tunes steadily for the past three days and nights. The miners and whores had hollered for dance music. He had rounded up young Charlie Wilson, a native banjo picker, and they went up by motorboat. Those wild rough folks had insisted on high jinks and kept Clem and Charlie playing day and night. Wouldn't let them rest, threw gold and dollar bills to them, yelled for them to keep going, offered bad bootleg he and Charlie waved away. The boys worked themselves so dizzy that Charlie had stayed on with kinfolks for a visit. Clem was dog-tired, he was homesick, he'd been away from Mary Joe too long already.

His biceps were numb from the kick of the tiller against him; that fast leaping current was deadly; he kept veering into it. Twenty- and thirty-foot trees tumbled up like matchsticks, roots clawing toward the sky. He swung over, pivoted the boat into still water. Even after he dropped anchor, the river kept grabbing, trying to yank him back. He knuckled his eyes. When his vision cleared, he saw tall green reeds in a slough 60 yards off. Suddenly a clump of ducks rose, bunched, started climbing. Shots cracked. Clem flattened fast. Four birds dropped; the flock fluttered south out of gunsight.

Who the hell is it? I didn't see a boat, he thought. Nothing moved. Then Floyd Tommy pried out of the reeds, holding a bunch of mallards. He ambled over. "Got a couple." He held up the birds. "I come down here early, before the sun. Sometimes a few duck stop here."

"Nice fat mallard," Clem said.

"Not so bad, been feedin' all summer." Floyd's gangling young body was wet to his waist.

"Scared them up, I guess," Clem said, climbing out of the boat, his red rubber Pacs plopping in the water. Ice tingled clear through the heavy rubber, the thick wool socks, on up the long johns.

"Feeding off of the bottom," Floyd said and grabbed a duck by its ringed neck, and a second. He dropped them on the grass. "Grub for the pot, anyways."

"That's swell. Thanks." Clem admired the birds, the green shine of their feathers.

"Nothing extra," Floyd said.

Clem fished out a tin of King Albert. "Take a smoke," he offered.

Floyd pocketed the tobacco. He coughed deeply and spit. The spit hung on a weed, a strand of pink swaying in the wind. He walked away and Clem saw his sharp shoulderblades, thin butt. Consumption, he thought. Kid shouldn't smoke. Sorry I gave him tobacco.

Clem crawled up the bank, lay flat under a tree. Fine here, let his whole body go quiet, he thought, let the stillness float into and around him while he stared at the scrambled pale blue sky.

Kid's cough made him think of Mary Joe.

*Right after Clem had come to Nulato, he'd struck up an acquaintance with Cap Jaeger, the trader. They played fiddle and guitar for dances, with Freddy Kriska jingling and clinking away on his banjo. They practiced in Cap's store.*

*One evening Clem went outside to take a breath. Mary Joe was sitting on the porch step. He couldn't resist. He laid his hand on her gleaming, waist-long hair, bound with a bright purple band. "What a beautiful girl," he said. Once he'd seen her running through the village, hair flying, had seen that even in shapeless trousers and faded cotton shirt, she was lovely.*

*She got up; her smile seemed to glow in the dusk as she floated closer in a movement sensuous as a cat's; they faced each other. He smelled wind and furs, and something elusive like sweet grass.*

*They stood motionless, barely breathing. Then she broke the hush. "I'm about as tall as you, Clem Stone. You're my brother's friend. You know, Andy. I come and listen to you play music, but I always go away. This time, I risk it."*

*"That's no risk, girl. I'm not dangerous,"* he murmured. *The very air felt electric with the closeness of her.*

*"Oh, yes, you are,"* she said. *She pulled out a large white handkerchief, coughed lightly into it. A tingling—was it a foreshadowing of an unknowable sorrow?—shivered along his nerves. Somehow, he sensed, it broke an impasse.*

*She told him she'd just turned 21. She lived with her father, her brother Andy, and a younger brother, Steven. Her mother, Matmiya, two sisters, and a third brother had died of TB. Times were bad for the people. She did laundry for soldiers at the station. They wore "Alaska Warmies," a special Army issue of long johns, and the damned brown Army soap shrank them midget-sized. Mary Joe had a special way to wash them. It kept her busy, along with looking after her menfolk, getting in a little fishing, tending a few traps.*

*Just surviving, she had skills he'd never known existed. The traps and snares she so carefully laid, empty when the animals couldn't come out to tackle the howling cold. Wolves running hungry. Moose, caribou, galloping broomstick thin before the wolves.*

*And in the village, the hungry children.*

Affection for her family was part of the whole business of hunger, he thought. It hadn't been like that with his folks, back in California. Hardly a time he could remember when Pa or even Ma showed their love for him and brother Jass, except when they were tykes, and then it was like he dreamed it. Becky, his mother, was always wrapped in thought, eyes far away, lips moving. How badly he wanted to get into her head! She kept her thoughts wrapped up inside, the way she wrapped her outside, in dark dresses and big white aprons with tails that tied round and round and hid her tiny waist. He hoped she was happy at last. She'd finally married Balch Jopson, the hired man, after she divorced Pa. Right away, Pa married that woman from Hoptown. Pure orneriness. Pa had that terrible temper ... suspicioned Balch and Becky so hard he finally had to leave her. Clem frowned. He'd never figured out why as a kid he'd been jealous over Becky and Balch too ... Vaguely, he knew he'd inherited a trait of jealousy. He supposed he'd got it from Pa. When he thought of Mary Joe and Taria, he got too mad to talk. She had married that old man when she was 14, had a son the next year. Not long ago, Taria had gone down to live in Kaltag and had taken their son with him. Why had she let that boy go, and him only five? When Clem tried to talk to her about it, she always got him off the track with a funny remark or dinner on the table, or lovemaking, anything to derail him.

Mary Joe was jealous too, in her secret way. There was the day he'd been talking to young Talla and Mary Joe came along the boardwalk, stalked right up to them, and walloped him a good one on the jaw. She never mentioned it afterwards, but it kind of lay there between them. Mary Joe had wanted one of those little medicine sacks made of caribou hide, to hang on her belt. He'd asked Talla to make one, and he'd been telling her how the initials ought to be. Mary Joe thought he was sparking the girl! Well, jealousy or no, Clem and Mary Joe had given Lidwynne and Michael enough love to last a lifetime.

His mind magnetized to a worry that had been shoved back, these few hectic days. He and Mary Joe were about to lose their kids. He had found out from Doc Merrick that she had consumption, and he had offered to adopt them. Mary Joe had got so worked up over that, he realized, she'd forgotten Clem's last hitch was about up. Strange, but no use worrying yet. He'd just have to let things take their course. Hell, like he always figured, it would come out in the wash. . . .

A jay screamed from a lodgepole pine. Clem stood, whirled his arms, kneaded his shoulders, took a fast run along the beach and back. New energy shuttled through his blood. Kicking the boat off, he noticed his tiller arm had eased up. He'd make it. He had a damn good bulge of strength in those biceps. But his calculation had misfired again. As usual, he had underrated the river. The damned thing yanked him every which way. Time blurred. No-Oy, as the natives called the sun, was well up the sky. Its light dazzled him and he centered in again on the tiller. God! that sprint of energy hadn't lasted! At last, through his daze, he saw Pete Slough alongside. Soft grayblue wings of a pair of teal flapped, rose. His eyes swarmed with blurs as he turned from the river glare, staggered stiffly up the bank.

Willy Pitka was netting whitefish in the ruffled water of the slough. He hauled in three fish, 10 to 14 inches long, threw them into a washtub. Willy looked as if he had always been there. He was strong, fierce-looking like most of the Ten'a Athabascans; good hunter, ten kids working every day, well fed. "Fishing pretty good today," Willy said, pointing to the nearly filled tub.

Clem pummeled his cramp-knotted arm. "Good big fish," he said.

"You come down from Ruby, yah?" Willy eased the handwoven net into the water. It flowed between his chunky fingers, barely rippling into the water.

"Been playing for a dance up there," Clem said, walking back and forth, the numbness inching out of his knees.

"River pretty fast, plenty wood coming down," Willy said.

"It was real bad a few miles. Got tired fighting it and stopped up yonder, below Tommy's camp. Floyd was getting a few mallard."

Willy nodded. "There's a few places up there, duck come every year about this time. Floyd knows them pretty good. Oh, yeah, you got to watch that river."

"Need eyes in back of your head. Easier in winter when she's frozen over," Clem said.

"You still got your lead dog Beauty?" Willy asked.

"You bet. She's my brood mother, pure malamute. I've got the best team on the river. Hey, you know Manuska built me a dogsled all spruce, not a nail, bound with walrus hide. Laid it around the joints wet, and it dried like iron."

"How much you pay him?"

"Couple sawbucks."

"Worth it. You take care of your team there at the station?"

"Yeah. Got a pot outside to boil their fish. I got three males, two females, out of Beauty. Bought my breeder, Moose, from old man Patsy, set me back fifty but he's worth every cent. Saved my bacon more'n once on the trail. He knows everything, even in the worst storms."

Willy chuckled. "Like you got money in the bank. Uncle Sam has to pay every time you use that team for Army business, yah?"

"Paid for itself a hundred times over." Clem pulled out a package of salmon strip and biscuit. The rich smoke made his taste buds water. He lay back and eased his shoulder muscles into the sunwarm padding of dry reeds. He looked up at the willows. They leaned nearly horizontal over the water. Fallen trees had been bleached to ivory skeletons, and lay crushed and scattered. Small waves slapped the sides of Willy's dory. The watery sounds soothed Clem to sleep.

"You got it made better'n three-quarters downriver to home now." The voice was just loud enough. Guess Willy figured I'd snooze too long, Clem thought. Time to get on. The voice continued, "You going to Nulato?" Willy's dense eyebrows almost grazed his straight soot-colored lashes.

"That's where I'm heading. Two, maybe three hours?"

"Three hours do it, I guess," Willy said, hauling net. He tossed another pair of whitefish into the tub, piled the net with great care into the dory. His teeth gleamed with good humor.

"Your camp downriver a ways?" Clem asked. He stretched and yawned. He thought, I'm rested now, maybe I can make it before dark.

"Yeah, we use the same old camp. Had that camp many years. Good run on kings this summer. Usually I come up here, get whitefish, let my boys handle the wheel."

Clem looked south. Away, faint in the clear air, the purple crest of the Kaiyuh range rested on the horizon. "Willy!" He pointed. "You think there's a Woodsman in Kaiyuh?"

Willy's face crinkled around the grin in tiny rolls of brown, velvety skin. "Oh, sure. Lotsa Woodsman over there."

"You ever see one?" Clem wasn't sure Willy was on the level. Probably joshing him.

"Yep. Mad like bear, bad like bear. Steal babies." Willy's crinkles deepened and formed fans. They laughed.

"So long, Willy."

"See you."

Clem stepped into his boat and pulled the starter cord. The engine barked and on the next yank snapped to life. Almost at once, the boat kept trying to get out of his hands and pull out into the heavy rip. He needed all his wits just keeping her steady outside the churning middle river. A red horde of dog salmon thrashed upriver. They leaped against the edges of the riptide, fell back. He steered away, the tiller held hard against his body. It's a stampede out there, he thought, looking over his shoulder at the line of furious red dog salmon action. There's something besides fish alive, out in that river.

He had a sudden sense of repeated time, of some old and half forgotten grief.

*He was carrying Lidwynne along a village path, and her frosty breaths puffed out on the windless air. Mary Joe's boots padded behind him as his heavy steps angrily crunched the snow. He held the swinging lantern; its light bobbed in yellow winkings. His mind babbled. We will go on through the night snow and we will never come back. We will go to the hills, Mary Joe. They will never part us. She caught up with him. There was no sound as Mary Joe looked into the baby's face. The moon reflected roundly silver in her pupils. Snow drifted down out of the spruces. The silence was broken by a sighing sound, descending from an immense distance. His anger left him. Only weariness remained. He turned with Mary Joe and they went back. Inside the cabin, he laid the baby in bed and kissed the corner of her sleeping mouth.*

*At his shoulder, Mary Joe said, "You can't have her. She must go somewhere else." His breath was heavy; he heard the muffled beating of his heart. Her face was deep in the shadows. "Clem, I have a new baby in here." She laid his hand on her belly and they rested on the lynx-fur blankets. His mind played a small wandering melody; they drifted to sleep.*

He did not know whether it was a dream or a strange, obscure knowledge; now it had come again to him in the fury of the river, the somber weariness of his body; he saw their faces in the aimless, enclosing mists of the Yukon, and he knew it would be so for all of his life.

He looked at his hands, rigidly white on the tiller. Needles of ice prodded them. The beaver-lined moosehide mittens he had forgotten to bring flashed into his mind. Mary Joe had sewn and beaded them.

Her face came toward him. The high flush of her flaring cheekbones. The gentle hollows beneath. The eyes he could never describe. The children, their laughter flashing white. Three faces together, wavering in the thin and growing mist.

Indian. Indianness. The words floated through his thoughts. He jerked his head, trying to flick away the daze. He shouted into the mist, "What difference now, how much the blood is mixed? Our kids are as much Irish or Russian or Scotch as Indian. What difference now?"

His words were snatched away by the wind.

## For Better Reading: Aftereffects

It's useless to ask, "Which comes first, the title or the story?" because the answer is, "It all depends ..."

Some titles, like "The Guided Tour of 7th Avenue," help focus your thoughts as you begin reading. Others, like *The Third Life of Per Smevik*, raise a question answered near the start.

"Snatched Away" is another kind of title, one intended to make you keep thinking about life and its meaning after you finish the story. Such titles are less closely related to action than theme—those ideas about life and human nature the writer explores. Not until the ending do all the threads of action, thought, and characterization come together. Then, by looking back to the title, you see how carefully and silently the author has woven them into a whole that often can "make people feel something more than they understood."

This is the afteraffect of a good thematic title. It's an idea about life, stated in a few words, that may remain in your mind long after you forget precise details of the story itself.

## Key Ideas

1. The Indian fishermen on the Yukon River are described as (a) being superstitious about the Great River Spirit (b) seeming part of sky, river, earth itself (c) refusing to adapt to modern ways (d) about to lose their tribal hunting grounds.
2. Clem had come to Alaska seven years earlier (a) to do research on the Athabascan Indians (b) as a prospector during the Yukon Gold Rush (c) as a soldier stationed at Nulato Garrison (d) to escape being arrested in California.
3. Clem thought Andy was (a) the best hunter, fisherman, and trapper around (b) too willing to take unnecessary risks (c) prejudiced against Gisakk white men (d) the only native he liked and admired.

## Questioning the Story

1. How and when had Clem first met Andy? Once Andy was caught in the fast rips of the Yukon, why would struggle against the deadly tides be hopeless? What was the only physical evidence of what happened to him?
2. What signals the flashback to Clem's afternoon talk with Andy and Little Jim on the riverbank? Of what former practice concerning babies did Clem learn that day?
3. What "old joke" explains how the word *Gisakk* originated? List two reasons why life is dangerous and often short for many in the Yukon.
4. Upon arriving in the Yukon, why was Clem already a "rugged fellow"? What outdoor jobs occupied him the seven years since? How is music also part of his life?
5. While Clem thinks back to Andy as well as events in the boomtown of Ruby, he is also fighting the river. Find at least three examples showing its fierceness.
6. What gift did Floyd Tommy offer Clem? Why did Clem regret giving the boy tobacco in return? How does this echo Clem's conversation with Little Jim in a flashback?
7. Who was Mary Joe? Describe two "survival skills" that helped her keep herself and her family alive.
8. How does the affection in Mary Joe's family compare with Clem's in California? What mismatched marriage was in Mary Joe's past? How did both she and Clem show their jealousy of one another?
9. As Clem navigated the river, his mind "magnetized" to his chief worry.

What offer had Doc Merrick made to Clem and Mary Joe, and why? What had Mary Joe forgotten, and why is this also a cause for concern?

10. During the talk with Willy Pitka, what proves Clem does quite well financially? What acts are the "Woodsman" of the Kaiyuh mountain range said to perform? Find at least two clues that the Woodsman are probably supernatural evil spirits, which some Alaskans believe in.

## Looking Deeper

### I. Was It a Dream?

According to the third passage in italics, "His mind babbled. We will go on through the night snow and we will never come back.... They will never part us." Explain what Clem is trying to convince himself. Although Clem wonders if it's a dream or "strange, obscure knowledge," what part can't be literally true and why?

Near the end of the story, what does Clem know "would be so for all of his life"? How does this uphold his thinking, "they will never part us"?

### II. What Really Matters

At the end, Clem shouts into the wind, "What difference now?" Explain the differences that have troubled him while living in Alaska.

From the entire story, find at least three examples of someone's being "snatched away" from life. At the end, Clem's words were also "snatched away" by the wind. Based on your reading, explain how would you answer his question.

Including the idea expressed by the title, write your version of the story's theme in a 12–20 word sentence.

# Saturday Belongs to the Palomía

## by Daniel L. Garza

| | |
|---|---|
| **Born:** | *Hillsboro, Texas, 1938* |
| **Family background:** | *Parents fled to USA from 1916 Mexican Revolution* |
| **Graduate:** | *Texas Christian University* |
| **Career:** | *Served in US Army, worked in public relations, continuing to write short stories* |
| **This selection:** | *First written in Spanish, Garza's first language* |

EVERY YEAR, IN THE MONTH of September, the cotton pickers come up from the Valley, and the *braceros* come from Mexico itself. They come to the town in Texas where I live, all of them, the whole *palomía*. "*Palomía*" is what we say; it is slang among my people, and I do not know how to translate it exactly. It means maybe gang. It means a bunch of people. It means ... the cotton pickers when they come. You call the whole bunch of them the *palomía*, but one by one they are cotton pickers, *pizcadores*.

Not many of them have traveled so far north before, and for the ones who have not it is a great experience. And it is an opportunity to know other kinds of people, for the young ones. For the older ones it is only a chance to make some money picking cotton. Some years the cotton around my town is not so good, and then the *pizcadores* have to go farther north, and we see them less.

But when they come, they come in full force to my little town that is full of gringos. Only a few of us live there who speak Spanish among ourselves, and whose parents maybe came up like the *pizcadores* a long time ago. It is not like the border country where there are many of both kinds of people; it is gringo country mostly, and most of the time we and the gringos live there together without worrying much about such matters.

In September and October in my town, Saturdays belong to the *pizcadores*. During the week they are in the fields moving up and down the long cotton rows with big sacks and sweating frightfully, but making *centavitos* to spend on Saturday at the movie, or on clothes, or on food. The gringos come to town during the week to buy their merchandise and groceries, but finally Saturday arrives, and the *pizcadores* climb aboard their trucks on the cotton farms, and the trucks all come to town. It is the day of the *palomía*, and most of the gringos stay at home.

"*Ay, qué gringos!*" the *pizcadores* say. "What a people to hide themselves like that. But such is life. . . ."

For Saturday the *pizcadores* dress themselves in a special and classy style. The girls comb their black hair, put on new bright dresses and low-heeled shoes, and the color they wear on their lips is, the way we say it, enough. The boys dress up in black pants and shoes with taps on the heels and toes. They open their shirts two or three buttons to show their chests and their Saint Christophers; then at the last they put a great deal of grease on their long hair and comb it with care. The old men, the *viejos*, shave and put on clean plain clothes, and the old women put on a tunic and comb their hair and make sure the little ones are clean, and all of them come to town.

They come early, and they arrive with a frightful hunger. The town, being small, has only a few restaurants. The *pizcadores*—the young ones and the ones who have not been up from Mexico before—go into one of the restaurants, and the owner looks at them.

One who speaks a little English says they want some *desayuno*, some breakfast.

He looks at them still. He says: "Sorry. We don't serve Meskins."

Maybe then one of the *pachuco* types with the long hair and the Saint Christopher says something ugly to him in Spanish, maybe not. Anyhow, the others do not, but leave sadly, and outside the old men who did not go in nod among themselves, because they knew already. Then maybe, standing on the sidewalk, they see a gringo go into the restaurant. He needs a shave and is dirty and smells of sweat, and before the doors closes they hear the owner say: "What say, Blacky? What'll it be this morning?"

The little ones who have understood nothing begin to holler about the way their stomachs feel, and the papás go to the market to buy some food there.

I am in the grocery store, me and a few gringos and many of the *palomía*. I have come to buy flour for my mother. I pass a *pizcador*, a father who is busy keeping his little ones from knocking cans down out of the big piles, and he smiles to me and says: "*Qué tal, amigo?*"

"*Pues, así no más,*" I answer.

He looks at me again. He asks in a quick voice. "You are a Chicano?"

"*Sí.*"

"How is it that you have missed the sun in your face, muchacho?" he says. "A big hat, maybe?"

"No, señor," I answer. "I live here."

"You have luck."

And I think to myself, yes. I have luck; it is good to live in one place. And all of a sudden the *pizcador* and I have less to say to each other, and he says *adiós* and gathers up his flow of little ones and goes out to the square where the boys and girls of the *palomía* are walking together.

On the square too there is usually a little lady selling hot tamales. She is dressed simply, and her white hair is in a bun, and she has a table with a big can of tamales on it which the *palomía* buy while they are still hot from the stove at the little lady's home.

"Mamacita, mamacita," the little ones shout at their mothers. "Doña Petra is here. Will you buy me some tamalitos?"

Doña Petra lives there in the town, and the mothers in the *palomía* are her friends because of her delicious tamales and because they go to her house to talk of the cotton picking, of children, and maybe of the fact that in the north of Texas it takes somebody like Doña Petra to find good masa for tamales and tortillas. Away from home as the *pizcadores* are, it is good to find persons of the race in a gringo town.

On the street walk three *pachucos*, seventeen or eighteen years old. They talk *pachuco* talk. One says: "Listen, *chabos*, let's go to the good movie."

"O. K." another one answers. "Let's go flutter the good eyelids."

They go to the movie house. Inside, on a Saturday, there are no gringos, only the *palomía*. The *pachucos* find three girls, and sit down with them. The movie is in English, and they do not understand much of it, but they laugh with the girls and make the *viejos* angry, and anyhow the cartoon—the mono, they call it—is funny by itself, without the need for English.

Other *pachucos* walk in gangs through the streets of the town, looking for something to do. One of them looks into the window of Mr. Jones's barber shop and tells the others that he thinks he will get a haircut. They laugh, because haircuts are something that *pachucos* do not get, but one of them dares him. "It will be like the restaurant," he says. "Gringo scissors do not cut Chicano hair."

So he has to go in, and Mr. Jones looks at him as the restaurant man looked at the others in the morning. But he is a nicer man than the restaurant man, and what he says is that he has to go to lunch when he has finished with the customers who are waiting. "There is a Mexican barber across the square," he says. "On Walnut Street. You go there."

The *pachuco* tells him a very ugly thing to do and then combs his long hair in the mirror and then goes outside again, and on the sidewalk he and his friends say bad things about Mr. Jones for a while until they get tired of it, and move on. The gringo customers in the barber shop rattle the magazines they are holding in their laps, and one of them says a thing about cotton pickers, and later in the day it is something that the town talks about, gringos and *pizcadores* and those of my people who live there, all of them. I hear about it, but forget, because September in my town is full of such things, and in the afternoon I go to the barber shop for a haircut the way I do on Saturdays all year long.

Mr. Jones is embarrassed when he sees me. "You hear about that?" he says. "That kid this morning?"

I remember then, and I say yes, I heard.

"I'm sorry, Johnny," he says, "Doggone it. You know I'm not ..."

"I know," I say.

"The trouble is, if they start coming, they start bringing the whole damn family, and then your regular customers get mad," he says.

"I know," I say, and I do. There is no use in saying that I don't, because I live in the town for the other ten or eleven months of the year when the *palomía* is not here but in Mexico and the Valley. I know the gringos of the town and what they are like, and they are many different ways. So I tell Mr. Jones that I know what he means.

"Get in the chair," he says. "You want it short or medium this time?"

And I think about the *pizcador* in the grocery store and what he said about my having luck, and I think again it is good to live in one place and not to have to travel in trucks to where the cotton is.

At about six in the afternoon all the families begin to congregate at what they call the *campo*. *Campo* means camp or country, and this *campo* is an area with a big tin shed that the state Unemployment Commission puts up where the farmers who have cotton to be picked can come and find the *pizcadores* who have not yet found a place to work. But on Saturday nights in September the *campo* does not have anything to do with work. The families come, bringing tacos to eat and maybe a little beer if they have it. After it is dark, two or three of the men bring out guitars, and some others have concertinas. They play the fast, twisty mariachi music of the places they come from, and someone always sings. The songs are about women and love and sometimes about a town that the song says is a fine town, even if there is no work there for *pizcadores*. All the young people begin to dance, and the old people sit around making certain that the *pachucos* do not get off into the dark with their daughters. They talk, and they eat, and they drink a little beer, and then at twelve o'clock it is all over.

The end of Saturday has come. The old men gather up their sons and daughters, and the mothers carry the sleeping little ones like small sacks of cotton to the trucks, and the whole *palomía* returns to the country to work for another week, and to earn more *centavitos* with which, the Saturday that comes after the week, to go to the movies, and buy groceries, and pay for *tamalitos* of Doña Petra and maybe a little beer for the dance at the *campo*. And the mothers will visit with Doña Petra, and the *pachucos* will walk the streets, and the other things will happen, all through September and October, each Saturday the same, until finally, early in November, the cotton harvest is over, and the *pizcadores* go back to their homes in the Valley or in Mexico.

The streets of my town are empty then, on Saturdays. It does not have many people, most of the year. On Saturday mornings you see a few gringo children waiting for the movie to open, and not much else. The streets are empty, and the gringos sit in the restaurant and the barber shop and talk about the money they made or lost on the cotton crop that fall.

# For Better Reading: Going to the Source

Sigmund Freud (1856–1939) is called the founder of psychoanalysis. Yet the man who became world famous for his revolutionary ideas about people's subconscious mental processes did not develop his theories by scientific studies, alone.

Long before the beginnings of psychiatry, great writers have probed beneath the surface and tried to express people's innermost thoughts and feelings. William Shakespeare and Russian novelist Feodor Dostoyevski are two, and both are credited with influencing Freud himself.

Like Freud, every good reader can gain a better understanding of human pyschology by reading plays, short stories, novels, and poems, as well as scientific texts.

First, you must decide whether the writer seeks to portray life as it is—or merely invites you to "take an exciting ride" with unrealistic characters and suspenseful but unlikely plots. And, you can only judge by putting yourself in the characters' place. To be true to human nature, writing must allow you to put yourself in the picture—not as you dream of being sometime, but as you know yourself now.

It's a simple test that helps you understand human pyschology and also become a better judge of good writing and literature.

## Words in Context

1. "Saturdays belong to the *pizcadores.*" *Pizcadores* means (a) cotton pickers as individuals (b) illegal migrant workers from Mexico (c) Mexican-Americans who speak only Spanish (d) those who've never crossed the border before.
2. "Other *pachucos* walk in gangs through the streets ..." *Pachucos* are (a) striking migrant workers (b) Mexican-American protest marchers (c) *gringo* patrols policing the streets (d) long-haired teenage boys.
3. The smiling father asked, "Qué tal, amigo?" The answer was, "Pues, así no más." To the question, "How's everything, friend?", the answer probably meant (a) I don't understand (b) Not bad (c) Get lost (d) Don't ask me.

## Questioning the Selection

1. How does the narrator, Johnny, differ from most people who live year-round in this small northern Texas town? Most of the year, how are Mexican-Americans' lives different here than in towns nearer the border?

2. Compare the attitudes of the younger and older *pizcadores* to traveling so far north. What proves Johnny is young himself?
3. In the first paragraph, Johnny says *palomía* means "maybe gang." What subconscious feeling about them does this reveal? Why might he unknowingly resent the *palomía* as a threat to his acceptance in the community?
4. How do "most of the gringos" or white population behave differently on Saturdays from other days? What is obviously unfair about the restaurant owner's treatment of the young *pizcadores*, in comparison with the unshaven and dirty gringo?
5. What would having "sun in his face" show about Johnny? What made Johnny lucky, and why did he and the *pizcador* suddenly "have less to say to each other"?
6. What are the joke and dare behind the *pachucos'* decision to ask for a haircut? Why is the barber a "nicer man than the restaurant man"?
7. Why did Mr. Jones, the barber, act embarrassed and apologetic toward Johnny? What does Johnny "know" about some gringos' attitudes?
8. Explain whether the state Unemployment Commission camp seems a happy or dull place Saturday night in September, and why.
9. Compare Johnny's hometown on Saturdays in September with the activity in other months. Does the final paragraph make it seem a happy or dull place? Explain your reasons, giving specific words that influenced you.

## Looking Deeper

### I. Protecting Your Turf

According to psychologists, both human beings and animals, by nature, seek to protect their own territory or space. In what ways did the *palomía* threaten Johnny's "turf"?

The barber told Johnny, "Doggone it. You know I'm not . . ." Complete his intended meaning, and explain whether or not you find his feelings understandable or blameworthy, and why.

Johnny said he understood the barber's feelings, adding "There is no use in saying that I don't." What does he find difficult to understand?

### II. Taking a Stand

Both Johnny and the barber had their own reasons for feeling as they did towards the *palomías*. Compare their attitudes, and explain how they are both alike and different.

Do you think either or both should have taken a stand against what they knew was wrong? Explain why or why not.

In response to Mr. Jones's phony excuse for not giving him a haircut, do you feel the *pachuco* was justified in telling him "a very ugly thing to do"? Why or why not?

## III. The Influence of Place

This story is very concerned with the influence of place on people's lives. How might Johnny's life have been different if he were living closer to the Mexican border?

Johnny felt himself lucky "to live in one place." In what sense might he have not been lucky?

# Easter: Wahiawa, 1959

## by Cathy Song

| | |
|---|---|
| **Born:** | *Honolulu, Hawaii, in 1955* |
| **Holds degrees:** | *From Wellesley College, Boston University* |
| **Career:** | *Lives and teaches in Hawaii; published two books of poetry* |

1

The rain stopped for one afternoon.
Father brought out
his movie camera and for a few hours
we were all together
under a thin film                                                     5
that separated the rain showers
from that part of the earth
like a hammock
held loosely by clothespins.

Grandmother took the opportunity                                     10
to hang the laundry
and Mother and my aunts
filed out of the house
in pedal pushers and poodle cuts,
carrying the blue washed eggs.                                       15

Grandfather kept the children
penned in on the porch,
clucking at us in his broken English
whenever we tried to peek
around him. There were bread crumbs                                  20
stuck to his blue gray whiskers.

I looked from him to the sky,
a membrane of egg whites
straining under the weight
of the storm that threatened                    25
to break.


We burst loose from Grandfather
when the mothers returned
from planting the eggs
around the soggy yard.                           30
He followed us,
walking with stiff but sturdy legs.
We dashed and disappeared
into bushes,
searching for the treasures;                     35
the hard-boiled eggs
which Grandmother had been simmering
in vinegar and blue color all morning.


      2
When Grandfather was a young boy
in Korea,                                        40
it was a long walk
to the riverbank,
where, if he were lucky,
a quail egg or two
would gleam from the mud                         45
like gigantic pearls.
He could never eat enough
of them.


It was another long walk
through the sugarcane fields                     50
of Hawaii,
where he worked for eighteen years,
cutting the sweet stalks
with a machete. His right arm
grew disproportionately large                    55
to the rest of his body.
He could hold three
grandchildren in that arm.

I want to think
that each stalk that fell                                        60
brought him closer
to a clearing,
to that palpable field
where from the porch
to the gardenia hedge                                            65
that day he was enclosed
by his grandchildren,
scrambling around him,
for whom he could at last buy
cratefuls of oranges,                                            70
basketfuls of sky blue eggs.

I found three that afternoon.
By evening, it was raining hard.
Grandfather and I skipped supper.
Instead, we sat on the porch                                     75
and I ate what he peeled
and cleaned for me.
The scattering of the delicate
marine-colored shells across his lap
was something like what the ocean gives                          80
the beach after a rain.

## Questioning the Poem

1. Easter egg hunts and colored eggs are traditional on this Christian
   holy day. Quote lines in part 1 showing that Easter on Wahiawa, 1959,
   included both.
2. In what way did the weather "separate" this day from the ones before?
   How would the father's movie camera also "separate" these hours from
   others?
3. What does Grandmother do that shows this day is not actually separate
   from the rest? How is Grandfather contrasted with the "up-to-date
   American" mother and aunts?
4. Basing your answer on part 1, what are two reasons the eggs would
   seem like "treasures" to the children?
5. Find evidence in part 2 that eggs were also a treasure to Grandfather
   as a boy.
6. Lines 41 and 49 both refer to "long walks." What even longer journey
   had to occur between stanzas six and seven? What questions about
   this journey are left unanswered?
7. Judged by stanza seven, was Grandfather's life in Hawaii easy or difficult? Use specific evidence to support your answer.

8. In lines 63–67, "that palpable field" is the actual scene from the porch on Easter day. What element of the landscape represents its beauty? How else was Grandfather "enclosed"?
9. What "treasures" does Grandfather offer his grandchildren? By stating he "could at last buy" these things, what does the poem imply about his life?
10. What shows a child's appreciation of the grandfather? What, more than sky blue eggs, has he given his grandchild?

## Looking Deeper

### "A Long Walk"

List three details in part 1 that make the grandfather seem useless and unimportant. How does this viewpoint change in part 2?

Lines 59–62 state, "I want to think that each stalk that fell brought him closer to a clearing." Explain how the poem relates "clearing" to each of the following: (1) a clearing in the weather, (2) an actual piece of land, (3) a time of life.

How might "each stalk that fell" contribute to this "clearing" in Grandfather's life? What has the grandfather given his family, and what does he still give, according to the underlying meaning of the last stanza? In what ways has he accomplished or fallen short of the American dream, in your opinion?

# My Heart Has Reopened to You
## The Place Where I Was Born

*by Alice Walker*

| | |
|---|---|
| ***Born:*** | *Eatonton, Georgia* |
| ***Graduate:*** | *Sarah Lawrence College, New York* |
| ***Literary career:*** | *Poet, novelist, winner of an American Book Award and Pulitzer Prize for the novel,* The Color Purple |

**I** AM A DISPLACED PERSON. I sit here on a swing on the deck of my house in Northern California admiring how the fog has turned the valley below into a lake. For hours nothing will be visible below me except this large expanse of vapor; then slowly, as the sun rises and gains in intensity, the fog will start to curl up and begin its slow rolling drift toward the ocean. People here call it the dragon; and, indeed, a dragon is what it looks like, puffing and coiling, winged, flaring and in places thin and discreet, as it races before the sun, back to its ocean coast den. Mornings I sit here in awe and great peace. The mountains across the valley come and go in the mist; the redwoods and firs, oaks and giant bays appear as clumpish spires, enigmatic shapes of green, like the stone forests one sees in Chinese paintings of Guilin.

It is incredibly beautiful where I live. Not fancy at all, or exclusive. But from where I sit on my deck I can look down on the backs of hawks, and the wide, satiny wings of turkey vultures glistening in the sun become my present connection to ancient Egyptian Africa. The pond is so still below me that the trees reflected in it seem, from this distance, to be painted in its depths.

All this: the beauty, the quiet, the cleanliness, the peace, is what I love. I realize how lucky I am to have found it here. And yet, there are days when my view of the mountains and redwoods makes me nostalgic for small rounded hills easily walked over, and for the look of big leaf poplar and the scent of pine.

I am nostalgic for the land of my birth, the land I left forever when I was thirteen—moving first to the town of Eatonton, and then, at seventeen, to the city of Atlanta.

I cried one day as I talked to a friend about a tree I loved as a child. A tree that had sheltered my father on his long cold walk to school each morning: it was midway between his house and the school and because there was a large cavity in its trunk, a fire could be made inside it. During my childhood, in a tiny, overcrowded house in a tiny dell below it, I looked up at it frequently and felt reassured by its age, its generosity despite its years of brutalization (the fires, I knew, had to hurt), and its tall, old-growth pine nobility. When it was struck by lightning and killed, and then was cut down and made into firewood, I grieved as if it had been a person. Secretly. Because who among the members of my family would not have laughed at my grief?

I have felt entirely fortunate to have had this companion, and even today remember it with gratitude. But why the tears? my friend wanted to know. And it suddenly dawned on me that perhaps it *was* sad that it was a tree and not a member of my family to whom I was so emotionally close.

As a child I assumed I would always have the middle Georgia landscape to live in, as Brer Rabbit, a native also, and relative, had his brier patch. It was not to be. The pain of racist oppression, and its consequence, economic impoverishment, drove me to the four corners of the earth in search of justice and peace, and work that affirmed my whole being. I have come to rest here, weary from travel, on a deck—not a southern front porch—overlooking another world.

I am content; and yet, I wonder what my life would have been like if I had been able to stay home?

I remember early morning fogs in Georgia, not so dramatic as California ones, but magical too because out of the Southern fog of memory tramps my dark father, smiling and large, glowing with rootedness, and talking of hound dogs, biscuits and coons. And my equally rooted mother bustles around the corner of our house preparing to start a wash, the fire under the black wash pot extending a circle of warmth in which I, a grave-eyed child, stand. There is my sister Ruth, beautiful to me and dressed elegantly for high school in gray felt skirt and rhinestone brooch, hurrying up the road to catch the yellow school bus which glows like a large glow worm in the early morning fog.

> O, landscape of my birth
> because you were so good to me as I grew
> I could not bear to lose you.
> O, landscape of my birth
> because when I lost you, a part of my soul died.          5
> O, landscape of my birth
> because to save myself I pretended it was *you*
> who died.
> You that now did not exist
> because I could not see you.                              10
> But O, landscape of my birth
> now I can confess how I have lied.
> Now I can confess the sorrow
> of my heart
> as the tears flow                                        15

and I see again with memory's bright eye
my dearest companion cut down
and can bear to resee myself
so lonely and so small
there in the sunny meadows                                          20
and shaded woods
of childhood
where my crushed spirit
and stricken heart
ran in circles                                                      25
looking for a friend.

Soon I will have known fifty summers.
Perhaps that is why
my heart
an imprisoned tree                                                 30
so long clutched tight
inside its core
insists
on shedding
like iron leaves                                                   35
the bars
from its cell.

You flow into me.
And like the Aborigine or Bushperson or Cherokee
who braves everything                                              40
to stumble home to die
no matter that cowboys
are herding cattle where the ancestors slept
I return to you, my earliest love.

Weeping in recognition at the first trees                          45
I ever saw, the first hills I ever climbed and rested
        my unbearable cares
upon, the first rivers I ever dreamed myself across,
the first pebbles I ever lifted up, warm from the sun,
        and put into
my mouth.

    O landscape of my birth                                        50
you have never been far from my heart.
It is *I* who have been far.
    If you will take me back
    Know that I
    Am yours.                                                      55

# For Better Reading: A Visible Difference

*Poetry* is sometimes said to sing, *prose* to speak.

Poetry is usually printed line by line, to direct the reader by emphasizing certain words and phrases.

Prose is usually written out in sentences and paragraphs, fitted to a page by space rather than a writer's directions.

Sometimes it seems that prose speaks from the head, and poetry from a person's heart and inner being. Prose often reads as if someone is talking to you, one to one, and presenting you with information. Poetry asks you to spring into unknown depths, take risks, and stretch into spaces and ideas that are new, often to the poet writing.

For reasons of her own, Alice Walker has chosen to write "My Heart Has Reopened to You," in a form that makes the first half look like prose, the second poetry. As you question her selection, try to decide why she chose to have such a "visible difference" in its two halves.

## Questioning the Poem

### First Half

1. A "displaced person" is usually driven from a homeland by war or an unjust ruler. Why does Walker's situation seem different?

2. Why can the early morning fog over the valley be compared to a dragon? Besides her description of fog, list three other specific points of beauty that Walker sees from her deck.

3. Walker twice mentions having found peace here. How does that relate to her being a displaced person? Considering her birthplace, what kind of war or injustice might she have faced there?

4. Describe the contrasts between her "view of the mountains and redwoods" and the scenes she remembers with nostalgia or longing from the land of her birth.

5. How had the pine tree, which she loved as a child, sheltered Walker's father on cold mornings? List two details showing the hardships Walker and her family experienced.

6. When the tree was cut down, Walker "grieved as if it had been a person." Find at least three earlier examples of her giving the tree human characteristics.

7. Why does Walker realize "perhaps it *was* sad" to feel so close to this tree? Give at least three examples proving Walker did care for members of her family.

8. As a child, what had Walker falsely assumed about her life and future? Why did she feel both her parents were "rooted"? Why was Walker "driven away," and for what did she search?

9. How does the idea of fog tie the first part's beginning and end together? How might the "fog of memory" affect her thoughts?

**Second Half**

1. To whom is Walker apparently speaking in the first half? Whom does she address when beginning to write in poetic form?
2. From both parts of the selection, find at least three examples to support Walker's calling the landscape "so good to me as I grew."
3. "To save" herself, what did Walker falsely pretend? What in the first half explains the "pain" she needed to cure?
4. Walker writes of her "crushed spirit and stricken heart." What realizations caused these feelings? Why couldn't her father and mother give her emotional support?
5. By pretending the landscape "died," how did Walker also cause "part of my soul" to die?
6. Walker compares her heart to an "imprisoned tree" because this was her dearest childhood companion. How had she tried to imprison both? How is she now "shedding . . . the bars" from her own "cell"?
7. How do lines 38–44 emphasize the difference between a landscape and those living there?
8. Walker writes that she is "weeping in recognition" at the sights of her childhood. Does "recognition" mean that she actually sees them, that she realizes and accepts their importance to her, or both? Explain the reasons for your opinion.

# Looking Deeper

## I. "Overlooking Another World"

At the end of the selection, Walker states "It is *I* who have been far" and asks her childhood landscape to take her back. Do you believe she plans to make her home in Georgia again or not? Explain the reasons for your conclusion.

Walker speaks of the "great peace" of her home in Northern California. What other peace has she attained by the poem's end?

Walker also writes of her search for "justice . . . and work that affirmed my whole being." Does the poem lead you to believe this search has ended or will continue? State the reasons for your belief.

## II. A Visible Difference

What were Walker's reasons for separating "My Heart Has Reopened to You" into two such different parts? How does one serve to reinforce the other? Do you believe either part would be effective alone, as a prose essay or a poem? Why or why not?

Walker wonders about her life if she had been able to stay home. Why do you think she chose the word "able"? Your teacher might wish to compare

Robert Frost's poem, "The Road Not Taken," with this selection by Alice Walker.

## REFLECTIONS

It's called "a sense of place." It means the sights and sounds, the smells of traffic fumes or newly plowed fields or the tang of an ocean breeze, the special feeling of a place's climate that seems to wrap itself around your shoulders like a cloak.

Every place in America has its own particular combination of landscape and climate, scents and sounds and flavors, too.

In this unit, you can hear the voices of Americans living in places from New England to Hawaii, from Alaska to Georgia. As you recall the selections, consider the varying demands that each place makes upon those who choose to live and settle there. Compare these Americans with each other and yourself—to discover what makes them seem different from yourself and what you find in common.

Americans have long been known as seekers. In fact, you may have noticed how many writers and poets have lived in a number of different states, as well as their native ones. Why is this characteristic of so many Americans?

As you reflect on this unit, you'll also note several selections concern newcomers to America. What special problems do recent immigrants face? Unless you are native American, your ancestors too were once recent arrivals—and even American Indians have often been treated as "outsiders" by other Americans. What fears and lack of understanding account for such attitudes?

## To Write About or Discuss

What is your special "corner of the world"? It may be the area or town where you live, your neighborhood or room, a tree. Describe your "sense of it" and why you feel it belongs to you.

# UNIT 8

# A Sense of Pride

"What so proudly we hailed . . ."
"Land of the pilgrims' pride . . ."

AMERICANS OFTEN FEEL LUCKIER THAN peoples of other lands, for they live in a country with beliefs in freedom and an equal voice for all Americans—a country worthy of their pride.

Yet pride is always a tricky quality. A sense of pride leads a person or nation to set high standards and strive to reach and maintain them. Yet pride can also lead to an air of smug superiority and boastfulness.

At its best, the American sense of pride comes from self-respect and a belief in the worthiness of America's goals and achievements.

At its worst, it expresses an attitude of "myself and my country, right or wrong," closing out all others because of narrow, selfish pride.

Being proud does not mean holding America above reproach. Because Americans make a habit of complaining about elected officials, the younger generation, taxes—the list goes on and on—some mistakenly assume Americans take no pride in their country or themselves.

Yet, pride allows Americans to be self-critical, just as family, friends, or those of similar backgrounds can make comments considered "fighting words" if said by an outsider.

And, so it is with the "sense of pride," giving Americans the freedom to criticize freely out of recognition of America's accomplishments, faith in its goals, and belief in the possibility of change for the better.

# Listening and Learning

*by James A. Autry*

**Born:**      *Memphis, Tennessee, 1933*
**Graduate:**   *University of Mississippi*
**Residence:**   *Des Moines, Iowa*
**Profession:**  *President of Meredith Corporation,*
               *publisher of* Better Homes and
               Gardens *magazine*

There was a time I listened
to the men at the store,
thinking I could learn about farming
as they came dusty from the fields
in bib overalls and long-sleeved shirts, 5
their hands and faces dark red
save a white band where their straw hats sat.
They kicked their boots on the ground,
red clay dust rising to their knees,
and shook their heads as they came in the door. 10
Always shook their heads and met the eyes
of other farmers who shook their heads
and stood at the co-cola boxes
with a Coke or a Dr. Pepper or RC.
I listened about the weather 15
and the government
and the prices,
all of it turned against them.

Now, I watch businessmen
stretch and squeeze time on planes 20
and in offices,
measuring their days by meetings and phone calls,
then gather in clubs
and bars and restaurants
and shake their heads and talk and talk, 25

about inflation and disinflation,
about the government and the deficit
and the margins
and the share fights.

After a while, it sounds the same,                    30
farmers and businessmen,
and what I hear
is how hard it is
for them to say how much they love it.

## For Better Reading: Understanding the Unsaid

Words are the raw material of poetry—as for all writing and speaking. Yet sometimes words not said can be just as significant as those written or uttered.

To some people, "I'm sorry" are nearly impossible words to say for a number of reasons. Left unspoken, do they mean the same as "not sorry" and show no regrets? It's easy to jump to that conclusion—but often not so.

Sometimes words say too much, sometimes not enough. And often careful attention must be paid to what is not said as well as what is.

It's a truth good poets know, and good readers should realize also.

"Listening and Learning" requires you to look beneath the surface—and understand the meaningfulness of words left unsaid. It attempts to show that, under the skin of our differences, there is a shared core of feeling and hopes, impulses, and desires that make us human.

### Questioning the Poem

1. In lines 1–3, the speaker says he listened to the men at the store thinking he "could learn about farming." What do lines 15–17 list as three things he heard about?
2. What specific points did the farmers probably make about each, considering "all of it turned against them"?
3. From lines 4–9, list two elements in the farmers' description that result from being out in their fields, and explain what each reveals about the difficulty of farm work.
4. What repeated phrase in lines 10–12 indicates the farmers' reliance on silent communication? How would you express this silent message in words?
5. In stanza two, what is most likely the speaker's reason for watching businessmen? Judge by the reasoning in stanza one.

6. Why would businessmen seek to both "stretch" and "squeeze" time?
7. According to line 22, businessmen are "measuring their days by meetings and phone calls." Deciding by inference, what do you believe farmers use to "measure their days"?
8. Explain three ways the businessmen's actions in lines 23–29 are similar to the farmers' in stanza one. How do they differ and why?

# Looking Deeper

## I. "Listening and Learning"

Near the beginning of the poem, the speaker said he wanted to "learn about farming." Does the poem lead you to think that he wanted to learn about the "what's" of farming and business—or "how" people feel about their life work? Use evidence from the poem to support your answer.

## II. The Language of Poetry

In this poem, James A. Autry uses fewer than 15 descriptive adjectives. List at least ten of them, and tell whether you would classify them as flowery or straightforward.

Lines 4–7 could have been written:

> as they came from fields powdered grey with dust
> in hard-worn bib overalls and sweat-streaked shirts,
> their roughened hands and faces fiery hot scarlet
> but for a ghostly white band
> where battered straw hats sat.

Explain which version is more effective and why.

## III. "How Much They Love It"

The speaker hears "how hard it is" for both farmers and businessmen to express their feelings about their work. Why do you think this is so? About what other subjects and areas do people have similar difficulties?

# A California Ad Man Celebrates His Art

## by David Alpaugh

| | |
|---|---|
| ***Profession:*** | *Owner of desk-top publishing business in San Francisco, California* |
| ***Career steps:*** | *Advertising director for bank, colleges, National Education Center* |

**Vocabulary**

*fecund:* (FEE kund) very productive or intellectually creative

*Beowulf:* (BAY oh woolf) English epic poem of the early 8th century AD in which the hero, Beowulf, battles the monster, Grendel

*Bert Brecht:* German dramatist and poet, 1898–1956, whose first name is actually Bertolt

*cataclysms:* violent or world-shaking disturbances or changes, especially of a social or political nature

*Milton:* John Milton, English poet, 1608–1674

*mnemonic:* (nee MON ik) meant to assist the memory

*Muse:* Any of the nine daughters of Zeus and Mnemosyne (nee MOSS a nee), goddesses of the arts

*odes:* poems expressing praise and/or enthusiasm; *ecologues:* poems picturing charmingly simple, rural scenes; *paeans:* songs of praise, joy, or triumph; *Juvenalian satire:* a form of mockery associated with the Roman poet Juvenal (Decimus Junius Juvenalis) who lived about 60–140 AD

*perdition:* damnation, hell

> For those of you
> who come here
> out of spite
> expecting to hear
> a con man apologize—     5
> prepare to gnash your teeth.

I am here to celebrate
the TV commercial—
the authentic poetry of our time:
lovingly produced,                                            10
widely received,
technically dazzling—
*It really changes lives.*

My title? "Tubular Poetics."

We deal in time and space:                                    15
thirty seconds of sound and light
rolling from earth to sky,
sky to earth,
kitchen to bedroom.

Our spirit is democratic.                                     20
We have made a pact
with Walt Whitman
to celebrate fecund America,
embracing all creeds, all colors:
men and women, young and old,                                 25
the runt as well as the athlete.

We praise hearth and home
in a manner that Beowulf
would understand.
Our art is tribal, mnemonic ...                               30
designed to be sung into the heart
by families gathered round the fire—
not warehoused in a public library
or read in private on a printed page.

Our words are deeds.                                          35
Like iron weapons
warriors carry into battle
to brandish at the foe
they must contribute to the victory.
If they don't sell cars or condoms                            40
Grendel comes out of the fen
people lose food, status, power—
and like a singer of unwanted songs
under the castle wall
we are not allowed to get on the elevator                     45
and rise to the thirty-eighth floor.

Like Bert Brecht, we believe that art
is an instrument for social progress.
We are concerned about the sick,
the homeless, those denied justice.                                    50
Much of our best work is in praise
of cold tablets, real estate chains
and motorcycle lawyers—
and every afternoon when school lets out
we suffer the little children to come unto us.                         55


Like all great craftsmen
we find the material reality imposes
only partly to our purpose.
Our task is to build a world elsewhere,
with porcelain teeth, perfect complexions,                             60
fully rounded bosoms and bottoms:
a pastoral living room . . .
an electronic bower of bliss . . .


Into this world creep many dragons:
zits, dandruff, athlete's foot,                                        65
bras that sag or ride up,
bad breath, fatal to love—
relentless fiends called
"Ring Around the Collar,"
"Hemorrhoidal Tissue,"                                                 70
and surly appliances
that snap, snarl
and refuse to work.


In the cataclysms that ensue
we let good have its way with evil,                                    75
demonstrating the wisdom
shown a hundred times each day
by our hero with a thousand faces,
*The Consumer.*


Finally, like Milton                                                   80
we have the highest moral purpose,
calling upon our Muse to justify
the ways of any product our agency assigns
to whatever target market is specified.

In doing so we've stumbled on free will                                85
and with it a whole new tragic vision:
the knowledge that despite triumphal odes,
hymns, eclogues, paeans, songs of love,
and Juvenalian satire at its bitterest—
millions ignore the good and choose Brand X              90
dropping down to darkness and perdition.

These are just a few of the qualities
that link us to The Great Tradition.

## Questioning the Poem

1. The poem begins "For those of you who come here . . ." Based on lines 1–14, what should you imagine yourself attending?
2. Although the title in line 14 tries to link the writing of TV commercials and the art of poetry, how do their purposes differ? What makes "tubular" a humorous word choice?
3. Why might some people think an ad man no better than a "con man" and come hear him "out of spite"? What is the speaker's attitude towards these?
4. How do lines 15–19 support the idea of TV commercials' being "widely received, technically dazzling"?
5. Why is it fair to say "our spirit is democratic" about advertisements on TV? According to lines 21–23, TV ad men have made a pact or agreement with American poet Walt Whitman to "celebrate" America. Since Whitman lived from 1819–1892, why can't this be literally true? Why would an ad man wish to claim this pact existed and also choose the title "Tubular Poetics"?
6. What techniques of TV advertising are "mnemonic" or meant to assist the memory? How do lines 31–34 contrast TV with books?
7. How is TV similar to the telling of folk tales in tribal groups "gathered round the fire"? How does a TV ad man's purpose differ?
8. The speaker compares advertisers' words to weapons. Who is the foe? What determines a victory? What happens if the ad man "warrior" loses, according to lines 45–46? What does this mean to his future?
9. Stanza seven states ad men share beliefs of "Bert Brecht." Name three of Brecht's concerns listed in lines 47–50. Why call him "Bert," not "Bertolt"? (Consider the effect desired by the poet.)
10. Name three "social" topics listed in lines 51–53. Why does and doesn't each express a concern for social progress and justice?
11. Concerning lines 56–63, what kind of fantasy "world elsewhere" do TV ad men "build"? Lines 64–73 introduce the "dragons" and "relentless fiends" that threaten this world. Name three or more examples of the

"devastating tragedies" and "horrors," such as dandruff, that TV ads peddle products to protect people from.

12. Judging by lines 74–79, who is the "hero" of TV commercials? Why does this hero have "a thousand faces"? How does the hero demonstrate wisdom? In what way is each TV ad a "cataclysm" representing "good over evil"?

13. Despite being "like Milton," why do ad men agree to promote any given product, according to lines 83–84? Judging by lines 90–91, whose "free will" have ad men "stumbled" on, and how is it demonstrated? Why might ad men think this a "tragic vision"?

## Looking Deeper

### I. Seriously, Now

Such expressions as "highest moral purpose" and "cataclysm" illustrate the exaggerated and overdrawn language that emphasizes the poet's humorous approach to the subject of television advertising. List three or more additional examples.

What is meant by "The Great Tradition" the speaker says TV ad men are linked to? Why might a "California ad man" feel "sneered" at and wish this association? In view of his calling TV commercials "authentic poetry," why would he use so many high-sounding literary terms, such as "paean" and "Juvenalian satire"? Why does choosing between Brand X and another product fail to qualify as a moral conflict between good and evil?

### II. Assuming a Celebration

In "Song of Myself," Walt Whitman wrote:
"I celebrate myself, and sing myself,
And what I assume you shall assume,
For every atom belonging to me as good belongs to you."
How does the poem reflect these words and ideas of Whitman? Do you believe that TV advertising "really changes lives"? Is it accurate to state its "spirit is democratic"? Is it really "the authentic poetry of our time"? Have good reasons and examples to back your opinions—because there's room for disagreement.

Considering that the poet is also a desk-top publisher and former advertising director, what serious points do you feel Alpaugh wants to make about TV advertising and ad men?

How does the language in this poem differ from that in James A. Autry's poem about farmers and businessmen? Why is each appropriate to its subject?

# For Rattlesnake: A Dialogue of Creatures

*by Peter Blue Cloud*

| | |
|---|---|
| ***Tribe:*** | *Mohawk* |
| ***Mohawk name:*** | *Aroniawenrate* |
| ***Born:*** | *Caughnowaga Reserve in Quebec, Canada, in 1927* |
| ***Adult life:*** | *California, Canada* |
| ***Career:*** | *Poet, ironworker, logger, carpenter, woodcarver, drummaker* |

## (A Voice Play)

(Each speaker introduced by _____)

Snow Plant; child of winter:
    See now the curving browness emerging from snow
    as earth her winter robe begins to fold,
    a trickle of moisture          5
    a gurgle   then   sand
      rolling,
    so like a pebble-filled gourd
    clasped between hands
    to mute to gentle murmur.          10

    Then freshets sigh the hillsides
    and stones to roundness tumble
      their praise.

Cedar; oldest of trees:
    Yes, my friend,          15
    and dawn breezes lend me voice
    my branches whisper

and sweet
           my scent
mingles your own breath                                20
as we await the others.


Woodpecker:
    It seems then a short night and day
    that berries sweet have mantled
    the mountain's greenness.                           25
    Then Bear-who-used-to-be, would . . .
(Long pause)


Oak Tree:
    Yes, brothers and sisters
    Bear no more his soft and heavy walk,               30
    Bear no more
                his strange and sacred manner.


Flicker: (Quickly)
    Are we about to speak of THEM again?                35


Fox: (As a chanting)
    I remember the last of Bear's tribe
        dragged
        by fear-sweating horse
    Foaming from whip and bear smell                    40
        eyes rolling
        and Bear
                great clots of blood
    and the human   a most awful smell
        of hate                                         45
    and fear and lust
    and the thought-pictures
        of his mind   hurting all,
    and we wondered at such cruelty
    for his thought-pictures                            50
        were of himself
        torn and devoured
    by the others of his likeness.


Squirrel:
    Wasn't this get together supposed to be             55
        for Rattlesnake?
    Hey, Coyote, what of you,
    your silence is like a burr
        beneath my tail.

Coyote: (In old long coat, floppy hat, stroking tail)  60
    Yes, well, Rattlesnake
    is on his way
    and should be here soon.
    And don't forget
              it's said,  65
    that we are here to stay
    as long as one of us remains,
               and . . .

Bluejay: (Interrupting)
    Who said that?  70

Coyote: (Innocently)
    Why I guess I just did.

Lizard: (Stamping his or her foot in agitation)
    You know, this is beginning to sound
    like a made-up lie and the liar  75
    don't know what to say next.

Rattlesnake: (Just the voice)
    I am a manner
            a custom
    a tribal creature.  80

Coyote:
    He's here! (She's here!)

Rattlesnake: (Emerging from concealment, carrying
    its head)
    I come to you cut in half
    and cut again   headless  85
    with strong heart beating a
        constant pulse
    I crawl to you bloody
        a nightmare of man's genius.

    I too am Springtime  90
    like my brother Bear
    for together   we emerge
    from sleep
    to the dancers pounding feet
        and the wormwood smell.  95
    I rattle them a music of my nearness

but they fear song
and axe, or knife, or gun, is the feast
   I am given.


I tell again of the Creation                        100
and beg the peace of their council
and name the many clans and tribes
   of man and all Creation
   that none be omitted.
I teach them the necessary lesson                  105
of alertness
of mind and body ever ready
for the tribal will
   but
they have forgotten the allness                  110
   of the Creation
in their eager quest of vanity.


I lie headless and bloody at their feet
   who am
   their former brother.                       115
(Begins to chant)
   I dream Bear
   I vision Bear
   I call Bear
      we must all become Bear.        120


Bear: (A dark mass, slowly shuffling in dance,
     four times in circle slowly, humming, as to himself,
     then pauses to speak)
   They kill my body
     they
   skin me and leave my body
     as in shame,                       125
 let us
     then
   begin again the praise
   forgotten by man.
   Snow Plant, please begin again.        130


Snow Plant: (As at the beginning)
   See now the curving browness emerging
     from snow
   as earth her winter robe begins to fold.
   A trickle of moisture                135

a gurgle    then    sand
    rolling,
so like a pebble-filled gourd
clasped between hands
to mute to gentle murmur.                                    140
Then freshets sigh the hillsides
and stones to roundness tumble
    their praise.

Cedar:
    Yes, my friend,                                          145
    and dawn breeze lends me voice
and my branches whisper
    a weeping as from an evil dream
    of creatures born of hate.

    Let us again                                             150
                then
    chant the evil back
    into earth's womb
    to be re-born
                or not                                       155
    as will be.

All the voices: (A chorus in chant)

    Man no more
        look
    he is fading,                                            160
    man no more
        see
    he lies dreaming,
    man no more
        forever                                              165
    let us forget the pain,
    man no more
        forever
    his bones of dust
    the wind is taking                                       170
        to scatter
            to scatter
                to scatter
                    to scatter

## For Better Reading: A Voice Play

It is a play, a dialogue, and a poem.

In "For Rattlesnake," Peter Blue Cloud uses techniques of Indian chant and the oral tradition in a selection that steps outside human awareness and views the world as a dozen different creatures of nature see it.

Having animals talk is common in nursery tales, but "For Rattlesnake" is not written for children.

In addition to reading it silently to consider the questions, you will surely want to read it aloud to receive its full effect. In the blank space after "Each speaker introduced by _____" at the beginning you may put the name of the person narrating the words that identify the different speakers.

Although "For Rattlesnake" represents the world of nature's vision of the negative side of human pride, you should also discover much to identify with, yourself.

## Questioning the Selection

1. Based on Snow Plant and Cedar's opening speeches, name the season of year. List at least two phrases to support your decision.
2. After mentioning "berries sweet," Woodpecker starts speaking of "Bear-who-used-to-be." What does this name reveal? What explains the long pause?
3. How does Oak Tree echo Woodpecker's words? What do the creatures avoid saying? With what four adjectives does Oak Tree describe Bear, and what effect do they create? Why does the expression "brothers and sisters" seem unusual, considering the biological kingdoms of the speakers?
4. When the other woodpecker, Flicker, speaks, who must "THEM" be? Why won't the creatures name "THEM"?
5. In lines 37–41, find at least two reasons the horse also seems a victim of THEM. What human "thought pictures" amaze and horrify Fox? Why is "such cruelty" impossible for animals to understand?
6. Why doesn't Coyote seem wholly of nature in appearance, like the others? Among farmers, coyotes have a bad reputation for stealing livestock. How does this make him different from the other creatures of nature in the play? How do both Squirrel and Lizard express distrust of Coyote? Why do their doubts seem justified?
7. Note: Coyote's "He's here! (She's here!)" depends upon who is reading the part.

    How was Rattlesnake a victim of humans? Why does his or her coming back to life seem to follow the laws of nature more closely than Bear's reappearance would?

8. Why are both Rattlesnake and Bear "Springtime"? How do the human dancers mistake and misuse Rattlesnake?

9. From lines 100–104, sum up the message Rattlesnake wants humans to hear. What "lesson" do lines 106–108 contain? What have humans forgotten in "their eager quest for vanity?"

10. Judging by Rattlesnake's chant, lines 117–120, what are three possibilities that might account for Bear's reappearance?

11. What "evil dream of creatures born of hate" causes Cedar to weep? What solution does Cedar suggest the creatures should seek?

12. How does the final chant about "man no more" echo Oak Tree's opening speech? How does this chant show the creatures' "humaneness"?

# Looking Deeper

## I. An "Eager Quest for Vanity"

Vanity is excessive pride in one's own achievements. To the creatures, why do humans appear to have this sort of pride?

What lesson does Rattlesnake want to teach humans by naming "the many clans and tribes of man"? Although the poet is a Mohawk Indian and the speakers not even human, what elements in the poem reflect American beliefs and aims, if not the actuality? If you feel there are none, explain why.

## II. "To Scatter . . . to Scatter"

What effect is created by the words "to scatter" repeated four times at the play's end?

In what way might this poem/play express a warning as well as a wish? What side do you find yourself taking as you read this voice play—humans or nature's creatures, and why?

# from *Walden or, Life in the Woods*

## *by Henry David Thoreau*

| | |
|---|---|
| ***Born:*** | *Concord, Massachusetts* |
| ***Educated:*** | *Harvard University* |
| ***Occupations:*** | *(as listed for 10th anniversary class questionnaire) "I am a School master—a private Tutor, a Surveyor—a Gardener, a Farmer—a Painter, I mean a House Painter, a Carpenter, a Mason, a Day-Laborer, a Pencil-Maker, Glasspaper Maker, a Writer, and sometimes a Poetaster."* |
| ***Protested:*** | *His government's toleration of slavery and invasion of Mexico; sympathized with Indian discontent* |
| ***Lifetime:*** | *1817–1862* |

**W**HEN I WROTE THE FOLLOWING pages, or rather the bulk of them, I lived alone, in the woods, a mile from any neighbor, in a house which I had built myself, on the shore of Walden Pond, in Concord, Massachusetts, and earned my living by the labor of my hands only. I lived there two years and two months. At present I am a sojourner in civilized life again.

I should not obtrude my affairs so much on the notice of my readers if very particular inquiries had not been made by my townsmen concerning my mode of life. . . . I will therefore ask those of my readers who feel no particular interest in me to pardon me if I undertake to answer some of these questions in this book. In most books, the *I*, or first person, is omitted; in this it will be retained; that, in respect to egotism, is the main difference. We commonly do not remember that it is, after all, always the first person that is speaking. I should not talk so much about myself if there were anybody else whom I knew as well. Unfortunately, I am confined to this theme by the narrowness of my experience. . . .

Nature and human life are as various as our several constitutions. Who shall say what prospect life offers to another? Could a greater miracle take place than for us to look through each other's eyes for an instant? We should live in all the ages in the world in an hour; ay, in all the worlds of the ages. History, Poetry, Mythology!—I know of no reading of another's experience so startling and informing as this would be. It would be some advantage to live a primitive and frontier life, though in the midst of an outward civilization, if only to learn what are the gross necessaries of life and what methods have been taken to obtain them; or even to look over the old day-books of the merchants, to see what it was that men more commonly bought at the stores, what they stored, that is, what are the grossest groceries. For the improvements of ages have had but little influence on the essential laws of man's existence; as our skeletons, probably, are not to be distinguished from those of our ancestors.

By the words, *necessary of life*, I mean whatever, of all that man obtains by his own exertions, has been from the first, or from long use has become, so important to human life that few, if any, whether from savageness, or poverty, or philosophy, ever attempt to do without it. To many creatures there is in this sense but one necessary of life, Food. To the bison of the prairie it is a few inches of palatable grass, with water to drink; unless he seeks the Shelter of the forest or the mountain's shadow. None of the brute creation requires more than Food and Shelter. The necessaries of life for man in this climate may, accurately enough, be distributed under the several heads of Food, Shelter, Clothing, and Fuel; for not till we have secured these are we prepared to entertain the true problems of life with freedom and a prospect of success. Man has invented, not only houses, but clothes and cooked food; and possibly from the accidental discovery of the warmth of fire, and the consequent use of it, at first a luxury, arose the present necessity to sit by it. We observe cats and dogs acquiring the same second nature. By proper Shelter and Clothing we legitimately retain our own internal heat; but with an excess of these, or of Fuel, that is, with an external heat greater than our own internal, may not cookery properly be said to begin? Darwin, the naturalist, says of the inhabitants of Tierra del Fuego, that while his own party, who were well clothed and sitting close to a fire, were far from too warm, these naked savages, who were farther off, were observed, to his great surprise, "to be streaming with perspiration at undergoing such a roasting." ... According to Liebig, man's body is a stove, and food the fuel which keeps up the internal combustion in the lungs. In cold weather we eat more, in warm less. The animal heat is the result of a slow combustion, and disease and death take place when this is too rapid; or for want of fuel, or from some defect in the draught, the fire goes out. Of course the vital heat is not to be confounded with fire; but so much for the analogy. It appears, therefore, from the above list, that the expression, *animal life*, is nearly synonymous with the expression, *animal heat*; for while Food may be regarded as the Fuel which keeps up the fire within us,—and Fuel serves only to prepare that Food or to increase the warmth of our bodies by addition from without,—Shelter and Clothing also serve only to retain the *heat* thus generated and absorbed.

The grand necessity, then, for our bodies, is to keep warm, to keep the vital heat in us. What pains we accordingly take, not only with our Food, and Clothing, and Shelter, but with our beds, which are our night-clothes, robbing the nests and breasts of birds to prepare this shelter within a shelter, as the mole has its bed of grass and leaves at the end of its burrow! The poor man is wont to complain that this is a cold world; and to cold, no less physical than social, we refer directly a great part of our ails. The summer, in some climates, makes possible to man a sort of Elysian life. Fuel, except to cook his Food, is then unnecessary; the sun is his fire, and many of the fruits are sufficiently cooked by its rays; while Food generally is more various, and more easily obtained, and Clothing and Shelter are wholly or half unnecessary....

When a man is warmed by the several modes which I have described, what does he want next? Surely not more warmth of the same kind, as more and richer food, larger and more splendid houses, finer and more abundant clothing, more numerous incessant and hotter fires, and the like. When he has obtained those things which are necessary to life, there is another alternative than to obtain the superfluities; and that is, to adventure on life now, his vacation from humbler toil having commenced....

I do not mean to prescribe rules to strong and valiant natures, who will mind their own affairs whether in heaven or hell, and perchance build more magnificently and spend more lavishly than the richest, without ever impoverishing themselves, not knowing how they live,—if, indeed, there are any such, as has been dreamed; nor to those who find their encouragement and inspiration in precisely the present condition of things, and cherish it with the fondness and enthusiasm of lovers,—and, to some extent, I reckon myself in this number; I do not speak to those who are well employed, in whatever circumstances, and they know whether they are well employed or not;—but mainly to the mass of men who are discontented, and idly complaining of the hardness of their lot or of the times, when they might improve them....

What I Lived For

I went to the woods because I wished to live deliberately, to front only the essential facts of life, and see if I could not learn what it had to teach, and not, when I came to die, discover that I had not lived. I did not wish to live what was not life, living is so dear; nor did I want to practise resignation, unless it was quite necessary. I wanted to live deep and suck out all the marrow of life, to live so sturdily and Spartan-like as to put to rout all that was not life, to cut a broad swath and shave close, to drive life into a corner, and reduce it to its lowest terms, and, if it proved to be mean, why then to get the whole and genuine meanness of it, and publish its meanness to the world; or if it were sublime, to know it by experience, and be able to give a true account of it in my next excursion ...

Conclusion

To the sick the doctors wisely recommend a change of air and scenery. Thank Heaven, here is not all the world. The buck-eye does not grow in New England,

and the mocking-bird is rarely heard here. The wild-goose is more of a cosmopo-lite than we; he breaks his fast in Canada, takes a luncheon in the Ohio, and plumes himself for the night in a southern bayou. Even the bison, to some extent, keeps pace with the seasons, cropping the pastures of the Colorado only till a greener and sweeter grass awaits him by the Yellowstone. Yet we think that if rail-fences are pulled down, and stone-walls piled up on our farms, bounds are henceforth set to our lives and our fates decided. If you are chosen town-clerk, forsooth, you cannot go to Tierra del Fuego this summer: but you may go to the land of infernal fire nevertheless. The universe is wider than our views of it. . . .

I left the woods for as good a reason as I went there. Perhaps it seemed to me that I had several more lives to live, and could not spare any more time for that one. It is remarkable how easily and insensibly we fall into a particular route, and make a beaten track for ourselves. I had not lived there a week before my feet wore a path from my door to the pond-side; and though it is five or six years since I trod it, it is still quite distinct. It is true, I fear that others may have fallen into it, and so helped to keep it open. The surface of the earth is soft and impressible by the feet of men; and so with the paths which the mind travels. How worn and dusty, then, must be the highways of the world, how deep the ruts of tradition and conformity! I did not wish to take a cabin passage, but rather to go before the mast and on the deck of the world, for there I could best see the moonlight amid the mountains. I do not wish to go below now.

I learned this, at least, by my experiment: that if one advances confidently in the direction of his dreams, and endeavors to live the life which he has imagined, he will meet with a success unexpected in common hours. He will put some things behind, will pass an invisible boundary; new, universal, and more liberal laws will begin to establish themselves around and within him; or the old laws be expanded, and interpreted in his favor in a more liberal sense, and he will live with the license of a higher order of beings. In proportion as he simplifies his life, the laws of the universe will appear less complex, and solitude will not be solitude, nor poverty poverty, nor weakness weakness. If you have built castles in the air, your work need not be lost; that is where they should be. Now put the foundations under them. . . .

Why should we be in such desperate haste to succeed, and in such desperate enterprises? If a man does not keep pace with his companions, perhaps it is because he hears a different drummer. Let him step to the music which he hears, however measured or far away. . . .

# For Better Reading: Bits and Pieces

"Something's missing." You may have felt this way when you're reading. All readers do sometimes. And, you may have thought, "I don't get it. It must be me."

Yet good readers know that perhaps something *is* missing. It might be that what they're reading isn't exactly the same as originally written, and it's only natural to feel puzzled. To become a better reader, you should know about and identify these ways a writer's work is sometimes altered:

1. *Excerpts.* These are paragraphs or passages "plucked," "pulled," or "extracted" from a selection to provide a sample of the original. Excerpts are frequently identified by the word "from" preceding their title, as "from *Walden*" and "from 'Self-Reliance.'"

A series of three dots (. . .) also indicates a portion of the text that follows has been left out.

Excerpts sometimes give famous quotations from the center of a work, omitting introductory and closing sections that explain the writer's purpose. Even when meant to include sufficient passages to indicate the author's overall plan, excerpts require decisions that take away the sense of completeness.

2. *Abridgments.* Think of abridgments as shortened versions that condense or omit certain sections, while keeping to the original idea or story. It's not unusual to find novels and plays presented in abridged versions in school texts, with cuts made in dialogue, description, and/or action.

3. *Expurgation.* To expurgate is to remove or "clean out" certain words or other offensive material considered inappropriate to the editor or publication reproducing it.

4. *Adaptations.* When a selection is adapted, the usual goal is to make it easier to read. Words are simplified, sentences are shortened, or the selection may actually be retold. Fairy tales and fables are often read in adaptations—and sometimes lose the flow and magic of the original tale.

How much is missing? How much does it matter? It is always necessary for you to decide—and, when in doubt, check the original.

## Important Details

1. Thoreau said he was writing *Walden* because (a) the townspeople expressed curiosity about his life there (b) he hoped to contribute to environmental research (c) attempts had been made to force him to leave (d) he wished to persuade others to join the colony.
2. The opening paragraph must have been written (a) while Thoreau was living at Walden Pond (b) after Thoreau returned to live in town (c) during Thoreau's brief period of imprisonment (d) when he was broke and needed money to support himself.

3. Regarding his use of *I* or first person, Thoreau expressed the idea that (a) the first person would make readers feel closer to him (b) not using first person might create the effect of preaching (c) he deserved credit for his accomplishment (d) with or without *I*, writers always speak for themselves.

## Questioning the Selection

1. According to the first paragraph, what are two things that Thoreau did for himself while at Walden? In what two ways was he away from "civilized life"?
2. What did Thoreau hope to learn by living a "primitive and frontier life"? How might this also help him partially achieve his wish to look through others' eyes?
3. According to Thoreau, what are the two "necessaries" of life for "the brute creation" or animals? What two additional needs do human beings have, and how are these related to the first two?
4. From Darwin's experience on the Tierra del Fuego islands at the tip of South America, what conclusions did Thoreau draw about civilization's effect on one need of human beings?
5. Thoreau states that the German chemist Liebig (1803–1873) compared the human body to a stove. In your own words, explain what makes this comparison seem to fit. In regard to human health, how might "too rapid" combustion or heating be associated with disease or death? Why might its opposite, a defect resulting in lack of heat or fuel, have similar associations?
6. Thoreau says, "... the vital heat is not to be confounded with fire." How does food "keep up the fire within us"? Although food is necessary for life, how is it merely fuel for the body and different from the "vital heat" that sparks life itself?
7. Explain how the expression "this is a cold world" applies to both physical and social matters. Include examples to clarify your answer.
8. What characteristics of climate would offer "a sort of Elysian" or perfectly happy life? What places on Earth fit this, in your opinion?
9. Since Thoreau believes people require only the "necessaries," what would be "superfluities" to him? What must he feel is the only valid reason for "humbler toil" or everyday jobs? What is his advice to those who have "obtained those things which are necessary to life"?
10. What are three types of natures or people to whom Thoreau chooses not to "prescribe"? Into which group does Thoreau class himself? To what kind of person does he prescribe?
11. Thoreau says he went to the woods to "front" or face "only the essential facts of life." Explain whether you feel his life there fulfilled his goal, using proof from the selection as support.
12. What in the second paragraph of the conclusion explains why Thoreau

left the woods? How do the "path from my door to the pond-side" and "the beaten track" serve as metaphors for "the ruts of tradition and conformity"?

13. What attitude toward life is expressed by Thoreau's desire to "go before the mast" as a ship's captain instead of being a passenger?

14. In what ways can Thoreau's "going to the woods" be accurately termed an experiment?

## Looking Deeper

### I. "Going to the Woods"

Does Thoreau feel others should "follow his path" to live alone in the woods? Use the next to last paragraph to help support your opinion. With regard to "necessaries" and "luxuries," what realization is involved in "simplifying" one's life?

What is meant by "building castles in the air"? What is Thoreau's attitude toward this? By leaving the woods because he "had several more lives to live and could not spare any more time for that one," how does Thoreau show himself taking his own advice?

### II. "A Different Drummer"

A famous quotation often excerpted from *Walden* is the following: "The mass of men lead lives of quiet desperation."

In line with Thoreau's thinking, why might an emphasis on "superfluities" instead of "necessaries" have this result? Do you believe the quotation is true today? Why or why not?

How does the final paragraph of the selection also relate to this quotation? Explain the last two sentences, beginning "If a man does not keep pace with his companions," and discuss your view on how they apply to people today.

# from *Self-Reliance*

## *by Ralph Waldo Emerson*

| | |
|---|---|
| ***Lifetime:*** | *1803–1882* |
| ***Born:*** | *Boston, Massachusetts* |
| ***Early life:*** | *Suffered from illness and poor vision* |
| ***Adult life:*** | *Settled in Concord, Mass., traveled Italy, France, Egypt, and England* |
| ***Famous as:*** | *Philosopher, poet, lecturer, and essayist* |

. . . To BELIEVE YOUR OWN THOUGHT, to believe that what is true for you in your private heart is true for all men—that is genius. . . . A man should learn to detect and watch that gleam of light which flashes across his mind from within. . . . Yet he dismisses without notice his thought, because it is his. In every work of genius we recognize our own rejected thoughts; they come back to us with a certain alienated majesty. Great works of art have no more affecting lesson for us than this. They teach us to abide by our spontaneous impression with good-humored inflexibility then most when the whole cry of voices is on the other side. Else, tomorrow a stranger will say with masterly good sense precisely what we have thought and felt all the time, and we shall be forced to take with shame our own opinion from another.

There is a time in every man's education when he arrives at the conviction that envy is ignorance; that imitation is suicide; that he must take himself for better or worse as his portion; that though the wide universe is full of good, no kernel of nourishing corn can come to him but through his toil bestowed on that plot of ground which is given to him to till. The power which resides in him is new in nature, and none but he knows what that is which he can do, nor does he know until he has tried. Not for nothing one face, one character, one fact, makes much impression on him, and another none. This sculpture in the memory is not without preestablished harmony. The eye was placed where one ray should fall, that it might testify of that particular ray. We but half express ourselves, and are ashamed of that divine idea which each of us represents. It may be safely trusted as proportionate and of good issues, so it be faithfully imparted, but God will not have his work made manifest by cowards. A man is relieved and gay when he has put his heart into his work and done his best; but what he has said or done otherwise shall give him no peace. It is a deliverance which does not deliver. In the attempt his genius deserts him; no muse befriends; no invention, no hope.

Trust thyself: every heart vibrates to that iron string. . . .

Society everywhere is in conspiracy against the manhood of every one of its members. Society is a joint-stock company, in which the members agree, for the better securing of his bread to each shareholder, to surrender the liberty and culture of the eater. The virtue in most request is conformity. Self-reliance is its aversion. It loves not realities and creators, but names and customs.

Whoso would be a man, must be a nonconformist. He who would gather immortal palms must not be hindered by the name of goodness, but must explore if it be goodness. Nothing is at last sacred, but the integrity of your own mind. . . .

What I must do is all that concerns me, not what the people think. This rule, equally arduous in actual and in intellectual life, may serve for the whole distinction between greatness and meanness. It is the harder because you will always find those who think they know what is your duty better than you know it. It is easy in the world to live after the world's opinion; it is easy in solitude to live after our own; but the great man is he who in the midst of the crowd keeps with perfect sweetness the independence of solitude. . . .

For nonconformity the world whips you with its displeasure. And therefore a man must know how to estimate a sour face. The by-standers look askance on him in the public street or in the friend's parlor. If this aversion had its origin in contempt and resistance like his own, he might well go home with a sad countenance; but the sour faces of the multitude, like their sweet faces, have no deep cause, but are put on and off as the wind blows and a newspaper directs.

The other terror that scares us from self-trust is our consistency; a reverence for our past act or word because the eyes of others have no other data for computing our orbit than our past acts, and we are loth to disappoint them.

But why should you keep your head over your shoulder? Why drag about this corpse of your memory, lest you contradict somewhat you have stated in this or that public place? Suppose you should contradict yourself; what then? It seems to be a rule of wisdom never to rely on your memory alone, scarcely even in acts of pure memory, but to bring the past for judgment into the thousand-eyed present, and live ever in a new day. . . .

A foolish consistency is the hobgoblin of little minds, adored by little statesmen and philosophers and divines. With consistency a great soul has simply nothing to do. He may as well concern himself with his shadow on the wall. Speak what you think now in hard words, and tomorrow speak what tomorrow thinks in hard words again, though it contradict every thing you said today—"Ah, so you shall be sure to be misunderstood."—Is it so bad then to be misunderstood? Pythagoras was misunderstood, and Socrates, and Jesus, and Luther, and Copernicus, and Galileo, and Newton, and every pure and wide spirit that ever took flesh. To be great is to be misunderstood. . . .

I must be myself. I cannot break myself any longer for you, or you. If you can love me for what I am, we shall be the happier. If you cannot, I will still seek to deserve that you should. I will not hide my tastes or aversions. I will so trust that what is deep is holy, that I will do strongly before the sun and moon whatever inly rejoices me and the heart appoints. If you are noble, I will love you; if you are not, I will not hurt you and myself by hypocritical attentions. If you are true, but not in the same truth with me, cleave to your companions. I will seek my own. I do this not selfishly but humbly and truly. It is alike your interest, and mine, and all men's, however long we have dwelt in lies, to live in truth. Does this sound harsh today? You will soon love what is dictated by your nature as well as mine, and if we follow the truth it will bring us out safe at last. But so may you give these friends pain. Yes, but I cannot sell my liberty and my power, to save their sensibility. Besides, all persons have their moments of reason, when they look out into the region of absolute truth; then will they justify me and do the same thing. . . .

If any man consider the present aspects of what is called by distinction *society*, he will see the need of these ethics. The sinew and heart of man seem to be drawn out, and we are become timorous, desponding whimperers. We are afraid of truth, afraid of fortune, afraid of death, and afraid of each other. Our age yields no great and perfect persons. We want men and women who shall renovate life and our social state, but we see that most natures are insolvent, cannot satisfy their own wants, have an ambition out of all proportion to their practical force and do lean and beg day and night continually. . . .

It is easy to see that a greater self-reliance must work a revolution in all the offices and relations of men; in their religion; in their education; in their pursuits; their modes of living; their association; in their property; in their speculative views. . . .

Nothing can bring you peace but yourself. Nothing can bring you peace but the triumph of principles.

## For Better Reading: Neighbors

Although Boston-born, Ralph Waldo Emerson spent most of his life in Concord, Massachusetts, and owned the land near Walden pond where Thoreau "lived alone, in the woods, a mile from any neighbor."

From this little town came writers who expressed ideas that stand as the foundation of American pride: belief in the individual, in trusting your own thoughts, in doing what you know is right, no matter what others say.

Not only were Emerson and Thoreau neighbors, but also living in Concord were Nathaniel Hawthorne, author of *The Scarlet Letter* and *The House of the Seven Gables*; writer and reformer Bronson Alcott; and his daughter, Louisa May Alcott, famous for her beloved stories, *Little Women* and *Little Men*.

Their ideas live in America today.

## Inference

1. Emerson expresses the belief that most people (a) have little respect for others' opinions (b) don't recognize the genius of others (c) think their own thoughts have little value (d) consider themselves one against the majority.
2. According to Emerson, great works of art are important because they show that (a) what is true for you is true for all (b) genius is rare, certain, and immortal (c) flashes of brilliance should be man's guiding stars (d) only genius truly understands genius.
3. Emerson believes people sometimes feel shame for (a) not having recognized another's genius (b) not trusting their opinion till expressed by someone else (c) having friends make fun of their pet beliefs (d) having a stranger point out errors in their logic.

## Questioning the Selection

### Concerning paragraph 2:
1. What does Emerson mean by stating that everyone "must take himself for better or worse" as his share in the world? Explain how his comparison concerning "toil . . . on that plot of ground" or work on a piece of land relates to this conclusion.
2. What supports Emerson's belief that each person's power is "new in nature"? Emerson states that each person's "eye was placed where one ray should fall." How is this thought related to Thoreau's wish to look through someone else's eyes?
3. According to Emerson, what are three negative results that occur when someone "has said or done otherwise" than his best? Explain each in your own words.

### Concerning paragraphs 4 & 5:
4. In comparing society to a joint-stock company, what are two things Emerson feels individuals must give up to earn their livelihood more easily? What "virtue" does society most value?
5. Loving "names and customs" means admiring someone for having the "right" family name and background, wearing the "right" clothes, and doing the "right things." Explain why such "names and customs" matter greatly to a conformist society. Why wouldn't such a society love "realities and creators"?
6. To a conformist society, how might "goodness" be simply a "name"? Include an example. How does a nonconformist determine goodness?

### Concerning paragraph 6:
7. To Emerson, what are hard and easy ways to live according to your own beliefs of right? How does the great person live?

### Concerning paragraphs 7 & 8:
8. Compared to a self-reliant person, Emerson believes attitudes of con-

formists have no deep cause. Why do their attitudes seem "put on and off as the wind blows"? Why as a "newspaper directs"?

9. What is "the other terror" that makes people stick to a past "act or word," even though it now seems wrong? For what two reasons do the "eyes of others" make them guilty of such "foolish consistency"?

**Concerning paragraph 9:**

10. How does keeping "your head over your shoulder" describe someone fearful of being inconsistent? How does the expression "drag about this corpse of your memory" clarify Emerson's attitude?

**Concerning paragraph 10:**

11. What is a great soul's attitude toward being consistent? After listing some of the greatest names in history, what does Emerson conclude is the natural result of greatness?

## Looking Deeper

### I. For Fear of Hobgoblins

"A foolish consistency is the hobgoblin of little minds, adored by little statesmen and philosophers and divines."

This is one of the most-often quoted statements from "Self-Reliance." Why would politicians, philosophers, and religious leaders with "little minds" be afraid to admit rethinking their opinions? Why is this only a "hobgoblin" or an imaginary, goblin-like fear?

Emerson uses seven names to illustrate his belief, "to be great is to be misunderstood." Choose at least three, and explain why each illustrates this quotation, basing your answer on your own knowledge or additional research. Do any famous figures in more recent history also fit this category? Explain the reasons for your view, including examples.

### II. Gaining Acceptance

In the last four paragraphs of these excerpts from "Self-Reliance," Emerson directly addresses "you," the reader, and speaks not of romantic love but of deep feelings towards another human being. What does Emerson insist is so, regardless of a would-be friend's reaction? How does trusting "whatever inly" or inwardly "rejoices me and the heart appoints" fit Emerson's belief in self-reliance and non-conformity?

In paragraph 11, Emerson raises a number of possibilities about you. They include: 1. You can love him for what he is; 2. You cannot love him for what he is; 3. You are true, but not in the same truth with him. How would he respond differently to each? Why would he consider "hypocritical attentions" hurtful?

## III. "If We Follow the Truth . . ."

Emerson believes the truth "will bring us out safe at last." How does this relate to the opening paragraph of this essay?

Why does Emerson blame society for men's fear of truth? Are Emerson's ideas about society true today? Why or why not?

Explain why you agree or disagree with each of the following: More self-reliance is necessary, now as in Emerson's time. Nothing can bring peace but yourself.

The final sentence stresses the "triumph of principles," the standards someone lives by. Explain what principles, if any, you feel are lacking in today's society, and how self-reliance might allow them to triumph.

# My Cow, She Was Almost Arrested

## by Tobias Leyba

**Background:** Not a professional writer, but a village farmer in New Mexico whose land was originally part of a Spanish and Mexican land grant, made before the U.S. conquest of the Southwest in 1846–48

**First published:** In El Grito del Norte (The Cry of the North) in 1970

MY COW, SHE WAS ALMOST arrested last week. The Forest Service was going to arrest her because she walked over the line and ate some grass. She got a little better head, my cow, than the forest rangers, but still she can't read the signs and she doesn't see the lines too pretty good.

I keep my cows on private land near the Echo Amphitheatre. This land is private where my cows are and it is across the road from where the Forest Service has its park for the tourists. The State Highway Department has land along both sides of the road and there is a little bit of forest land that goes across the road. Next to where my cows are, there is land that the University of New Mexico says it owns. All this once belonged to the people.

Now, *mira* my cow is eating the grass and it looks the same, and the land looks the same, so I guess she thinks it is still the same—the land still belongs to all of the people. But this ranger, a *gauvacho* who doesn't know much about the land—or the people—he's watching my cow. And when she steps over the line, he sends me a letter saying he's going to arrest my cow, he's going to "impound" her.

This ranger says my cow has walked over onto the University of New Mexico land and over another line of the forest and he is going to arrest her. This land the University of New Mexico has, it is just sitting there, but the university, it doesn't let the people use it. How many taxes does the university pay for that land? I tell you: *Nada.* But they keep it, and the rangers, they keep the people off of it. Like police. It is the same with the Highway Department land. What is it used for—*nada*. How many taxes are paid—*nada*. But the rangers keep the people off.

My cow, she doesn't understand such things and she can't read the signs. But the ranger says he saw her cross the lines and I get a letter saying she's going to be arrested in two weeks, she and six other cows I have there. I don't know if they were eating the grass too, because the ranger says he saw only this one walk from the university to the forest and back. But he says he's going to arrest them all.

Why do they do this? Why does the university of New Mexico do this? Why can't the people use these lands of the university, which are doing nothing now? Why can't the poor people use the Highway Department land for their cows, when it is just sitting there? *Porqué?* Why does the forest and the university and the highway all work together to hurt our people and keep us off the land?

I would laugh at them, but when they do this, they hurt our people. They have the land, and our people have become poor. When they arrest the people's cows, people have to get them back by paying. To get your cow back, it costs $20. *Mira*, here in the North, that's a lot of money. This ranger, he says he's going to arrest seven of my cows. That would cost $140 to get them back. *Hijo*, where am I supposed to get that much money? Where would any of the poor people get that much money to pay the rangers?

It is like the Presbyterian Ghost Ranch. Why can't the people use the water that's over there a little north of Ghost Ranch? It is because all that water, the Forest Service, they give it to the Ghost Ranch for nothing. Only they can use it. The people, they tell the people they can go to hell.

The university is doing the same thing. This ranger, he was called by EL GRITO and he told the paper this: "It was the university land that caused this letter (the letter that said they were going to arrest my cows). They were on the forest when we saw them, but they were walking back and forth."

How come this ranger is working as a police for the university? Why can't the people use the university's land? Last week I hear about what they're having called EARTH DAY and at the University of New Mexico they're talking about how much they love the land. They have a big demonstration at the university about loving the earth and the people. At the same time, they're arresting my cow. I don't hear about any demonstrations about my cow being arrested.

Tobias Leyba and his cattle have lived in Canjilon a long time, all of his life. And this ranger, he is a stranger. What does this ranger know about the land and the people? The way it is, Tobias Leyba and the ranger, they can't never have between each other any real trust. Because Tobias Leyba doesn't have any use for the ranger. The ranger is like he is a policeman for the forest, the university, the highway, the state, the U.S. Government in Washington. The ranger, he is just a police to keep the people off of the land.

For my little bit of land, I have to pay taxes. What does the university pay in taxes for our children in the schools in the North—*nada*. What does the highway pay—*nada*. What does the forest pay—*nada*. But they have the land, and these rangers, they are their police. The poor people pay their taxes, and this money is used to keep us poor.

I remember once I saw this ranger and another one, two of them, driving one cow. It cost the people more than $20 to get that cow back. They were poor people. They paid because they needed that cow and because they were afraid of the rangers. I don't think the rangers have a right to do this to our people. Now they send me this letter. It seems like they want Tobias Leyba to eat some *mierda.*

And they have put notices in the paper saying they are going to arrest the people's cattle if they cross the lines. It seems like they are saying to our Spanish people—"You just go on and just get out, get out of this land."

No, no, no, no, no—not me, not Tobias Leyba, not my people. This land is ours, and we will be here when the rangers, they all are gone.

## For Better Reading: "Civil Disobedience"

Henry David Thoreau, like Emerson, believed in standing by his principles, even though it opposed the will of society. In 1846, to protest America's invasion of Mexico and the existence of slavery, Thoreau would not pay a poll tax set on every person and was sentenced to jail for his refusal.

It was only a brief imprisonment, one night away from Walden. Yet Thoreau's act and his "Essay on Civil Disobedience" have inspired leaders like India's Mahatma Gandhi as well as our own Martin Luther King, Jr. to uphold their beliefs, even though law and society called them wrong.

Tobias Leyba was perhaps not familiar with the words and deeds of Henry David Thoreau or "Civil Disobedience" when he wrote "My Cow, She Was Almost Arrested."

Not well-educated nor a professional writer, Leyba speaks as a farmer living all his life in Canjilon, New Mexico, and the father of 16 children, who feels the need to protest what he sees as wrong.

Leyba's village was part of original Spanish and Mexican land grants, confirmed "in spirit" by a treaty signed after the Mexican-American War. Yet the villagers, knowing neither English nor law, were soon deprived of nearly 80 percent of their lands. In later years, more land went for national forests and parks.

About 120 years after Thoreau's night in jail, Tobias Leyba was one of eight men facing charges from a so-called "courthouse raid" and wrote "My Cow, She Was Almost Arrested."

## Fact or Opinion

Identify the following as fact, opinion, or a combination. Be prepared with proof to support your answer.

1. Leyba grazed his cow on public lands because he hoped to stage a protest.

2. The Highway Department does not pay taxes on its land.
3. The ranger was legally authorized to impound Leyba's cow.


## Questioning the Selection

1. How does Leyba use a humorous comparison in the opening paragraph to express his opinion of the forest rangers?
2. What proves Leyba himself is fully aware of the history of the land grants and the boundaries of the public lands? What are two reasons the cow wasn't aware of breaking the law?
3. How does Leyba's saying his cow thinks the grass is "still the same" relate to the source of his protest?
4. What are two things Leyba finds objectionable about the University of New Mexico's use of land?
5. What seems unfair about "arresting" not just one but six other cows? What "fair" reason might be the excuse for this decision?
6. The cows are not exactly arrested, but rather impounded. Describe the terms for getting them back. Why does Leyba object?
7. What does Leyba think unfair involving the Presbyterian Ghost Ranch?
8. In a newspaper interview with *El Grito*, which also published Leyba's article, whom did the ranger blame for the letter threatening the cows' arrest? Where were the cows when the Forest Service saw them?
9. What, to Leyba, is ironical about the university's celebration of Earth Day?
10. What are two reasons he distrusts the ranger?
11. What suggestions does Leyba make about tax dollars the university might, but doesn't, pay? Why does he feel poor people pay "more than $20" when two rangers return one cow?


## Looking Deeper

## I. Society's "Joint-stock Company"

How would the university, Forest Service park for tourists, and State Highway Department explain the necessity for them to possess and protect "their" public lands? Consider each separately. How would they justify their not paying taxes?

How would the ranger defend his "arrest" of farmers' cows? From society's view, why is he justified? What does the ranger personally gain by refusing to accept the farmers' point of view? How do the university, Ghost Ranch, and Highway Department also gain by conforming to society's view?

## II. "Through Someone Else's Eyes"

After hearing Leyba's viewpoint, what decision would you make about letting the farmers use public lands, and why? Basing your answer on the works of Emerson and Thoreau, why do "the university and the highway all work together"? Do they intend to hurt the poor people by keeping them off the land, as Leyba believed? Explain the reasons for your opinions.

How does Tobias Leyba show the kind of self-reliance and pride that Emerson and Thoreau believed in? How does his writing lead to his willingness to participate in an act of civil disobedience, protesting a law he felt unfair?

# Freeman Field

### *For Edward Wilson Woodward, Captain USAF (ret.) and the 101 of the 477th*

*by Marilyn Nelson Waniek*

| | |
|---|---|
| ***Born:*** | *Cleveland, Ohio* |
| ***Career:*** | *Teacher, professor, poet, translator* |
| ***Education:*** | *Universities of California (BA), Pennsylvania (MA), and Minnesota (PhD)* |
| ***Has taught in:*** | *Denmark, Minnesota, Connecticut* |

It was a cool evening
in the middle of April.
The 477th, the only Negro
bombardier group in the Air Corps,
had just been transferred                                    5
to Freeman Field.

Some of the guys
said they were hungry
and left to find food.
The others went on                                          10
playing bridge,
mending socks,
writing letters home.

A few minutes later
the hungry guys came back,                                  15
still hungry.
*We're under arrest.*

Note: During World War II, Freeman Field was an Air Force training base near Seymour, Indiana. It has since been closed.

The others thought they were kidding.

The next morning
the Base Commander                                   20
issued new regulations:
Negro officers were assigned
to the NCO Club;
white officers were assigned
to the Officers' Club.                               25

The Base Commander,
who had deliberately busted
an entire Negro outfit
so he wouldn't have to be
their flight-leader in combat,                       30
was a graduate of West Point.

He issued a statement:
*If we do not allow*
*Negro and white officers to mix,*
*the accident rate*                                  35
*will go down two*
*and two-tenths*
*percent.*

Sixty-one Negro officers
were ordered to report                               40
one by one
to his office.
*Lieutenant, have you read the regulations?*
*Sign here if you have read and understood.*

Sixty-one Negro officers                             45
refused to sign.
*A man of your intelligence*
*must be able to recognize*
*the dangers of fraternization.*

They refused to sign.                                50
*This is an order:*
*Sign the document.*

They refused to sign.
*This is a direct order!*
*You will sign the document!*                        55

Six cargo planes were called in;
pilots, navigators, and bombardiers
were shoved on board and flown
to Godman Field, Kentucky.

Across the river                                                    60
was Fort Knox.
The sixty-one
had grown by now
to one hundred and one
American fliers trained                                            65
to fight Nazis.
They were confined
to the BOQ
under guard
of armed MP's.                                                     70

By night, searchlights watched
every window. By daylight
the men leaned in the windows
to smoke, watching
the German POW's pump gas,                                         75
wash windshields
and laugh
at the motorpool
across the street.

## For Better Reading: Beyond Simplicity

"Hungry guys . . . mending socks . . ." and "busted." Such phrases as these don't fit the usual image of poetic language.

Yet "Freeman Field" and the two poems following it prove that simple words do not necessarily equal easy reading.

All three poets choose to use common American speech in writing about ordinary people—ordinary Americans, some of whom may seem quite extraordinary as you reflect on these poems.

Simple language doesn't mean these poets ask less of their readers, and you needn't expect to find all the answers on first reading.

It's often a good idea to read a poem once, just to listen for the sounds of its words and spot the questions of your own that arouse your curiosity. Second time through, look for clues—and decide whether the poem provides the evidence you seek or you need to check elsewhere—or perhaps understanding the poem doesn't require your knowing.

In "Freeman Field," for example, you might wonder about such military abbreviations as NCO (Noncommissioned Officers) and POW (Prisoner of War). Good readers usually try first to puzzle out answers on their own from context and clues—yet don't hesitate to seek more information when it's needed. It's another part of the decision-making process that builds to better reading.

## Questioning the Poem

1. Find two clues that place the time of this poem as World War II.
2. During World War II black servicemen were assigned to black units. In addition to such segregation, what does the 477th's being the "only" Negro Air Corps bombardier group show about the official military attitude?
3. By their actions in stanza two, do the bombardiers seem different or like any officers in a similar situation? What effect does the poet create by calling them "guys," not men?
4. The Base Commander ordered the black officers assigned to the lower-ranking NCO Club for sergeants or corporals. Why was the order unfair? Why does his issuing it "the next morning" make their punishment seem unjust?
5. In lines 27–28, what reason is given for "busting" the black officers to a lower rank? What excuse does the Commander use (lines 33–38) to cover up his prejudice? Give two reasons his excuse is unconvincing.
6. Why would the Commander prefer the officers to report one by one? Why does Waniek now call them "Negro officers" instead of "guys"?
7. At the ends of stanzas eight through eleven, what are the different psychological techniques used to convince the officers to sign?
8. Although lines 56–59 do not emphasize the treatment members of the 477th received when transferred, what two specific words indicate it was not good. Describe the scene more fully, based on these details.
9. Regarding lines 62–65, what made the sixty-one "grow"? What waste resulted, both of the men of the 477th and the MP's guarding them?
10. What is ironic about the searchlights that "watched every window"? How does Waniek contrast the attitudes of the black officers and the German prisoners of war?

## Looking Deeper
### "The Dangers of Fraternization"

A key meaning of fraternize means "to associate with enemy troops or natives of an occupied country."

By signing the order, what additional attitude would the black officers have agreed to accept? Does the poem depict the officers as like or different from typical WWII servicemen, who wish to fight for their country? Use evidence from the poem for support.

What is ironic about the incident's taking place at a base called "Freeman Field"? Does the poet's dedication lead you to believe this a real or imagined incident? Explain your reasoning.

How does the behavior of the 101 black officers compare with the beliefs of Emerson and Thoreau?

# I'm Nobody

## by Emily Dickinson

| | |
|---|---|
| **Born:** | *Amherst, Massachusetts* |
| **Lived:** | *All of her life (1830–86) at her birthplace* |
| **Wrote:** | *Over 1,000 poems* |
| **Gained fame:** | *With first editions of her verse (1890–91), published after her death* |

I'm nobody! Who are you?
    Are you nobody, too?
Then there's a pair of us—don't tell!
    They'd banish us, you know.

How dreary to be somebody!                                    5
    How public like a frog
To tell your name the livelong day
    To an admiring bog!

## Questioning the Poem

1. How does the speaker expect "you," the reader, to answer the question in line 2? Find two clues from lines 1 and 2 as proof.
2. By saying "there's a pair of us," what two things does the speaker assume? In what ways is this an echo of Emerson's statement about believing "what is true for you is true for all men"?
3. Even though you are "a pair," what does the speaker warn and why?
4. In line 4, what words indicate "you" and the speaker have a special understanding?
5. In stanza two, Dickinson invites you to imagine a "public" frog and an "admiring bog" or piece of wet, spongy ground. Describe the scene as you picture it—perhaps draw it, as a cartoon if you wish.
6. By its comparison to such a frog, what does Dickinson make the purpose

of "being somebody" seem to be? In what sense does she use the word "somebody"?

7. By doing the same thing "the livelong day," what does the frog seem to accomplish? As a result, why does the speaker conclude it's "dreary to be somebody"?

## Looking Deeper

### Pair of Nobodies

Although Dickinson's poems look simple at first glance, they are anything but that. For this reason, the reader must be alert for subtle clues that determine the precise meanings of words and that depend upon context and phrasing.

With this in mind, explain the difference between the following uses of indefinite pronouns:

      a. "He's a nobody," and "Nobody came."

      b. "She's a somebody," and "Somebody came."

Does Dickinson make the frog seem foolish or wise? Explain your choice. Dickinson implies the way to be "somebody" is "tell your name." What must this expression mean?

How do the ideas in this poem echo those about society's "names and customs" in Emerson's "Self-Reliance"?

Even though they're envied as rich, successful, and famous, do you believe most people would agree they're "nobody, too" if willing to admit their innermost thoughts? You may wish to include some examples, along with the reasons.

# Touching the Past

## *by Robert Sargent*

| | |
|---|---|
| ***Born:*** | *New Orleans, Louisiana* |
| ***World War II:*** | *Officer in US Navy* |
| ***Later career:*** | *Civil servant in Washington DC;* *later, returned to live in New Orleans* |
| ***Noted as:*** | *Poet, lover of jazz* |

Uptown New Orleans, 1940,
And here was a man of the right color,
Old enough to have been there,

Who maybe heard. So I inquired
From the old man doing his yard work,                                  5
"Ever hear Buddy Bolden play?"

"Ah me," he said, stopping his work.
"Yes. But you mean *King, King* Bolden.
That's what we called him then."

He leaned on his rake a while, resting.                               10
"Used to play in Algiers, played so loud
We could hear him clear 'cross the river."

He seemed listening. "King Bolden, now,
There was a man could play." We stood there,
Thinking about it, smiling.                                          15

Note: Buddy Bolden was a legendary trumpeter and leader in 1895 of a New Orleans band believed the first ever to play jazz, now known throughout the world as "America's music."

## Questioning the Poem

1. By using 1940 in the first line, what does the speaker suggest about the "man of the right color"?
2. Since jazz originated in black gospel music, work songs, and blues, what would the "right color" be? Why would the man's color be "right"?
3. From the question in line 6, what does the speaker mean by "been there" and "maybe heard"?
4. Judging by the few words of description in lines 5, 7, and 10, would you say the old man was most likely a hired gardener, a modest householder, or a poverty-stricken homeless person. Supply support for your choice.
5. The old man tells the speaker that "we called him" King Bolden. Who would "we" be? According to the dictionary, "ah" can express pain, appreciation, pity, or complaint, depending upon how it is said. Which does the old man's "Ah me" reflect, and how would you express his meaning in words?
6. In line 11, is Algiers most likely the city in North Africa or a district in New Orleans? Have logical support for your choice.
7. Lines 11–12 show that Bolden played loud. What of the old man's words show that he also played well?
8. Which words in stanza five are concerned with silence? In this silence, what must both have been doing to cause them to smile?


# Looking Deeper

## About the Music

In "Touching the Past," little is said about the actual sound of King Bolden's music except, "There was a man could play." Why is this more effective than saying, "He was great, the best there was"?

Although the poem does refer to the color of the old man, it does not mention the speaker's. Since music is sometimes called a universal language, does the speaker's skin tone matter? Why or why not?

What was the speaker's apparent reason for being in Uptown New Orleans? Considering the date, 1940, why would the poem be titled "Touching the Past"? As well as the old man's words and attitude, what detail or details in the background note also support Bolden's right to be called, "King"?

Is Bolden like or unlike someone of whom the speaker in "I'm Nobody" says, "How dreary to be somebody!" Explain the reason for your opinion.

# Being a Public Character

## *by Don Marquis*

***Born:*** *Illinois, 1878*
***Career:*** *New York newspaper columnist,*
*humorist*

**E**VER SINCE I BIT A CIRCUS lion, believing him to be another dog, only larger, I've been what Doc Watson calls a Public Character in our town.

Freckles, my boy, was a kind of Public Character, too. All the other boys and dogs in town sort of looked up to him and thought how lucky he was to belong to a dog like me. And he deserved all the glory he got out of it. For if I do say it myself, there's not a dog in town got a better boy than my boy Freckles. I'll back him against any dog's boy anywhere near his size for fighting, swimming, climbing, foot-racing or throwing stones farthest and straightest. Or I'll back him against any stray boy, either.

Well, some dogs may be born Public Characters and like it. And some may be brought up to like it. But with me, becoming a Public Character happened all in a flash, and it was sort of hard for me to get used to it. One day I was just a private sort of dog. And the next day I had bit that lion and fame came so sudden I scarcely knew how to act.

Even Heinie Hassenyager, the butcher got stuck on me after I got to be a Public Character. Heinie would come two blocks up Main Street with lumps of Hamburg steak, which is some kind one has already chewed for you, and give them to me. Steak, mind you, not old gristly scraps. And before I became a Public Character Heinie even begrudged me the bones I would drag out of the box under his counter when he wasn't looking.

My daily hope was that I could live up to it all. I had always tried, before I happened to bite that lion, to be a friendly kind of dog towards boys and humans and dogs, all three. I'd always been expected to do a certain amount of tail-wagging and be friendly. But as soon as I got to be a Public Character, I saw right away that I wasn't expected to be *too* friendly any more.

So when Heinie would bring me the ready-chewed steak I'd growl at him a little bit. And then I'd bolt and gobble the steak like I didn't think so darned much of it and was doing Heinie a big favor to eat it. That way of acting made a big hit with Heinie, too. I could see that he was honored and flattered because

I didn't go any further than just a growl. And the more I growled, the more steak he brought. Everybody in town fed me. I pretty near ate myself to death for awhile, besides all the meat I buried back of Doc Watson's store to dig up later.

The worst of it was that people, after a week or so, began to expect me to pull something else remarkable. Freckles, he got up a circus, and charged pins and marbles, and cents, when he found anyone that had any, to get into it, and I was the principal part of that circus. I was in a cage. I didn't care for being caged and circused that way myself. And it was right at that circus that considerable trouble started.

Seeing me in a cage like that, all famoused-up, with more meat poked through the slats than two dogs could eat, made Mutt Mulligan and some of my old friends jealous. Mutt, he nosed by the cage and sniffed. I nosed a piece of meat out of the cage to him. Mutt grabbed it and gobbled it down, but he didn't thank me any. Mutt, he says:

"There's a new dog down town that says he blew in from Chicago. He says he used to be a Blind Man's Dog on a street corner there. He's a pretty wise dog, and he's a right ornery-looking dog, too. He's peeled considerably where he has been bit in fights.

"You got such a swell head on you the last week or so that you gotta be licked. You can fool boys and humans all you want to about that accidental old lion, but us dogs got your number all right. What that Blind Man's Dog from Chicago would do to you would be a plenty!"

"Well then," I says, "I'll be out of this cage about supper time. Suppose you bring that Blind Man's Dog around here. And if he ain't got a spiked collar on him, I'll fight him. I won't fight a spiked-collared dog to please anybody."

And I wouldn't neither, without I had one on myself. If you can't get a dog by the throat or the back of his neck, what's the use of fighting him? You might just as well try to eat a blacksmith shop as fight one of those spike-collared dogs.

Well, that night after supper, along comes the Blind Man's Dog. Never did I see a Blind Man's Dog that was as tight-skinned. I had been used to fighting loose-skinned dogs that you can get some sort of a reasonable hold on while you are working around for position. And running into a tight-skinned dog that way, all of a sudden and all unprepared for it, would make anybody nervous.

Lots of dogs wouldn't have fought him at all when they realized how they had been fooled about him, and how tight-skinned he was. But I was a Public Character now, and I had to fight him. More than that, I ain't ready to say yet that that dog actually licked me. Freckles he hit him with a lump of soft coal, and he got all off me and run away before I could get my second wind. There's no telling what I would have done to that Blind Man's Dog, tight-skinned as he was, if he hadn't run away before I got my second wind.

Well, there's some mighty peculiar dogs in this world, let alone boys and humans. The word got around town, in spite of his running away before I got my second wind, that the Blind Man's Dog had actually licked me! Every time Freckles and me went down the street some one would say:

"Well, the dog that licked the lion got licked himself, did he?"

And if it was a lady said it, Freckles would spit on the sidewalk through the place where his front teeth are out and pass on politely as if he hadn't heard and say nothing. And if it was a man that said it Freckles would thumb his nose at him. And if it was a girl, he would rub a handful of sand into her hair. And if it was a boy anywhere near his size, there would be a fight. If it was too big a boy, Freckles would sling railroad iron at him.

I didn't care so awful much for myself, but I hated it for Freckles. For one Saturday afternoon when there wasn't any school, instead of going swimming with the other kids or playing baseball, or anything, he went and played with girls. He must have been pretty well down hearted and felt himself pretty much of an outcast, or he wouldn't have done that. I am an honest dog, and the truth must be told, the disgrace along with everything else, and the truth is that he played with girls of his own accord that day. Any boy will play with girls when all the boys and girls are playing together; but no boy is going to go off alone and look up a bunch of girls and play with them unless he has had considerable of a downfall.

Right next to our side of the yard was the Wilkinses. Freckles was sitting on the top of their fence when the three Wilkins girls came out to play. There was only two boys in the Wilkins family, and they were twins; but they were only year-old babies and didn't amount to anything. The two oldest Wilkins girls each had one of the twins taking care of it. And the other Wilkins girl had one of those big dolls made as big as a baby. They were rolling those babies and the doll around the grass in a wheelbarrow, and the wheel came off, and that's how Freckles happened to go over.

"Up in the attic," says one, when he had fixed up the wheelbarrow, "there's a little old express wagon with one wheel off that would be better'n this wheelbarrow. Maybe you could fix that wheel on, too."

Freckles, he fell for it. After he got the wagon fixed, they got to playing charades and fool girl games like that. The hired girl was off for the afternoon, and pretty soon Mrs. Wilkins hollered up the stairs that she was going to be gone for an hour, and to take good care of the twins, and then we were alone in the place.

Well, it wasn't much fun for me. They played and they played and I stuck to Freckles. I stuck to him because a dog should stick to his boy, and a boy should stick to his dog, no matter what the disgrace. But after a while I got pretty tired and lay down on a rug, and a new kind of flea struck me. After I had chased him down and cracked him with my teeth I went to sleep.

I must have slept pretty sound and pretty long. All of a sudden I waked up with a start and almost choking, for the place was smoky. I barked and no one answered.

The house was on fire, and it looked like I was alone in it. I went down the back stairway but the door that led out on the first floor landing was locked and I had to go up again. By the time I got back up, the front stairway was a great deal fuller of smoke, and I could see glints of flame through it way down below. But it was the only way out of the place.

On the top step I stumbled over a gray wool bunch of something or other, and I picked it up in my mouth. Think I, "That's Freckle's gray sweater that he is so stuck on. I might as well take it down to him."

I got kind of confused and excited. And it struck me all of a sudden, by the time I was down to the second floor, that the sweater weighed an awful lot. I dropped it on the second floor, and ran into one of the front bedrooms and looked out.

The whole town was in the front yard and in the street. And in the midst of the crowd was Mrs. Wilkins, carrying on like mad. "My baby!" she yelled. "Save my baby. Let me loose! I'm going after my baby!"

I stood up on my hind legs, with my head just out of that bedroom window, and the flame and smoke licking up all around me, and barked. "My doggie! My doggie!" yells Freckles, who was in the crowd. And he made a run for the house, but someone grabbed him and slung him back.

And Mrs. Wilkins made a run, but they held her, too. Old Pop Wilkins, Mrs. Wilkins's husband, was jumping up and down in front of Mrs. Wilkins yelling, here was her baby. He had a real baby on one arm and that big doll in the other, and was so excited he thought he had both babies. Later I heard what had happened. The kids had thought that they were getting out with both twins but one of them had saved the doll and left a twin behind.

Well, I thinks that the baby will likely turn up in the crowd, and I'd better get out of there myself while the getting was good. I ran out of the bedroom, and run into that hunched-up gray bundle again.

I ain't saying I knew it was the missing twin in a gray shawl when I picked it up a second time. And I ain't saying I didn't know it. The fact is I did pick it up. It may be that I was so rattled I just picked it up because I had had it in my mouth before and didn't quite know what I was doing. But the *record* is something you can't go behind, and the record is that I got out the back way and into the backyard with that bundle swinging from my mouth, and walked around into the front yard and laid that bundle down—*and it was the twin!*

I don't make any claim that I knew it was the twin till I got into the front yard. But you can't prove I *didn't* know it was. And nobody tried to prove it. The gray bundle let out a squall.

"My baby!" yells Mrs. Wilkins. And she kissed me.

"Three cheers for Spot!" yelled the whole town. And they give them.

And then I saw what the lay of the land was, so I wagged my tail and barked. It called for hero stuff, and I throwed my head up and looked noble—and pulled it.

An hour before Freckles and me had been outcasts. And now we was Public Characters again. We walked down Main Street and we owned it. And we hadn't any more got to Doc Watson's drug store than in rushed Heinie Hassenyager with a Hamburg steak, and with tears in his eyes.

"It's got chicken livers mixed in it, too!" says Heinie.

I ate it. But while I ate it, I growled at him.

# For Better Reading: A Different Persona

It's usual to equate the word *person* with someone's actual self or individual being. Yet, checking into its origin reveals an angle quite different.

*Person* has evolved from an earlier word, *persone,* meaning "role"—as in life, in a play, in a tale. At an even earlier stage, it probably meant the mask worn by an actor as well as the part being played.

Almost everyone sometimes "plays a role" in everyday life—when trying to appear cool, professional, and full of confidence the first day on the job, for example. Yet there's a special word that means purposely taking or assuming another character or personality, not only for business or social reasons but in an attempt to see through someone else's eyes.

The term is *persona,* and it's often used in a literary sense. Good readers find that "taking on" the persona of a character can help them participate more fully. Adopting another persona this way is not an escape but a means of discovering the inner workings of the character's mind and, often, learning more about yourself.

Although writers often assume personae other than their own, humorist Don Marquis is famous for adopting unusual ones. His most famous work, *lives and times of archy and mehitabel,* is about a sophisticated alley cat and literary cockroach, archy, who found it hard to hop from one typewriter key to another and so had trouble correctly typing up his stories.

In "Being a Public Character," Marquis adopts the persona of a dog who has a boy named Freckles, and, in doing so, points up the pressures and humor of "being a somebody."

## Important Details

1. Spot, the narrator, bit a circus lion because Spot (a) was trying to protect his boy, Freckles (b) thought it was just a very big dog (c) wanted to prove he wasn't a sissy (d) was told "get him" by his master.
2. Spot felt being a Public Character was (a) a role that came naturally (b) worth nothing of value (c) filled with fun, friends, and excitement (d) hard to get used to.
3. Before becoming a Public Character, Spot felt his main role was to (a) wag his tail and be friendly (b) chase cars, cats, and chickens (c) patrol Freckles' house and yard (d) prove himself the "top dog" in the neighborhood.

## Questioning the Story

1. In addition to Spot's calling him "my boy Freckles," what are three other ways the author reverses the normal relationship between dog and master in the second paragraph?

2. How did Heinie, the butcher, change his behavior after Spot became famous? What act did Spot put on that made a hit with him?
3. To live up to his reputation as a Public Character, how did Spot see "right away" he had to change? What mistake did he make when he started getting a great many food treats? What did he think the "worst thing" about being famous?
4. Why did Spot's old friends grow jealous? Why was there no cause for jealousy?
5. Before the fight with the Blind Man's Dog from Chicago, what motives and reactions typical of humans did both Mutt and Spot exhibit? Include examples. What details, especially geared to a dog's viewpoint, add to the humor?
6. What is Spot's excuse for coming off badly when fighting Blind Man's Dog? If he hadn't run away, Spot says "there's no telling what I would have done" to him. Why is this statement ambiguous, with Spot attempting both to uphold his reputation and be truthful as well?
7. After the fight, what "word got around town"? What is the truth?
8. What did Spot hate worst about the town's attitude? How did Freckles both stand by Spot, yet act in a way Spot disapproved?
9. By going to the Wilkinses, how did Spot show both loyalty and boredom? In escaping the fire, what mistake caused Spot to pick up the "gray wool bunch of something or other" the first time?
10. When Spot looked out the front bedroom window, how did Freckles and Mrs. Wilkins react similarly?
11. What two possible reasons does Spot give for picking up the "hunched-up gray bundle" again? Which is most likely and why? Base your decision on Spot's thought.

# Looking Deeper

## I. Going Public

Describe three ways in which Spot's public persona was different from his former and private self. What are three good qualities Spot shows that proved he retained his pride, whether a hero or an outcast?

After becoming a Public Character, how did Spot seemingly fool himself into thinking he was better than he was? Explain why both of the episodes which brought him fame are really much alike.

## II. The Humor in Language

In "Being a Public Character," Marquis has Spot misuse language for a humorous effect. Spot invents words like "circused," misuses others such as "we was" for "we were," and talks "tough guy" slang like "he blew in from Chicago." Find one or two additional examples of each.

Although Spot shares human feelings, some of his viewpoints are strictly canine. For example, to Spot, hamburger is steak that's "already chewed for you." Find two or three additional examples of humor achieved by Marquis's dog's eye view.

# The Scapegoat*

## by Paul Laurence Dunbar

| | |
|---|---|
| ***Born:*** | *Dayton, Ohio, 1872* |
| ***Early job:*** | *Elevator operator* |
| ***Famous for:*** | *Authoring four novels, six poetry and four short story collections* |

$T$HE LAW IS USUALLY SUPPOSED to be a stern mistress, not to be lightly wooed, and yielding only to the most ardent pursuit. But even law, like love, sits more easily on some natures than on others.

This was the case with Mr. Robinson Asbury. Mr. Asbury had started life as a bootblack in the growing town of Cadgers. From this he had risen one step and become porter and messenger in a barbershop. This rise fired his ambition, and he was not content until he had learned to use the shears and the razor and had a chair of his own. From this, in a man of Robinson's temperament, it was only a step to a shop of his own, and he placed it where it would do the most good.

Fully one-half of the population of Cadgers was composed of Negroes, and with their usual tendency to colonize, a tendency encouraged, and in fact compelled, by circumstances, they had gathered into one part of the town. Here in alleys, and streets as dirty and hardly wider, they thronged like ants.

It was in this place that Mr. Asbury set up his shop, and he won the hearts of his prospective customers by putting up the significant sign, "Equal Rights Barbershop." This legend was quite unnecessary, because there was only one race about, to patronize the place. But it was a delicate sop to the people's vanity, and it served its purpose.

Asbury came to be known as a clever fellow, and his business grew. The shop really became a sort of club and, on Saturday nights especially, was the gathering-place of the men of the whole Negro quarter. He kept the illustrated and race journals there, and those who cared neither to talk nor listen to someone else might see pictured the doings of high society in very short skirts or read in the Negro papers how Miss Boston had entertained Miss Blueford to tea on

*scapegoat* someone who bears the blame or punishment for the wrongs or crimes of others.

such and such an afternoon. Also, he kept the policy returns, which was wise, if not moral.

It was his wisdom rather more than his morality that made the party managers after a while cast their glances towards him as a man who might be useful to their interests. It would be well to have a man—a shrewd, powerful man—down in that part of the town who could carry his people's vote in his vest pocket, and who at any time its delivery might be needed, could hand it over without hesitation. Asbury seemed that man, and they settled upon him. They gave him money, and they gave him power and patronage. He took it all silently and he carried out his bargain faithfully. His hands and his lips alike closed tightly when there was anything within them. It was not long before he found himself the big Negro of the district and, of necessity, of the town. The time came when, at a critical moment, the managers saw that they had not reckoned without their host in choosing this barber of the black district as the leader of his people.

Now, so much success must have satisfied any other man. But in many ways Mr. Asbury was unique. For a long time he himself had done very little shaving—except of notes, to keep his hand in. His time had been otherwise employed. In the evening hours he had been wooing the coquettish Dame Law, and wonderful to say, she had yielded easily to his advances.

It was against the advice of his friends that he asked for admission to the bar. They felt that he could do more good in the place where he was.

"You see, Robinson," said old Judge Davis, "it's just like this: If you're not admitted, it'll hurt you with the people; if you are admitted, you'll move uptown to an office and get out of touch with them."

Asbury smiled an inscrutable smile. Then he whispered something into the judge's ear that made the old man wrinkle from his neck up with appreciative smiles.

"Asbury," he said, "you are—you are—well, you ought to be white, that's all. When we find a black man like you we send him to State's prison. If you were white, you'd go to the Senate."

The Negro laughed confidently.

He was admitted to the bar soon after, whether by merit or by connivance is not to be told.

"Now he will move uptown," said the black community. "Well, that's the way with a colored man when he gets a start."

But they did not know Robinson Asbury yet. He was a man of surprises, and they were destined to disappointment. He did not move uptown. He built an office in a small open space next to his shop, and there hung out his shingle.

"I will never desert the people who have done so much to elevate me," said Mr. Asbury. "I will live among them and I will die among them."

This was a strong card for the barber-lawyer. The people seized upon the statement as expressing a nobility of an altogether unique brand.

They held a mass meeting and endorsed him. They made resolutions that extolled him, and the Negro band came around and serenaded him, playing various things in varied time.

All this was very sweet to Mr. Asbury, and the party managers chuckled with satisfaction and said, "That Asbury, that Asbury!"

Now there is a fable extant of a man who tried to please everybody, and his failure is a matter of record. Robinson Asbury was not more successful. But be it said that his ill success was due to no fault or shortcoming of his.

For a long time his growing power had been looked upon with disfavor by the colored law firm of Bingo & Latchett. Both Mr. Bingo and Mr. Latchett themselves aspired to be Negro leaders in Cadgers, and they were delivering Emancipation Day orations and riding at the head of processions when Mr. Asbury was blacking boots. Is it any wonder, then, that they viewed with alarm his sudden rise? They kept their counsel, however, and treated with him, for it was best. They allowed him his scope without open revolt until the day upon which he hung out his shingle. This was the last straw. They could stand no more. Asbury had stolen their other chances from them, and now he was poaching upon the last of their preserves. So Mr. Bingo and Mr. Latchett put their heads together to plan the downfall of their common enemy.

The plot was deep and embraced the formation of an opposing faction made up of the best Negroes of the town. It would have looked too much like what it was for the gentlemen to show themselves in the matter, and so they took into their confidence Mr. Isaac Morton, the principal of the colored school, and it was under his ostensible leadership that the new faction finally came into being.

Mr. Morton was really an innocent young man, and he had ideals which should never have been exposed to the air. When the wily confederates came to him with their plan he believed that his worth had been recognized, and at last he was to be what nature destined him for—a leader.

The better class of Negroes—by that is meant those who were particularly envious of Asbury's success—flocked to the new man's standard. But whether the race be white or black, political virtue is always in a minority, so Asbury could afford to smile at the force arrayed against him.

The new faction met together and resolved. They resolved, among other things, that Mr. Asbury was an enemy to his race and a menace to civilization. They decided that he should be abolished; but as they couldn't get out an injunction against him, and as he had the whole undignified but still voting black belt behind him, he went serenely on his way.

"They're after you hot and heavy, Asbury," said one of his friends to him.

"Oh, yes," was the reply, "they're after me, but after a while I'll get so far away that they'll be running in front."

"It's all the best people, they say."

"Yes. Well, it's good to be one of the best people, but your vote only counts one just the same."

The time came, however, when Mr. Asbury's theory was put to the test. The Cadgerites celebrated the first of January as Emancipation Day. On this day there was a large procession, with speechmaking in the afternoon and fireworks at night. It was the custom to concede the leadership of the colored people of the town to the man who managed to lead the procession. For two years past this honor had fallen, of course, to Robinson Asbury, and there had been no disposition on the part of anybody to try conclusions with him.

Mr. Morton's faction changed all this. When Asbury went to work to solicit contributions for the celebration, he suddenly became aware that he had a fight upon his hands. All the better-class Negroes were staying out of it. The next thing he knew was that plans were on foot for a rival demonstration.

"Oh," he said to himself, "that's it, is it? Well, if they want a fight they can have it."

He had a talk with the party managers, and he had another with Judge Davis.

"All I want is a little lift, Judge," he said, "and I'll make 'em think the sky has turned loose and is vomiting niggers."

The judge believed that he could do it. So did the party managers. Asbury got his lift. Emancipation Day came.

There were two parades. At least, there was one parade and the shadow of another. Asbury's, however, was not the shadow. There was a great deal of substance about it—substance made up of many people, many banners, and numerous bands. He did not have the best people. Indeed among his cohorts there were a good many of the pronounced ragtag and bobtail. But he had noise and numbers. In such cases, nothing more is needed. The success of Asbury's side of the affair did everything to confirm his friends in their good opinion of him.

When he found himself defeated, Mr. Silas Bingo saw that it would be policy to placate his rival's just anger against him. He called upon him at his office the day after the celebration.

"Well, Asbury," he said, "you beat us, didn't you?"

"It wasn't a question of beating," said the other calmly. "It was only an inquiry as to who were the people—the few or the many."

"Well, it was well done, and you've shown that you are a manager. I confess that I haven't always thought that you were doing the wisest thing in living down here and catering to this class of people when you might, with your ability, be much more to the better class."

"What do they base their claims of being better on?"

"Oh, there ain't any use discussing that. We can't get along without you, we see that. So I, for one, have decided to work with you for harmony."

"Harmony. Yes, that's what we want."

"If I can do anything to help you at any time, why you have only to command me."

"I am glad to find such a friend in you. Be sure, if I ever need you, Bingo, I'll call on you."

"And I'll be ready to serve you."

Asbury smiled when his visitor was gone. He smiled, and knitted his brow. "I wonder what Bingo's got up his sleeve," he said. "He'll bear watching."

It may have been pride at his triumph, it may have been gratitude at his helpers, but Asbury went into the ensuing campaign with reckless enthusiasm. He did the most daring things for the party's sake. Bingo, true to his promise, was ever at his side ready to serve him. Finally, association and immunity made danger less fearsome; the rival no longer appeared a menace.

With the generosity born of obstacles overcome, Asbury determined to forgive Bingo and give him a chance. He let him in on a deal, and from that time they worked amicably together until the election came and passed.

It was a close election and many things had had to be done, but there were men there ready and waiting to do them. They were successful, and then the first cry of the defeated party was, as usual, "Fraud! Fraud!" The cry was taken up by the jealous, the disgruntled, and the virtuous.

Someone remembered how two years ago the registration books had been stolen. It was known upon good authority that money had been freely used. Men held up their hands in horror at the suggestion that the Negro vote had been juggled with, as if that were a new thing. From their pulpits ministers denounced the machine and bade their hearers rise and throw off the yoke of a corrupt municipal government. One of those sudden fevers of reform had taken possession of the town and threatened to destroy the successful party.

They began to look around them. They must purify themselves. They must give the people some tangible evidence of their own yearnings after purity. They looked around them for a sacrifice to lay upon the altar of municipal reform. Their eyes fell upon Mr. Bingo. No, he was not big enough. His blood was too scant to wash the political stains. Then they looked into each other's eyes and turned their gaze away to let it fall upon Mr. Asbury. They really hated to do it. But there must be a scapegoat. The god from the Machine commanded them to slay him.

Robinson Asbury was charged with many crimes—with all that he had committed and some that he had not. When Mr. Bingo saw what was afoot he threw himself heart and soul into the work of his old rival's enemies. He was of incalculable use to them.

Judge Davis refused to have anything to do with the matter. But in spite of his disapproval it went on. Asbury was indicted and tried. The evidence was all against him, and no one gave more damaging testimony than his friend Mr. Bingo. The judge's charge was favorable to the defendant, but the current of popular opinion could not be entirely stemmed. The jury brought in a verdict of guilty.

"Before I am sentenced, Judge, I have a statement to make to the court. It will take less than ten minutes."

"Go on, Robinson," said the judge kindly.

Asbury started, in a monotonous tone, a recital that brought the prosecuting attorney to his feet in a minute. The judge waved him down, and sat transfixed by a sort of fascinated horror as the convicted man went on. The before-mentioned attorney drew a knife and started for the prisoner's dock. With difficulty he was restrained. A dozen faces in the courtroom were red and pale by turns.

"He ought to be killed," whispered Mr. Bingo audibly.

Robinson Asbury looked at him and smiled, and then he told a few things of him. He gave the ins and outs of some of the misdemeanors of which he stood accused. He showed who were the men behind the throne. And still, pale and transfixed, Judge Davis waited for his own sentence.

Never were ten minutes so well taken up. It was a tale of rottenness and corruption in high places told simply and with the stamp of truth upon it.

He did not mention the judge's name. But he had torn the mask from the face of every other man who had been concerned in his downfall. They had shorn him of his strength, but they had forgotten that he was yet able to bring the roof and pillars tumbling about their heads.

The judge's voice shook as he pronounced sentence upon his old ally—a year in State's prison.

Some people said it was too light, but the judge knew what it was to wait for the sentence of doom, and he was grateful and sympathetic.

When the sheriff led Asbury away the judge hastened to have a short talk with him.

"I'm sorry, Robinson," he said, "and I want to tell you that you were no more guilty than the rest of us. But why did you spare me?"

"Because I knew you were my friend," answered the convict.

"I tried to be, but you were the first man that I've ever known since I've been in politics who ever gave me any decent return for friendship."

"I reckon you're about right, Judge."

In politics, party reform usually lies in making a scapegoat of someone who is only as criminal as the rest, but a little weaker. Asbury's friends and enemies had succeeded in making him bear the burden of all the party's crimes, but their reform was hardly a success, and their protestations of a change of heart were received with doubt. Already there were those who began to pity the victim and to say that he had been hardly dealt with.

Mr. Bingo was not of these; but he found, strange to say, that his opposition to the idea went but a little way, and that even with Asbury out of his path he was a smaller man than he was before. Fate was strong against him. His poor, prosperous humanity could not enter the lists against a martyr. Robinson Asbury was now a martyr.


## II

A year is not a long time. It was short enough to prevent people from forgetting Robinson, and yet long enough for their pity to grow strong as they remembered. Indeed, he was not gone a year. Good behavior cut two months off the time of his sentence, and by the time people had come around to the notion that he was really the greatest and smartest man in Cadgers he was at home again.

He came back with no flourish of trumpets, but quietly, humbly. He went back again into the heart of the black district. His business had deteriorated during his absence, but he put new blood and new life into it. He did not go to work in the shop himself but, taking down the shingle that had swung idly before his office door during his imprisonment, he opened the little room as a news- and cigar-stand.

Here anxious, pitying customers came to him and he prospered again. He was very quiet. Uptown hardly knew that he was again in Cadgers, and it knew nothing whatever of his doings.

"I wonder why Asbury is so quiet," they said to one another. "It isn't like him to be quiet." And they felt vaguely uneasy about him.

So many people had begun to say, "Well, he was a mighty good fellow after all."

Mr. Bingo expressed the opinion that Asbury was quiet because he was crushed, but others expressed doubt as to this. There are calms and calms, some after and some before the storm. Which was this?

They waited a while, and, as no storm came, concluded that this must be the afterquiet. Bingo, reassured, volunteered to go and seek confirmation of this conclusion.

He went, and Asbury received him with an indifferent, not to say impolite, demeanor.

"Well, we're glad to see you back, Asbury," said Bingo patronizingly. He had variously demonstrated his inability to lead during his rival's absence and was proud of it. "What are you going to do?"

"I'm going to work."

"That's right. I reckon you'll stay out of politics."

"What could I do even if I went in?"

"Nothing now, of course; but I didn't know—"

He did not see the gleam in Asbury's half-shut eyes. He only marked his humility, and he went back swelling with the news.

"Completely crushed—all the run taken out of him," was his report.

The black district believed this, too, and a sullen, smouldering anger took possession of them. Here was a good man ruined. Some of the people whom he had helped in his former days—some of the rude, coarse people of the low quarter who were still sufficiently unenlightened to be grateful—talked among themselves and offered to get up a demonstration for him. But he denied them. No, he wanted nothing of the kind. It would only bring him into unfavorable notice. All he wanted was that they would always be his friends and would stick by him.

They would to the death.

There were again two factions in Cadgers. The schoolmaster could not forget how once on a time he had been made a tool of by Mr. Bingo. So he revolted against his rule and set himself up as the leader of an opposing clique. The fight had been long and strong, but had ended with odds slightly in Bingo's favor.

But Mr. Morton did not despair. As the first of January and Emancipation Day approached, he arrayed his hosts, and the fight for supremacy became fiercer than ever. The schoolteacher brought the schoolchildren in for chorus singing, secured an able orator, and the best essayist in town. With all this, he was formidable.

Mr. Bingo knew that he had the fight of his life on his hands, and he entered with fear as well as zest. He, too, found an orator, but he was not sure that he was good as Morton's. There was no doubt but that his essayist was not. He secured a band, but still he felt unsatisfied. He had hardly done enough, and for the schoolmaster to beat him now meant his political destruction.

It was in this state of mind that he was surprised to receive a visit from Mr. Asbury.

"I reckon you're surprised to see me here," said Asbury, smiling.

"I am pleased, I know." Bingo was astute.

"Well, I just dropped in on our business."

"To be sure, to be sure, Asbury. What can I do for you?"

"It's more what I can do for you that I came to talk about," was the reply.

"I don't believe I understand you."

"Well, it's plain enough. They say that the schoolteacher is giving you a pretty hard fight."

"Oh, not so hard."

"No man can be too sure of winning though. Mr. Morton once did me a mean turn when he started the faction against me."

Bingo's heart gave a great leap, and then stopped for the fraction of a second.

"You were in it, of course," pursued Asbury, "but I can look over your part in it in order to get even with the man who started it."

It was true, then, thought Bingo gladly. He did not know. He wanted revenge for his wrongs and upon the wrong man. How well the schemer had covered his tracks! Asbury should have his revenge and Morton would be the sufferer.

"Of course, Asbury, you know that I did what I did innocently."

"Oh, yes, in politics we are all lambs and the wolves are only to be found in the other party. We'll pass that, though. What I want to say is that I can help you to make your celebration an overwhelming success. I still have some influence down in my district."

"Certainly, and very justly, too. Why I should be delighted with your aid. I could give you a prominent position in the procession."

"I don't want it; I don't want to appear in this at all. All I want is revenge. You can have all the credit, but let me down my enemy."

Bingo was perfectly willing, and with their heads close together, they had a long and close consultation. When Asbury was gone, Mr. Bingo lay back in his chair and laughed. "I'm a slick duck," he said.

From that hour Mr. Bingo's cause began to take on the appearance of something very like a boom. More bands were hired. The interior of the State was called upon and a more eloquent orator secured. The crowd hastened to array itself on the growing side.

With surprised eyes, the schoolmaster beheld the wonder of it, but he kept to his own purpose with dogged insistence, even when he saw that he could not turn aside the overwhelming defeat that threatened him. But in spite of his obstinacy, his hours were dark and bitter. Asbury worked like a mole, all underground, but he was indefatigable. Two days before the celebration time everything was perfected for the biggest demonstration that Cadgers had ever known. All the next day and night he was busy among his allies.

On the morning of the great day, Mr. Bingo, wonderfully caparisoned, rode down to the hall where the parade was to form. He was early. No one had yet come. In an hour a score of men all told had collected. Another hour passed, and no more had come. Then there smote upon his ear the sound of music. They were coming at last. Bringing his sword to his shoulder, he rode forward to the middle of the street. Ah, there they were. But—but—could he believe his eyes? They were going in another direction, and at their head rode—Morton! He gnashed his teeth in fury. He had been led into a trap and betrayed. The procession passing had been his—all his. He heard them cheering, and then, oh! climax of infidelity, he saw his own orator go past in a carriage, bowing and smiling to the crowd.

There was no doubting who had done this thing. The hand of Asbury was apparent in it. He must have known the truth all along, thought Bingo. His allies left him one by one for the other hall, and he rode home in a humiliation deeper than he had ever known before.

Asbury did not appear at the celebration. He was at his little newsstand all day.

In a day or two the defeated aspirant had further cause to curse his false friend. He found that not only had the people defected from him, but that the thing had been so adroitly managed that he appeared to be in fault, and three-fourths of those who knew him were angry at some supposed grievance. His cup of bitterness was full when his partner, a quietly ambitious man, suggested that they dissolve their relations.

His ruin was complete.

The lawyer was not alone in seeing Asbury's hand in his downfall. The party managers saw it too, and they met together to discuss the dangerous factor which, while it appeared to slumber, was so terribly awake. They decided that he must be appeased, and they visited him.

He was still busy at his newsstand. They talked to him adroitly, while he sorted papers and kept an impassive face. When they were all done, he looked up for a moment and replied, "You know, gentlemen, as an ex-convict I am not in politics."

Some of them had the grace to flush.

"But you can use your influence," they said.

"I am not in politics," was his only reply.

And the spring elections were coming on. Well, they worked hard, and he showed no sign. He treated with neither one party nor the other. "Perhaps," thought the managers, "he is out of politics," and they grew more confident.

It was nearing eleven o'clock on the morning of election when a cloud no bigger than a man's hand appeared upon the horizon. It came from the direction of the black district. It grew, and the managers of the party in power looked at it, fascinated by an ominous dread. Finally it began to rain Negro voters, and as one man they voted against their former candidates. Their organization was perfect. They simply came, voted, and left, but they overwhelmed everything. Not one of the party that had damned Robinson Asbury was left in power save old Judge Davis. His majority was overwhelming.

The generalship that had engineered the thing was perfect. There were loud threats against the newsdealer. But no one bothered him except a reporter. The reporter called to see just how it was done. He found Asbury very busy sorting papers. To the newspaperman's questions he had only this reply, "I am not in politics, sir."

But Cadgers had learned its lesson.

## For Better Reading: With Tongue in Cheek

Nobody's perfect.

"I'm nobody, who are you?"

When the two preceding sentences are taken together, what "reading" would you give the first one?

It could be, "No person is perfect." Or, "Since I'm nobody, I'm perfect."

Good reading depends not only on what a writer says but how the reader "takes" it. In "The Scapegoat," Paul Laurence Dunbar uses words in a manner often called "tongue in cheek." It means not speaking straightforwardly but with a type of insincerity that the reader is meant to notice, find humorous, and recognize as pointing up a weakness or flaw in an individual or group.

For example, Dunbar says that Robinson Asbury opened his first barber shop "where it would do the most good." That's Dunbar's tongue in cheek way of inviting you to ask, "For whose or what good? The good of Asbury's customers or his own ambition?"

As you see, the tongue in cheek approach is different from verbal irony, which means the opposite of what is said. Doing good—for somebody—was the true intention.

In a similar way, the sign "Equal Rights Barbershop" really did "serve its purpose." The main reason for its wording was to convince the community of Asbury's concern for justice.

In this unit, you've seen how writers from Thoreau and Emerson to today have felt free to point out flaws in American society, seeking its betterment. Dunbar does the same, though with one difference. With his tongue in cheek manner, he seems to make fun of society with "fondness and enthusiasm," like those who, Thoreau said, find "inspiration . . . in the present condition of things."

## Inference

1. Since a "stern mistress" is one that strictly controls those under its authority, Dunbar must mean law in relation to (a) everyone subject to the laws of a specific place (b) criminals caught, charged, and jailed (c) those who practice the law profession (d) those responsible for policing society.
2. By writing "law . . . sits more easily on some natures than on others,"

Dunbar refers to (a) the differences between laws in different states (b) nature's laws being more just and fair than man's laws (c) the importance of not judging before the facts are known (d) the fact some people use the law to their own advantage.

3. Stating that the black population of Cadgers was "compelled" to settle in one part of town "by circumstance" is Dunbar's tongue in cheek way of calling attention to (a) vanity (b) ambition (c) prejudice (d) gambling.

## Questioning the Selection

**Part I.**

1. In addition to the "policy returns," what are two other attractions for those gathering at Asbury's barbershop?

2. "Policy" is a type of gambling on lottery numbers. In what way might this be "wise"? Why perhaps "not moral"?

3. What did the town's political party managers want from Asbury? Name at least two things they gave him in exchange. Why are Asbury's "questionable morality" and his wisdom both helpful to them?

4. Why did Asbury's political "friends" discourage his becoming a lawyer? What could Asbury have said that caused Judge Davis to comment, "You ought to be white"? In what way does this slyly criticize the town's justice system?

5. Why was the law firm, Bingo & Latchett, alarmed by Asbury's opening a law office beside his barber shop? Give two reasons for Mr. Isaac Morton's choice to head the new black faction.

6. According to Dunbar, those who "flocked to the new man's standard" are "the better class of Negro." Why is this a tongue in check comment? How did Asbury react to losing this element?

7. Give two reasons Asbury's Emancipation Day parade was more successful than Morton's. After this success, what offer did Bingo make, and how did Asbury's outward and private response differ?

8. After the victory of Asbury, Bingo, and Judge Davis's party, what accusation did losing side make? List three specific charges.

9. Why was Asbury, not Bingo, chosen as scapegoat? How did Bingo react to Asbury's downfall? How and why had Asbury previously fooled himself concerning Bingo?

10. How does Judge Davis behave differently from Asbury's other party "friends"? At the trial, how does Asbury "repay" both his false friends and Judge Davis?

11. At the trial, why did Judge Davis feel "what it was to wait for the sentence of doom"? How did the judge return Asbury's favor? What qualities do both men have that make them different from the others?

12. After sentencing, what realization led people to consider Asbury a "martyr" or someone sacrificed to a cause?

**Part II.**

13. After release from prison, what are two ways Asbury changed his way of life in Cadgers? What two guesses do people make about his motives?

14. During Asbury's imprisonment, how did party factions change in the black community?

15. Why would Bingo believe Asbury's claim about giving up politics? What two advantages did Asbury gain by this?

16. Explain the meaning behind Bingo's words: "How well the schemer had covered his tracks!" Why was he wrong?

17. How and why did Bingo feel "led into a trap and betrayed"? What did Asbury do during the parade and celebration?

18. Although "not in politics," what must Asbury have "engineered" for the spring election? Why would nobody except one reporter bother him? What "lesson" had Cadgers learned?

# Looking Deeper

## I. A Cautionary Fable

Near the beginning of the story, Dunbar alludes to the saying, "He who tries to please everybody ends up pleasing nobody." How does Asbury fit this saying in part I? Do you agree that "his ill success was due to no fault or shortcoming of his"? Explain the reasons behind your opinion.

Explain how this story illustrates that skin tone is less important than the kind of person one is. In a fable, good triumphs over evil. How is this true of "The Scapegoat"?

## II. Sincerely Speaking

Explain what lies behind each of the following "tongue in cheek" statements.

1. "Bingo, true to his promise, was ever at his side ready to serve him."

2. "Men held up their hands in horror" at the idea that fraud was involved in Cadger's elections.

3. "In politics we are all lambs and the wolves are only to be found in the other party."

At the beginning of the story, Dunbar states that Asbury "carried out his bargain faithfully" and said, "I will never desert the people" and expressed "a nobility of an altogether unique brand."

Explain why these might seem tongue in cheek at the beginning, yet true at the end.

# A New City in Colorado

## by Helen Hunt Jackson

| | |
|---|---|
| **Born:** | *Amherst, Massachusetts. 1830* |
| **Noted for:** | *Writing of the injustices done to American Indians in the novel* Ramona *and nonfiction book,* A Century of Dishonor |
| **Also wrote:** | *Other novels, children's stories, accounts of travels* |

GARLAND CITY IS SIX MILES from Fort Garland. The road to it from the fort lies for the last three miles on the top of a sage-grown plateau. It is straight as an arrow, looks in the distance like a brown furrow on the pale gray plain, and seems to pierce the mountains beyond. Up to within an eighth of a mile of Garland City, there is no trace of human habitation. Knowing that the city must be near, you look in all directions for a glimpse of it; the hills ahead of you rise sharply across your way. Where is the city? At your very feet, but you do not suspect it.

The sunset light was fading when we reached the edge of the ravine in which the city lies. It was like looking unawares over the edge of a precipice; the gulch opened beneath us as suddenly as if the earth had that moment parted and made it. With brakes set firm, we drove cautiously down the steep road; the ravine twinkled with lights, and almost seemed to flutter with white tents and wagon tops. At the farther end it widened, opening out on an inlet of the San Luis Park; and, in its center, near this widening mouth, lay the twelve-days-old city. A strange din arose from it.

"What is going on?" we exclaimed. "The building of the city," was the reply. "Twelve days ago there was not a house here. Today there are one hundred and five, and in a week more there will be two hundred; each man is building his own home, and working day and night to get it done ahead of his neighbor. There are four sawmills going constantly, but they can't turn out lumber half fast enough. Everybody has to be content with a board at a time. If it were not for that, there would have been twice as many houses done as there are."

We drove on down the ravine. A little creek on our right was half hid in willow thickets. Hundreds of white tents gleamed among them: tents with poles; tents made by spreading sailcloth over the tops of bushes; round tents; square tents; big tents; little tents; and for every tent a camp fire; hundreds of white-topped wagons, also, at rest for the night, their great poles propped up by sticks, and their mules and drivers lying and standing in picturesque groups around them.

It was a scene not to be forgotten. Louder and louder sounded the chorus of the hammers as we drew near the center of the "city;" more and more the bustle thickened; great ox teams swaying unwieldily about, drawing logs and planks, backing up steep places; all sorts of vehicles driving at reckless speed up and down; men carrying doors; men walking along inside of window sashes,—the easiest way to carry them; men shoveling; men wheeling wheelbarrows; not a man standing still; not a man with empty hands; every man picking up something, and running to put it down somewhere else, as in a play; and, all the while, "Clink! clink! clink!" ringing above the other sounds,—the strokes of hundreds of hammers, like the "Anvil Chorus."

"Where is Perry's Hotel?" we asked. One of the least busy of the throng spared time to point to it with his thumb, as he passed us. In some bewilderment we drew up in front of a large unfinished house, through the many uncased apertures of which we could see only scaffoldings, rough boards, carpenters' benches, and heaps of shavings. Streams of men were passing in and out through these openings, which might be either doors or windows; no steps led to any of them.

"Oh, yes! oh, yes! can accommodate you all!" was the landlord's reply to our hesitating inquiries. He stood in the doorway of his dining-room; the streams of men we had seen going in and out were the fed and the unfed guests of the house. It was supper time; we also were hungry. We peered into the dining room: three tables full of men; a huge pile of beds on the floor, covered with hats and coats; a singular wall, made entirely of doors propped upright; a triangular space walled off by sailcloth,—this is what we saw. We stood outside, waiting among the scaffolding and benches. A black man was lighting the candles in a candelabrum made of two narrow bars of wood nailed across each other at right angles, and perforated with holes. The candles sputtered, and the hot fat fell on the shavings below.

"Dangerous way of lighting a room full of shavings," some one said. The landlord looked up at the swinging candelabra and laughed. "Tried it pretty often," he said. "Never burned a house down yet."

I observed one peculiarity in the speech at Garland City. Personal pronouns, as a rule, were omitted; there was no time for a superfluous word.

"Took down this house at Wagon Creek," he continued, "just one week ago; took it down one morning while the people were eating breakfast; took it down over their heads; putting it up again over their heads now."

This was literally true. The last part of it we ourselves were seeing while he spoke, and a friend at our elbow had seen the Wagon Creek crisis.

"Waiting for that round table for you," said the landlord; " 'll bring the chairs out here's fast's they quit 'em. That's the only way to get the table."

So, watching his chances, as fast as a seat was vacated, he sprang into the room, seized the chair and brought it out to us; and we sat there in our "reserved seats," biding the time when there should be room enough vacant at the table for us to take our places.

What an indescribable scene it was! The strange-looking wall of propped doors which we had seen, was the *impromptu* wall separating the bedrooms from the dining-room. Bedrooms? Yes, five of them; that is, five bedsteads in a row, with just space enough between them to hang up a sheet, and with just room enough between them and the propped doors for a moderate-sized person to stand upright if he faced either the doors or the bed. Chairs? Oh, no! What do you want of a chair in a bedroom which has a bed in it? Washstands? One tin basin out in the unfinished room. Towels? Uncertain.

The little triangular space walled off by the sailcloth was a sixth bedroom, quite private and exclusive; and the big pile of beds on the dining-room floor was to be made up into seven bedrooms more between the tables, after everybody had finished supper.

Luckily for us we found a friend here,—a man who has been from the beginning one of Colorado's chief pioneers; and who is never, even in the wildest wilderness, without resources of comfort.

"You can't sleep here," he said. "I can do better for you than this."

"Better!"

He offered us luxury. How movable a thing is one's standard of comfort! A two-roomed pine shanty, board walls, board floors, board ceilings, board partitions not reaching to the roof, looked to us that night like a palace. To have been entertained at Windsor Castle would not have made us half so grateful.

It was late before the "city" grew quiet; and, long after most of the lights were out, and most of the sounds had ceased, I heard one solitary hammer in the distance, clink, clink, clink. I fell asleep listening to it.

## For Better Reading: Sources of Pride

Born well over 150 years ago, Helen Hunt Jackson represents some of the sources of American pride . . . and many of the qualities that Americans value today.

When Thoreau writes of a man's choice to "adventure on life," it does not rule out its being a woman's choice, too, as Jackson proves in this account from her book, *Bits of Travel at Home*.

Nor did Jackson accept, without protest, the unjust treatment of Indians. She spoke out against it both in nonfiction and fiction.

Jackson also offers a close-up view of the "can-do" spirit on which Americans pride themselves. As she shows, a chief source of Americans' pride is not the belief that America is perfect, but faith in its possibilities for betterment. This belief is illustrated by the city rising out of nowhere, "A New City in Colorado."

It's the kind of pride that makes criticism and change a typically American way of expressing belief in America and its future.

## Important Details

1. As close as $\frac{1}{8}$ mile away from Garland City, travelers (a) could see no signs of a settlement (b) met guards, posted to discourage trespassing (c) spotted smoke curling upward from campfires (d) saw "for sale" signs advertising land.
2. The city itself was located (a) at the bottom of a ravine or steep-sided valley (b) atop a level, sage-grown plateau (c) in the midst of a brown, furrowed plain (d) near the site of a newly-found diamond mine.
3. Jackson, who writes of going cautiously "with brakes set firm," was most likely traveling in a (a) wood-fired railroad train (b) U.S. cavalry caravan (c) public motorcoach (d) mule or horse-drawn vehicle.

## Questioning the Selection

1. In building the city, what did the people of Garland City accomplish in just 12 days? What prevented their doing "twice as much"?
2. As well as work fast, what other accomplishment gave each man in Garland the right to feel proud? How was competition involved?
3. In addition to new homes, what other type of shelter made up the city? What does its variety reveal about the people settling there?
4. Describing "a scene not to be forgotten," Jackson states there was "not a man standing still." What American attitude toward work does this illustrate?
5. What two things made Jackson feel bewildered when she arrived at Perry's Hotel?
6. Give two examples how successful results in the hotel landlord's past had helped him acquire a "can-do" attitude.
7. Explain what Jackson found unusual about the townmen's use of personal pronouns, and give an example. How did she account for this peculiarity?
8. In the hotel, what substituted for dining room and bedroom walls? How did the dining room do double duty?
9. How did "one of Colorado's chief pioneers" come to Jackson's aid?

## Looking Deeper

### I. Movable Standards

Why did Jackson believe she would not be "half so grateful" as a guest at Windsor Castle as in the two-room shanty? If the offer had not come, do you think Jackson would have complained to the hotel landlord about her quarters? Why or why not?

## II. Building

Name at least three qualities exhibited by the men building "A New City in Colorado" that Americans can take pride in, and give an example of each.

Do you think people today still hold to the American work ethic, admiring hard work and putting forth their best effort? Explain why or why not. Do you feel society today encourages or discourages these kinds of standards? Give reasons for your belief.

## III. A Good Reporter

Most of "A New City in Colorado" is presented as a first-person report, full of details, facts, and descriptions that let readers draw their own conclusions.

Name two or three elements; explain why they impressed you and what conclusions they lead you to draw about this period in America's past.

# I Hear America Singing

## by Walt Whitman

| | |
|---|---|
| **Born:** | *Long Island, N.Y. 1819* |
| **Education:** | *Left school at age 11* |
| **Early jobs:** | *Office boy, doctor's helper, printer's assistant, printer, carpenter, teacher, journalist; quit as newspaper editor to protest publisher's support of slavery* |
| **Military service:** | *Volunteer nurse during Civil War* |
| **Later years:** | *In Camden, New Jersey* |
| **Famous as:** | *Poet whose* Leaves of Grass *revolutionized poetry; author of* Democratic Vistas |

I hear America singing, the varied carols I hear,
Those of mechanics, each one singing his as it should be
    blithe and strong,
The carpenter singing his as he measures his plank or
    beam,
The mason singing his as he makes ready for work, or
    leaves off work,
The boatman singing what belongs to him in his boat,
    the deckhand singing on the steamboat deck,    5
The shoemaker singing as he sits on his bench, the
    hatter singing as he stands,
The woodcutter's song, the plowboy's on his way in the
    morning, or at noon intermission or at sundown,
The delicious singing of the mother, or of the young wife
    at work, or of the girl sewing or washing,
Each singing what belongs to him or her and to none
    else,
The day what belongs to the day—at night the party
    of young fellows, robust, friendly,    10
Singing with open mouths their strong melodious songs.

# For Better Reading: Lasting Influences

As you have seen, the northeastern part of the United States is the birthplace of many poets and writers whose words still stir American pride and define the qualities Americans claim proudly.

The reason is understandable. The time was before the Civil War. The West was still in the process of building, as Helen Hunt Jackson describes.

Yet Massachusetts was already the home of famous thinkers, writers, and poets. New York City was providing the fuel for Horatio Alger's stories and the promise of the American Dream.

In your search to find America, you must look to these Americans, their times, and their ideas. Then look back to the stories and poems, which have taken you as far west as Hawaii, north to Alaska, and south to Texas and Florida—to discover how all of them fit as parts of the whole.

## Questioning the Poem

1. A *mechanic* is anyone skilled with tools and machinery, not only a repairman. Why was and is this profession important to America? Whitman might feel their song "should be ... strong" because this would show they felt confident, vigorous, and able to exert great physical power. Why would he feel their song should also be "blithe," meaning joyous?
2. In lines 3 and 4, what contributions do the carpenter and mason make to Americans' lives?
3. In line 5, what difference in status might seem to exist between a boatman and deckhand? By describing them both as "singing," what does Whitman want you to accept as true, in spite of this apparent difference?
4. How are the occupations in line 7 alike?
5. Although Whitman does not mention a setting, what different kind of place fits the woodcutter and plowboy, compared to those in lines 2–6?
6. How does the "delicious singing" of line 8 also express the more usual role of women in early America? Does Whitman seem to value it more, less, or the same as the others? Explain the reasons for your opinion.
7. How does line 9 express the ideas of American equality, individualism, and pride? Consider each separately.
8. Does Whitman want you to imagine "the party of young fellows" as dissatisfied getting low pay for hard work or pleased and cheerful about their workday lives? Explain your reasons.
9. Whitman describes thse young fellows as "robust," meaning strong and healthy. What in the poem supports their being this way?
10. Whitman also describes their song as "strong" and "melodious," both

tuneful and sweet-sounding. Do you believe that Whitman meant you to picture the young men as having the same line of work or various occupations? Explain the logic behind your decision.

## Looking Deeper

### I. "The Varied Carols"

A *carol* is a song of joy. After reading the poem, why do you think that Whitman wrote that "America singing" was made up of "varied carols"?

In Whitman's time there were also poverty, disease, violence, war, and even slavery, which the poet opposed. Yet Whitman overlooked all these elements in writing this poem. Explain what you feel were his reasons, and whether you think them justified.

Do you think Whitman would say, "I hear America singing" if he had visited Garland City at the time Jackson did? Why or why not?

Do you feel that a "song of joy" could be written about America today? Explain why or why not.

### II. In Today's Terms

What occupations named in Whitman's poem are still called by the same name today? Which have basically the same job description but a different name? Which, if any, are obsolete?

List at least three additional occupations for men and three for women that were unknown to Whitman. Do they fit the spirit of Whitman's poem. Explain why or why not. If you believe they do, you might wish to try fitting several of these into added lines of the poem.

# I, Too, Sing America

*by Langston Hughes*

| | |
|---|---|
| **Born:** | *Joplin, Missouri. 1902* |
| **Early schooling:** | *Kansas, Ohio* |
| **Youthful experience:** | *Did odd jobs, shipped on freighters to Africa, Europe, lived a year in Mexico* |
| **Famous as:** | *Poet, novelist, lecturer, and playwright* |

I, too, sing America.

I am the darker brother.
They send me to eat in the kitchen
When company comes,
But I laugh,                                                    5
And eat well,
And grow strong.

Tomorrow,
I'll be at the table
When company comes.                                            10
Nobody'll dare
Say to me,
"Eat in the kitchen,"
Then.

Besides,                                                       15
They'll see how beautiful I am
And be ashamed—

I, too, am America.

# For Better Reading: An Echoing Song

Born in the century following Walt Whitman, poet Langston Hughes clearly knows and comments on America's song.

## Questioning the Poem

1. Considering your reading of "I Hear America Singing," why would Langston Hughes feel it necessary to emphasize "too" in the first line?
2. Although no healthy human flesh is actually a color such as paper white, what ethnic backgrounds might qualify someone to say, "I am the darker brother," compared to that commonly termed "white"?
3. In mentioning being sent to eat in the kitchen, what kind of treatment does Hughes object to? How might "the darker brother" face similar treatment on the job and elsewhere? Give two or three examples.
4. Does the stanza following lines 5–7 show that the speaker intends to "grow strong" in order to join those who sent him to the kitchen or to attack them? Support your answer.
5. Compare Hughes' choice of "I laugh" in line 5 with other possible choices, such as "I moan" or "I curse." Explain the differences in effect caused by each. What was Hughes' purpose in making the choice he did?
6. Whom do you believe Hughes intends the reader to identify as the unnamed "they" in the poem? Who would the "company" or guests be?
7. In line 11, what does the speaker think will bring him to the place where nobody will "dare" send him away "tomorrow"?
8. Hughes sets off the words "Tomorrow" in line 8 and "Then" in line 14. What do these words show about the speaker's feelings toward the present? Does this stanza most clearly express a mood of hopeful waiting, mocking indifference, or bitter striving? Explain the reasons for your choice.
9. Although lines 5–6 speak of what "I" will do, what change does the speaker see "they" going through in lines 16–17?
10. In terms of the poem, of what would "they ... be ashamed"? How should you apply this idea in broader terms?

## Looking Deeper

### I. "Tomorrow"

To what degree has Hughes' prediction about "tomorrow" come true? Give examples to support your opinion.

In relation to the title and last line, whom would you include in the words, "I, too, am America," that neither Whitman nor Hughes might have had in mind? Explain the reasons behind this change of view.

## II. Singing America

How does Hughes's poem represent the pride and self-reliance that make "I, too, am America" seem to fit? How does it also show belief in the American promise?

Write a poem or essay about what you see or you would like to see in America's future. You might wish to title it, "America's Song in the Twenty-first Century."

---
### REFLECTIONS
---

It's time to look out at the America and Americans around you as well as reflect on what you've read.

The search to find America is never finished—for Americans never stop looking for ways to make their lives and nation better. As you reflect on all the ideas you've met, all the places that are America, and the many different voices that speak as Americans, it's time to remember where finding America must always begin—with you and where you are.

From "Trying Your Wings" to "A Sense of Pride" there are unspoken assumptions and beliefs about America that tie each to the other as parts of a whole. What do Americans have in common? In considering the answer, think about the variety of influences that affect every American. For example, how does where you live affect your first attempts at trying your wings? And, how often does one person's focus prevent recognition of another's expression of true American pride?

The American dream, the legends that inspire us, Americans' beliefs and values—all are part of the makeup of every American. As you reflect on the stories, essays, and poems you've read, choose two or three that impressed you most, and consider how each is affected by elements not directly associated with its specific theme. For example, how was the short story "One Throw" influenced by the American dream? Or "The Person of the Moment" by the place Maya Angelou lived?

Because the American dream and its promise are so deeply rooted in the ideas America is built on, Americans sometimes forget how much they contribute to everyday life.

The right to speak openly . . . to receive equal justice . . . to pursue your dreams . . .

These are the foundations on which Americans lay their plans and expectations. Though not always expressed openly, they can't be separated from what Americans say and do. They exist at the heart of American life.

The right to speak openly . . . to receive equal justice . . . to pursue your dreams . . .

Each is so much a part of America that no Americans hesitate to claim their share, while not always recognizing the claims of others.

To find America, you must also look around you—to your neighborhood, your school, the people you know and meet, the news and entertainment you watch and read. Because of their closeness and yours, it's sometimes hardest to see American values and beliefs in the places most familiar.

Perhaps it's because Americans ask so much that they sometimes forget the importance of seeking what lies beneath the surface and close at hand, as well as pursuing distant dreams.

## To Write About or Discuss

1. Do Americans take too much about America for granted? Discuss one or several factors. Include examples from your experience or reading.
2. Will today's young people be ready to inherit America? Some say no. Take either side—or both sides—of this question, basing your opinion on sound reasoning and examples.
3. "I Hear America Singing" and "Listening and Learning" are both inspired by ordinary Americans. Write a poem, story, or essay about what you learned by making a point to observe and listen to Americans where you are.
4. Choose a topic about "Finding America" that expresses your special interests or concerns.